NONLINEAR THEORY OF CONTINUOUS MEDIA

McGRAW-HILL SERIES IN ENGINEERING SCIENCES

STEPHEN H. CRANDALL AND PAUL M. NAGHDI, *Consulting Editors*

CRANDALL AND DAHL · An Introduction to the Mechanics of Solids
ERINGEN · Nonlinear Theory of Continuous Media
FRANKEL · Principles of the Properties of Materials
HODGE · Plastic Analysis of Structures
KARPLUS AND SOROKA · Analog Methods
LANGMUIR · Electromagnetic Fields and Waves
McKINLEY · Meteor Science and Engineering
YEH AND ABRAMS · Principles of Mechanics of Solids and Fluids

# NONLINEAR THEORY OF CONTINUOUS MEDIA

A. CEMAL ERINGEN
Professor of Aeronautical and Engineering Sciences
Purdue University

McGRAW-HILL BOOK COMPANY, INC.
New York San Francisco Toronto London

NONLINEAR THEORY OF CONTINUOUS MEDIA

 *Library of Congress Catalog Card Number* 62-13810

19580

# PREFACE

This book is an outgrowth of class notes used by the author in teaching a graduate course, "Theory of Continuous Media," during the past seven years at Purdue University. Several early versions of these notes were privately distributed to students and to interested colleagues. The growing demand at various universities for the teaching of a course covering this subject matter and the encouragement received from colleagues are largely responsible for the publication of this book.

The book is written for use in graduate teaching in any school of the type commonly called Engineering Sciences, Engineering Physics, Applied Mathematics, or Applied Mechanics, where a definite program to cultivate the physical and mathematical foundations of continuum physics exists. Prerequisites for a course based on the present book are a first course in linear continuum mechanics covering the theory of elasticity and fluid dynamics, and some understanding of vector and tensor calculus; a separate course in tensor calculus is not mandatory, however, since an account of this subject, adequate for our purposes, is included in the Appendix. The author has found that approximately seven lectures on tensors, covering the material in the Appendix, provide sufficient background.

This book will also be valuable to research workers in this field since it collects under one cover the results of many significant investigations.

The present book consists of eleven chapters. Chapter 1 deals with the concepts of deformation, strain, and rotation. It gives a thorough study of local deformations and their various measures, from both analytical and geometrical viewpoints. Chapter 2 deals with the motion of deformable bodies. Deformation-rate, spin, vorticity, and strain-rate tensors are introduced and studied. The concept of mass is presented and the global conservation laws are postulated. Chapter 3 deals with stress vectors, couples, and tensors and the principle of the local balance of momenta. Chapter 4 is devoted to the presentation and discussion of some thermodynamical concepts. The principle of the local conservation of energy and the principle of entropy are the main topics.

Chapter 5 is an exposition of the general ideas and principles of the theory of constitutive equations. Simple applications are given for illustrative purposes. In particular, the constitutive equations of the theory of elasticity, from the viewpoints of both Green and Cauchy, and those of the stokesian fluids are presented.

In later chapters, i.e., Chaps. 8 to 11, we find more sophisticated applications of the theory. Chapter 6 on the theory of elasticity and Chap. 7 on stokesian fluids give some simple exact solutions obtained during the past decade. Chapter 8 deals with the theory of hypoelasticity developed in the years since 1955. Chapter 9 presents two essentially different recent approaches to finite plasticity theory. In Chap. 10 there is presented an account of finite viscoelasticity. Chapter 11 on electroelasticity is a combination and modification of Toupin's and our work on the elastic dielectric.

Some of the materials included in this book certainly are in their early stages of development. The foundation on which they are laid is solid, however, and methodologically they are so full of potential that the gain to be realized in teaching these topics far outweighs the risk of impermanence inherent in the teaching of any new material.

The approach and composition of the book are believed to be novel. In addition, the book contains a number of new results in various chapters, some of which are identified in the text.

It is a pleasure to thank Professor C. Truesdell and Dr. R. A. Toupin for their kindness in lending me for inspection some of their monumental work in the "Handbuch der Physik" prior to its publication, and to thank Professor W. Noll for the use of some mimeographed material. I am deeply indebted to Professors P. M. Naghdi and J. E. Adkins for their generosity in reading and criticizing the whole manuscript and to Dr. R. A. Toupin for valuable criticism of Chap. 11. Early encouragement by Dr. Paul F. Chenea is appreciated. Without the careful reading and checking of the whole manuscript by my students S. L. Koh and N. F. Jordan the work would not have gone to press. To them goes my deepest appreciation. Considerable assistance with the proofreading was rendered by V. R. Parfitt, J. D. Ingram, and R. C. Dixon.

Valuable typing and reproduction services were provided by the U.S. Office of Naval Research, the School of Aeronautical and Engineering Sciences, and General Technology Corporation. The burden of this work fell upon Mrs. A. Light, Mrs. L. Schrock, Mrs. G. Fanning, and Mrs. R. Williams. My thanks are also due to the following organizations for permission to use the indicated figures:

Royal Society of London, Figs. 61.1, 61.2, 61.4, 61.5, 61.8 to 61.10, 70.3 to 70.6

*Quarterly of Applied Mathematics*, Fig. 68.1
Graduate Institute of Mechanics and Applied Mathematics of Indiana University, Figs. 78.1, 78.2, 106.2, 106.3
Interscience Publishers, Inc., Figs. 70.7, 76.1
American Society of Mechanical Engineers, Figs. 88.1 to 88.9
American Institute of Physics, Fig. 90.2
The Macmillan Company, Fig. 65.1
Oxford University Press, Fig. 61.6
North-Holland Publishing Company, Fig. 70.1

*A. CEMAL ERINGEN*

# CONTENTS

# INTRODUCTION

The theory of continuous media is a scientific discipline concerned with the global behavior of substances (including empty space as a limit) under the influence of external disturbances. A satisfactory training in this field requires the study of the interrelations among (1) external agents, (2) the constitution of the medium, and (3) the response.

*External Agents.* The external agents that produce changes in the state of the medium may appear in the form of surface and body forces and/or displacements, the initial state of the body, or the effect produced by the changes made in the environment of the system. These changes may appear in the form of contact forces, heat, and electrical, chemical, mechanical, or any other type of disturbance. The nature of these agents, the laws governing them, their mathematical characterization, and the physical measurements of the external effects must be an integral part of any program of study in the theory of continuous media.

*Constitution of the Medium.* When different substances of the same geometry are subjected to the same external agents, the response is generally observed to be different. This is caused mainly by differences in the constitution of the various substances. Therefore in the description of physical phenomena the constitution of bodies plays an essential role. From a continuum viewpoint, constitution must be understood in a macroscopic sense. Although an extensive knowledge of the atomic and molecular structure of materials is not required, some knowledge of statistical mechanics and transport phenomena, leading to a macroscopic description of the characteristics of the material, is useful in the understanding of continuum physics.

The theory of continuous media, at the outset, must define the medium in accordance with the scope it intends to encompass. At the beginning of this century we find serious attempts toward a unified theory of continuous media. As exemplified by the works of Jaumann [1911] and Lohr [1917], these theories encompass large numbers of physical phenomena. The unwieldy nature of such theories has now been recognized, and we are forced to restrict our attention to formulations of smaller but no less significant scope.

It is important that the medium be a continuous one. This means that the field quantities (e.g., displacements, stresses, electric fields, etc.) are piecewise-continuous functions of the coordinates of the material points and the time.

*The Response.* In engineering, the ultimate interest lies in predicting the way in which a medium responds to the external agents. An engineer cannot design and build his machine without reasonable assurance in regard to predicted performance. In this *input-output* relationship, the physical model assumed for the constitution of the body occupies a central position. The validity of models must of course be checked by experiment. We must therefore have recourse to experimentation and/or statistical mechanical considerations both for the determination of constitutive coefficients (e.g., elastic constants, viscosity, heat conductivity, etc.) and for the verification of the results predicted by our theories.

The theory of continuous media nourishes us with the strength of a unified theory, the power of generalization, and the stimulus of aesthetic appreciation, all essential to research. The unified approach to the study of the global behavior of materials consists of, first, a thorough study of basic principles common to all media and, second, a clear demonstration of the types of media (such as the elastic solid, stokesian fluids, hygrosteric materials, etc.) within the structure of the theory. The theory so constructed makes available methods which are useful in the creation of new fields of research. New and more precise descriptions of physical phenomena are born by the introduction of special functional equations as constitutive equations. The recent birth of hypoelasticity, non-newtonian fluids, and electroelasticity is sufficient to illustrate this point.

Finally in the exact theories one finds not only a satisfying permanence but also an aesthetic structure that is fundamental to all basic research. Exact theories are frequently criticized for the seemingly insurmountable mathematical difficulties they present in the treatment of nontrivial engineering problems. This objection is balanced, however, by the simplicity of the exact theories, and generally the basic phenomena contained in the theory can be displayed by a choice of simple, but physically meaningful, problems. Moreover exact theories provide a perpetual source from which all approximate theories may spring.

The foregoing considerations indicate that in the design of a theory of continuous media there exist two definite expositions constituting the backbone of the theory: (1) basic principles and (2) a constitutive theory.

*The Basic Principles.* These are the fundamental axioms essential in the construction of the foundations of the theory. They are considered to be self-evident as a result of our experience with the physical world. The domain of applicability of these principles determines the strength of the theory. Certainly they are not unchangeable; however, any change in these principles must arise from the failure of the theory. The replacement of newtonian mechanics by relativistic mechanics and by quantum mechanics exemplifies such changes. The basic principles upon which the theory is constructed are:

Axiom 1. Conservation of mass
Axiom 2. Balance of momentum
Axiom 3. Balance of moment of momentum
Axiom 4. Conservation of energy
Axiom 5. Principle of entropy
Axiom 6. Conservation of charge
Axiom 7. Faraday's law of induction
Axiom 8. Ampère's law

*Constitutive Theory.* The basic principles are valid for all materials irrespective of their constitution. It is therefore expected that their mathematical expressions generally are not sufficient to predict uniquely the behavior of all substances under prescribed boundary and initial conditions. In order to take account of the nature of different materials, we must therefore find additional equations identifying the basic characteristics of the body with respect to the response sought. In the theory of continuous media this is done by introducing models appropriate to the particular class of phenomena under scrutiny. There exist certain rules and invariance requirements (cf. Chap. 5) which must be satisfied by all such models. After these requirements are met, there still remain unknown constitutive functions which must be determined through experiments. Once this is done, the theory is fully constructed and ready for application. It remains acceptable until such time as once again the phenomena predicted by the theory do not agree with the experimental results.

Alternatively, constitutive coefficients may be determined from a molecular theory. Rich as the microscopic world may be, the nature of molecular forces is so complicated and our knowledge so incomplete that even a rational transport theory leading to the prediction of constitutive coefficients is still well out of reach.

The first four chapters of the present book are devoted to a systematic study of the first five of the basic principles listed above. The fifth chapter is a discussion of the theory of constitutive relations. The final six chapters are excursions in widely varied applications of these basic principles and the constitutive theory. Very restricted forms of Axioms 6 to 8 are used in Chap. 11.

# 1

# STRAIN

## 1. SCOPE OF THE CHAPTER

This chapter is concerned with an exposition of the geometry of deformation. It may be considered as a discussion of differential geometry appropriate to deformable bodies. The main purpose is to connect the elements of a deformed body to their original locations and measures. To describe the positions of material points, we introduce, in Art. 2, two sets of curvilinear coordinate systems, one for the undeformed and one for the deformed body. These coordinate systems are characterized through their relations to any rectangular frame of reference. The axioms of continuity and indestructibility of matter are discussed.

In Art. 3 base vectors, metric tensors, and shifters essential to the representation of vectors and to their parallel transport are introduced. The concept of deformation and its measure in terms of the deformation tensors of Cauchy and of Green are given in Art. 4. The square of elements of length for both deformed and undeformed bodies is obtained.

Strain tensors and the displacement vector are introduced in the subsequent article, followed by a discussion of infinitesimal strains and rotations in Art. 6. The geometrical significance of strains is made clear through the study of length and angle changes in Art. 7. The strain ellipsoid of Cauchy, which often provides a clear geometrical understanding of the directional dependence of deformation, is the subject of Art. 8. In Art. 9 we give a detailed discussion of strain invariants, so important subsequently in the characterization of isotropic tensor functions in the systematic treatment of the constitutive equations of isotropic media. Finite rotation and the fundamental theorem of local deformation are discussed in Art. 10. We give a brief account in Art. 11 of direction-preserving fibers, and in Art. 12 of the calculation of area and volume changes in any deformation.

Deformation tensors are second-order tensors which are expressed in terms of gradients of the deformation vector. A question arises as to the conditions under which any second-order tensor may be a deformation tensor. These conditions, known as the compatibility conditions, are derived in Art. 13.

In Art. 14 we give a brief account of various types of approximations to the expressions of strain and rotation. For example, the questions of what we mean when we speak of small deformations, small rotations, infinitesimal deformations, etc., are briefly discussed in that article. The final article of this chapter is written to illustrate some of the fundamental results by means of elementary applications, physically easy to visualize and experimentally simple to construct. Rigid deformation, pure strain, potential deformation, isochoric deformation, uniform dilatation, simple extension, simple shear, pure torsion of a circular cylinder, and pure bending of a cylindrical bar are among the examples discussed in that article.

## 2. COORDINATES

The material points of a continuous medium at $t = 0$ occupy a region $B$ that consists of the material volume $\mathcal{V}$ and its surface $\mathcal{S}$. The position of a material point $P$ in this region is denoted by a curvilinear coordinate system $X^K$, $(K = 1, 2, 3)$ or by a vector $\mathbf{P}$ that extends from an origin $O$ of the coordinates to the point $P$. After the deformations take place, at time $t$ the material points of $\mathcal{V} + \mathcal{S}$ go into a region $b$ consisting of a spatial volume $v$ and its surface $s$. A point $p$ in the deformed state may be represented by a new set of curvilinear coordinates $x^k$, $(k = 1, 2, 3)$ or a position vector $\mathbf{p}$ that extends from the origin $o$ of the new coordinates to the point $p$. Often it may be advantageous to select these two reference frames to be nonidentical. For example, if a rectangular parallelepiped becomes a circular cylinder after deformation, a rectangular coordinate system for the undeformed block and circular cylindrical coordinates for the deformed configuration may prove to be advantageous.

In the description of motion of a continuous body we shall find a definite need for the use of these two types of coordinates (Fig. 2.1). Some authors prefer the use of the so-called *convected* or *intrinsic* coordinates which are obtained from the foregoing coordinates by selecting $x^k$ in such a way that at each time $t$ the numerical value of the coordinates $x^k$ of a given point is the same as that of $X^K$. Therefore each motion of the deformed configuration requires the choice of a second coordinate frame. In this book we shall use only the more conventional two frames of reference described above, since this practice is more general in nature and renders itself particularly suitable in the analysis of some new problems. Moreover, as a special case, by equating the numerical values of $X^K$ and $x^k$, we obtain the intrinsic system.

When points of $B$ are referred to a rectangular reference frame, often we use $Z^K$ in place of $X^K$, and for individual components we write $X = Z^1$, $Y = Z^2$, $Z = Z^3$. The rectangular reference frame employed for the deformed configuration $v + s$ is frequently denoted by $z^k$, and for individual components we write $x = z^1$, $y = z^2$, $z = z^3$. Following the current terminology, we shall call $X^K$ and $Z^K$ the *material* or *lagrangian* coordinates and $x^k$ and $z^k$ the *spatial* or *eulerian* coordinates.[1]

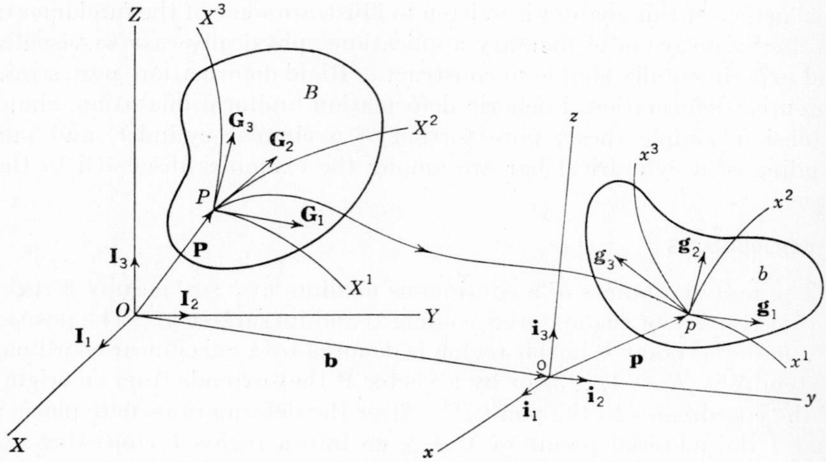


FIG. 2.1. Coordinate system.

The motion of the body carries various material points through various spatial positions. This is expressed by

$$x^k = x^k(X^K, t) \quad \text{or} \quad X^K = X^K(x^k, t) \tag{2.1}$$

Thus each point $p$ in $b$ at time $t$ comes from a point $P$ in $B$ at time $t = 0$.

We assume that the mappings (2.1) are single-valued and have continuous partial derivatives with respect to their arguments to whatever order desired except possibly at some singular points, curves, and surfaces. Moreover each member of (2.1) is the unique inverse of the other in a neighborhood of the material point $P$. A unique inverse of the first of (2.1) exists, at least in a $\delta$ neighborhood of $p$, if and only if the jacobian $j$ is not identically zero, i.e.,

$$j \equiv \left| \frac{\partial x^k}{\partial X^K} \right| \neq 0 \qquad |x^k - x_0^k| < \delta \tag{2.2}$$

The foregoing assumption is known as the *axiom of continuity*, which expresses the *indestructibility of matter*. No region of positive, finite

[1] Notation used here closely follows that of Truesdell and Toupin [1960].

volume is deformed into one of zero or infinite volume. It also implies the *impenetrability of matter*. The motion (2.1) carries every region into a region, every surface into a surface, and every curve into a curve. One portion of matter never penetrates into another. We assume, however, that there exist singular surfaces, curves, and points over an interval of time at which the axiom of continuity may be violated. To these, special attention must be given.

The quantities associated with the undeformed body $B$ will be denoted by majuscules and those associated with the deformed body $b$ will be denoted by minuscules. When these quantities are referred to coordinates $X^K$, their indices will be majuscules; and when they are referred to $x^k$, their indices will be minuscules. For example, $G_{KL}(\mathbf{X})$ and $g_{kl}(\mathbf{x})$ respectively denote metric tensors of $B$ and $b$.

## 3. BASE VECTORS, METRIC TENSORS, SHIFTERS

The position vector $\mathbf{P}$ of a point $P$ in $B$ and $\mathbf{p}$ of one in $b$ referred respectively to rectangular coordinates $Z^K$ and $z^k$ are given by

$$\text{(3.1)} \qquad \mathbf{P} = Z^K(X^1, X^2, X^3)\,\mathbf{I}_K \qquad \mathbf{p} = z^k(x^1, x^2, x^3)\,\mathbf{i}_k$$

where $\mathbf{I}_K$ and $\mathbf{i}_k$ are the rectangular base vectors in $Z^K$ and $z^k$ (Fig. 2.1). Henceforth the usual summation convention is applied to every *diagonally* repeated index.

The curvilinear coordinates are usually introduced by expressing rectangular coordinates in terms of them, i.e.,

$$\text{(3.2)} \qquad Z^K = Z^K(X^1, X^2, X^3) \qquad z^k = z^k(x^1, x^2, x^3)$$

Infinitesimal vectors $d\mathbf{P}$ in $B$ and $d\mathbf{p}$ in $b$ may be expressed as

$$\text{(3.3)} \qquad d\mathbf{P} = \frac{\partial \mathbf{P}}{\partial X^K}\,dX^K = \mathbf{G}_K\,dX^K \qquad d\mathbf{p} = \frac{\partial \mathbf{p}}{\partial x^k}\,dx^k = \mathbf{g}_k\,dx^k$$

where

$$\text{(3.4)} \qquad \mathbf{G}_K(\mathbf{X}) \equiv \frac{\partial \mathbf{P}}{\partial X^K} = \frac{\partial Z^M}{\partial X^K}\,\mathbf{I}_M \qquad \mathbf{g}_k(\mathbf{x}) \equiv \frac{\partial \mathbf{p}}{\partial x^k} = \frac{\partial z^m}{\partial x^k}\,\mathbf{i}_m$$

are the *base vectors* at $X^K$ and $x^k$ respectively. The base vectors are tangential to the coordinate curves $X^K$ and $x^k$.

The squares of the lengths in $B$ and $b$ are respectively

$$\text{(3.5)} \qquad dS^2 = d\mathbf{P}\cdot d\mathbf{P} = G_{KL}\,dX^K\,dX^L \qquad ds^2 = d\mathbf{p}\cdot d\mathbf{p} = g_{kl}\,dx^k\,dx^l$$

where

$$\text{(3.6)} \qquad \begin{aligned} G_{KL}(\mathbf{X}) &= \mathbf{G}_K\cdot\mathbf{G}_L = \delta_{MN}\frac{\partial Z^M}{\partial X^K}\frac{\partial Z^N}{\partial X^L} \\ g_{kl}(\mathbf{x}) &= \mathbf{g}_k\cdot\mathbf{g}_l = \delta_{mn}\frac{\partial z^m}{\partial x^k}\frac{\partial z^n}{\partial x^l} \end{aligned}$$

are the *covariant metric tensors* of $B$ and $b$ respectively. The Kronecker deltas $\delta_{MN}$, $\delta_{mn}$, $\delta^M{}_N$, $\delta^m{}_n$, etc., take the value 1 or 0 depending on whether the indices are identical or not.

Associated with the covariant metric tensors $G_{KL}$ and $g_{kl}$ are the contravariant metric tensors $G^{KL}(\mathbf{X})$ and $g^{kl}(\mathbf{x})$, which are defined by

$$G^{KL} = \frac{\text{cofactor } G_{KL}}{|G_{KL}|} \qquad g^{kl} = \frac{\text{cofactor } g_{kl}}{|g_{kl}|} \tag{3.7}$$

where single vertical bars enclosing the quantities represent a determinant, and double vertical bars a matrix, e.g.,

$$|g_{kl}| = \begin{vmatrix} g_{11} & g_{12} & g_{13} \\ g_{21} & g_{22} & g_{23} \\ g_{31} & g_{32} & g_{33} \end{vmatrix} \qquad \|g_{kl}\| = \begin{bmatrix} g_{11} & g_{12} & g_{13} \\ g_{21} & g_{22} & g_{23} \\ g_{31} & g_{32} & g_{33} \end{bmatrix} \tag{3.8}$$

The metric tensors satisfy the relations

$$G_{KL}\, G^{LM} = \delta_K{}^M \qquad g_{kl}\, g^{lm} = \delta_k{}^m \tag{3.9}$$

Metric tensors, $G_{KL}$, $G^{KL}$, are used to raise and lower indices of vectors and tensors referred to $X^K$; $g_{kl}$ and $g^{kl}$ are employed for this purpose in $x^k$, e.g.,

$$\begin{aligned} C^K{}_L &= G^{KM}\, C_{ML} \qquad & C_L{}^K &= G^{KM}\, C_{LM} \\ C^{KL} &= G^{LM}\, C^K{}_M \qquad & C^K{}_L &= G_{LM}\, C^{KM} \qquad \cdots \end{aligned} \tag{3.10}$$

The reciprocal base vectors $\mathbf{G}^K(\mathbf{X})$ and $\mathbf{g}^k(\mathbf{x})$ are defined by the orthonormality conditions

$$\mathbf{G}^K \cdot \mathbf{G}_L = \delta^K{}_L \qquad \mathbf{g}^k \cdot \mathbf{g}_l = \delta^k{}_l \tag{3.11}$$

The solutions of these equations are

$$\mathbf{G}^K = G^{KL}\, \mathbf{G}_L \qquad \mathbf{g}^k = g^{kl}\, \mathbf{g}_l \tag{3.12}$$

as may be verified by substituting (3.12) into the left of (3.11) and by using (3.9). The formalism apparent in the raising of indices in (3.12) to get the reciprocal base vectors is in general not valid for other types of *three-vectors*.

In all of these representations the vectors and tensors referred to $X^K$ and those expressed in $x^k$ are treated separately.

For comparison purposes it will often be necessary to *shift* vectors and tensors to the same system in parallel transport. For example, by definition, components of position vectors $\mathbf{P}$ and $\mathbf{p}$ in $X^K$ and $x^k$ are

$$P^K = \mathbf{P} \cdot \mathbf{G}^K \qquad p^k = \mathbf{p} \cdot \mathbf{g}^k$$

Suppose now we want to shift $\mathbf{p}$ to the point $P$ ($\mathbf{X}$) in parallel transport. If $p^K$ are the components of $\mathbf{p}$ in $X^K$, then

$$\mathbf{p} = p^K \mathbf{G}_K(\mathbf{X}) = p^k \mathbf{g}_k(\mathbf{x}) \tag{3.13}$$

or by taking inner products with $\mathbf{G}^L$ and $\mathbf{g}^l$, we get

$$p^K = g^K{}_k\, p^k \qquad p^k = g^k{}_K\, p^K \tag{3.14}$$

where

$$g^K{}_k(\mathbf{X},\mathbf{x}) = \mathbf{G}^K(\mathbf{X}) \cdot \mathbf{g}_k(\mathbf{x}) \qquad g^k{}_K(\mathbf{X},\mathbf{x}) = \mathbf{g}^k(\mathbf{x}) \cdot \mathbf{G}_K(\mathbf{X}) \tag{3.15}$$

are the *shifters* required for this parallel transport. The shifters relate components of a vector in two coordinate systems. The shifters are *two-point* tensor fields; i.e., they transform as tensors with respect to the transformation of both coordinates $X^K$ and $x^k$. The Latin majuscule index transforms with $X^K$ and the Latin minuscule with $x^k$.[1]

We may in a fashion similar to (3.15) define

$$\begin{aligned} g_{Kk}(\mathbf{X},\mathbf{x}) &= g_{kK}(\mathbf{X},\mathbf{x}) = \mathbf{g}_k(\mathbf{x}) \cdot \mathbf{G}_K(\mathbf{X}) \\ g^{Kk}(\mathbf{X},\mathbf{x}) &= g^{kK}(\mathbf{X},\mathbf{x}) = \mathbf{g}^k(\mathbf{x}) \cdot \mathbf{G}^K(\mathbf{X}) \end{aligned} \tag{3.16}$$

It is now apparent that the lowering and raising of Latin minuscule indices can be done with the metric tensors $g_{kl}$ and $g^{kl}$, while the Latin majuscule indices require $G_{KL}$ and $G^{KL}$. For example, by writing $\mathbf{g}_k = g_{kl}\,\mathbf{g}^l$ and/or $\mathbf{G}_K = G_{KL}\,\mathbf{G}^L$ in $(3.16)_1$, we see that

$$g_{Kk} = g_{kl}\, g^l{}_K = G_{KL}\, g^L{}_k = g_{kl}\, G_{KL}\, g^{lL} \tag{3.17}$$

Similarly one may easily verify the expressions

$$\begin{aligned} g^{Kk} &= g^{kl}\, g^K{}_l = G^{KL}\, g^k{}_L = g^{kl}\, G^{KL}\, g_{lL} \\ g^K{}_k &= g_{kl}\, g^{lK} = G^{KL}\, g_{kL} = g_{kl}\, G^{KL}\, g^l{}_L \\ g^K{}_k\, g^l{}_K &= \delta^l{}_k \qquad g^K{}_k\, g^k{}_L = \delta^K{}_L \end{aligned} \tag{3.18}$$

of which the last line proves the reciprocity of $g^k{}_K$ and $g^K{}_k$.

If we substitute (3.4) into (3.16), we get

$$g_{Kk} = \delta_{Ll} \frac{\partial Z^L}{\partial X^K} \frac{\partial z^l}{\partial x^k} \qquad \delta_{Ll} \equiv \mathbf{I}_L \cdot \mathbf{i}_l \tag{3.19}$$

which not only shows the two-point tensor character of $g_{Kk}$, but also indicates that when both coordinates $X^K$ and $x^k$ are rectangular,

$$g_{Kk} = \delta_{Kk} \qquad g^K{}_k = \delta^K{}_k \tag{3.20}$$

[1] Michal [1927, 1947] noted the importance of two-point tensor fields in the deformation of continuous media. Toupin [1956] and Ericksen and Truesdell [1958] further developed and used these tensors. For a short account see Art. A6.

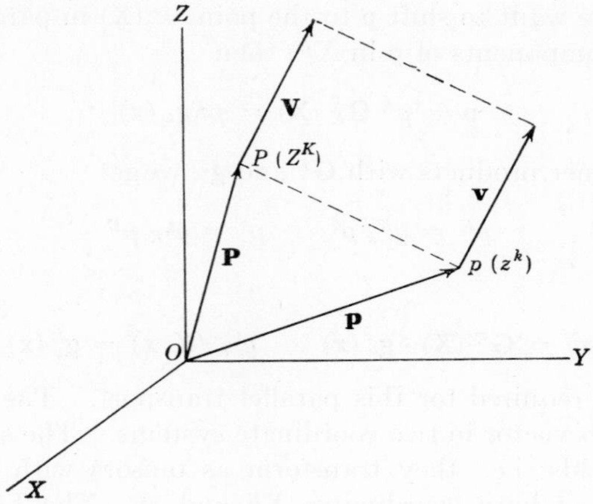


FIG. 3.1

In a rectangular frame of reference (Fig. 3.1), a vector $v^k$ at $z^k$ may be transported to the point $Z^K$ remaining parallel to itself if we write

$$V^K = \delta^K{}_k\, v^k \tag{3.21}$$

Here $\delta^K{}_l$ is the usual Kronecker delta, since the same frame of reference is used for both $Z^K$ and $z^k$. We see that the same thing is done in a curvilinear frame of reference by using $g^K{}_k$ instead of $\delta^K{}_k$, i.e.,

$$V^K = g^K{}_k\, v^k \tag{3.22}$$

Indeed we may show this by taking the scalar product of

$$\mathbf{v} = V^K\,\mathbf{G}_K = v^k\,\mathbf{g}_k$$

with $\mathbf{G}^K$. Hence we have the justification for the name "shifters" for $g^k{}_K$, $g^K{}_k$, etc. These tensors will find further important applications in the course of the present study.

## 4. DEFORMATION GRADIENTS, DEFORMATION TENSORS

Through the equation of motion (2.1) we have

$$dx^k = x^k{}_{,K}\, dX^K \qquad dX^K = X^K{}_{,k}\, dx^k \tag{4.1}$$

where indices after a comma indicate differentiation with respect to $X^K$ when they are majuscules and with respect to $x^k$ when they are minuscules. The two sets of quantities defined by

$$x^k{}_{,K} \equiv \frac{\partial x^k}{\partial X^K} \qquad X^K{}_{,k} \equiv \frac{\partial X^K}{\partial x^k} \tag{4.2}$$

are called *deformation gradients.* Through the chain rule of partial differentiation it is clear that they satisfy

(4.3) $$x^k{}_{,K}\, X^K{}_{,l} = \delta^k{}_l \qquad X^K{}_{,k}\, x^k{}_{,L} = \delta^K{}_L$$

Each of the sets is a set of nine linear equations for nine unknowns $x^k{}_{,K}$ or $X^K{}_{,k}$. A unique solution exists since the jacobian of the transformation is assumed not to vanish. Using Cramer's rule of determinants, the solution for $X^K{}_{,k}$ is given by

(4.4) $$X^K{}_{,k} = \frac{\text{cofactor } x^k{}_{,K}}{j} = \frac{1}{2\,j}\, e^{KLM}\, e_{klm}\, x^l{}_{,L}\, x^m{}_{,M}$$

where $e$ is the permutation symbol and

(4.5) $$j = |x^k{}_{,K}| = \tfrac{1}{6}\, e^{KLM}\, e_{klm}\, x^k{}_{,K}\, x^l{}_{,L}\, x^m{}_{,M}$$

is the jacobian. An important identity due to Jacobi follows from differentiating $j$, i.e.,

(4.6) $$\frac{\partial j}{\partial x^k{}_{,K}} = \text{cofactor } x^k{}_{,K} = j\, X^K{}_{,k}$$

If we substitute (4.1) into (3.5), we get

(4.7) $$dS^2 = c_{kl}\,(\mathbf{x}, t)\, dx^k\, dx^l \qquad ds^2 = C_{KL}\,(\mathbf{X}, t)\, dX^K\, dX^L$$

where

(4.8) $$c_{kl}\,(\mathbf{x}, t) = G_{KL}\,(\mathbf{X})\; X^K{}_{,k}\, X^L{}_{,l} \qquad C_{KL}\,(\mathbf{X}, t) = g_{kl}\,(\mathbf{x})\; x^k{}_{,K}\, x^l{}_{,L}$$

which are called respectively *Cauchy's deformation tensor* and *Green's deformation tensor. Both of these tensors are symmetrical,* i.e., $c_{kl} = c_{lk}$, $C_{KL} = C_{LK}$, *and both are positive-definite.*

If at time $t$ we look upon the motion (2.1) as a coordinate transformation (imbedded coordinates), then $c_{kl}\,(\mathbf{x}, t)$ may be interpreted as the metric tensor of $B$ in coordinates $x^k$ at time $t$; i.e., the metric tensor $G_{KL}\,(\mathbf{X})$ is transformed into $c_{kl}\,(\mathbf{x}, t)$ through the motion. An analogous interpretation is valid for $C_{KL}$ in inverse motion.

Corresponding to these tensors, new base vectors $\mathbf{c}_k\,(\mathbf{x}, t)$ and $\mathbf{C}_K\,(\mathbf{X}, t)$ may be defined by

(4.9) $$\begin{aligned} \mathbf{c}_k\,(\mathbf{x}, t) &\equiv \frac{\partial \mathbf{P}}{\partial x^k} = \frac{\partial \mathbf{P}}{\partial X^K}\frac{\partial X^K}{\partial x^k} = \mathbf{G}_K\,(\mathbf{X})\; X^K{}_{,k} \\ \mathbf{C}_K\,(\mathbf{X}, t) &= \frac{\partial \mathbf{p}}{\partial X^K} = \frac{\partial \mathbf{p}}{\partial x^k}\frac{\partial x^k}{\partial X^K} = \mathbf{g}_k\,(\mathbf{x})\; x^k{}_{,K} \end{aligned}$$

from which it follows that

(4.10) $$c_{kl} = c_{lk} = \mathbf{c}_k \cdot \mathbf{c}_l \qquad C_{KL} = C_{LK} = \mathbf{C}_K \cdot \mathbf{C}_L$$

Expressions (4.9) indicate that the base vectors $\mathbf{G}_K$ and $\mathbf{g}_k$, through the motion, are transformed into $\mathbf{c}_k$ and $\mathbf{C}_K$ respectively. From (4.9) we also have

$$\mathbf{G}_K = \mathbf{c}_k \, x^k{}_{,K} \qquad \mathbf{g}_k = \mathbf{C}_K \, X^K{}_{,k} \tag{4.11}$$

The vectors $\mathbf{c}^k(\mathbf{x}, t)$ and $\mathbf{C}^K(\mathbf{X}, t)$ reciprocal to the new set $\mathbf{c}_k$ and $\mathbf{C}_K$ are defined by

$$\mathbf{c}^k \cdot \mathbf{c}_l = \delta^k{}_l \qquad \mathbf{C}^K \cdot \mathbf{C}_L = \delta^K{}_L \tag{4.12}$$

The solutions of these equations are

$$\mathbf{c}^k(\mathbf{x}, t) = \mathbf{G}^K(\mathbf{X}) \, x^k{}_{,K} \qquad \mathbf{C}^K(\mathbf{X}, t) = \mathbf{g}^k(\mathbf{x}) \, X^K{}_{,k} \tag{4.13}$$

as may be verified by substituting (4.9) and (4.13) into (4.12). The raising and lowering of indices in the curvilinear coordinates $x^k$ are accomplished by the use of the metric tensors $g^{kl}$ and $g_{kl}$, and in $X^K$ by $G^{KL}$ and $G_{KL}$. Hence, for example,

$$\begin{aligned} c^k{}_l &= g^{km} \, c_{ml} \qquad & c^{kl} &= g^{lm} \, c^k{}_m \\ C^K{}_L &= G^{KM} \, C_{ML} \qquad & C^{KL} &= G^{LM} \, C^K{}_M \end{aligned} \tag{4.14}$$

Note, however, that we cannot apply these operations to vectors $\mathbf{c}_k$ and $\mathbf{c}^k$. That is, in general,

$$\mathbf{c}^k \neq g^{kl} \, \mathbf{c}_l$$

Since $\mathbf{c}^k$ is defined by $(4.13)_1$, the question arises as to the relations of $\mathbf{c}^k \cdot \mathbf{c}^l$ to $c_{kl}$. We write

$$\overset{-1}{c}{}^{kl} = \mathbf{c}^k \cdot \mathbf{c}^l = G^{KL} \, x^k{}_{,K} \, x^l{}_{,L} \qquad \overset{-1}{C}{}^{KL} = \mathbf{C}^K \cdot \mathbf{C}^L = g^{kl} \, X^K{}_{,k} \, X^L{}_{,l} \tag{4.15}$$

and proceed to show that these quantities are indeed the inverse matrices to $c_{kl}$ and $C_{KL}$. For the Cauchy deformation tensor, we have

$$\begin{aligned} c_{km} \, \overset{-1}{c}{}^{ml} &= (G_{KL} \, X^K{}_{,k} \, X^L{}_{,m}) \, (G^{MN} \, x^m{}_{,M} \, x^l{}_{,N}) \\ &= G_{KL} \, G^{LN} \, X^K{}_{,k} \, x^l{}_{,N} = \delta^N{}_K \, X^K{}_{,k} \, x^l{}_{,N} = X^K{}_{,k} \, x^l{}_{,K} = \delta^l{}_k \end{aligned}$$

Since $c_{kl}$ is a nonsingular matrix, we have the proof. Proof for $(4.15)_2$ is similar.[1]

By lowering the indices of $\overset{-1}{c}{}^{km}$ we also get

$$\overset{-1}{c}{}^k{}_l = g_{lm} \, \overset{-1}{c}{}^{km} \qquad \overset{-1}{c}_{kl} = g_{km} \, \overset{-1}{c}{}^m{}_l = g_{km} \, g_{ln} \, \overset{-1}{c}{}^{mn} \tag{4.16}$$

By substituting $(4.8)_1$ into $(4.14)_1$, and $(4.15)_1$ into $(4.16)_1$, we obtain the dual expressions

$$c^k{}_l = X^{K,k} \, X_{K,l} \qquad \overset{-1}{c}{}^k{}_l = x^{k,K} \, x_{l,K} \tag{4.17}$$

[1] The tensor $\overset{-1}{\mathbf{C}}$ was introduced by Piola [1833, 1836] and $\overset{-1}{\mathbf{c}}$ by Finger [1894*a*].

where
$$X^{K,k} \equiv g^{kl} X^K{}_{,l} \qquad x^{k,K} \equiv G^{KL} x^k{}_{,L}$$
$$X_{K,l} \equiv G_{KL} X^L{}_{,l} \qquad x_{l,K} \equiv g_{lk} x^k{}_{,K}$$

We now have two different representations for the differential vectors $d\mathbf{P}$ and $d\mathbf{p}$, one in the reference frame $X^K$ and the other in $x^k$, i.e.,

$$\begin{aligned} d\mathbf{P} &= \mathbf{G}_K(\mathbf{X})\, dX^K = \mathbf{c}_k(\mathbf{x}, t)\, dx^k \\ d\mathbf{p} &= \mathbf{C}_K(\mathbf{X}, t)\, dX^K = \mathbf{g}_k(\mathbf{x})\, dx^k \end{aligned} \tag{4.18}$$

Similarly for the square of length elements we have

$$\begin{aligned} dS^2 &= G_{KL}(\mathbf{X})\, dX^K dX^L = c_{kl}(\mathbf{x}, t)\, dx^k dx^l \\ ds^2 &= C_{KL}(\mathbf{X}, t)\, dX^K dX^L = g_{kl}(\mathbf{x})\, dx^k dx^l \end{aligned} \tag{4.19}$$

## 5. STRAIN TENSORS, DISPLACEMENT VECTORS

The difference of the squares of the line elements containing the same material points in $B$ and in $b$ implies a length change due to deformation. If $ds^2 = dS^2$ for any pair of neighboring material points, then the deformation has not changed the distance of the pair. We say that *a body has undergone a rigid-body displacement whenever $ds^2 = dS^2$ for all material points.* Therefore the difference $ds^2 - dS^2$ is a measure of the deformation produced during a displacement. Subtracting expressions (4.19) of $dS^2$ from $ds^2$ expressed in the same coordinate system, we obtain

$$ds^2 - dS^2 = 2\, E_{KL}(\mathbf{X}, t)\, dX^K dX^L = 2\, e_{kl}(\mathbf{x}, t)\, dx^k dx^l \tag{5.1}$$

where

$$\begin{aligned} 2\, E_{KL} &= 2\, E_{LK} \equiv C_{KL}(\mathbf{X}, t) - G_{KL}(\mathbf{X}) \\ 2\, e_{kl} &= 2\, e_{lk} \equiv g_{kl}(\mathbf{x}) - c_{kl}(\mathbf{x}, t) \end{aligned} \tag{5.2}$$

are respectively called *lagrangian* and *eulerian strain tensors.* From (5.1) we readily find

$$E_{KL} = e_{kl}\, x^k{}_{,K}\, x^l{}_{,L} \qquad e_{kl} = E_{KL}\, X^K{}_{,k}\, X^L{}_{,l} \tag{5.3}$$

The *displacement vector* $\mathbf{u}$ is defined as the vector that extends from a material point in the undeformed body to the same material point in the deformed body (Fig. 5.1). Thus

$$\mathbf{u} = \mathbf{p} - \mathbf{P} + \mathbf{b} \tag{5.4}$$

This vector will have components $U^K$ referred to $X^K$ and $u^k$ referred to $x^k$, i.e.,

$$\mathbf{u} = U^K \mathbf{G}_K = u^k \mathbf{g}_k \tag{5.5}$$

To obtain $U^K$, we take the scalar product of (5.4) with $\mathbf{G}^K$, i.e.,

$$U^K = \mathbf{u} \cdot \mathbf{G}^K = \mathbf{p} \cdot \mathbf{G}^K - \mathbf{P} \cdot \mathbf{G}^K + \mathbf{b} \cdot \mathbf{G}^K$$

or

$$U^K = p^K - P^K + B^K \tag{5.6}$$

where $p^K$, $P^K$, and $B^K$ are the components of **p**, **P**, and **b** in $X^K$. For $p^K$ we have

$$p^K = g^K{}_k \, p^k$$

which is the shift of $p^k$ from the point $p$ to $P$.

The displacement vector **u** may also be expressed in terms of its covariant components $U_K$ and $u_k$:

$$\mathbf{u} = U_K \, \mathbf{G}^K = u_k \, \mathbf{g}^k \tag{5.7}$$

By scalar multiplication of this with $\mathbf{G}_K$ and $\mathbf{g}_k$ we find

$$U_K = g^k{}_K \, u_k \qquad u_k = g^K{}_k \, U_K \tag{5.8}$$

of which the first is the expression for the parallel displacement of $u_k$ from $p$ to $P$, and the second is the inverse operation. Of course, at the same

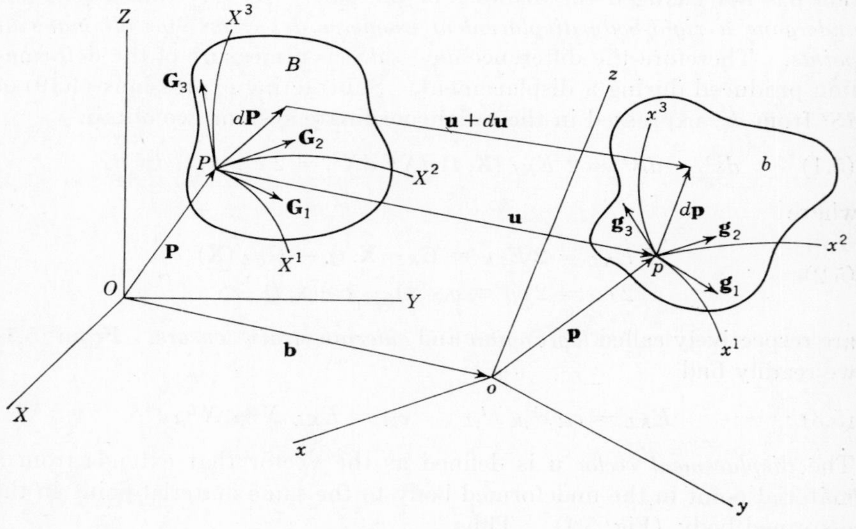


FIG. 5.1. Displacement vector.

point $X^K$ and $x^k$ among the covariant and contravariant components of the displacement vector we have

$$\begin{aligned} U^K &= G^{KL} \, U_L \qquad & U_K &= G_{KL} \, U^L \\ u^k &= g^{kl} \, u_l \qquad & u_k &= g_{kl} \, u^l \end{aligned} \tag{5.9}$$

We now should like to express the strain tensors in terms of the displacement vector.

THEOREM 1. *The lagrangian and eulerian strain tensors are related to the displacement vector by*

$$
\begin{aligned}
2\,E_{KL} &= C_{KL} - G_{KL} = U_{K;L} + U_{L;K} + U_{M;K}\,U^{M}{}_{;L} \\
2\,e_{kl} &= g_{kl} - c_{kl} = u_{k;l} + u_{l;k} - u_{m;k}\,u^{m}{}_{;l}
\end{aligned}
\tag{5.10}
$$

where a semicolon represents covariant partial differentiation.

PROOF. From (4.18) and (5.4) for the Green and Cauchy base vectors we have

$$
\begin{aligned}
\mathbf{C}_K &= \frac{\partial \mathbf{p}}{\partial X^K} = \frac{\partial \mathbf{P}}{\partial X^K} + \frac{\partial \mathbf{u}}{\partial X^K} = \mathbf{G}_K + U_{M;K}\,\mathbf{G}^M \\
\mathbf{c}_k &= \frac{\partial \mathbf{P}}{\partial x^k} = \frac{\partial \mathbf{p}}{\partial x^k} - \frac{\partial \mathbf{u}}{\partial x^k} = \mathbf{g}_k - u_{m;k}\,\mathbf{g}^m
\end{aligned}
\tag{5.11}
$$

where we have used the expression for the partial derivative of a vector given by $\partial \mathbf{u}/\partial x^k = u_{m;k}\,\mathbf{g}^m$. Now calculate the deformation tensor $C_{KL}$ by scalar multiplication of $\mathbf{C}_K$ by $\mathbf{C}_L$. Hence

$$
\begin{aligned}
C_{KL} &= (\mathbf{G}_K + U_{M;K}\,\mathbf{G}^M)\cdot(\mathbf{G}_L + U_{N;L}\,\mathbf{G}^N) \\
&= G_{KL} + U_{K;L} + U_{L;K} + U_{M;K}\,U^{M}{}_{;L}
\end{aligned}
$$

which proves $(5.10)_1$. Similarly, by calculating $\mathbf{c}_k \cdot \mathbf{c}_l$ with the use of $(5.11)_2$, we get $(5.10)_2$.

Two important relations that connect the deformed infinitesimal vector $d\mathbf{p}$ to the undeformed vector $d\mathbf{P}$ are obtained through (5.11)

$$
\begin{aligned}
d\mathbf{p} &= \mathbf{C}_K\,dX^K = (\mathbf{G}_K + U_{M;K}\,\mathbf{G}^M)\,dX^K \\
d\mathbf{P} &= \mathbf{c}_k\,dx^k = (\mathbf{g}_k - u_{m;k}\,\mathbf{g}^m)\,dx^k
\end{aligned}
\tag{5.12}
$$

which may also be written in terms of components of $d\mathbf{p}$ and $d\mathbf{P}$ at $P\,(\mathbf{X})$ and $p\,(\mathbf{x})$ as

$$
\begin{aligned}
dx_l \equiv g_{kl}\,dx^k &= (G_{LK} + U_{L;K})\,g^{L}{}_{l}\,dX^K \\
dX_L \equiv G_{KL}\,dX^K &= (g_{lk} - u_{l;k})\,g^{l}{}_{L}\,dx^k
\end{aligned}
\tag{5.13}
$$

Here again we see the use of shifters in the transport of vectors to the same point.

Returning to the strain tensor, we can, by raising the indices, obtain mixed and contravariant components of the strain tensor

$$
\begin{aligned}
E^{K}{}_{L} &= G^{KM}\,E_{ML} \qquad e^{k}{}_{l} = g^{km}\,e_{ml} \\
e^{kl} &= g^{lm}\,e^{k}{}_{m} = g^{lm}\,g^{kn}\,e_{nm}
\end{aligned}
\tag{5.14}
$$

The expressions for the components of the strain tensor in rectangular coordinates $z^k$ and $Z^K$ simplify a great deal, since the covariant derivatives reduce to partial derivatives and the covariant, mixed, and contravariant components have identical expressions. For example, the lagrangian strain components read

$$
\begin{aligned}
&2\,E_{XX} = C_{XX} - 1 = 2\frac{\partial U}{\partial X} + \left(\frac{\partial U}{\partial X}\right)^2 + \left(\frac{\partial V}{\partial X}\right)^2 + \left(\frac{\partial W}{\partial X}\right)^2 \\
(5.15)\quad &2\,E_{XY} = C_{XY} = \frac{\partial U}{\partial Y} + \frac{\partial V}{\partial X} + \frac{\partial U}{\partial X}\frac{\partial U}{\partial Y} + \frac{\partial V}{\partial X}\frac{\partial V}{\partial Y} + \frac{\partial W}{\partial X}\frac{\partial W}{\partial Y} \\
&\cdots\cdots\cdots\cdots\cdots\cdots\cdots\cdots\cdots\cdots
\end{aligned}
$$

Similarly the eulerian strain components become

$$
\begin{aligned}
&2\,e_{xx} = 1 - c_{xx} = 2\frac{\partial u}{\partial x} - \left(\frac{\partial u}{\partial x}\right)^2 - \left(\frac{\partial v}{\partial x}\right)^2 - \left(\frac{\partial w}{\partial x}\right)^2 \\
(5.16)\quad &2\,e_{xy} = -c_{xy} = \frac{\partial u}{\partial y} + \frac{\partial v}{\partial x} - \frac{\partial u}{\partial x}\frac{\partial u}{\partial y} - \frac{\partial v}{\partial x}\frac{\partial v}{\partial y} - \frac{\partial w}{\partial x}\frac{\partial w}{\partial y} \\
&\cdots\cdots\cdots\cdots\cdots\cdots\cdots\cdots\cdots\cdots
\end{aligned}
$$

The rectangular components of displacement $U$, $V$, $W$ in $Z^K$ and $u$, $v$, $w$ in $z^k$ have dimensions of length $L$. Therefore the deformation tensors $C_{XX}$, $c_{xy}$ and the strain tensors $E_{XX}$, $e_{xy}$ are dimensionless. In curvilinear coordinates this, in general, is not the case, since the base vectors may have dimensions themselves. Thus, to obtain the physical components $u^{(k)}$ of the displacement vector $u^k$, we write

$$
(5.17)\qquad \mathbf{u} = \sum_k u^k \sqrt{g_{kk}} \left(\frac{\mathbf{g}_k}{\sqrt{g_{kk}}}\right)
$$

Now $\mathbf{g}_k/\sqrt{g_{kk}}$ is a unit vector. Hence, through

$$
(5.18)\qquad u^{(k)} = u^k \sqrt{g_{\underline{kk}}} \qquad u^k = \frac{u^{(k)}}{\sqrt{g_{\underline{kk}}}}
$$

where an underscore suspends the summation, we relate the components of the displacement vector to its physical components. Using $(5.18)_2$, one can express the components of the strain tensor in terms of the physical components of the displacement vector (cf. Art. A3).

## 6. INFINITESIMAL STRAINS AND ROTATIONS

Various approximate theories of continuum mechanics are based on the dropping or approximating of the nonlinear terms of (5.10). This may be done systematically by introducing *infinitesimal strain tensors* $\tilde{E}_{KL}$, $\tilde{e}_{kl}$ and *infinitesimal rotation tensors* $\tilde{R}_{KL}$, $\tilde{r}_{kl}$:

$$
(6.1)\qquad
\begin{aligned}
\tilde{E}_{KL} &\equiv \tfrac{1}{2}(U_{K;L} + U_{L;K}) \equiv U_{(K;L)} \qquad & \tilde{e}_{kl} &\equiv \tfrac{1}{2}(u_{k;l} + u_{l;k}) \equiv u_{(k;l)} \\
\tilde{R}_{KL} &\equiv \tfrac{1}{2}(U_{K;L} - U_{L;K}) \equiv U_{[K;L]} \qquad & \tilde{r}_{kl} &\equiv \tfrac{1}{2}(u_{k;l} - u_{l;k}) \equiv u_{[k;l]}
\end{aligned}
$$

where parentheses enclosing indices indicate the symmetric part of the quantity and brackets the antisymmetric part. The above quantities are the strains and rotations of the classical linear theory. From (6.1) we clearly have

$$u_{k;l} = \tilde{e}_{kl} + \tilde{r}_{kl} \qquad U_{K;L} = \tilde{E}_{KL} + \tilde{R}_{KL} \tag{6.2}$$

Since the analyses for the lagrangian and eulerian quantities are identical, we carry out the further treatment in terms of the eulerian representation except when a specific reference to the lagrangian picture is needed.

By raising the indices, we also have the associated tensors

$$\tilde{e}^k{}_l = g^{km}\,\tilde{e}_{ml} \qquad \tilde{e}^{kl} = g^{lm}\,\tilde{e}^k{}_m = g^{lm}\,g^{kn}\,\tilde{e}_{nm} \tag{6.3}$$

The infinitesimal strain tensor $\tilde{e}_{kl}$ is a *symmetric* tensor, and the infinitesimal rotation tensor $\tilde{r}_{kl}$ is a *skew-symmetric* tensor, i.e.,

$$\tilde{e}_{kl} = \tilde{e}_{lk} \qquad \tilde{r}_{kl} = -\tilde{r}_{lk} \tag{6.4}$$

From a skew-symmetric tensor, in three dimensions, we can always form a dual vector by the operation

$$2\,\tilde{r}^k = \epsilon^{klm}\,\tilde{r}_{ml} \qquad 2\,\tilde{R}^K = \epsilon^{KLM}\,\tilde{R}_{ML} \tag{6.5}$$

or explicitly

$$\begin{gathered} 2\sqrt{g}\,\tilde{r}^1 = 2\,\tilde{r}_{32} = u_{3;2} - u_{2;3} \qquad 2\sqrt{g}\,\tilde{r}^2 = 2\,\tilde{r}_{13} = u_{1;3} - u_{3;1} \\ 2\sqrt{g}\,\tilde{r}^3 = 2\,\tilde{r}_{21} = u_{2;1} - u_{1;2} \end{gathered} \tag{6.6}$$

Substituting (6.2) into (5.10), we shall have

$$\begin{aligned} E_{KL} &= \tilde{E}_{KL} + \tfrac{1}{2}\,(\tilde{E}_{MK} + \tilde{R}_{MK})\,(\tilde{E}^M{}_L + \tilde{R}^M{}_L) \\ e_{kl} &= \tilde{e}_{kl} - \tfrac{1}{2}\,(\tilde{e}_{mk} + \tilde{r}_{mk})\,(\tilde{e}^m{}_l + \tilde{r}^m{}_l) \end{aligned} \tag{6.7}$$

These expressions suggest many possibilities for various degrees of approximations for the strain tensors. For example, in the product terms for small $\tilde{e}_{kl}$, the products of $\tilde{e}_{mk}\,\tilde{e}^m{}_l$ may be dropped while such products as $\tilde{e}_{mk}\,\tilde{r}^m{}_l$ may be retained; or one may retain only certain components of these product terms.[1]

An important conclusion that follows from (6.7) is that in general $\tilde{e}_{kl} = 0$ does not imply $e_{kl} = 0$; that is, vanishing infinitesimal strains (i.e., the linear part of the strain tensor) are not sufficient for a rigid deformation. Note that $\tilde{e}_{kl}$ is not a strain measure.

A geometrical interpretation of $\tilde{E}_{KL}$ may be made as follows. Con-

[1] A complete systematic study does not exist. Various plate and shell theories, however, make use of this approach. For a discussion see Novozhilov [1948]. For a more complete treatment see Eringen [1954]. See also Art. 14.

sider an infinitesimal vector $d\mathbf{X}$ at $\mathbf{X}$; after deformation this vector becomes $d\mathbf{x}$ at $\mathbf{x}$. Now translate $d\mathbf{x}$ from $\mathbf{x}$ to $\mathbf{X}$ (Fig. 6.1). Let $\mathbf{N}$ be the unit vector along $d\mathbf{X}$. Hence

$$\mathbf{N} \equiv \frac{d\mathbf{X}}{|d\mathbf{X}|}$$

We now calculate *elongation* $\epsilon_{(\mathbf{N})}$ along the direction $\mathbf{N}$, defined by

$$\epsilon_{(\mathbf{N})} \equiv \frac{|d\mathbf{x}| \cos\theta - |d\mathbf{X}|}{|d\mathbf{X}|}$$
$$= \frac{d\mathbf{x} \cdot d\mathbf{X}}{|d\mathbf{X}|^2} - 1 = \frac{d\mathbf{x} \cdot \mathbf{N}}{|d\mathbf{X}|} - 1$$

or

$$\epsilon_{(\mathbf{N})} = \frac{dx_K N^K}{|d\mathbf{X}|} - 1 \tag{6.8}$$

where, according to $(5.13)_1$,

$$dx_K = g^k{}_K\, dx_k = g^k{}_K\, g^M{}_k\, (G_{ML} + U_{M;L})\, dX^L$$

or using $(6.2)_2$

$$dx_K = (G_{KL} + \tilde{E}_{KL} + \tilde{R}_{KL})\, dX^L \tag{6.9}$$

If we now substitute (6.9) into (6.8), we get

$$\epsilon_{(\mathbf{N})} = \tilde{E}_{KL} N^K N^L \tag{6.10}$$

which shows that *the normal component of* $\tilde{\mathbf{E}}$ *in the direction of* $\mathbf{N}$ *is the elongation in that direction.* The dual result for the tensor $\tilde{\mathbf{e}}$ may be seen

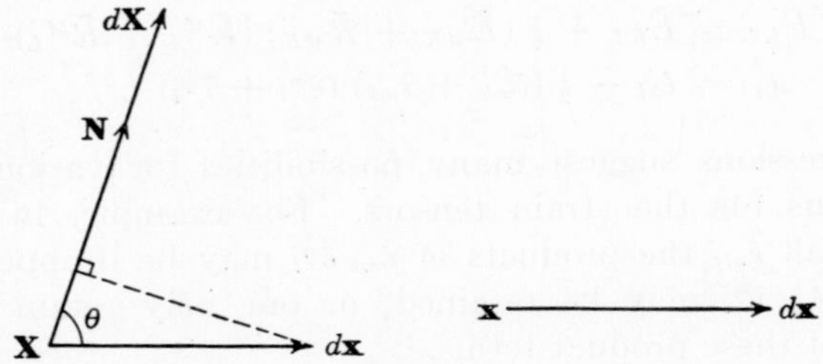


FIG. 6.1

to hold in an analogous way. If we select the directions of $\mathbf{N}$ to be the direction of the $X^1$ axis in rectangular coordinates, then $N^1 = 1$, $N^2 = N^3 = 0$. Hence $\epsilon_{(1)} = \tilde{E}_{11}$ or in general $\epsilon_{(K)} = \tilde{E}_{\underline{KK}}$; that is, *the elongations along the coordinate axes are none other than the normal components* $\tilde{E}_{11}$, $\tilde{E}_{22}$, *and* $\tilde{E}_{33}$ *of* $\tilde{\mathbf{E}}$ *in these directions.*

A geometrical meaning for the infinitesimal rotation tensor $\tilde{R}_{KL}$ will be found in Art. 10. We shall prove that $\tilde{\mathbf{R}} = 0$ is a necessary but not sufficient condition for a pure strain.

## 7. LENGTH AND ANGLE CHANGES

A geometrical meaning of the strain tensor is obtained if we consider the edge vectors $\mathbf{G}_{\underline{K}}\, dX^{\underline{K}}$ of a curvilinear parallelepiped in their deformations. We have found that, referred to the same coordinate system $X^K$, the edge vectors $\mathbf{G}_{\underline{K}}\, dX^{\underline{K}}$ deform into $\mathbf{C}_{\underline{K}}\, dX^{\underline{K}}$ (Fig. 7.1).

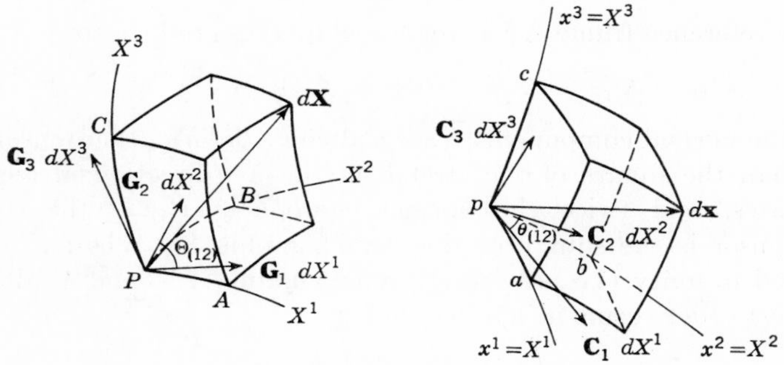


FIG. 7.1. Deformation of a curvilinear parallelepiped.

The ratio $ds/dS$ of the lengths of vectors $d\mathbf{x}$ and $d\mathbf{X}$ is a function of the direction of either $d\mathbf{X}$ or $d\mathbf{x}$ and is called the *stretch*. Let $\mathbf{N}$ and $\mathbf{n}$ be respectively the unit vectors along $d\mathbf{X}$ and $d\mathbf{x}$. Then the stretch $\Lambda_{(\mathbf{N})} = \lambda_{(\mathbf{n})}$ is defined by

$$(7.1)\qquad \begin{aligned} \Lambda_{(\mathbf{N})} &= \frac{ds}{dS} = \sqrt{C_{KL}\, N^K N^L} \\ \lambda_{(\mathbf{n})} &= \frac{ds}{dS} = \frac{1}{\sqrt{c_{kl}\, n^k n^l}} \end{aligned}$$

where

$$(7.2)\qquad N^K \equiv \frac{dX^K}{dS} \qquad n^k \equiv \frac{dx^k}{ds}$$

are the cosine directors of $\mathbf{N}$ and $\mathbf{n}$ respectively. Physically $\Lambda_{(\mathbf{N})}$ and $\lambda_{(\mathbf{n})}$ are the same. We use two different expressions for the stretch to indicate whether the directions are referred to $X^K$ at $P$ or $x^k$ at $p$.

From (7.1) we see that *the normal components of* $\mathbf{C}$ *and* $\mathbf{c}$ *in the directions* $\mathbf{N}$ *and* $\mathbf{n}$ *are, respectively, the squares and inverse squares of the stretches in those directions.*

The *extension* $E_{(\mathbf{N})} = e_{(\mathbf{n})}$ is defined by

$$(7.3)\qquad E_{(\mathbf{N})} = e_{(\mathbf{n})} \equiv \Lambda_{(\mathbf{N})} - 1 = \frac{ds - dS}{dS}$$

When the direction $\mathbf{N}$ is tangent to the coordinate curve $X^1$, we have $N^1 = dX^1/dS = 1/\sqrt{G_{11}}$, $N^2 = N^3 = 0$. Therefore

$$
\begin{aligned}
\Lambda_{(1)} &= \sqrt{C_{11}(\mathbf{X}, t)/G_{11}(\mathbf{X})} = \sqrt{1 + 2(E_{11}/G_{11})} \\
E_{(1)} &= \sqrt{1 + 2(E_{11}/G_{11})} - 1
\end{aligned} \tag{7.4}
$$

From this it follows that

$$
\frac{C_{11}}{G_{11}} = \Lambda_{(1)}^2 \qquad \frac{2E_{11}}{G_{11}} = (1 + E_{(1)})^2 - 1 \tag{7.5}
$$

If the reference frame $X^K$ is rectangular, these reduce to

$$
C_{11} = \Lambda_{(1)}^2 \qquad 2E_{11} = (1 + E_{(1)})^2 - 1 = \Lambda_{(1)}^2 - 1 \tag{7.6}
$$

Hence the normal component $C_{11}$ of Cauchy's deformation tensor is none other than the square of the stretch in the $X^1$ direction in rectangular coordinates, and twice the normal component $E_{11}$ of the lagrangian strain tensor is the square of the stretch minus 1. When $E_{11}$ is small compared to unity (i.e., $E_{11} \ll 1$), by expanding (7.5) and retaining only the lowest-order terms in $E_{11}$, we find

$$
E_{11} \cong E_{(1)} \tag{7.7}
$$

The foregoing is of course valid for all normal components $C_{KK}$ and $E_{KK}$. We may similarly find relations of $c_{kk}$ and $e_{kk}$ to the stretches and extensions through (5.1) and (5.2). To this end consider the extension of any element along the $x^1$ axis. For this we have $n^1 = dx^1/ds = 1/\sqrt{g_{11}}$, $n^2 = n^3 = 0$. Hence

$$
\begin{aligned}
\lambda_{(1)} &= \frac{\sqrt{g_{11}(\mathbf{x})}}{\sqrt{c_{11}(\mathbf{x}, t)}} = \left(1 - 2\frac{e_{11}}{g_{11}}\right)^{-\frac{1}{2}} \\
e_{(1)} &= \lambda_{(1)} - 1
\end{aligned}
$$

or

$$
\begin{aligned}
\frac{c_{11}}{g_{11}} &= \lambda_{(1)}^{-2} \\
2\frac{e_{11}}{g_{11}} &= 1 - \lambda_{(1)}^{-2} = 1 - (1 + e_{(1)})^{-2}
\end{aligned} \tag{7.8}
$$

The dissymmetry of (7.8) to (7.5) arises from the definitions of stretch and extension which were not expressed in dual forms. For small extensions in a rectangular frame of reference we again find

$$
e_{11} \cong e_{(1)} \tag{7.9}
$$

Next we proceed to show the relation between the angle changes and the mixed components of the Cauchy and Euler tensors. Let two elements $d\mathbf{X}_1$ and $d\mathbf{X}_2$ at $\mathbf{X}$ be deformed into the elements $d\mathbf{x}_1$ and $d\mathbf{x}_2$ at $\mathbf{x}$.

We take $\mathbf{N}_1$, $\mathbf{N}_2$ and $\mathbf{n}_1$, $\mathbf{n}_2$ as the unit vectors respectively along $d\mathbf{X}_1$, $d\mathbf{X}_2$ at $\mathbf{X}$, and $d\mathbf{x}_1$ and $d\mathbf{x}_2$ at $\mathbf{x}$. The angle $\Theta_{(\mathbf{N}_1,\mathbf{N}_2)}$ between $d\mathbf{X}_1$ and $d\mathbf{X}_2$ becomes $\theta_{(\mathbf{n}_1,\mathbf{n}_2)}$ between $d\mathbf{x}_1$ and $d\mathbf{x}_2$ (Fig. 7.2).

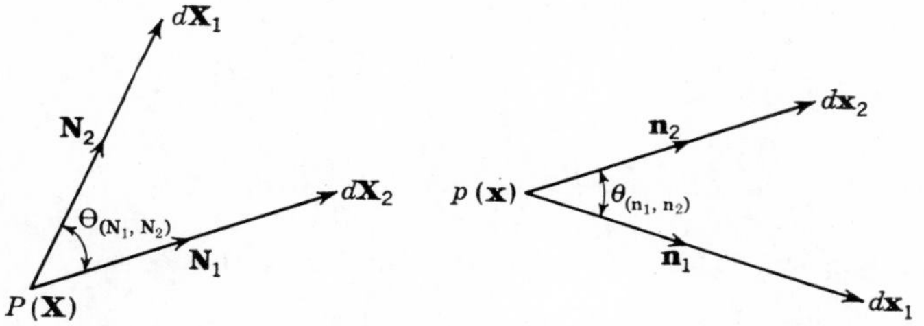


FIG. 7.2. Angle change.

We have

$$\text{(7.10)} \qquad \mathbf{N}_\alpha = \frac{d\mathbf{X}_\alpha}{|d\mathbf{X}_\alpha|} \qquad \mathbf{n}_\alpha = \frac{d\mathbf{x}_\alpha}{|d\mathbf{x}_\alpha|} \qquad (\alpha = 1, 2)$$

Now calculate the angles $\Theta_{(\mathbf{N}_1,\mathbf{N}_2)}$ and $\theta_{(\mathbf{n}_1,\mathbf{n}_2)}$ from

$$\cos \Theta_{(\mathbf{N}_1,\mathbf{N}_2)} = \frac{d\mathbf{X}_1 \cdot d\mathbf{X}_2}{|d\mathbf{X}_1|\,|d\mathbf{X}_2|} = \frac{G_{KL}\,dX_1{}^K\,dX_2{}^L}{|d\mathbf{X}_1|\,|d\mathbf{X}_2|}$$

or

$$\text{(7.11)} \qquad \cos \Theta_{(\mathbf{N}_1,\mathbf{N}_2)} = G_{KL}\;N_1{}^K\;N_2{}^L$$

Similarly

$$\cos \theta_{(\mathbf{n}_1,\mathbf{n}_2)} = \frac{d\mathbf{x}_1 \cdot d\mathbf{x}_2}{|d\mathbf{x}_1|\,|d\mathbf{x}_2|} = \frac{C_{KL}\,dX_1{}^K\,dX_2{}^L}{\sqrt{C_{MN}\,dX_1{}^M\,dX_1{}^N}\,\sqrt{C_{PQ}\,dX_2{}^P\,dX_2{}^Q}}$$

or

$$\text{(7.12)} \qquad \cos \theta_{(\mathbf{n}_1,\mathbf{n}_2)} = \frac{C_{KL}\;N_1{}^K\;N_2{}^L}{\Lambda_{(\mathbf{N}_1)}\,\Lambda_{(\mathbf{N}_2)}}$$

The *shear* in the plane determined by $\mathbf{N}_1$ and $\mathbf{N}_2$ is defined as the *decrease in angle:*

$$\text{(7.13)} \qquad \Gamma_{(\mathbf{N}_1,\mathbf{N}_2)} = \gamma_{(\mathbf{n}_1,\mathbf{n}_2)} = \Theta_{(\mathbf{N}_1,\mathbf{N}_2)} - \theta_{(\mathbf{n}_1,\mathbf{n}_2)}$$

Here again dual representation $\Gamma$ and $\gamma$ for the same physical quantity, i.e., the shear, is introduced primarily to distinguish lagrangian and eulerian representations. It is now clear that the knowledge of $C_{KL}$, $K \neq L$, is not sufficient to determine the shear $\Gamma_{(\mathbf{N}_1,\mathbf{N}_2)}$; we must in addition know the normal components $C_{KK}$ so that stretches $\Lambda_{(\mathbf{N}_1)}$ and $\Lambda_{(\mathbf{N}_2)}$ can be determined. If we write $H$ for the right side of (7.12) and use this in

(7.13), we may solve for

$$\sin \Gamma_{(\mathbf{N}_1,\mathbf{N}_2)} = H \sin \Theta_{(\mathbf{N}_1,\mathbf{N}_2)} - \sqrt{1 - H^2} \cos \Theta_{(\mathbf{N}_1,\mathbf{N}_2)} \tag{7.14}$$

which for originally orthogonal directions, i.e., $\Theta_{(\mathbf{N}_1,\mathbf{N}_2)} = \pi/2$, reduces to

$$\sin \Gamma_{(\mathbf{N}_1,\mathbf{N}_2)} = H = \frac{C_{KL}\, N_1{}^K\, N_2{}^L}{\Lambda_{(\mathbf{N}_1)}\, \Lambda_{(\mathbf{N}_2)}} \tag{7.15}$$

Therefore, *for two orthogonal directions, the vanishing of* $C_{KL}\, N_1{}^K\, N_2{}^L$ *is necessary and sufficient for the vanishing of the corresponding shear.*

If we select the directions $\mathbf{N}_1$ and $\mathbf{N}_2$ along the tangents of the coordinates $X^K$, (7.11) and (7.12) reduce to

$$\begin{aligned} \cos \Theta_{(KL)} &= \frac{G_{KL}}{\sqrt{G_{\underline{KK}}\, G_{\underline{LL}}}} \\ \cos \theta_{(KL)} &= \frac{C_{KL}}{\sqrt{C_{\underline{KK}}\, C_{\underline{LL}}}} = \frac{G_{KL} + 2\, E_{KL}}{[(G_{\underline{KK}} + 2\, E_{\underline{KK}})\, (G_{\underline{LL}} + 2\, E_{\underline{LL}})]^{\frac{1}{2}}} \end{aligned} \tag{7.16}$$

When the coordinates $X^K$ are rectangular, this simplifies to

$$\begin{aligned} \cos \Theta_{(KL)} &= \delta_{KL} \\ \cos \theta_{(KL)} &= \sin \Gamma_{(KL)} = \frac{\delta_{KL} + 2\, E_{KL}}{\sqrt{(1 + 2\, E_{\underline{KK}})\, (1 + 2\, E_{\underline{LL}})}} \end{aligned} \tag{7.17}$$

Thus, using $(7.6)_2$ in $(7.17)_2$, we may also write

$$2\, E_{KL} = (1 + E_{(K)})\, (1 + E_{(L)}) \sin \Gamma_{(\underline{KL})} \qquad (K \neq L) \tag{7.18}$$

When the extensions are small compared to unity, this reduces to

$$2\, E_{KL} \cong \sin \Gamma_{(KL)} \qquad (K \neq L) \tag{7.19}$$

We therefore find that the mixed component of the strain tensor for small extensions is one-half of the sine of the shear. For small shears we may further take $\sin \Gamma_{(KL)} \cong \Gamma_{(KL)}$, obtaining the classical result in the theory of infinitesimal deformations. It is clear that the foregoing result applies in the same way in the eulerian representation. The dual of (7.16) in eulerian representation reads

$$\begin{aligned} \cos \theta_{(kl)} &= \frac{g_{kl}}{\sqrt{g_{\underline{kk}}\, g_{\underline{ll}}}} \\ \cos \Theta_{(kl)} &= \frac{c_{kl}}{\sqrt{c_{\underline{kk}}\, c_{\underline{ll}}}} = \frac{g_{kl} - 2\, e_{kl}}{[(g_{\underline{kk}} - 2\, e_{\underline{kk}})\, (g_{\underline{ll}} - 2\, e_{\underline{ll}})]^{\frac{1}{2}}} \end{aligned} \tag{7.20}$$

Since eulerian and lagrangian coordinates can be chosen independently, it is not in general possible to relate the shears $\Gamma_{(KL)}$ and $\gamma_{(kl)}$. For

$\Theta_{(KL)} = \pi/2$ and $\theta_{(kl)} = \pi/2$ respectively, they are given by

$$(7.21) \qquad \sin \Gamma_{(KL)} = \frac{1}{\Lambda_{(K)}\,\Lambda_{(L)}} \frac{C_{KL}}{\sqrt{G_{\underline{KK}}\,G_{\underline{LL}}}} \qquad \sin \gamma_{(kl)} = -\lambda_{(k)}\,\lambda_{(l)} \frac{c_{kl}}{\sqrt{g_{\underline{kk}}\,g_{\underline{ll}}}}$$

From the geometrical meaning of the deformation tensors $C_{KL}$ and $c_{kl}$ and the strain tensors $E_{KL}$ and $e_{kl}$, it is now clear that the necessary and sufficient condition for the deformation to be rigid at each point is

$$(7.22) \qquad C_{KL} = \delta_{KL} \qquad c_{kl} = \delta_{kl} \qquad \text{or} \qquad E_{KL} = e_{kl} = 0$$

## 8. STRAIN ELLIPSOID

The state of local deformation in the neighborhood of a point $P$ $(\mathbf{X})$ in the undeformed body or $p$ $(\mathbf{x})$ in the deformed body can be understood more clearly by a geometrical treatment due to Cauchy. The method presented here is applicable without change to any second-order symmetric tensor.

An infinitesimal sphere[1] at $X^K$ swept by a vector $dX^K$ is given by

$$(8.1) \qquad G_{KL}\, dX^K\, dX^L = dS^2 = K^2$$

Through the motion (2.1) the material points of this sphere are carried into a quadric surface at the point $x^k$ of the deformed body

$$(8.2) \qquad c_{kl}\, dx^k\, dx^l = dS^2 = K^2$$

The mapping (2.1) is nonsingular and $G_{KL}$ is positive-definite. From $(4.8)_1$ it is clear that $c_{kl}$ is positive-definite. Consequently the quadric surface (8.2) is an *ellipsoid*. This ellipsoid is called the *material strain ellipsoid*. Similarly, by inverse mapping, the infinitesimal sphere

$$(8.3) \qquad g_{kl}\, dx^k\, dx^l = ds^2 = k^2$$

at $x^k$ is carried into an ellipsoid at $X^K$

$$(8.4) \qquad C_{KL}\, dX^K\, dX^L = ds^2 = k^2$$

called the *spatial strain ellipsoid*.

It is of interest to know how an orthogonal triad of radii of the sphere at $X^K$ deforms. To this end we have the following theorem.

THEOREM 1. (*Cauchy's First Theorem*) *Perpendicular diameters of an infinitesimal sphere at* $\mathbf{X}$ *are deformed into conjugate diameters of the material ellipsoid at* $\mathbf{x}$.

PROOF. Let $d\mathbf{X}_1$ and $d\mathbf{X}_2$ be two orthogonal vectors at $\mathbf{X}$, i.e.,

$$d\mathbf{X}_1 \cdot d\mathbf{X}_2 = 0$$

[1] The fact that (8.1) is a sphere can be seen by noting that in rectangular coordinates $G_{KL} = \delta_{KL}$, and hence (8.1) reads $(dX)^2 + (dY)^2 + (dZ)^2 = K^2$.

Now according to $(4.18)_1$, $d\mathbf{X}_1$ deforms into $\mathbf{c}_k\, dx_1^k$; hence, we get

$$c_{kl}\, dx_1^k\, dx_2^l = 0 \tag{8.5}$$

This shows that the gradient vector $c_{kl}\, dx_1^k$ of the ellipsoid at the end point of the vector $d\mathbf{x}_1$ is perpendicular to the vector $d\mathbf{x}_2$ (Fig. 8.1). Hence the proof of the theorem.

A quadric has three diameters that are each perpendicular to its conjugate plane. These mutually orthogonal diameters are the axes of the quadric. These axes, according to the foregoing theorem, are the mappings of an orthogonal triad of the sphere at $\mathbf{X}$. Hence we have the following corollary.

COROLLARY 1. *At a point $P(\mathbf{X})$ of $B$ there exist at least three mutually perpendicular directions which remain orthogonal to each other after deforma-*

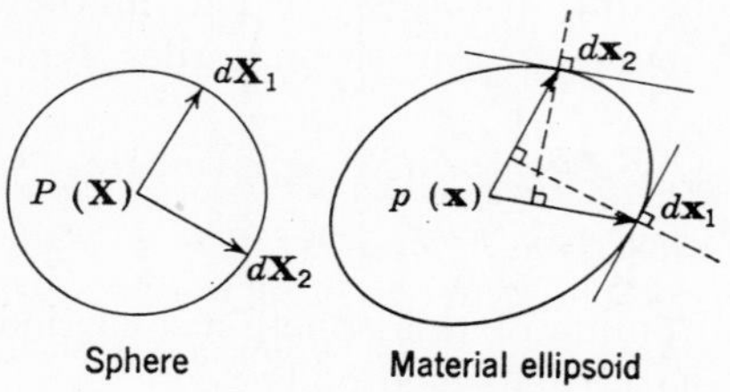


FIG. 8.1

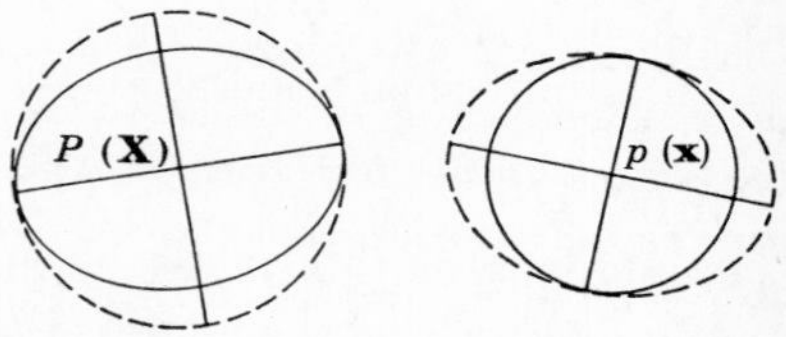


FIG. 8.2. Spatial and material strain ellipsoids.

*tion and constitute the principal axes of the strain ellipsoid at $p(\mathbf{x})$.* A deformation that carries the orthogonal triad of radii into the principal semiaxes of the ellipsoid does not alter the angles between each pair of the radii. Therefore, according to (7.20) and (7.21), we have Corollary 2.

COROLLARY 2. *Referred to principal axes of the strain ellipsoid, the mixed components $c_{kl}$ $(k \neq l)$ of the Cauchy deformation tensor and the eulerian strain tensor $e_{kl}$ $(k \neq l)$ vanish.* All of these, of course, are also valid for the spatial strain ellipsoid. In fact, we have a dual picture as follows. The triad at $\mathbf{X}$ considered as the orthogonal radii of a sphere deforms into the triad at $\mathbf{x}$ which constitutes the principal semiaxes of the material strain ellipsoid. Conversely an orthogonal triad of radii of the sphere at $\mathbf{x}$ is a triad of the principal semiaxes of the spatial ellipsoid at $\mathbf{X}$. Consequently a third corollary follows.

COROLLARY 3. *The deformation rotates the principal axes of the spatial ellipsoid at $\mathbf{X}$ into those of the material ellipsoid at $\mathbf{x}$* (Fig. 8.2).

This result is based on the assumption that the lengths of the principal axes of the material ellipsoid at $\mathbf{x}$ are unequal. When any two principal axes have equal lengths, we have an ellipsoid of rotation. In this case there is a plane through $\mathbf{X}$ perpendicular to the axis of rotation. On this plane every pair of orthogonal directions through **X** constitutes two principal axes, the third being the axis of rotation of the ellipsoid.

When all three axes of the material ellipsoid at **x** are equal, the ellipsoid degenerates into a sphere. In this case we have infinitely many choices of principal directions since any orthogonal triad of radii may be selected for this purpose.

The deformation carries the diameters of a sphere at **X** into the diameters of an ellipsoid at **x**. *The ratio of the diameters of the ellipsoid to the corresponding diameters of the sphere are the stretches.* Therefore the magnitudes of the stretches in different undeformed directions at **X** vary as the distance from **x** to the surface of the ellipsoid. The determination of the direction of corresponding deformed and undeformed diameters with respect to each other requires a knowledge of the local rotation.[2]

In an ellipsoid the lengths of principal axes may be ordered as the largest, the middle-sized, and the smallest. Hence we have the following theorem.

THEOREM 2. (*Cauchy's Second Theorem*) *At any point* **X** *there exists at least one set of three mutually perpendicular directions for one of which the stretch is not less than in any other direction, for another one it is not greater than in any other direction, and for the third one it is a minimax. When they are ordered as* $\Lambda_{(1)} \geq \Lambda_{(2)} \geq \Lambda_{(3)}$, *they stand in the same ratio* $\Lambda_{(1)} : \Lambda_{(2)} : \Lambda_{(3)}$ *as the lengths of the axes of the strain ellipsoid.* These stretches, associated with the principal axes of strain, are called *principal stretches.*

## 9. STRAIN INVARIANTS

In the previous article we have found that at a point **X** in $B$ there exist at least three mutually perpendicular directions which are carried into the principal axes of an ellipsoid at **x**. Along these three directions the stretches $\Lambda_{(\mathbf{N})}$ take extremum values. A dual picture applies for the inverse deformation. The analytical determination of the principal directions may thus be effected by minimizing

$$(9.1) \qquad \Lambda^2_{(\mathbf{N})} = C_{KL}\, N^K N^L = 2\, E_{KL}\, N^K N^L + 1 \qquad \left(N^K \equiv \frac{dX^K}{dS}\right)$$

with respect to $N^K$ subject to the condition that **N** is a unit vector, i.e.,

$$(9.2) \qquad G_{KL}\, N^K N^L = 1$$

Lagrange's method of multipliers may be utilized for this purpose. Thus

$$\frac{\partial}{\partial N^M} \Lambda^2_{(\mathbf{N})} = \frac{\partial}{\partial N^M} [C_{KL}\, N^K N^L - C\,(G_{KL}\, N^K N^L - 1)] = 0$$

[2] For a definitive treatment see the fundamental theorem of rotation (Art. 10).

where $C$ is an unknown Lagrange multiplier. This gives three linear homogeneous equations for $N^K$

$$(C_{KL} - C\,G_{KL})\,N^L = 0 \tag{9.3}$$

Upon using $C_{KL} = G_{KL} + 2\,E_{KL}$, we may also write this as

$$(E_{KL} - E\,G_{KL})\,N^L = 0 \tag{9.4}$$

where

$$2\,E \equiv C - 1 \tag{9.5}$$

We may solve either (9.3) or (9.4). Once this is done, using the relations of $C_{KL}$ to $E_{KL}$ and $C$ to $E$, we can always convert from the $C$ language to the $E$ language or vice versa.

It is simpler to work with the following equations, which are obtained from (9.3) by raising the index $K$:

$$(C^K{}_L - C\,\delta^K{}_L)\,N^L = 0 \tag{9.6}$$

A nontrivial solution of (9.6) exists if the coefficient determinant (often called the *characteristic determinant*) is equal to zero, i.e.,

$$|C^K{}_L - C\,\delta^K{}_L| = 0 \tag{9.7}$$

Expansion of this determinant gives a cubic equation in $C$, i.e.,

$$-\,C^3 + \mathrm{I}_C\,C^2 - \mathrm{II}_C\,C + \mathrm{III}_C = 0 \tag{9.8}$$

where

$$\begin{aligned} \mathrm{I}_C &= \frac{1}{1!}\,\delta^K{}_L\,C^L{}_K \qquad \mathrm{II}_C = \frac{1}{2!}\,\delta^K{}_L{}^M{}_N\,C^L{}_K\,C^N{}_M \\ \mathrm{III}_C &= \frac{1}{3!}\,\delta^K{}_L{}^M{}_N{}^P{}_Q\,C^L{}_K\,C^N{}_M\,C^Q{}_P = \det C^K{}_L \end{aligned} \tag{9.9}$$

are the *invariants of deformation tensor* **C**. The symbols $\delta^K{}_L{}^M{}_N$ and $\delta^K{}_L{}^M{}_N{}^P{}_Q$ are *generalized Kronecker deltas.* These tensors are defined as

$$\delta^K{}_L{}^M{}_N{}^P{}_Q{}^{\cdots}_{\cdots} = \begin{cases} 1\,(-1) & \text{when subscripts are distinct numbers taken from } 1, 2, 3, \ldots \text{ and the superscripts can be brought to the same sequence of the subscripts by an even (odd) permutation;} \\ 0 & \text{otherwise} \end{cases}$$

It can be shown that

$$\delta^K{}_L{}^M{}_N{}^P{}_Q = e^{KMP}\,e_{LNQ} \qquad \delta^K{}_L{}^M{}_N = \delta^K{}_L{}^M{}_N{}^P{}_P$$

where $e^{KMP}$ and $e_{LNQ}$ are permutation symbols defined by (A4.18).

The characteristic equation (9.8) possesses three roots $C_\alpha$, $(\alpha = 1, 2, 3)$[1] called *proper numbers* or *principal values* or *eigenvalues*. The coefficients $\mathrm{I}_C$, $\mathrm{II}_C$, and $\mathrm{III}_C$ of the cubic equation (9.8) are the sums of products of these roots, taken one, two, and three at a time, i.e.,

$$(9.10) \qquad \mathrm{I}_C = C_1 + C_2 + C_3 \qquad \mathrm{II}_C = C_2 C_3 + C_3 C_1 + C_1 C_2$$
$$\mathrm{III}_C = C_1 C_2 C_3$$

Corresponding to each of $C_\alpha$, through (9.6) we obtain a direction $N^L{}_\alpha$. If the proper numbers are *real* and *distinct*, corresponding to these we will have three *real* and *distinct proper (principal) directions*. We now prove the following lemmas.

LEMMA 1. *The proper numbers are real.*

PROOF. Suppose that the contrary is true; then the cubic equation (9.8) will have two complex roots

$$C_1 = C_1' + i\,C_2' \qquad \overset{*}{C}_1 = C_1' - i\,C_2' \qquad (i = \sqrt{-1})$$

Corresponding to these, through (9.6) we obtain a complex direction $N^K{}_1$ and its conjugate $\overset{*}{N}{}^K{}_1$ satisfying (9.3), i.e.,

$$C_{KL} N^L{}_1 = C_1 G_{KL} N^L{}_1 \qquad C_{KL} \overset{*}{N}{}^L{}_1 = \overset{*}{C}_1 G_{KL} \overset{*}{N}{}^L{}_1$$

Now multiply the first of these by $\overset{*}{N}{}^K{}_1$ and the second by $N^K{}_1$, and subtract the second from the first. Remembering that $C_{KL} = C_{LK}$, we obtain

$$0 = (C_1 - \overset{*}{C}_1)\, G_{KL} \overset{*}{N}{}^K{}_1 N^L{}_1$$

Since $G_{KL} \overset{*}{N}{}^K{}_1 N^L{}_1 > 0$, we must have

$$C_1 - \overset{*}{C}_1 = 2i\,C_2' = 0$$

which proves the theorem. Note that the crucial point in this proof is the symmetry of the tensors $C_{KL}$ and $G_{KL}$.

LEMMA 2. *The principal directions* $\mathbf{N}_1$ *and* $\mathbf{N}_2$ *corresponding to two distinct proper numbers* $C_1$ *and* $C_2$ *are orthogonal to each other.*

PROOF. Principal directions $N^L{}_1$ and $N^L{}_2$ satisfy (9.3), i.e.,

$$C_{KL} N^L{}_1 = C_1 G_{KL} N^L{}_1 \qquad C_{KL} N^L{}_2 = C_2 G_{KL} N^L{}_2$$

Multiply the first of these by $N^K{}_2$ and the second by $N^K{}_1$, and subtract the second from the first. Hence

$$0 = (C_1 - C_2)\, G_{KL} N^K{}_1 N^L{}_2$$

[1] Greek indices are used as labels, not necessarily as tensor indices.

Now $C_1 \neq C_2$ by hypothesis. Hence

$$G_{KL} N^K{}_1 N^L{}_2 = 0 \qquad \text{or} \qquad \mathbf{N}_1 \cdot \mathbf{N}_2 = 0$$

which is the proof of the theorem.

The basic assumption in arriving at this result is that the roots of the characteristic equation (9.8) are distinct. The question arises as to what happens when (9.8) has multiple roots. In such cases the associated directions become indeterminate. For a double root there will be infinitely many directions in a plane, satisfying (9.3). Any two orthogonal directions in this plane may be chosen as the proper directions, the third one being perpendicular to this plane. The strain ellipsoid in this case will have rotational symmetry with respect to the axis of revolution. Two orthogonal directions in a plane through $P$ ($\mathbf{X}$) perpendicular to the axis of rotation may be chosen at will to constitute a principal triad together with the axis of rotation.

When all three roots of the characteristic equation coincide, then the quadric surface becomes a sphere. In this case any three mutually orthogonal directions may be selected as the principal directions.

The state of strain referred to a principal triad takes a simple form. We have

$$N^L{}_\alpha = \delta^L{}_\alpha$$

Hence through (9.6) we get

$$C^K{}_\alpha = C_\alpha \, \delta^K{}_\alpha \tag{9.11}$$

For $\alpha = 1, 2, 3$ we get

$$C^1{}_1 = C_1 \qquad C^2{}_2 = C_2 \qquad C^3{}_3 = C_3 \qquad C^K{}_\alpha = 0 \qquad (K \neq \alpha)$$

which proves the following lemma.

LEMMA 3. *Proper numbers are the normal components of the deformation tensor (principal deformations) in the principal triad, and the shear components in this frame of reference are zero.*

We therefore see that *the determination of the principal directions and the principal deformations of a tensor $C^K{}_L$ at a point* $\mathbf{X}$ *is simply equivalent to finding an orthogonal triad in which $C^K{}_L$ reduces to a diagonal form,*[2] *i.e.,*

$$\begin{bmatrix} C^1{}_1 & C^1{}_2 & C^1{}_3 \\ C^2{}_1 & C^2{}_2 & C^2{}_3 \\ C^3{}_1 & C^3{}_2 & C^3{}_3 \end{bmatrix} = \begin{bmatrix} C_1 & 0 & 0 \\ 0 & C_2 & 0 \\ 0 & 0 & C_3 \end{bmatrix} \tag{9.12}$$

The foregoing process is valid for any symmetric second-order tensor.

Clearly the principal directions $\mathbf{N}_\alpha$ are the principal axes of the strain

[2] A standard theorem in tensor analysis; cf. Sokolnikoff [1951, art. 12].

ellipsoid at $\mathbf{X}$. Referred to a principal triad, the equation of the strain ellipsoid becomes simpler.

$$ds^2 = k^2 = C_{KL}\, dX^K\, dX^L = \sum_\alpha C_\alpha\, (dX^\alpha)^2 \tag{9.13}$$

Now $C_{11}$, $C_{22}$, and $C_{33}$ are positive; hence $C_\alpha > 0$. Therefore, in rectangular coordinates, the strain ellipsoid has semiaxis lengths $a_\alpha = ds/\sqrt{C_\alpha} = k/\sqrt{C_\alpha}$ (Fig. 9.1). The stretches $\Lambda_\alpha = \lambda_\alpha$ along the principal axes are given by[3]

$$\Lambda_\alpha = \frac{ds}{dS} = \sqrt{C_\alpha} = \frac{ds}{a_\alpha} \tag{9.14}$$

Through the consideration of the ellipsoid at $\mathbf{x}$, we find

$$\lambda_\alpha = \frac{ds}{dS} = \frac{1}{\sqrt{c_\alpha}} = \frac{a_\alpha}{dS} \tag{9.15}$$

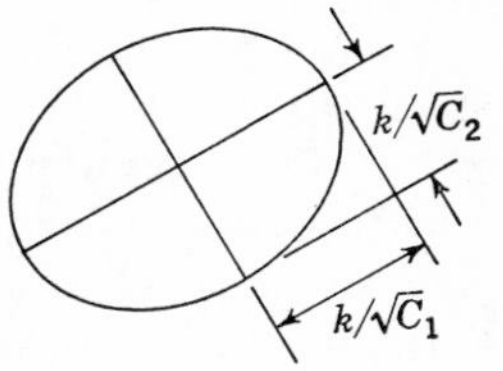


FIG. 9.1

where $c_\alpha$ are the proper numbers for $c^k{}_l$. Since $\lambda_\alpha = \Lambda_\alpha$, we have

$$C_\alpha = \frac{1}{c_\alpha} = \lambda_\alpha^2 \tag{9.16}$$

and the proof of the following theorem.

THEOREM 1. *The lengths of the semiaxes of the strain ellipsoid at* $\mathbf{X}$ *are reciprocal to those at* $\mathbf{x}$, *and the proper numbers are reciprocals of each other. The proper numbers* $C_\alpha$ *are equal to the squares of the stretches along the principal directions of the strain ellipsoid at* $\mathbf{X}$. *Along the principal directions the stretches have extremal values.* The foregoing also constitutes an algebraic proof of Cauchy's second theorem. An alternative form of (9.16) follows from $(4.8)_2$ and $(4.17)_2$:

$$C^K{}_L = x^{k,K}\, x_{k,L} \qquad \overset{-1}{c}{}^k{}_l = x^{k,K}\, x_{l,K}$$

Since any two matrices $\mathbf{AB}$ and $\mathbf{BA}$ have the same characteristic determinant, and hence the same proper values,[4] we have $C_\alpha = \overset{-1}{c}_\alpha$. But $\overset{-1}{c}_\alpha = (c_\alpha)^{-1}$, where $\overset{-1}{c}_\alpha$ are the proper values of $\overset{-1}{c}{}^k{}_l$. Hence

$$C_\alpha = \overset{-1}{c}_\alpha = (c_\alpha)^{-1} = \lambda_\alpha^2 \tag{9.17}$$

The dual of this is

$$c_\alpha = \overset{-1}{C}_\alpha = (C_\alpha)^{-1} = \lambda_\alpha^{-2} \tag{9.18}$$

[3] The parentheses enclosing the subscripts in stretches $\Lambda_{(\alpha)} = \lambda_{(\alpha)}$ are dropped for simplicity.

[4] Cf. Sokolnikoff [1951, p. 38].

According to (9.14) and (9.15) the proper values $C_\alpha$ and $c_\alpha$ uniquely determine the lengths of the semiaxes of the strain ellipsoids at **x** and **X**. Finally:

LEMMA 4. *The deformation rotates the principal axes of the spatial ellipsoid at* **X** *into those of the material ellipsoid at* **x**. This will constitute an analytical proof of Corollary 3 of Cauchy's first theorem. The proof of the theorem and its other corollaries is contained in Lemmas 1 to 4 above. The present lemma finally produces the solution of equation (9.3) for $\mathbf{N}_\alpha$ corresponding to each proper number $C_\alpha$. We shall now show that

$$N^K{}_\alpha = \frac{X^K{}_{,k}\, n^k{}_{\underline{\alpha}}}{\sqrt{c_{\underline{\alpha}}}} \tag{9.19}$$

is the desired solution in terms of the principal directions $\mathbf{n}_\alpha$ of the spatial ellipsoid at **X**. For this purpose we must prove that (1) $N^K{}_\alpha$ are mutually orthogonal unit vectors whenever $n^k{}_\alpha$ are mutually orthogonal and (2) $N^K{}_\alpha$, given by (9.19), satisfy (9.3) whenever $n^k{}_\alpha$ satisfy the equations dual to (9.3), i.e.,

$$(c_{kl} - c\, g_{kl})\, n^l = 0 \tag{9.20}$$

To prove (1), we form

$$\begin{aligned} G_{KL}\, N^K{}_\alpha\, N^L{}_\beta &= \frac{G_{KL}\, X^K{}_{,k}\, X^L{}_{,l}\, n^k{}_{\underline{\alpha}}\, n^l{}_{\underline{\beta}}}{\sqrt{c_{\underline{\alpha}}\, c_{\underline{\beta}}}} \\ &= \frac{c_{kl}\, n^k{}_{\underline{\alpha}}\, n^l{}_{\underline{\beta}}}{\sqrt{c_{\underline{\alpha}}\, c_{\underline{\beta}}}} \\ &= \frac{\sqrt{c_{\underline{\alpha}}}}{\sqrt{c_{\underline{\beta}}}}\, g_{kl}\, n^k{}_{\underline{\alpha}}\, n^l{}_{\underline{\beta}} = \delta_{\alpha\beta} \end{aligned}$$

where the second line follows from the first by using $(4.8)_1$ and the third is obtained by using (9.20) in the second line.

To prove (2), we form

$$\begin{aligned} C_{KL}\, N^L{}_\alpha &= \frac{1}{\sqrt{c_{\underline{\alpha}}}}\, g_{kl}\, x^k{}_{,K}\, x^l{}_{,L}\, X^L{}_{,m}\, n^m{}_{\underline{\alpha}} = \frac{1}{\sqrt{c_{\underline{\alpha}}}}\, g_{kl}\, x^k{}_{,K}\, n^l{}_{\underline{\alpha}} \\ &= \frac{c_{kl}\, n^l{}_{\underline{\alpha}}\, x^k{}_{,K}}{c_{\underline{\alpha}}\sqrt{c_{\underline{\alpha}}}} \\ &= \frac{G_{PM}\, X^P{}_{,k}\, X^M{}_{,l}\, x^k{}_{,K}\, n^l{}_{\underline{\alpha}}}{c_{\underline{\alpha}}\sqrt{c_{\underline{\alpha}}}} = \frac{G_{KM}\, X^M{}_{,l}\, n^l{}_{\underline{\alpha}}}{c_{\underline{\alpha}}\sqrt{c_{\underline{\alpha}}}} \\ &= \frac{G_{KM}\, N^M{}_{\underline{\alpha}}}{c_{\underline{\alpha}}} \end{aligned}$$

In the first line we have used $(4.8)_2$ for $C_{KL}$. The second line follows from the first with the use of (9.20). By using $(4.8)_1$ for $c_{kl}$ on the second line, we get the third line. The fourth line follows from the third with the use of (9.19). If we now compare this result with (9.3), we get $(9.16)_1$. These results assert that the transformation (9.19) carries the orthogonal triad of unit proper vectors $\mathbf{n}_\alpha$ with proper numbers $c_\alpha$ to the orthogonal unit triad of proper vectors $\mathbf{N}_\alpha$ with the proper numbers $C_\alpha$. This therefore sets a one-to-one correspondence between the principal axes of strain ellipsoids at **X** and **x**, thus proving the lemma. The dual of (9.19) is

$$n^k{}_\alpha = \frac{x^k{}_{,K} N^K{}_{\underline{\alpha}}}{\sqrt{C_{\underline{\alpha}}}} = x^k{}_{,K} N^K{}_{\underline{\alpha}} \sqrt{c_{\underline{\alpha}}} \tag{9.21}$$

We may give these results the following geometrical interpretation. *The Green and Cauchy deformation tensors* **C** *and* **c** *may be characterized as the unique symmetric tensors whose principal axes are the principal axes of the strain ellipsoids at* **X** *and* **x** *and whose proper numbers are the squares and the reciprocals of the squares of the principal stretches respectively.* The physical lengths remain unchanged in a coordinate transformation. Consequently $C_\alpha$ and, by (9.10), the quantities $\mathrm{I}_C$, $\mathrm{II}_C$, and $\mathrm{III}_C$ remain unchanged. Hence we have the following theorem.

THEOREM 2. *Quantities* $\mathrm{I}_C$, $\mathrm{II}_C$, *and* $\mathrm{III}_C$ *are invariant with respect to any coordinate transformation at* $X^K$. Moreover the number of principal axes that are needed to characterize uniquely a quadric surface is not more than three. Hence Theorem 3 follows.

THEOREM 3. *In three dimensions the number of independent invariants of a second-order tensor is not more than three.*[5] Using (7.8), (9.17), (9.18), (9.10), and analogous expressions to (9.10) for **c**, we may express the invariants of $C^K{}_L$ and $c^k{}_l$ in terms of the principal stretches $\lambda_\alpha$ and the extensions $e_\alpha$ by

$$\begin{aligned}
\mathrm{I}_C &= \mathrm{I}_{c^{-1}} = \lambda_1^2 + \lambda_2^2 + \lambda_3^2 = (1+e_1)^2 + (1+e_2)^2 + (1+e_3)^2 \\
\mathrm{II}_C &= \mathrm{II}_{c^{-1}} = \lambda_1^2\lambda_2^2 + \lambda_2^2\lambda_3^2 + \lambda_3^2\lambda_1^2 = (1+e_1)^2(1+e_2)^2 \\
&\qquad + (1+e_2)^2(1+e_3)^2 + (1+e_3)^2(1+e_1)^2 \\
\mathrm{III}_C &= \mathrm{III}_{c^{-1}} = \lambda_1^2\lambda_2^2\lambda_3^2 = (1+e_1)^2(1+e_2)^2(1+e_3)^2 \\
\mathrm{I}_c &= \mathrm{I}_{C^{-1}} = \frac{1}{\lambda_1^2} + \frac{1}{\lambda_2^2} + \frac{1}{\lambda_3^2} \\
\mathrm{II}_c &= \mathrm{II}_{C^{-1}} = \frac{1}{\lambda_1^2\lambda_2^2} + \frac{1}{\lambda_2^2\lambda_3^2} + \frac{1}{\lambda_3^2\lambda_1^2} \\
\mathrm{III}_c &= \mathrm{III}_{C^{-1}} = \frac{1}{\lambda_1^2\lambda_2^2\lambda_3^2}
\end{aligned} \tag{9.22}$$

[5] For analytical proofs of this and the previous theorems, see Eringen [1964].

From these follow the *fundamental* identities[6]

$$\text{(9.23)} \qquad \mathrm{I}_c = \frac{\mathrm{II}_C}{\mathrm{III}_C} \qquad \mathrm{II}_c = \frac{\mathrm{I}_C}{\mathrm{III}_C} \qquad \mathrm{III}_c = \frac{1}{\mathrm{III}_C}$$

Since we have $0 < \lambda_\alpha < \infty$, we see that

$$\text{(9.24)} \qquad 0 < \mathrm{I}, \mathrm{II}, \mathrm{III} < \infty$$

For a rigid deformation $e_1 = e_2 = e_3 = 0$; hence

$$\text{(9.25)} \qquad \mathrm{I} = \mathrm{II} = 3 \qquad \mathrm{III} = 1$$

*This is the necessary and sufficient condition for a rigid deformation.* For large values of stretches, $\mathrm{I}_C$, $\mathrm{II}_C$, and $\mathrm{III}_C$ are large and $\mathrm{I}_c$, $\mathrm{II}_c$, and $\mathrm{III}_c$ are small; for small values the reverse is true.

According to (9.8), once the invariants are given, the proper values are determined in a unique fashion. Hence, *given* $\mathrm{I}_C$, $\mathrm{II}_C$, $\mathrm{III}_C$ *satisfying* (9.24), *and given any principal triad at* **X**, *we can determine a unique deformation tensor* **C**.

The proper numbers $E_\alpha$ of strain tensor $E^K{}_L$ are related to $C_\alpha$ through (9.5), i.e.,

$$\text{(9.26)} \qquad 2\,E_\alpha = C_\alpha - 1$$

Using this, we may relate the invariants of the lagrangian strain tensor to the deformation tensor invariants. We have

$$\text{(9.27)} \qquad \mathrm{I}_E = E_1 + E_2 + E_3 \qquad \mathrm{II}_E = E_1 E_2 + E_2 E_3 + E_3 E_1$$
$$\mathrm{III}_E = E_1 E_2 E_3$$

Substituting (9.26) into (9.10) and (9.27), we obtain

$$\text{(9.28)} \qquad \begin{aligned} \mathrm{I}_C &= 3 + 2\,\mathrm{I}_E & 2\,\mathrm{I}_E &= -3 + \mathrm{I}_C \\ \mathrm{II}_C &= 3 + 4\,\mathrm{I}_E + 4\,\mathrm{II}_E & 4\,\mathrm{II}_E &= 3 - 2\,\mathrm{I}_C + \mathrm{II}_C \\ \mathrm{III}_C &= 1 + 2\,\mathrm{I}_E + 4\,\mathrm{II}_E + 8\,\mathrm{III}_E & 8\,\mathrm{III}_E &= -1 + \mathrm{I}_C \\ & & &\quad - \mathrm{II}_C + \mathrm{III}_C \end{aligned}$$

The dual expressions relating the invariants of $c^k{}_l$ and $e^k{}_l$ may be obtained in a similar fashion, e.g.,

$$\text{(9.29)} \qquad \mathrm{I}_c = 3 - 2\,\mathrm{I}_e \qquad \mathrm{II}_c = 3 - 4\,\mathrm{I}_e + 4\,\mathrm{II}_e$$
$$\mathrm{III}_c = 1 - 2\,\mathrm{I}_e + 4\,\mathrm{II}_e - 8\,\mathrm{III}_e$$

According to a rule in the theory of matrices, the determinant of the product of matrices is equal to the product of the determinants of the member matrices. Hence

[6] A proof of these was given by Murnaghan [1937, appendix].

(9.30) $$\mathrm{III}_C = \det C^K{}_L = (\det g_{mn})\,(\det G^{RS})\,(\det x^k{}_{,K})^2 = \frac{g}{G}\,j^2 = J^2$$

where $J = |\partial z^k/\partial Z^K| = \sqrt{g/G}\,j$ is the jacobian of the transformation $z^k = z^k\,(Z^K, t)$ for fixed $t$, as can be seen from the following:

$$\left|\frac{\partial z^k}{\partial Z^K}\right| = \left|\frac{\partial z^k}{\partial x^m}\frac{\partial x^m}{\partial X^M}\frac{\partial X^M}{\partial Z^K}\right| = \left|\frac{\partial z^k}{\partial x^m}\right|\left|\frac{\partial X^M}{\partial Z^K}\right|\left|\frac{\partial x^m}{\partial X^M}\right| = \frac{\sqrt{g}}{\sqrt{G}}\,j$$

Consequently, for the volume elements $dV$ in the reference state and $dv$ in the deformed state, we have

(9.31) $$dv = \sqrt{\mathrm{III}_C}\,dV \qquad dV = \sqrt{\mathrm{III}_c}\,dv$$

which provide a geometrical interpretation of $\mathrm{III}_C$ and $\mathrm{III}_c$; namely, *$\mathrm{III}_C$ and $\mathrm{III}_c$ are respectively the square and the inverse square of the ratio of the deformed to the undeformed volume elements.*

## 10. ROTATION

After deformation a vector $d\mathbf{X}$ at $\mathbf{X}$ becomes a new vector $d\mathbf{x}$ at $\mathbf{x}$ (Fig. 10.1). The angle $\theta$ that $d\mathbf{X}$ rotated during deformation may be calculated from

(10.1) $$\cos\theta = \frac{d\mathbf{X}\cdot d\mathbf{x}}{dX\,dx} = \frac{G_{KL}\,dX^K\,g^L{}_l\,dx^l}{dX\,dx} = \frac{g_{kl}\,dx^k\,g^l{}_L\,dX^L}{dX\,dx}$$

If we use the convention $0 \le \theta < \pi$ and introduce the unit vectors

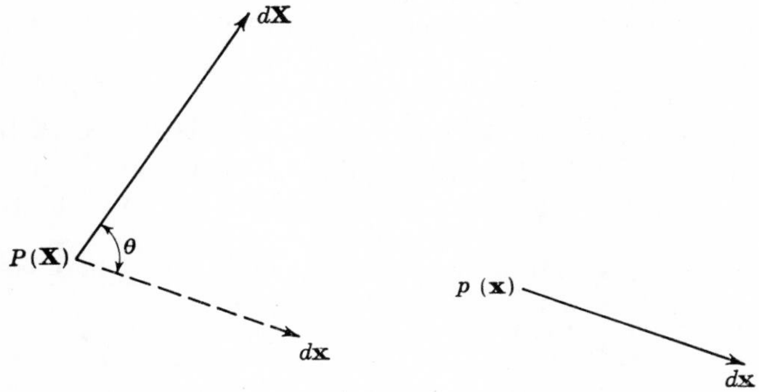


FIG. 10.1

$\mathbf{N}$ and $\mathbf{n}$ at $\mathbf{X}$ and $\mathbf{x}$ along $d\mathbf{X}$ and $d\mathbf{x}$ respectively given by

(10.2) $$N^K \equiv \frac{dX^K}{dX} \qquad n^k \equiv \frac{dx^k}{dx}$$

we obtain

$$\cos\theta = G_{KL}\, g^L{}_l\, N^K n^l = g_{kl}\, g^l{}_L\, n^k N^L \tag{10.3}$$

We may express this fully in terms of $N^K$ or $n^k$ if we write (10.1) as

$$\cos\theta = \frac{G_{KL}\, g^L{}_l\, x^l{}_{,M}\, (dX^K/dX)\,(dX^M/dX)}{dx/dX}$$

or

$$\cos\theta = \frac{1}{\Lambda_{(\mathbf{N})}}\, G_{KL}\, g^L{}_l\, x^l{}_{,M}\, N^K N^M \tag{10.4}$$

$$= g_{kl}\, g^l{}_L\, X^L{}_{,m}\, n^k n^m \lambda_{(\mathbf{n})}$$

where $(10.4)_2$ follows from $(10.1)_2$. In deriving (10.4), we have also used $\Lambda_{(\mathbf{N})} = \lambda_{(\mathbf{n})} = dx/dX$.

Now suppose $\mathbf{n}_\alpha$ is a proper vector of $\mathbf{c}$. Then for the angle $\theta_\alpha$ through which the deformation turns $\mathbf{n}_\alpha$, we get by using (9.16) and (9.20)

$$\cos\theta_\alpha = (c_\alpha)^{-\frac{3}{2}}\, c_{kl}\, g^l{}_L\, X^L{}_{,m}\, n^k{}_{\underline{\alpha}}\, n^m{}_{\underline{\alpha}} \tag{10.5}$$

When any two of the angles $\theta_\alpha$ vanish, the third also vanishes; and we obtain a deformation called *pure strain*. Thus in a state of pure strain the principal axes of the spatial and the material ellipsoids are parallel to each other. This, however, does not imply that the orientation of every radius vector not lying along the principal axes will remain unchanged. In fact, when the ratios of the corresponding principal axes of the two ellipsoids are different, we find that radius vectors not lying on the principal axes will in general rotate.

The measure of rotation introduced by (10.4) and (10.5) is complicated. The measure introduced by Novozhilov [1948, art. 7] for the mean rotation indicates the importance of the infinitesimal rotation tensors $\tilde{R}_{KL}$ and $\tilde{r}_{kl}$. We therefore give an account of this.

Let $\mathbf{N}_Z$ be a unit vector in the $XY$ plane of a rectangular frame of reference $X$, $Y$, $Z$ at $P$ (Fig. 10.2). After deformation $\mathbf{N}_Z$ becomes $\mathbf{n}_Z$ at $p$. Now bring $\mathbf{n}_Z$ to $P$ and let the angle between $\mathbf{N}_Z$ and the projection, $\mathbf{n}_Z^*$, of $\mathbf{n}_Z$ on the $XY$ plane be denoted by $\theta_Z$. From

$$\tan(\Phi + \theta_Z) = \frac{\tan\Phi + \tan\theta_Z}{1 - \tan\Phi\tan\theta_Z} = \frac{dy}{dx} = \frac{y_{,X}\, dX + y_{,Y}\, dY}{x_{,X}\, dX + x_{,Y}\, dY}$$

after substituting $dX = dS\cos\Phi$ and $dY = dS\sin\Phi$, we get

$$\tan\theta_Z = \frac{y_{,X}\cos^2\Phi + (y_{,Y} - x_{,X})\sin\Phi\cos\Phi - x_{,Y}\sin^2\Phi}{x_{,X}\cos^2\Phi + y_{,Y}\sin^2\Phi + (y_{,X} + x_{,Y})\sin\Phi\cos\Phi} \tag{10.6}$$

$$= \frac{-\tilde{R}_{XY} + \tilde{E}_{XY}\cos 2\Phi + \frac{1}{2}(\tilde{E}_{YY} - \tilde{E}_{XX})\sin 2\Phi}{1 + \frac{1}{2}(\tilde{E}_{XX} + \tilde{E}_{YY}) - \frac{1}{2}(\tilde{E}_{YY} - \tilde{E}_{XX})\cos 2\Phi + \tilde{E}_{XY}\sin 2\Phi}$$

The second line of (10.6) follows from the first by putting

$$y_{,X} = V_{,X} = \tilde{E}_{XY} - \tilde{R}_{XY}, \qquad y_{,Y} = 1 + V_{,Y} = 1 + \tilde{E}_{YY}, \ \ldots$$

Expression (10.6) is periodic in $\Phi$ with period $\pi$. Therefore $\theta_Z$ subject to $0 \leq \theta_Z \leq \pi$, except for the indistinguishable angles $\theta_Z = 0$ and $\theta_Z = \pi$, is well-defined.

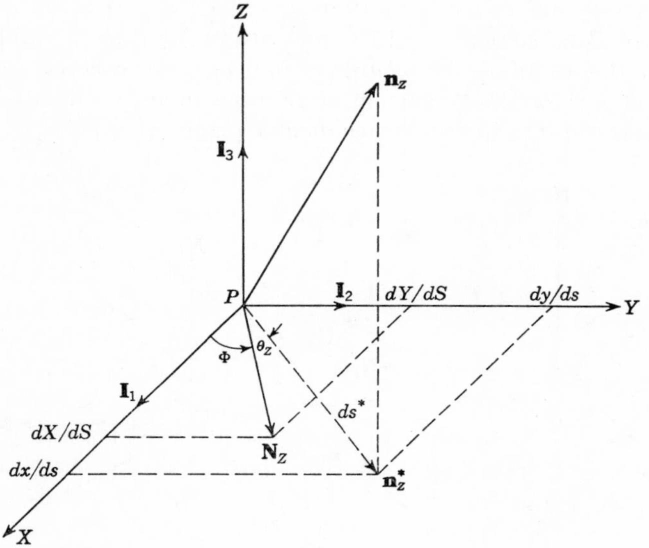


FIG. 10.2

Novozhilov has defined the following mean as his measure of rotation:

$$\langle \tan \theta_Z \rangle \equiv \frac{1}{2\pi} \int_0^{2\pi} \tan \theta_Z \, (\Phi) \, d\Phi \tag{10.7}$$

In performing the integration, we note that the numerator of $(10.6)_2$ excluding the term $-\tilde{R}_{XY}$ is the derivative of the denominator. Furthermore this part of the fraction integrates to zero. Thus

$$\begin{aligned} \langle \tan \theta_Z \rangle &= \frac{-1}{2\pi} \tilde{R}_{XY} \int_0^{2\pi} \frac{d\Phi}{1 + \frac{1}{2}(\tilde{E}_{XX} + \tilde{E}_{YY}) + \frac{1}{2}(\tilde{E}_{XX} - \tilde{E}_{YY}) \cos 2\Phi + \tilde{E}_{XY} \sin 2\Phi} \\ &= \frac{-\tilde{R}_{XY}}{\sqrt{(1 + \tilde{E}_{XX})(1 + \tilde{E}_{YY}) - \tilde{E}^2_{XY}}} \end{aligned} \tag{10.8}$$

We can also express this result as

$$(10.9) \qquad \langle \tan \theta_Z \rangle = -\frac{\tilde{R}_{12}}{\sqrt{1 + \mathrm{I}_{{}_3\tilde{E}} + \mathrm{II}_{{}_3\tilde{E}}}}$$

where $\mathrm{I}_{{}_3\tilde{E}}$ and $\mathrm{II}_{{}_3\tilde{E}}$ are the two-dimensional invariants of ${}_3\tilde{\mathbf{E}}$ obtained from $\tilde{\mathbf{E}}$ by suppressing all components having the index 3. In this form Novozhilov's measure of mean rotation has an invariant form, thus justifying the name of mean rotation tensor for $\tilde{\mathbf{R}}$. It is not difficult to write expressions similar to (10.8) and (10.9) for $\langle \tan \theta_X \rangle$ and $\langle \tan \theta_Y \rangle$ merely by the use of a *cyclic change* of indices. Since $\tilde{\mathbf{R}}$ is a tensor, if it vanishes in one coordinate system, it vanishes in all coordinates. Thus, if the mean rotation in two perpendicular planes at a point is zero or $\pi$

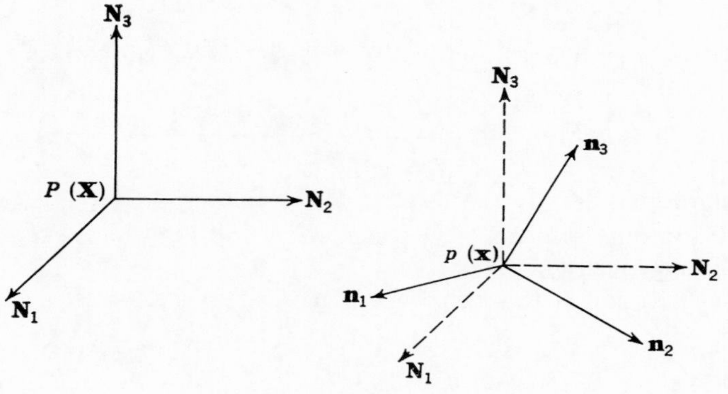


FIG. 10.3

radians, then the mean rotation in any plane at that point is zero or $\pi$ radians. The mean rotation is zero if and only if there exists a displacement potential $V$ such that

$$(10.10) \qquad U_K = V_{,K}$$

Such deformations may therefore be called *potential deformations.*

The mean rotation is incapable of describing the state of rotation of any fiber through a point. It gives only the average of the rotations of all fibers through that point. For the description of the local rotation of a given fiber we now define a rotation tensor $\mathbf{R}$ as follows.

Let $\mathbf{N}_\alpha$ be an orthogonal triad along the principal axes of strain at $\mathbf{X}$. According to Lemma 4 of the previous article, after deformation the original triad is rotated into the orthogonal triad $\mathbf{n}_\alpha$ lying along the principal axes of strain at $\mathbf{x}$. If we shift $\mathbf{N}_\alpha$ to $\mathbf{x}$, we can define a unique orthogonal tensor $\mathbf{R}$ which rotates the shifted $\mathbf{N}_\alpha$ into $\mathbf{n}_\alpha$ (Fig. 10.3).

$$(10.11)\qquad \begin{aligned} n^k{}_\alpha &= R^k{}_m\, g^m{}_K\, N^K{}_\alpha = R^k{}_K\, N^K{}_\alpha \\ N^K{}_\alpha &= g^K{}_m\, \overset{-1}{R}{}^m{}_k\, n^k{}_\alpha = \overset{-1}{R}{}^K{}_k\, n^k{}_\alpha \end{aligned}$$

where the components

$$(10.12)\qquad R^k{}_K = R^k{}_m\, g^m{}_K$$

represent the translation from **X** to **x** followed by a rotation. Suppose $\mathbf{N}^\alpha$ and $\mathbf{n}^\alpha$ are the reciprocal triads, i.e.,

$$(10.13)\qquad N^\alpha{}_K\, N^L{}_\alpha = \delta^L{}_K \qquad\qquad n^\alpha{}_k\, n^l{}_\alpha = \delta^l{}_k$$

Now multiply $(10.11)_1$ by $N^\alpha{}_L$ and use $(10.13)_1$. Likewise multiply $(10.11)_2$ by $n^\alpha{}_l$ and use $(10.13)_2$. This gives

$$(10.14)\qquad R^k{}_K = n^k{}_\alpha\, N^\alpha{}_K \qquad\qquad \overset{-1}{R}{}^K{}_k = N^K{}_\alpha\, n^\alpha{}_k$$

If we write $R^k{}_K = R^L{}_K\, g^k{}_L$ in $(10.11)_1$, we also find the equivalent formulas

$$(10.15)\qquad \begin{aligned} n^k{}_\alpha &= g^k{}_L\, R^L{}_K\, N^K{}_\alpha = R^k{}_K\, N^K{}_\alpha \\ N^K{}_\alpha &= g^L{}_k\, \overset{-1}{R}{}^K{}_L\, n^k{}_\alpha = \overset{-1}{R}{}^K{}_k\, n^k{}_\alpha \end{aligned}$$

which show that $\mathbf{R}^{-1}$ is the dual of $\mathbf{R}$. In other words, $\mathbf{R}$ rotates the shifted $\mathbf{N}_\alpha$ into $\mathbf{n}_\alpha$, while $\mathbf{R}^{-1}$ rotates $\mathbf{n}_\alpha$ back into the shifted $\mathbf{N}_\alpha$, a result that is geometrically obvious.

For the rotation of the reciprocal triads we have

$$(10.16)\qquad \begin{aligned} N^\alpha{}_K &= R^k{}_K\, n^\alpha{}_k \\ n^\alpha{}_k &= R_k{}^K\, N^\alpha{}_K \\ R_k{}^K &= G^{KL}\, g_{kl} R^l{}_L = n^\alpha{}_k\, N^K{}_\alpha = \overset{-1}{R}{}^K{}_k \end{aligned}$$

It is now clear that *the necessary and sufficient condition for pure strain is*

$$(10.17)\qquad \mathbf{R} = \mathbf{I}$$

or in coordinate notation $R^k{}_m = \delta^k{}_m$, $R_{km} = g_{km}$, $R^k{}_K = g^k{}_K$, . . .

LEMMA 1. (*Finger*) *The nth powers of the Cauchy and Green deformation tensors are related to each other by*[1]

$$(10.18)\qquad \overset{-n}{C}{}^K{}_L = \overset{-1}{R}{}^K{}_k\, \overset{n}{c}{}^k{}_l\, R^l{}_L \qquad\qquad \overset{-n}{c}{}^k{}_l = R^k{}_K\, \overset{n}{C}{}^K{}_L\, \overset{-1}{R}{}^L{}_l$$

To prove $(10.18)_1$, we recall that $C_{KL}$ is a nonsingular symmetric matrix. Moreover any positive, negative, or fractional power of this matrix has the proper numbers of $C_{KL}$ raised to the same power, i.e.,

$$(10.19)\qquad \overset{-n}{C}{}^K{}_L\, N^L{}_\alpha = (C_{\underline{\alpha}})^{-n}\, N^K{}_{\underline{\alpha}}$$

[1] This theorem, in this generality, was given by Toupin [1956, art. 4].

From this we solve

$$\overset{-n}{C}{}^K{}_L = \sum_\alpha (C_\alpha)^{-n} N^K{}_\alpha N^\alpha{}_L \tag{10.20}$$

Now replace $N^K{}_\alpha$ and $N^\alpha{}_L$ by their equivalents given by $(10.11)_2$ and $(10.16)_1$, and write $C_\alpha = 1/c_\alpha$. Thus

$$\overset{-n}{C}{}^K{}_L = \sum_\alpha \overset{-1}{R}{}^K{}_k (c_\alpha)^n n^k{}_\alpha n^\alpha{}_l R^l{}_L = \overset{-1}{R}{}^K{}_k \overset{n}{c}{}^k{}_l R^l{}_L$$

The last step follows from using the expression dual to (10.20) for $\overset{n}{c}{}^k{}_l$. This proves $(10.18)_1$. The proof of $(10.18)_2$ is similar to this.

We give two other important formulas which were obtained by Toupin [1956, art. 4], as a lemma.

LEMMA 2. *The displacement gradients, the Cauchy and the Green deformation tensors, are related to each other by*

$$x^k{}_{,K} = R^k{}_L \overset{\frac{1}{2}}{C}{}^L{}_K = R^l{}_K \overset{-\frac{1}{2}}{c}{}^k{}_l \tag{10.21}$$

$$X^K{}_{,k} = \overset{-1}{R}{}^K{}_l \overset{\frac{1}{2}}{c}{}^l{}_k = \overset{-1}{R}{}^L{}_k \overset{-\frac{1}{2}}{C}{}^K{}_L \tag{10.22}$$

To prove these results, we solve for $x^k{}_{,K}$ from (9.21), i.e.,

$$x^k{}_{,K} = \sum_\alpha \sqrt{C_\alpha}\, N^\alpha{}_K n^k{}_\alpha \tag{10.23}$$

Now substitute $n^k{}_\alpha$ from $(10.11)_1$ into (10.23), and use (10.20) with $n = -\frac{1}{2}$. Hence

$$x^k{}_{,K} = \sum_\alpha \sqrt{C_\alpha}\, R^k{}_L N^L{}_\alpha N^\alpha{}_K = \overset{\frac{1}{2}}{C}{}^L{}_K R^k{}_L$$

thus proving $(10.21)_1$. We get $(10.21)_2$ from this by using $(10.18)_1$ with $n = -\frac{1}{2}$. The proof of (10.22) is similar to this. From (10.21) and (10.22) we also have

$$R^k{}_K = x^k{}_{,L} \overset{-\frac{1}{2}}{C}{}^L{}_K \qquad \overset{-1}{R}{}^K{}_k = X^K{}_{,l} \overset{-\frac{1}{2}}{c}{}^l{}_k \tag{10.24}$$

As a corollary to Lemma 2 we have

$$U_{K;M} = R_{KL} \overset{\frac{1}{2}}{C}{}^L{}_M - G_{KM} = R_K{}^L \overset{\frac{1}{2}}{C}_{LM} - G_{KM} \tag{10.25}$$

To show this, we recall $(5.13)_1$, which may be put into the form

$$x^k{}_{,K} = g^{kl} g^L{}_l (G_{LK} + U_{L;K}) \tag{10.26}$$

This may be solved for $U_{L;K}$ to give

$$U_{L;K} = g_{kl} g^l{}_L x^k{}_{,K} - G_{LK} \tag{10.27}$$

Substitution of $(10.21)_1$ into this gives (10.25). From this expression one obtains the relations between the tensors $\tilde{\mathbf{E}}$, $\tilde{\mathbf{R}}$, and $\mathbf{R}$

$$\tilde{E}_{KM} = R_{(M}{}^{L}\overset{\frac{1}{2}}{C}_{LK)} - G_{MK} \qquad \tilde{R}_{KM} = R_{[M}{}^{L}\overset{\frac{1}{2}}{C}_{LK]} \tag{10.28}$$

An additional result follows from using $(10.21)_1$ on the left of (10.26) and then solving for $R_{KM}$, i.e.,

$$R_{KM} = (G_{KL} + \tilde{E}_{KL} + \tilde{R}_{KL})\,\overset{-\frac{1}{2}}{C}{}^{L}{}_{M} \tag{10.29}$$

Formulas dual to these involving the eulerian representation are not difficult to find.

If the deformation gradients are small, retaining only the lowest-order terms, (10.29) gives

$$R_{KM} - G_{KM} \cong \tilde{R}_{KM} \qquad \tilde{R}_{KM} \cong g^{k}{}_{K}\, g^{m}{}_{M}\, \tilde{r}_{km} \tag{10.30}$$

hence the justification of the name "infinitesimal rotation" for $\tilde{R}_{KM}$ and $\tilde{r}_{km}$.

We are now ready for the fundamental theorem of rotation.

FUNDAMENTAL THEOREM. *The deformation of any line element at a point may be considered as resulting from a translation, a rigid rotation of the principal axes of strain, and stretches along these axes.* The translation, rotation, and stretch may be applied in any order.[2]

Consider the vector $dX^K$ at $\mathbf{X}$. This vector is carried by the deformation into $dx^k = x^k{}_{,K}\, dX^K$. Using (10.21), we have

$$dx^k = g^k{}_L\, R^L{}_M\, \overset{\frac{1}{2}}{C}{}^{M}{}_{K}\, dX^K = \overset{-\frac{1}{2}}{c}{}^{k}{}_{l}\, R^l{}_m\, g^m{}_K\, dX^K \tag{10.31}$$

We may decompose (10.31) as follows (Fig. 10.4):

1. *The vector $dX^K$ is rigidly translated in parallel displacement to $dx^k{}_{(T)}$.*

$$dx^k{}_{(T)} = g^k{}_K\, dX^K \tag{10.32a}$$

2. *The vector $dx^k{}_{(T)}$ is rigidly rotated into $dx^k{}_{(R)}$.*

$$dx^k{}_{(R)} = R^k{}_l\, dx^l{}_{(T)} \tag{10.32b}$$

3. *The vector $dx^k{}_{(R)}$ is stretched into $dx^k{}_{(S)} \equiv dx^k$.*

$$dx^k = \overset{-\frac{1}{2}}{c}{}^{k}{}_{l}\, dx^l{}_{(R)} \tag{10.32c}$$

Successive substitution of (10.32*a*) and (10.32*b*) into (10.32*c*) gives

[2] A proof of this theorem for infinitesimal deformations was given by Helmholtz [1858]. It was discussed by Kelvin and Tait [1867, art. 182] and explicitly stated by Love [1892, art. 10]. For finite deformation a clear proof may be found in Toupin [1956]. See also Truesdell and Toupin [1960, art. 37].

$(10.31)_2$, thus proving the fundamental theorem. Note that if and only if $dX^K$ is a proper vector of $C_{KL}$ will the stretching not involve a further rotation of the vector $dx^k{}_{(R)}$.

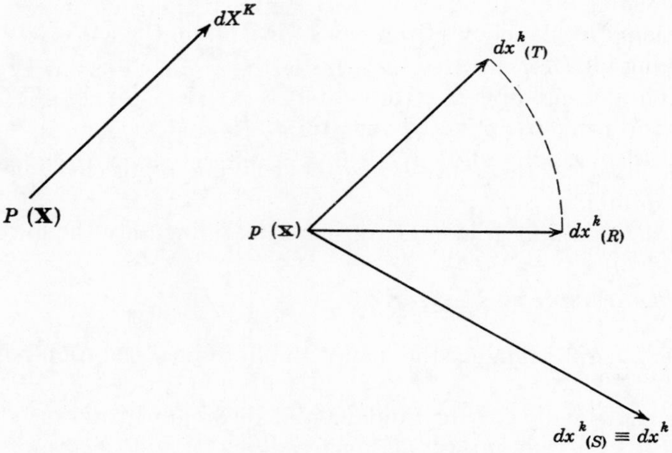


FIG. 10.4. The decomposition of deformation.

We can decompose (10.31) in another way as follows (Fig. 10.5):

$$
\begin{aligned}
dX^M{}_{(S)} &= \overset{\frac{1}{2}}{C}{}^M{}_K \, dX^K \\
dX^L{}_{(R)} &= R^L{}_M \, dX^M{}_{(S)} \qquad (10.33)\\
dx^k &= g^k{}_L \, dX^L{}_{(R)}
\end{aligned}
$$

According to this, the vector $dX^K$ is first stretched into $dX^K{}_{(S)}$. (This stretching as remarked above will, in general, involve a rotation except

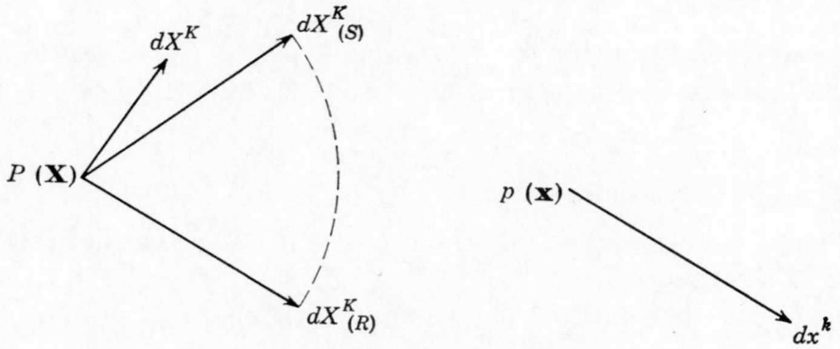


FIG. 10.5. The decomposition of deformation.

when $dX^K$ is taken along the principal axes of the strain ellipsoid at **X**.) The vector $dX^K{}_{(S)}$ is then rigidly rotated into a vector $dX^K{}_{(R)}$. Finally

$dX^K{}_{(R)}$ is shifted to the point $\mathbf{x}$ in a rigid parallel displacement. We therefore see that the order of the foregoing three operations is unimportant. Their tensorial measure is not independent, however, of the order in which they are applied.

The foregoing description of the deformation concerning an infinitesimal neighborhood of a point $\mathbf{X}$, the decomposition following the former sequence, may be summarized in terms of the strain ellipsoids as follows: (1) An infinitesimal sphere with center at $\mathbf{X}$ is rigidly translated to $\mathbf{x}$ carrying the principal triad of the strain ellipsoid at $\mathbf{X}$ to $\mathbf{x}$. (2) The sphere is then rigidly rotated about $\mathbf{x}$ until the transported principal triad coincides with that of the strain ellipsoid at $\mathbf{x}$. (3) Finally, all diameters of the transported sphere are stretched, but only those lying along the principal directions at $\mathbf{x}$ are stretched without further rotation.

## 11. DIRECTION-PRESERVING FIBERS

THEOREM. (*Kelvin and Tait*) *In any deformation at least one direction remains unchanged.*

PROOF. Vector $dX^K$ at $\mathbf{X}$ becomes $dx^k$ at $\mathbf{x}$ after deformation. Now bring $dx^k$ back to $\mathbf{X}$ in rigid parallel displacement. Since this latter vector $g^K{}_k\, dx^k$ is to be parallel to $dX^K$, we must have

$$g^K{}_k\, dx^k = g^K{}_k\, x^k{}_{,L}\, dX^L = (A + 1)\, dX^K \tag{11.1}$$

where $A + 1$ is a real factor of proportionality. Using (10.26) in this expression, we get

$$(G^{KL}\, U_{L;M} - A\, \delta^K{}_M)\, dX^M = 0 \tag{11.2}$$

Using $(6.2)_2$, we may also write this as

$$(\tilde{E}^K{}_M + \tilde{R}^K{}_M - A\, \delta^K{}_M)\, dX^M = 0 \tag{11.3}$$

The necessary condition for the existence of a direction-preserving fiber $dX^L$ is that the coefficient determinant of (11.3) must be zero.

$$|\tilde{E}^K{}_M + \tilde{R}^K{}_M - A\, \delta^K{}_M| = 0 \tag{11.4}$$

This is a cubic equation in $A$. Since it has at least one real root, we have the proof of the theorem.

Expanding the determinant (11.4), we will have

$$- A^3 + \mathrm{I}_{\tilde{E}+\tilde{R}}\, A^2 - \mathrm{II}_{\tilde{E}+\tilde{R}}\, A + \mathrm{III}_{\tilde{E}+\tilde{R}} = 0 \tag{11.5}$$

where $\mathrm{I}_{\tilde{E}+\tilde{R}}$, $\mathrm{II}_{\tilde{E}+\tilde{R}}$, and $\mathrm{III}_{\tilde{E}+\tilde{R}}$ are the invariants of $\tilde{\mathbf{E}} + \tilde{\mathbf{R}}$. They are given by

$$\mathrm{I}_{\tilde{E}+\tilde{R}} = \frac{1}{1!}\,\delta^K{}_L\,(\tilde{E}^L{}_K + \tilde{R}^L{}_K)$$

$$\text{(11.6)}\qquad \mathrm{II}_{\tilde{E}+\tilde{R}} = \frac{1}{2!}\,\delta^K{}_L{}^M{}_N\,(\tilde{E}^L{}_K + \tilde{R}^L{}_K)\,(\tilde{E}^N{}_M + \tilde{R}^N{}_M)$$

$$\mathrm{III}_{\tilde{E}+\tilde{R}} = \frac{1}{3!}\,\delta^K{}_L{}^M{}_N{}^P{}_Q\,(\tilde{E}^L{}_K + \tilde{R}^L{}_K)\,(\tilde{E}^N{}_M + \tilde{R}^N{}_M)\,(\tilde{E}^Q{}_P + \tilde{R}^Q{}_P)$$

To simplify these expressions, we notice the identities that stem from the symmetry of $\tilde{E}_{KL}$, the skew symmetry of $\tilde{R}_{KL}$, and the properties of Kronecker deltas, namely,

$$\tilde{R}^K{}_K = 0 \qquad \delta^K{}_L{}^M{}_N\,\tilde{E}^L{}_K\,\tilde{R}^N{}_M = 0,$$

$$\text{(11.7)}\qquad \delta^K{}_L{}^M{}_N{}^P{}_Q\,\tilde{E}^L{}_K\,\tilde{E}^N{}_M\,\tilde{R}^Q{}_P = 0 \qquad \det \tilde{R}^K{}_L = 0$$

$$\epsilon^{KLM}\,\epsilon^{RST}\,\tilde{R}_{TM}\,\tilde{R}_{SL} = \epsilon^{KLS}\,\epsilon^{RMT}\,\tilde{R}_{TM}\,\tilde{R}_{SL}$$

Hence

$$\mathrm{I}_{\tilde{E}+\tilde{R}} = \mathrm{I}_{\tilde{E}} \qquad \mathrm{II}_{\tilde{E}+\tilde{R}} = \mathrm{II}_{\tilde{E}} + \mathrm{II}_{\tilde{R}}$$

$$\text{(11.8)}\qquad \mathrm{III}_{\tilde{E}+\tilde{R}} = \mathrm{III}_{\tilde{E}} + \tfrac{1}{2}\,\delta^K{}_L{}^M{}_N{}^P{}_Q\,\tilde{E}^L{}_K\,\tilde{E}^N{}_M\,\tilde{E}^Q{}_P$$

$$= \mathrm{III}_{\tilde{E}} + 2\,\tilde{E}_{KL}\,\tilde{R}^K\,\tilde{R}^L$$

where $\tilde{R}^K$ is the infinitesimal rotation vector defined by $(6.5)_2$. From $(11.8)_3$ and $(11.8)_4$ it is clear that the last terms on the right are also invariants.

Existence of more than one real root of (11.5) depends on the discriminant $D$ of the cubic equation, i.e.,

$$\text{(11.9)}\qquad D \equiv P^3 - Q^2 \qquad 3P = \tfrac{1}{3}\,\mathrm{I}_{\tilde{E}}^2 - \mathrm{II}_{\tilde{E}} - \mathrm{II}_{\tilde{R}}$$

$$2\,Q = \tfrac{1}{3}\,\mathrm{I}_{\tilde{E}}\,(\mathrm{II}_{\tilde{E}} + \mathrm{II}_{\tilde{R}}) - \tfrac{2}{27}\,\mathrm{I}_{\tilde{E}}^3 - \mathrm{III}\tilde{E} - 2\,\tilde{E}_{KL}\,\tilde{R}^K\,\tilde{R}^L$$

Three cases can be cited:

1. *When* $D > 0$, *then there exist three and only three invariant directions.*
2. *When* $D < 0$, *there exists one and only one invariant direction.*
3. *When* $D = 0$, *there may be one, two, three, or an infinite number of invariant directions.*

In the last case we have multiple roots to which there may correspond any number of directions as would be seen from the following examples. In a simple shear (Fig. 15.2) $x = X + S\,Y$, $y = Y$, $z = Z$ where $S$ is a constant, there is a single triply repeated root $A = 0$. Thus the fibers initially parallel to the $(X, Z)$ plane remain parallel to themselves. In the simple extension (Fig. 15.1) $x = \lambda\,X$, $y = Y$, $z = Z$ where $\lambda$ is a constant, the characteristic equation will have a double root $A = 0$ and a single root $A = 1 - \lambda$. The lines parallel to the $X$, $Y$, or $Z$ axes remain parallel to their original directions.

If $\tilde{\mathbf{R}} = 0$, the characteristic cubic equation will have three real roots, since $\tilde{E}_{MN}$ is a symmetric tensor. Therefore *for* $\tilde{\mathbf{R}} = 0$ *the principal axes of the elongations remain unaltered*, and the principal axes of strain deform into themselves. We see that *the necessary and sufficient condition for the principal axes of strain to deform into themselves is that the principal axes of strain coincide with those of the elongations.*

*It can be shown that if at a point the maximum* $\tilde{R}_{KL}$ *are less than the maximum shears* $\tilde{E}_{KL}$ $(K \neq L)$, *then three direction-preserving fibers exist.* In general these directions are not mutually orthogonal. The proof of this follows by showing that under these conditions $D > 0$.

## 12. AREA AND VOLUME CHANGES

In the undeformed body a surface may be represented in a parametric form

$$X^K = X^K(U, V) \tag{12.1}$$

where $U$ and $V$ are two parameters and equation (12.1) is the gaussian equation of the surface. The element of area $dA^{KL}$ is a bivector

$$dA^{KL} = 2\,\frac{\partial X^{[K}}{\partial U}\,\frac{\partial X^{L]}}{\partial V}\,dU\,dV \tag{12.2}$$

The surface (12.1) after deformation becomes the surface

$$x^k = x^k[\mathbf{X}(U, V)]$$

with area element

$$\begin{aligned} da^{kl} &= 2\,\frac{\partial x^{[k}}{\partial U}\,\frac{\partial x^{l]}}{\partial V}\,dU\,dV = 2\,x^{[k}{}_{,K}\,x^{l]}{}_{,L}\,\frac{\partial X^K}{\partial U}\,\frac{\partial X^L}{\partial V}\,dU\,dV \\ &= 2\,x^k{}_{,K}\,x^l{}_{,L}\,\frac{\partial X^{[K}}{\partial U}\,\frac{\partial X^{L]}}{\partial V}\,dU\,dV \end{aligned}$$

or

$$da^{kl} = x^k{}_{,K}\,x^l{}_{,L}\,dA^{KL} \tag{12.3}$$

Equivalent to the skew-symmetric area bivectors, in three dimensions we have the covariant area vectors $dA_K$ and $da_k$

$$\begin{aligned} dA_K &= \tfrac{1}{2}\,\epsilon_{KLM}\,dA^{LM} \qquad & da_k &= \tfrac{1}{2}\,\epsilon_{klm}\,da^{lm} \\ dA^{LM} &= \epsilon^{KLM}\,dA_K \qquad & da^{lm} &= \epsilon^{klm}\,da_k \end{aligned} \tag{12.4}$$

Substituting (12.3) into $(12.4)_2$, we get

$$da_k = \tfrac{1}{2}\,\epsilon_{klm}\,x^l{}_{,L}\,x^m{}_{,M}\,dA^{LM} = \tfrac{1}{2}\,\epsilon_{klm}\,\epsilon^{KLM}\,x^l{}_{,L}\,x^m{}_{,M}\,dA_K$$

Using (4.4) and the fact that $\epsilon_{klm} = e_{klm}\sqrt{g}$ and $\epsilon^{KLM} = e^{KLM}/\sqrt{G}$, we find the important result

$$da_k = J\, X^K{}_{,k}\, dA_K \tag{12.5}$$

We can now calculate the square of the area

$$(da)^2 = g^{kl}\, da_k\, da_l = J^2\, g^{kl}\, X^K{}_{,k}\, X^L{}_{,l}\, dA_K\, dA_L$$

Recalling $(4.15)_2$ and (9.30), we obtain[1]

$$(da)^2 = \mathrm{III}_C\, \overset{-1}{C}{}^{KL}\, dA_K\, dA_L \tag{12.6}$$

This expression is analogous to the expression for the square of the element of length, i.e.,

$$ds^2 = C^{KL}\, dX_K\, dX_L$$

Thus we conclude that *with respect to the measuring of the change of area the tensor* $\mathrm{III}_C\, \overset{-1}{C}{}^{KL}$ *plays the same role as the tensor* $C^{KL}$ *plays with respect to change of length.* We also have results that are dual to (12.5) and (12.6), namely,

$$dA_K = J^{-1}\, x^k{}_{,K}\, da_k \qquad (dA)^2 = \mathrm{III}_c\, \overset{-1}{c}{}^{kl}\, da_k\, da_l \tag{12.7}$$

The above *duality* of the length and area suggests that we can construct an ellipsoid based on the tensor $\mathrm{III}_C\, \overset{-1}{C}{}^{KL}$ or $\mathrm{III}_c\, \overset{-1}{c}{}^{kl}$ and can then study this ellipsoid in order to understand the area changes which take place in going from the original to the final orientations. Clearly, all the theorems proved in Arts. 8 and 9 have dualities here.

For example, according to (9.17) and (9.18), $\overset{-1}{C}{}^K{}_L$ acquires its maximal (minimal) value along a principal axis of strain $c^k{}_l$ at which $c^k{}_l$ has minimal (maximal) value. Consequently the *greatest (least) area change occurs at the plane normal to the direction of maximum (minimum) stretch.* In fact, if the stretches are ordered as $\lambda_3 \leq \lambda_2 \leq \lambda_1$, in view of $(9.10)_3$ and $(9.22)_3$, we have the *principal areas* $\lambda_1\lambda_2$, $\lambda_2\lambda_3$, $\lambda_3\lambda_1$ which are ordered as $\lambda_2\lambda_3 \leq \lambda_3\lambda_1 \leq \lambda_1\lambda_2$.

The change of volume has already been calculated in Art. 9. According to (9.31), (9.28), and (9.29), for the ratio of the deformed volume element $dv$ to the undeformed volume element $dV$, we have

$$\begin{aligned} \frac{dv}{dV} &= J = \sqrt{\mathrm{III}_C} = \frac{1}{\sqrt{\mathrm{III}_c}} = (1 + 2\,\mathrm{I}_E + 4\,\mathrm{II}_E + 8\,\mathrm{III}_E)^{\frac{1}{2}} \\ &= (1 - 2\,\mathrm{I}_e + 4\,\mathrm{II}_e - 8\,\mathrm{III}_e)^{-\frac{1}{2}} \end{aligned} \tag{12.8}$$

## 13. COMPATIBILITY CONDITIONS

In three dimensions the deformation tensor $C_{KL}$ has *six* components which are related to the *three* components $U_K$ of the displacement vector

[1] This result is due to Truesdell [1958].

by $(5.10)_1$, i.e.,

$$C_{KL} - G_{KL} = 2\,E_{KL} = U_{K;L} + U_{L;K} + G^{MN}\,U_{M;K}\,U_{N;K} \tag{13.1}$$

If the displacement vector **U** is given, then by a mere substitution in the extreme right we can calculate $C_{KL}$ and $E_{KL}$, since the metric tensor $G_{KL}$ of the reference frame is chosen at the outset.

If, instead, $C_{KL}$ are six prescribed functions or, what is equivalent, if the six $E_{KL}$ components are given, then the determination of the displacement field requires the solution of six partial differential equations (13.1) for the three unknowns $U_K$. Such a system is overdetermined, and for the existence of a *single-valued continuous displacement* field certain restrictions must be imposed upon $C_{KL}$ or $E_{KL}$. These conditions are known as the *compatibility conditions.* Let us immediately remark that, in a formulation in which the displacement-field components are chosen as the basic dependent variables, the compatibility conditions are then automatically satisfied and no further reference needs to be made to compatibility conditions. If, however, the deformation tensors or strain tensors are selected as the basic dependent variables without reference to the displacement field, then the compatibility conditions constitute an essential part of the field equations.

An obvious way of obtaining the compatibility conditions is through the elimination of the three displacement components $U_K$ from the six equations of (13.1) by partial differentiation and elimination. This, however, is very tedious, if not hopelessly awkward. An alternative method makes use of a theorem of Riemann; namely, that *for a symmetric tensor $a_{kl}$ to be a metric tensor for a euclidean space, it is necessary and sufficient that $a_{kl}$ be a nonsingular positive-definite tensor and that the Riemann-Christoffel tensor $R^{(a)}{}_{klmn}$ formed from it vanish identically.* We recall that when this tensor vanishes identically, the order of covariant differentiation of a vector or a tensor, with respect to $a_{kl}$, is immaterial, e.g., $v_{k;lm} = v_{k;ml}$. Moreover this is also the necessary and sufficient condition for a space to be *flat.* All of these are different statements of Riemann's theorem. We have, by definition (cf. Art. A5),

$$R^{(a)}{}_{klmn} \equiv a_{kr}\left(\begin{Bmatrix} r \\ ln \end{Bmatrix}_{,m} - \begin{Bmatrix} r \\ lm \end{Bmatrix}_{,n} + \begin{Bmatrix} s \\ ln \end{Bmatrix}\begin{Bmatrix} r \\ sm \end{Bmatrix} - \begin{Bmatrix} s \\ lm \end{Bmatrix}\begin{Bmatrix} r \\ sn \end{Bmatrix}\right) \tag{13.2}$$

where

$$\begin{aligned} \begin{Bmatrix} r \\ lm \end{Bmatrix} &\equiv a^{rs}\,[lm,s] \\ [lm,r] &\equiv \tfrac{1}{2}\,(a_{lr,m} + a_{mr,l} - a_{lm,r}) \end{aligned} \tag{13.3}$$

are the second and the first kinds of the Christoffel symbols respectively.

Both Green and Cauchy tensors $C_{KL}$ and $c_{kl}$ are nonsingular positive-definite tensors of the euclidean three-dimensional space. Therefore we must have

$$R^{(C)}{}_{KLMN} = 0 \qquad R^{(c)}{}_{klmn} = 0 \tag{13.4}$$

The partial differentiation in the former is understood to be taken with respect to $X^K$ and that in the latter with respect to $x^k$. In a three-dimensional space only six of the eighty-one components of $R_{klmn}$ are algebraically independent and nonidentically vanishing. The first of (13.4) constitutes the compatibility conditions for $C_{KL}$ and the second for $c_{kl}$. In the literature the compatibility conditions are often referred to as the conditions satisfied by the strain tensors $E_{KL}$ or $e_{kl}$. Since we have

$$C_{KL} = G_{KL} + 2\,E_{KL} \qquad c_{kl} = g_{kl} - 2\,e_{kl}$$

and since both Riemann-Christoffel tensors formed from $G_{KL}$ and $g_{kl}$ vanish, by substituting these into the expressions (13.4), we get the compatibility conditions for $E_{KL}$ and $e_{kl}$. Below we give one of these.

$$\begin{aligned}
(13.5)\quad & e_{kn,lm} + e_{lm,kn} - e_{km,ln} - e_{ln,km} \\
&+ 2\,g^{rs}\,\{[kn,r]_e\,[lm,s]_g + [kn,r]_g\,[lm,s]_e - 2\,[kn,r]_e\,[lm,s]_e \\
&- [km,r]_e\,[ln,s]_g - [km,r]_g\,[ln,s]_e + 2\,[km,r]_e\,[ln,s]_e\} \\
&+ 2\,e^{rs}\,\{[kn,r]_g\,[lm,s]_g - [km,r]_g\,[ln,s]_g - 2\,[kn,r]_e\,[lm,s]_g \\
&- 2\,[kn,r]_g\,[lm,s]_e + 4\,[kn,r]_e\,[lm,s]_e + 2\,[km,r]_e\,[ln,s]_g \\
&\qquad + 2\,[km,r]_g\,[ln,s]_e - 4\,[km,r]_e\,[ln,s]_e\} = 0
\end{aligned}$$

where $[kl,m]_g$ and $[kl,m]_e$ are Christoffel symbols of the first kind based on $g_{kl}$ and $e_{kl}$ respectively, as defined in $(13.3)_2$.

It is important to note that the member equations of either set of the compatibility conditions (13.4) or (13.5) are not independent, since the Riemann-Christoffel curvature tensor $R_{klmn}$ satisfies the identity of Bianchi,

$$R_{klmn;p} + R_{klnp;m} + R_{klpm;n} = 0 \tag{13.6}$$

If in (13.5) we drop the terms containing products of $\mathbf{e}$ and replace $\mathbf{e}$ by $\tilde{\mathbf{e}}$, we obtain the compatibility conditions valid for the infinitesimal deformation theory, namely,

$$\tilde{e}_{kn;lm} + \tilde{e}_{lm;kn} - \tilde{e}_{km;ln} - \tilde{e}_{ln;km} = 0 \tag{13.7}$$

Of course, we have the duals of (13.5) to (13.7) for the strains $E_{KL}$ and $\tilde{E}_{KL}$. *The conditions* (13.7) *are the integrability conditions,* in euclidean space, for the strains

$$\tilde{e}_{kl} = u_{(k;l)} \tag{13.8}$$

If ${}^0u_k$ is any solution of (13.8) and $\tilde{e}_{kl}$ satisfies (13.7), then the most general solution of (13.8) is

$$u_k = {}^0u_k + \tilde{R}_{lk}\, p^l \tag{13.9}$$

where $\mathbf{p}$ is any vector satisfying $p^k{}_{,l} = \delta^k{}_l$ and $\tilde{\mathbf{R}}$ is a skew-symmetric tensor satisfying $\tilde{R}_{lk;m} = 0$. Physically the terms $\tilde{R}_{lk}\, p^l$ represent small rigid displacement. In the linear theory of elasticity, (13.9) is often used as the starting point for the derivation of the compatibility conditions. The literature on the subject is extensive. For an excellent collection we refer the reader to Truesdell and Toupin [1960, footnotes, art. 34].

## 14. APPROXIMATIONS

The classical linear elasticity and fluid-flow theories make use of the concept of small deformations at the outset. The treatment of problems of finite deformations with full generality [excluding some simple situations (cf. Chap. 6)] represents a task presently outside the realm of mathematical tools. Utilizing the nature of the deformation and the geometry of the body, one can make approximations that will take into account larger deformations than those admissible in the linear theory.

Approximations to the basic equations of continuous media, in general, appear in two loosely connected steps. (1) The extensions may be small while the rotations may be large. An example of this is found in a thin bar when it is bent into a ring without large or permanent deformation. (2) The extension may locally be large; the rotations, however, remain small. Such situations may occur in the region of applications of loads to bulky bodies (e.g., half space subject to concentrated load). While the full treatment of an approximation theory is neither timely nor possible with any acceptable rigor at this place, we feel that a small account here is useful even at the expense of precision.

Let us remark in passing that in case (1) above often the use of infinitesimal strain in place of finite strain together with a full use of the field equations (equations of mass, momentum, and energy conservations) is sufficient to provide physically acceptable results. In case (2), on the other hand, finite strain with approximate field equations referred to the reference state may (with adequate caution!) be used.

The following approximations are presented to provide only an intuitive ground in this incomplete theory.

The strain and rotation tensors and the invariants are expressible in terms of the gradients of three displacement components. Therefore we may speak of small displacements or any other *three* independent functions that can conveniently replace them. For example, the magnitudes of the principal extensions, the components of rotation vectors, etc., may be employed for approximations. Direct use of the magnitudes of the components of the strain or the rotation tensor presents difficulties since the compatibility conditions must be satisfied. Similarly, caution must be taken when the deformation gradients are considered as basic in an order of magnitude analysis.

*Small Displacement Theory.* In this theory the displacement components $u^k$ are considered small. Thus any product of these components and their various gradients may be neglected. Clearly then (5.10) reduce to

$$\begin{aligned} 2\,E_{KL} &= C_{KL} - G_{KL} \cong U_{K;L} + U_{L;K} \\ 2\,e_{kl} &= g_{kl} - c_{kl} \cong u_{k;l} + u_{l;k} \end{aligned} \tag{14.1}$$

Strain measures $\overset{\pm\frac{1}{2}}{\mathbf{C}}$ now read

$$\overset{\pm\frac{1}{2}}{\mathbf{C}} \cong \mathbf{I} \pm \tilde{\mathbf{E}} \tag{14.2}$$

Hence (10.29) gives

$$\begin{aligned} R_{KM} - G_{KM} \cong \tilde{R}_{KM} &= \tfrac{1}{2}\,(U_{K;M} - U_{M;K}) \\ \tilde{R}_{KM} &\cong g^k{}_K\, g^m{}_M\, \tilde{r}_{km} \end{aligned} \tag{14.3}$$

which have already been obtained in Art. 10.

The difference between $U^k$ and $u^k$ in this case disappears, and we have the classical theory of infinitesimal strain. A systematic theory based on perturbation series was developed by E. and F. Cosserat [1896] by taking

$$\mathbf{u} = \sum_{n=0}^{\infty} \epsilon^n\, \mathbf{u}_n \tag{14.4}$$

where $\mathbf{u}_n$ are given and kept fixed and $\epsilon$ is a small perturbation parameter.[1] In this formalism the coefficient of $\epsilon^n$ represents the $n$th-order approximation. Such a scheme has limitations in that the gradients may not be small even if the displacements are. In this theory a small physical elongation may produce a large strain.

*Small Principal Extensions.* In this case the principal extensions $e_{(\alpha)} \equiv E_{(\alpha)}$ are assumed to be small. Hence, through such relations as $(7.5)_2$, $(7.8)_3$, and (7.18), we get

$$\begin{aligned} E_{KK} &\cong E_{(K)} = e_{kk} = e_{(k)} \\ 2\,E_{KL} &\cong [1 + E_{(K)} + E_{(L)}] \sin \Gamma_{(KL)} \end{aligned} \tag{14.5}$$

[1] Signorini [1943] calculated the $n$th derivative at $\epsilon = 0$ of various quantities associated with $\mathbf{u}$.

From (9.22) and (9.23) it follows that

$$
\begin{aligned}
&\mathrm{I}_C = \mathrm{I}_{\underset{c}{-1}} \cong 3 + 2\,\mathrm{I}_e &\qquad \mathrm{I}_c = \mathrm{I}_{\underset{C}{-1}} \cong 3 - 2\,\mathrm{I}_e\\
(14.6)\qquad &\mathrm{II}_C = \mathrm{II}_{\underset{c}{-1}} \cong 3 + 4\,\mathrm{I}_e &\qquad \mathrm{II}_c = \mathrm{II}_{\underset{C}{-1}} \cong 3 - 4\,\mathrm{I}_e\\
&\mathrm{III}_C = \mathrm{III}_{\underset{c}{-1}} \cong 1 + 2\,\mathrm{I}_e &\qquad \mathrm{III}_c = \mathrm{III}_{\underset{C}{-1}} \cong 1 - 2\,\mathrm{I}_e
\end{aligned}
$$

The volume change from (12.8) in this case reduces to

$$
(14.7)\qquad \frac{dv - dV}{dV} \cong \mathrm{I}_E \cong \mathrm{I}_e
$$

Strain measures $\overset{\pm\frac{1}{2}}{\mathbf{C}}$ now read

$$
(14.8)\qquad \overset{\pm\frac{1}{2}}{\mathbf{C}} \cong \mathbf{I} \pm \mathbf{E}
$$

so that, using (10.28) and (10.29), we get

$$
(14.9)\qquad
\begin{aligned}
&R_{KM} \cong G_{KM} + U_{K;M} &\qquad &\overset{-1}{R}_{KM} \cong G_{KM} - U_{K;M}\\
&\tilde{R}_{KM} \cong R_{[KM]} &\qquad &\tilde{E}_{KM} \cong R_{(KM)} - G_{KM}
\end{aligned}
$$

*Small Rotations.* When the rotation $\theta$ of every element is small, we write $\tan \theta_Z \cong \theta_Z$; thus by $(10.8)_2$ we see that

$$
(14.10)\qquad \theta_Z \cong \frac{-\tilde{R}_{XY}}{\sqrt{(1 + \tilde{E}_{XX})\,(1 + \tilde{E}_{YY}) - \tilde{E}^2_{XY}}}
$$

Similar expressions being valid for $\theta_X$ and $\theta_Y$, we see that $\tilde{\mathbf{R}}$ is small when the rotation is small.

The strain tensor may now be approximated by

$$
(14.11)\qquad E_{KL} \cong \tilde{E}_{KL} + \tfrac{1}{2}\,(\tilde{E}_{MK}\,\tilde{E}^M{}_L + \tilde{E}_{MK}\,\tilde{R}^M{}_L + \tilde{R}_{MK}\,\tilde{E}^M{}_L)
$$

If the rotation is small, then the rotation vector $2\,\tilde{R}^K = \epsilon^{KLM}\,\tilde{R}_{ML}$ may be employed in place of rotation interchangeably. Therefore the theorem of superposition of infinitesimal rotations now becomes applicable.

In some instances certain components of $\tilde{R}^K$ may be small as compared to others; then $E_{KL}$ may be further simplified by dropping the terms containing these components as compared to others. Such an approximation depends on the geometry of the deformation and the shape of the body. For example, in the bending of thin plates rotation of a plane element about an axis normal to the median plane of the plate is small as compared to the rotation about any axis in this plane. This is used to obtain the second-order plate theory known as the Föppl-Kármán-Timoshenko theory.[2]

[2] Cf. Novozhilov [1948]; see also Eringen [1954].

*Small Extensions and Small Rotations.* In this case we have $\tilde{E}_{KL} \ll 1$ in addition to $\tilde{R}_{KL}$ being small. Hence (14.10) reduces to

$$\theta_Z \cong -\tilde{R}_{XY} = \tilde{R}_Z \tag{14.12}$$

We may now approximate $E_{KL}$ by

$$E_{KL} \cong \tilde{E}_{KL} + \tfrac{1}{2}(\tilde{E}_{MK}\,\tilde{R}^M{}_L + \tilde{R}_{MK}\,\tilde{E}^M{}_L) \tag{14.13}$$

Further simplification requires that we compare rotations and strains and assume that they are of the same order of magnitude. This amounts to an assumption of *small displacement gradients*, in which case we obtain the theory of infinitesimal deformations

$$E_{KL} \cong \tilde{E}_{KL} \qquad R^K{}_L \cong \delta^K{}_L + \tilde{R}^K{}_L \tag{14.14}$$

For the theory of infinitesimal deformations all nonlinear terms in the displacement gradients drop out, and we have the *superposition principle* applicable: *In a common frame the strains of two succeeding displacements are obtained by adding the strains corresponding to each displacement field, provided of course that the displacement gradients are small.* Mathematically

$$\mathbf{E} \cong \tilde{\mathbf{E}} \cong \tilde{\mathbf{E}}_1 + \tilde{\mathbf{E}}_2 = \tilde{\mathbf{E}}_2 + \tilde{\mathbf{E}}_1 \tag{14.15}$$

The superposition principle applies without change to infinitesimal rotations.

## 15. SOME SPECIAL DEFORMATIONS

For illustration purposes we cite here three classes of special deformations. This division into classes is not unique and the classes overlap.

1. Deformations resulting from restrictions on strains and rotations: these types of deformations do not make reference to any special geometry or direction. The types of deformations that fall into this class are *rigid deformation, pure homogeneous strain, potential deformation,* and *isochoric deformation.*

2. Deformations resulting from specifications of strains and rotations in a chosen frame of reference: *uniform dilatation, simple extension, simple shear, plane strain,* etc., fall into this class.

3. Deformations that result from an appropriate deformation of an object having a special geometry: *simple torsion, inflation of a cylinder, expansion or twist of a sphere,* etc.

Many interesting combinations of these special deformations exist. Below we give a brief account of some of them.

1*a*. *Rigid Deformation.* Deformation is said to be rigid if the distance between every pair of points remains unchanged. The necessary and sufficient condition for a rigid deformation is

$$\mathbf{C} = \mathbf{c} = \mathbf{I} \tag{15.1}$$

at each point. In this case we also have

$$C_\alpha = \lambda_\alpha^2 = 1 \qquad \mathrm{I}_C = \mathrm{II}_C = 3 \qquad \mathrm{III}_C = 1 \tag{15.2}$$

All of these have been given before (see Art. 9).

1b. *Pure Strain.* This was defined in Art. 10. In a pure strain the principal axes of strain are not rotated. The necessary and sufficient condition for pure strain is

$$\mathbf{R} = \mathbf{I} \tag{15.3}$$

1c. *Potential Deformation.* This was defined in Art. 10 as a deformation in which the mean rotation **R** vanishes. The necessary and sufficient condition for this is the existence of a scalar function $V$ such that

$$\mathbf{U} = \text{grad } V \tag{15.4}$$

In this case we found that at a point there exists an orthogonal triplet of invariant directions. The existence of the potential strain is also the necessary and sufficient condition for the principal axes of strain to be invariant lines.

1d. *Isochoric Deformation.* This is defined by the condition that the volumes remain unaltered. The necessary and sufficient condition according to (12.8) is given by any one of

$$J = 1 \qquad \mathrm{III}_C = 1 \qquad \mathrm{III}_c = 1 \qquad 1 - 2\,\mathrm{I}_e + 4\,\mathrm{II}_e - 8\,\mathrm{III}_e = 1 \tag{15.5}$$

Any *scalar isotropic function* of **c** is in general a function of $\mathrm{I}_c$, $\mathrm{II}_c$, and $\mathrm{III}_c$. For an *isochoric deformation, a scalar isotropic function of* **c** *therefore is a function of* $\mathrm{I}_c$ *and* $\mathrm{II}_c$ *alone.*

From (9.22) we have $\mathrm{III}_C = \lambda_1^2\lambda_2^2\lambda_3^2 = 1$. Hence from (9.23) we get

$$\mathrm{I}_c = \mathrm{II}_C = \mathrm{I}_{\overset{-1}{C}} = \frac{1}{\lambda_1^2} + \frac{1}{\lambda_2^2} + \lambda_1^2\lambda_2^2 \tag{15.6}$$

2. *Deformations Resulting from the Specification of Strains and Rotations in a Chosen Frame of Reference.* Many of these types of deformation are included in a homogeneous *affine* transformation relating the positions of $Z^K$ and $z^k$ of a material point before and after deformation as

$$z^k = D^k{}_K Z^K \qquad Z^K = \overset{-1}{D}{}^K{}_k z^k \qquad D^k{}_K \overset{-1}{D}{}^K{}_l = \delta^k{}_l \tag{15.7}$$

where $D^k{}_K$ and the inverse $\overset{-1}{D}{}^K{}_k$ are constant matrices. The deformation described by (15.7) carries straight lines into straight lines, ellipses into ellipses, and ellipsoids into ellipsoids. Such a deformation is called *homogeneous strain.* From (15.7) it follows that the homogeneous strain may also be defined by $\partial^2 z^k / \partial Z^K \partial Z^L = 0$, or in general curvilinear coordinates, equivalent forms are

$$(15.8) \qquad (x^k{}_{,K})_{:L} = 0 \qquad C_{KL:M} = 0$$

where a colon indicates total covariant differentiation (see Art. A6). These indicate that the deformation tensors are constants.

Besides the homogeneous strain described above, in this class are also included *plane strain, generalized plane strain,* and a generalization of the homogeneous strain in which the matrix elements $D^k{}_K$ may depend on the coordinates of the material point in a special way. Below we give a few special examples.

2*a*. *Uniform Dilatation.* Suppose now that in a homogeneous deformation the nondiagonal elements of $\mathbf{D}$ are zero and the diagonal elements are all equal, i.e.,

$$(15.9) \qquad \mathbf{D} = \begin{bmatrix} \lambda & 0 & 0 \\ 0 & \lambda & 0 \\ 0 & 0 & \lambda \end{bmatrix} \qquad 0 < \lambda < \infty$$

The state of deformation so obtained is known as *uniform dilatation.* The deformation and strain tensors are given by

$$(15.10) \qquad \mathbf{C} = \overset{-1}{\mathbf{c}} = \lambda^2 \mathbf{I} \qquad \mathbf{c} = \overset{-1}{\mathbf{C}} = \frac{\mathbf{I}}{\lambda^2} \qquad 2\,\mathbf{E} = (\lambda^2 - 1)\,\mathbf{I}$$

The strain ellipsoids are spheres. Thus uniform dilatation may be characterized by identical principal stretches. The strain invariants are

$$(15.11) \qquad \mathrm{I}_C = 3\,\lambda^2 \qquad \mathrm{II}_C = 3\,\lambda^4 \qquad \mathrm{III}_C = \lambda^6$$

Clearly $\lambda$ is the stretch in any direction. For $\lambda > 1$ we have a uniform expansion, and for $0 < \lambda < 1$ we have a uniform compression. A uniform dilatation deforms a sphere into another sphere.

2*b*. *Uniaxial Strain and Simple Extension.* Consider now a homogeneous strain characterized by

$$(15.12) \qquad D = \begin{bmatrix} \lambda & 0 & 0 \\ 0 & 1 & 0 \\ 0 & 0 & 1 \end{bmatrix} \qquad 0 < \lambda < \infty$$

Through (15.7) we calculate

$$(15.13) \qquad \mathbf{C} = \overset{-1}{\mathbf{c}} = \begin{bmatrix} \lambda^2 & 0 & 0 \\ 0 & 1 & 0 \\ 0 & 0 & 1 \end{bmatrix} \qquad \mathbf{c} = \overset{-1}{\mathbf{C}} = \begin{bmatrix} 1/\lambda^2 & 0 & 0 \\ 0 & 1 & 0 \\ 0 & 0 & 1 \end{bmatrix}$$

For various invariants we have

$$\text{(15.14)}\qquad \mathrm{I}_C = 2 + \lambda^2 \qquad \mathrm{II}_C = 1 + 2\lambda^2 \qquad \mathrm{III}_C = \lambda^2$$
$$\mathrm{I}_E = \frac{\lambda^2 - 1}{2} \qquad \mathrm{II}_E = \mathrm{III}_E = 0$$

The strain ellipsoids are spheroids. Thus *uniaxial strain* may be characterized as having two principal stretches equal to unity with the third being different. The deformation moves the planes perpendicular to the $Z^1$ axis parallel to themselves, and no deformation takes place in the $Z^2$ and $Z^3$ directions (Fig. 15.1).

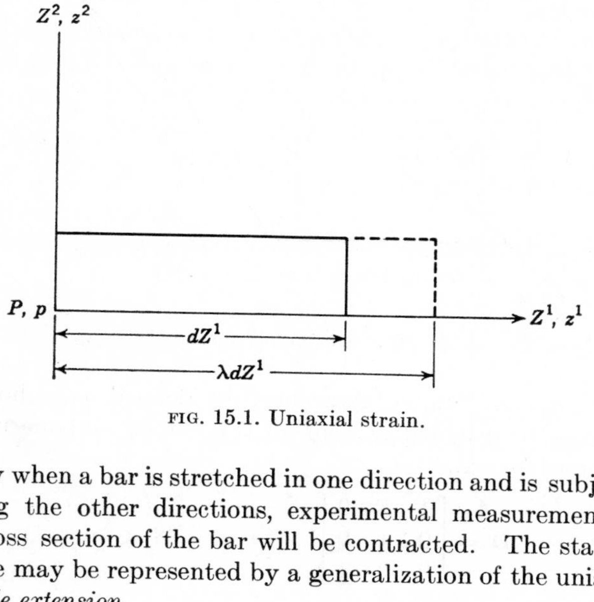


FIG. 15.1. Uniaxial strain.

Generally when a bar is stretched in one direction and is subjected to no forces along the other directions, experimental measurements indicate that the cross section of the bar will be contracted. The state of strain for this case may be represented by a generalization of the uniaxial strain called *simple extension*,

$$\text{(15.15)}\qquad \mathbf{C} = \overset{-1}{\mathbf{c}} = \begin{bmatrix} \lambda^2 & 0 & 0 \\ 0 & K^2\lambda^2 & 0 \\ 0 & 0 & K^2\lambda^2 \end{bmatrix}$$
$$\mathbf{c} = \overset{-1}{\mathbf{C}} = \begin{bmatrix} \lambda^{-2} & 0 & 0 \\ 0 & (K\lambda)^{-2} & 0 \\ 0 & 0 & (K\lambda)^{-2} \end{bmatrix}$$
$$\mathrm{I}_C = \lambda^2(1 + 2K^2) \qquad \mathrm{II}_C = K^2\lambda^4(2 + K^2) \qquad \mathrm{III}_C = K^4\lambda^6$$

and $\mathrm{I}_E$, $\mathrm{II}_E$, and $\mathrm{III}_E$ are obtained from (9.28).

In the $Z^2$ and $Z^3$ directions we have the stretches $K\lambda$ and extensions

$(K\lambda - 1)$; therefore the *transverse contraction ratio* is given by

$$\nu = -\frac{K\lambda - 1}{\lambda - 1} \qquad K = \frac{1+\nu}{\lambda} - \nu \tag{15.16}$$

The case of $\nu = -1$ or $K = 1$ leads to uniform dilatation. For $\nu = 0$ or $K = 1/\lambda$ we obtain uniaxial strain. For $\nu > 0$ the cross section perpendicular to the axis of stretch contracts, and for $\nu < 0$ it swells.

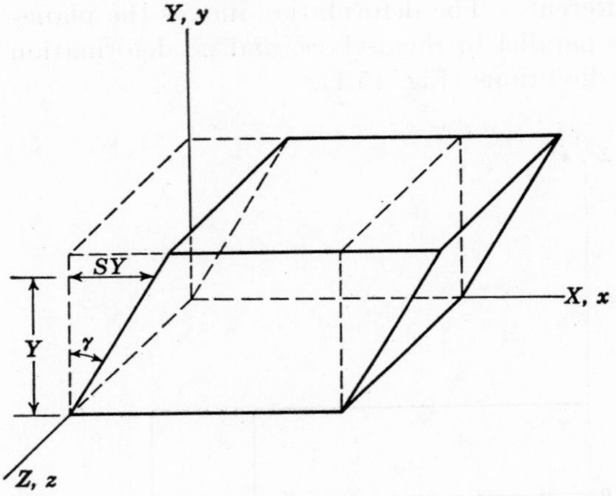


FIG. 15.2. Simple shear.

2c. *Simple Shear.* Simple shear may be defined as a homogeneous strain in which the diagonal elements of **D** are unity and one nondiagonal element is nonzero, e.g.,

$$\mathbf{D} = \begin{bmatrix} 1 & S & 0 \\ 0 & 1 & 0 \\ 0 & 0 & 1 \end{bmatrix} \qquad -\infty < S < \infty \tag{15.17}$$

where $S$ is a constant. Through (15.17) we have

$$x = X + SY \qquad y = Y \qquad z = Z \tag{15.18}$$

Therefore simple shear rotates $X =$ const planes rigidly about their lines of intersection with the $Y = 0$ plane, in an amount equal to the angle of shear $\gamma$, given by

$$\gamma = \arctan S$$

The $Y =$ const and $Z =$ const planes are unchanged (Fig. 15.2). Simple shear may be approximated by sliding the cards of a deck from its original rectangular parallelepiped geometry to a final rectilinear parallelepiped form. The Green and Cauchy deformation tensors, the strain tensors, and the invariants are

$$\mathbf{C} = \begin{bmatrix} 1 & S & 0 \\ S & 1+S^2 & 0 \\ 0 & 0 & 1 \end{bmatrix} \qquad \overset{-1}{\mathbf{C}} = \begin{bmatrix} 1+S^2 & -S & 0 \\ -S & 1 & 0 \\ 0 & 0 & 1 \end{bmatrix} \qquad \mathbf{E} = \begin{bmatrix} 0 & S/2 & 0 \\ S/2 & S^2/2 & 0 \\ 0 & 0 & 0 \end{bmatrix}$$

$$\mathbf{c} = \begin{bmatrix} 1 & -S & 0 \\ -S & 1+S^2 & 0 \\ 0 & 0 & 1 \end{bmatrix} \qquad \overset{-1}{\mathbf{c}} = \begin{bmatrix} 1+S^2 & S & 0 \\ S & 1 & 0 \\ 0 & 0 & 1 \end{bmatrix} \qquad \mathbf{e} = \begin{bmatrix} 0 & S/2 & 0 \\ S/2 & -S^2/2 & 0 \\ 0 & 0 & 0 \end{bmatrix}$$

(15.19)

$$\mathrm{I}_C = \mathrm{II}_C = 3 + S^2 \qquad \mathrm{III}_C = 1$$

$$-\mathrm{I}_E = \mathrm{I}_e = 2\,\mathrm{II}_E = 2\,\mathrm{II}_e = \frac{-S^2}{2} \qquad \mathrm{III}_E = \mathrm{III}_e = 0$$

Since $\mathrm{III}_C = 1$, we see that simple shear is isochoric. The proper numbers are obtained by solving (9.8). Hence

$$\begin{aligned} C_1 &= \lambda_1^2 = 1 + \tfrac{1}{2}S^2 + S\sqrt{1+\tfrac{1}{4}S^2} \\ C_2 &= \lambda_2^2 = \frac{1}{\lambda_1^2} = 1 + \tfrac{1}{2}S^2 - S\sqrt{1+\tfrac{1}{4}S^2} \\ C_3 &= \lambda_3^2 = 1 \end{aligned} \tag{15.20}$$

Proper directions $\mathbf{N}$ and $\mathbf{n}$ corresponding respectively to $\mathbf{C}$ and $\mathbf{c}$ are

$$\begin{aligned} \left.\begin{matrix}\mathbf{N}_1\\ \mathbf{N}_2\end{matrix}\right\} &= \frac{\mathbf{I}_1 + (\tfrac{1}{2}S \pm \sqrt{1+\tfrac{1}{4}S^2})\,\mathbf{I}_2}{\sqrt{2+\tfrac{1}{2}S^2 \pm S\sqrt{1+\tfrac{1}{4}S^2}}} \qquad \mathbf{N}_3 = \mathbf{I}_3 \\ \left.\begin{matrix}\mathbf{n}_1\\ \mathbf{n}_2\end{matrix}\right\} &= \frac{\mathbf{i}_1 + (-\tfrac{1}{2}S \pm \sqrt{1+\tfrac{1}{4}S^2})\,\mathbf{i}_2}{\sqrt{2+\tfrac{1}{2}S^2 \mp S\sqrt{1+\tfrac{1}{4}S^2}}} \qquad \mathbf{n}_3 = \mathbf{i}_3 \end{aligned} \tag{15.21}$$

In the $Y = 0$ plane, according to (15.18) a point $A\,(-S/2, 1, 0)$ after deformation occupies the position $a\,(S/2, 1, 0)$ (Fig. 15.3). We have

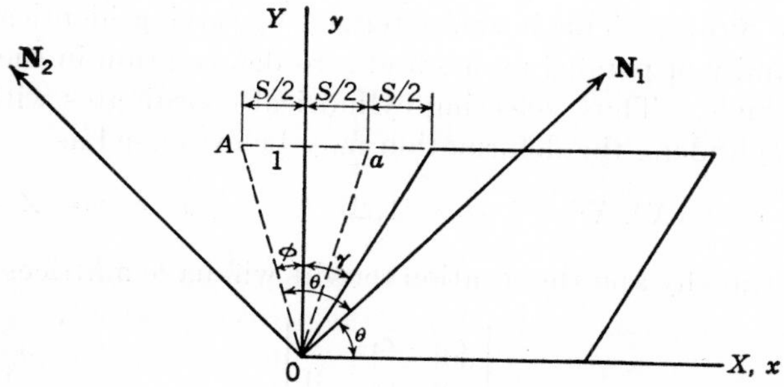


FIG. 15.3. Plane of shear.

$OA = Oa$. Consequently the fibers parallel to $OA$ making an angle $\phi = \arctan(S/2)$ with the $Y$ axis do not alter their length. Now from $(15.21)_1$ we have

$$\tan\theta = \tfrac{1}{2}S + \sqrt{1 + \tfrac{1}{4}S^2} \tag{15.22}$$

From Fig. 15.3 we find that $\theta$ is the angle between $OA$ and $\mathbf{N}_1$. Thus the *principal directions bisect the angle between the undeformed planes $ZOA$ and $ZOX$.* The principal stretches can be determined by calculating the ratio of the lengths after and before deformation for the fibers lying along $\mathbf{N}_1$ and $\mathbf{N}_2$ directions. This again produces (15.20). The greatest shear is seen to be experienced by the elements *bisecting the principal axes.* One of these elements makes an angle $\tfrac{1}{2}\arctan S/2$ with the $X$ axis. The magnitude of the maximum shear $\gamma_{\max}$ is thus given by

$$\tan\gamma_{\max} = \frac{2}{S}\left[-1 + \sqrt{\frac{S^2}{4} + 1}\right] \tag{15.23}$$

It is simple to see that for a small shearing $S \ll 1$, we have

$$\begin{gathered} \lambda_1 = 1 + \frac{S}{2} + 0\,(S^2) \qquad \lambda_2 = 1 - \frac{S}{2} + 0\,(S^2) \\ \tan\gamma_{\max} = S + 0\,(S^2) \end{gathered} \tag{15.24}$$

The principal axes approach the bisectors of the coordinate axes, and the maximum shear axes approach the coordinate axes. Finally we get the components of the rotation tensor by substituting (15.21) into $(10.14)_1$ in the same reference frame as above.

$$\mathbf{R} = \|R^k{}_K\| = \begin{bmatrix} (1 + \tfrac{1}{4}S^2)^{-\frac{1}{2}} & \tfrac{1}{2}S\,(1 + \tfrac{1}{4}S^2)^{-\frac{1}{2}} & 0 \\ -\tfrac{1}{2}S\,(1 + \tfrac{1}{4}S^2)^{-\frac{1}{2}} & (1 + \tfrac{1}{4}S^2)^{-\frac{1}{2}} & 0 \\ 0 & 0 & 1 \end{bmatrix} \tag{15.25}$$

where the row index is $k$ and the column is $K$. Clearly the axis of rotation is the $Z$ axis.

2d. *Plane Strain.* This is characterized by having identical deformations in a family of parallel planes and zero deformation in the directions of their normals. Thus, selecting cylindrical coordinates with $Z$ as the axis of the cylinders, the deformation may be expressed as

$$x^k = x^k(X^1, X^2) \qquad (k = 1, 2) \qquad x^3 = z = Z = X^3 \tag{15.26}$$

Clearly the Cauchy and the rotation tensors will have matrices of the type

$$\begin{bmatrix} c_{11} & c_{12} & 0 \\ c_{21} & c_{22} & 0 \\ 0 & 0 & 1 \end{bmatrix}$$

The $z$ axis is a principal axis of strain and the stretch in this direction is unity, i.e., $\lambda_3 = 1$. Invariants of **C** are

$$\text{(15.27)}\qquad \begin{aligned} \mathrm{I}_C &= C^1{}_1 + C^2{}_2 + 1 \qquad \mathrm{II}_C = C^1{}_1 C^2{}_2 - C^1{}_2 C^2{}_1 + C^1{}_1 + C^2{}_2 \\ \mathrm{III}_C &= C^1{}_1 C^2{}_2 - C^1{}_2 C^2{}_1 = \mathrm{II}_C - \mathrm{I}_C + 1 \end{aligned}$$

Hence the roots of the characteristic cubic equation (9.8) are

$$\text{(15.28)}\qquad \left.\begin{matrix} C_1 \\ C_2 \end{matrix}\right\} = \tfrac{1}{2}[\mathrm{I}_C - 1 \pm (\mathrm{I}_C^2 + 2\,\mathrm{I}_C - 4\,\mathrm{II}_C - 3)^{\frac{1}{2}}] \qquad C_3 = 1$$

These, of course, are also the squares of the stretches. The principal directions are determined by solving three simultaneous equations of the type (9.6) for each $C = C_\alpha$, $(\alpha = 1, 2, 3)$. The construction of Mohr's circle for this case and other graphical methods are well-known through books on strength of materials.

Since $\mathrm{III}_C = \lambda_1 \lambda_2 = \sqrt{C_1 C_2}$, we see that the plane strain is isochoric if the principal stretches are reciprocals of one another. For this case we also get $\mathrm{I}_C = \mathrm{II}_C$; hence, through (9.23), $\mathrm{I}_c = \mathrm{I}_C$. Therefore *in a plane isochoric strain each one of the strain invariants of* **C**, **c**, $\overset{-1}{\mathbf{C}}$, *and* $\overset{-1}{\mathbf{c}}$ *is equal to the corresponding one of any other.*

A generalization of the plane strain that has found application in the theory of elasticity is the *generalized plane strain* which is defined by deformations of the form

$$\text{(15.29)}\qquad x^k = x^k(X^1, X^2) \qquad (k = 1, 2) \qquad z = z(Z)$$

3. *Deformations That Result from an Appropriate Deformation of an Object Having a Special Geometry.* Finally we give a few examples for some special types of deformation of some simple objects. The theory of finite deformations has produced important results through its applications to such cases.

3a. *Torsion of a Circular Cylinder.* The uniform twist of a circular cylinder along its length may be represented by the deformations

$$\text{(15.30)}\qquad r = R \qquad \theta = \Theta + KZ \qquad z = Z$$

where $R$, $\Theta$, $Z$ are the cylindrical coordinates of a material point before deformation and $r$, $\theta$, $z$ are the cylindrical coordinates of the same point after deformation, both being referred to the same system. It is clear from (15.30) that material points of a normal cross section $Z$ = const remain in their original plane. The cross sections rotate with respect to each other by angles proportional to their axial distances from some reference plane. Also, the material points of coaxial cylinders do not leave their respective original surfaces (Fig. 15.4).

The constant $K$ is *the twist per unit length.* In cylindrical coordinates

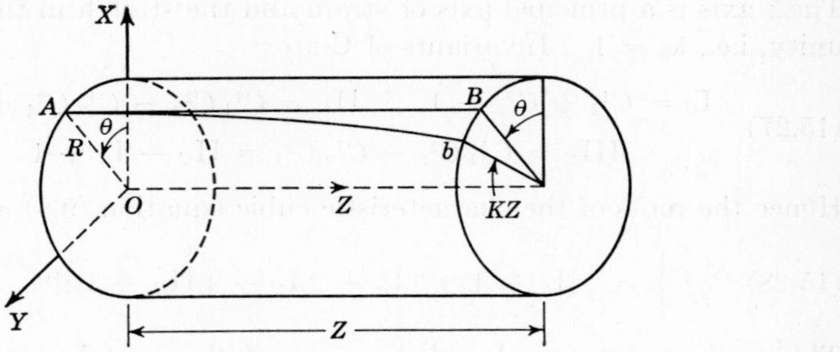


FIG. 15.4. Twist of a cylinder.

we have $G_{11} = G_{33} = 1$, $G_{22} = R^2$, $g_{11} = g_{33} = 1$, and $g_{22} = r^2$, and all other $G_{KL}$ and $g_{kl}$ vanish. From $(4.8)_2$ and $(4.15)_1$ we get

$$(15.31) \qquad \|C_{KL}\| = \begin{bmatrix} 1 & 0 & 0 \\ 0 & R^2 & KR^2 \\ 0 & KR^2 & 1 + K^2R^2 \end{bmatrix}$$

$$\|\overset{-1}{c}{}^{kl}\| = \begin{bmatrix} 1 & 0 & 0 \\ 0 & K^2 + 1/r^2 & K \\ 0 & K & 1 \end{bmatrix}$$

where the first index represents the row and the second the column. The invariants of **C** follow from (9.9)

$$(15.32) \qquad \mathrm{I}_C = \mathrm{II}_C = 3 + K^2R^2 \qquad \mathrm{III}_C = 1$$

It is clear that the torsion described by (15.30) is isochoric. Physical components $C^{(K)}{}_{(L)}$ and $\overset{-1}{c}{}^{(k)}{}_{(l)}$ are given by

$$(15.33) \qquad C^{(K)}{}_{(L)} = C^K{}_L \sqrt{G_{\underline{KK}}/G_{\underline{LL}}} \qquad \overset{-1}{c}{}^{(k)}{}_{(l)} = \overset{-1}{c}{}^k{}_l \sqrt{g_{\underline{kk}}/g_{\underline{ll}}}$$

or explicitly

$$(15.34) \qquad \|C^{(K)}{}_{(L)}\| = \begin{bmatrix} 1 & 0 & 0 \\ 0 & 1 & KR \\ 0 & KR & 1 + K^2R^2 \end{bmatrix}$$

$$\|\overset{-1}{c}{}^{(k)}{}_{(l)}\| = \begin{bmatrix} 1 & 0 & 0 \\ 0 & 1 + K^2r^2 & Kr \\ 0 & Kr & 1 \end{bmatrix}$$

When these are compared with the corresponding formulas (15.19) for the case of simple shear, in which case they are also the physical components of **C** and $\overset{-1}{\mathbf{c}}$, we find that the simple torsion is equivalent to simple shearing of concentric cylinders $R = \text{const}$ with $S = KR$. Therefore, with this correspondence, all formulas of simple shear apply to the case of simple torsion.

3b. *Pure Bending of a Block.* Suppose we deform a rectangular parallelepiped in such a way that the $X$ = const planes become circles, the $Y$ = const planes become radial lines, and the $Z$ = const planes are preserved[1] (Fig. 15.5). Such a deformation may be represented in two coordinate systems by

(15.35) $$r = f(X) \qquad \theta = g(Y) \qquad z = h(Z)$$

where $r$, $\theta$, $z$ are the cylindrical coordinates having the same origin as the rectangular coordinates $X$, $Y$, $Z$. We have $G_{KL} = \delta_{KL}$, $g_{11} = g_{33} = 1$,

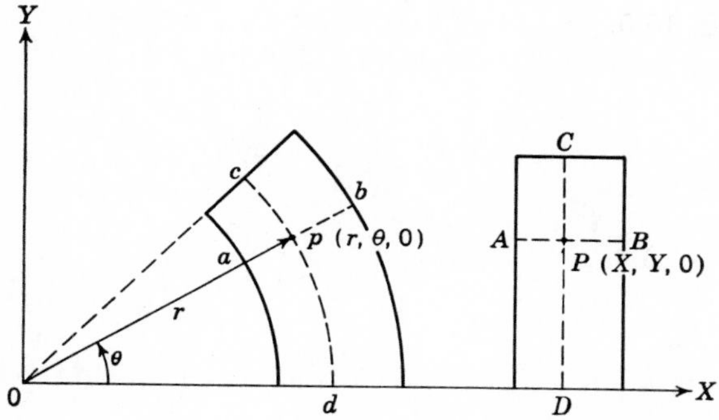


FIG. 15.5. Bending of a block.

$g_{22} = r^2$, and $g_{kl} = 0$ ($k \neq l$). Using $(4.8)_2$, $(4.15)_1$, and (9.9), we get

$$\|C^K{}_L\| = \|\overset{-1}{c}{}^k{}_l\| = \begin{bmatrix} f'^2 & 0 & 0 \\ 0 & r^2 g'^2 & 0 \\ 0 & 0 & h'^2 \end{bmatrix}$$

(15.36) $$\mathrm{I}_C = f'^2 + r^2 g'^2 + h'^2 \qquad \mathrm{II}_C = f'^2 h'^2 + r^2 g'^2 (f'^2 + h'^2)$$
$$\mathrm{III}_C = r^2 f'^2 g'^2 h'^2$$

where a prime represents differentiation with respect to the arguments of the functions, e.g., $f' \equiv df/dX$. In the foregoing formula, equivalence of the tensors **C** and **c** implies the equivalence of the numerical values of the components for a given particle. **C** as a function of **X** and **c** as a function of **x** are, of course, different.

Tensors **C** and **c** have diagonal forms; therefore the coordinates at **X** and **x** give the principal directions. Hence principal stretches are

(15.37) $$\lambda_1 = f' \qquad \lambda_2 = r g' \qquad \lambda_3 = h'$$

[1] Rivlin [1949*a*]. See also Signorini [1943, art. 29].

and the principal directions $\mathbf{N}_\alpha$ in rectangular coordinates and $\mathbf{n}_\alpha$ in cylindrical coordinates are given by

$$\text{(15.38)}\qquad \begin{aligned} &\mathbf{N}_1 = (1,0,0) \qquad \mathbf{N}_2 = (0,1,0) \qquad \mathbf{N}_3 = (0,0,1) \\ &\mathbf{n}_1 = (1,0,0) \qquad \mathbf{n}_2 = \left(0, \frac{1}{r}, 0\right) \qquad \mathbf{n}_3 = (0,0,1) \end{aligned}$$

According to (10.14) and $R^k{}_l = g^K{}_l R^k{}_K$, we get

$$\text{(15.39)}\qquad \|R^k{}_K\| = \begin{bmatrix} 1 & 0 & 0 \\ 0 & 1/r & 0 \\ 0 & 0 & 1 \end{bmatrix} \qquad \|R^k{}_l\| = \begin{bmatrix} \cos\theta & -r\sin\theta & 0 \\ r^{-1}\sin\theta & \cos\theta & 0 \\ 0 & 0 & 1 \end{bmatrix}$$

Hence the axis of rotation is the common $Z$-$z$ axis, which, of course, is clear from Fig. 15.5.

# 2

# MOTION

## 16. SCOPE OF THE CHAPTER

The present chapter deals with the kinematics and global kinetics of continuous media. The material time rates of tensors, velocity, and acceleration are defined in Art. 17. Material lines, surfaces, and volumes are treated in Art. 18. The material derivatives of line, surface, and volume elements and the kinematics of integrals are studied in Arts. 19 and 20. The concepts of deformation rate, spin, velocity, strain rates, and their physical significances occupy Arts. 21 and 22. A discussion on circulation is presented in Art. 23. Vorticity and the Helmholtz theorems are discussed in Art. 24. The concepts of mass, momentum, moment of momentum, and energy, and the four basic conservation principles of mechanics—namely, the conservation of mass, balance of momentum and moment of momentum, and conservation of energy—are given in Arts. 25 and 26. The discussion on the principles of global kinetics is thus completed. Article 27 is devoted to the principle of objectivity, which plays a central role in the determination of the constitutive relations.

## 17. MOTION, MATERIAL DERIVATIVES OF TENSORS, VELOCITY, AND ACCELERATION

A material point $\mathbf{X}$ at time $t = 0$ is carried to a spatial point $\mathbf{x}$ at time $t$. *The one-parameter family of transformations*

(17.1) $$\mathbf{x} = \mathbf{x}(\mathbf{X}, t) \qquad \text{or} \qquad x^k = x^k(X^K, t)$$

*that carries a fixed material point* $\mathbf{X}$ *to a spatial place* $\mathbf{x}$ *is known as the motion.* The parameter $t$ is real. The coordinate system $x^k$ is a single *fixed* one, and (17.1) should not be considered as a group of coordinate transformations. Unless stated explicitly, (17.1) is not understood to define an *intrinsic* or *convected* coordinate system.

By the *axiom of continuity* (17.1) and its *unique* inverse,

(17.2) $$\mathbf{X} = \mathbf{X}(\mathbf{x}, t) \qquad \text{or} \qquad X^K = X^K(x^k, t)$$

*are assumed to possess continuous partial derivatives with respect to their arguments to whatever order needed, except possibly at some singular points, lines, or surfaces.* Generally we shall not need more than the second- or third-order partial derivatives. Single-valuedness of (17.1) and (17.2) is essential for the *axiom of impenetrability of matter.* Otherwise the body may split or two disjoint bodies may intermingle.

In the kinematics of continuous media, time rates of vectors and tensors associated with the material points play an important role. In the determination of the time rate of change of field quantities carried by a material point, one must take account not only of the change at a fixed spatial point (local change) but also of the change in the field as observed by the particle due solely to its motion (convective change). A common example in hydrodynamics is encountered in the calculation of the acceleration of a material point [see (17.15)]. Other examples are deformation rate (19.4), stress flux (Arts. 35 and 72), etc.

DEFINITION. *The material derivative of an absolute spatial vector* $f^k(\mathbf{x}, t)$ *is defined by*

$$\dot{f}^k \equiv \frac{D}{Dt} f^k(\mathbf{x}, t) \equiv \frac{\partial f^k}{\partial t} + \frac{\delta f^k}{\delta t} = \frac{\partial f^k}{\partial t} + f^k{}_{;l}\, \dot{x}^l \tag{17.3}$$

where the partial time derivative $\partial f^k/\partial t$ is taken with $\mathbf{x}$ held constant and the *intrinsic derivative* $\delta f^k/\delta t$ with $t$ held constant, i.e.,

$$\frac{\partial f^k}{\partial t} \equiv \frac{\partial f^k}{\partial t}(\mathbf{x}, t)\bigg|_{\mathbf{x}=\text{const}}$$

$$\frac{\delta f^k}{\delta t} \equiv f^k{}_{;l}\, v^l \equiv \left(f^k{}_{,l} + \begin{Bmatrix} k \\ lm \end{Bmatrix} f^m\right) \dot{x}^l \tag{17.4}$$

$$\dot{x}^l \equiv \frac{Dx^l}{Dt} = \frac{\partial x^l}{\partial t}$$

In calculating the partial time derivative of a function, it is assumed that all variables other than $t$ are held constant. Thus, for example,

$$\frac{\partial f^k}{\partial t} \equiv \frac{\partial f^k(\mathbf{x}, t)}{\partial t}\bigg|_{\mathbf{x}=\text{const}} \qquad \frac{\partial F^K}{\partial t} \equiv \frac{\partial F^K(\mathbf{X}, t)}{\partial t}\bigg|_{\mathbf{X}=\text{const}}$$

Similar definitions apply to material derivatives of tensors, e.g.,

$$\frac{D}{Dt} f^k{}_l(\mathbf{x}, t) \equiv \frac{\partial f^k{}_l}{\partial t} + \frac{\delta f^k{}_l}{\delta t} = \frac{\partial f^k{}_l}{\partial t} + f^k{}_{l;m}\, \dot{x}^m \tag{17.5}$$

If the vectors and tensors are lagrangian, then the intrinsic derivatives vanish and we write

$$\frac{D}{Dt} F^K(\mathbf{X}, t) \equiv \frac{\partial F^K}{\partial t} \tag{17.6}$$

The material derivative defined above applies equally well to the lagrangian vectors and tensors.

LEMMA 1. *The material derivative obeys the rules of ordinary differentiation involving sums and products of tensors.*

$$\frac{D}{Dt}(f^k + g^k) = \frac{Df^k}{Dt} + \frac{Dg^k}{Dt}$$

$$\frac{D}{Dt}(f^k g^l) = \frac{Df^k}{Dt} g^l + f^k \frac{Dg^l}{Dt} \tag{17.7}$$

Proofs of these are obvious from the fact that both operators $\partial/\partial t$ and $\delta/\delta t$ obey these rules. An independent proof would follow from the definition of material derivative. The proof of $(17.7)_1$ is trivial; that for $(17.7)_2$ is as follows:

$$\frac{D}{Dt}(f^k g^l) = \frac{\partial (f^k g^l)}{\partial t} + (f^k g^l)_{;m} \dot{x}^m$$

$$= \left(\frac{\partial f^k}{\partial t} + f^k{}_{;m} \dot{x}^m\right) g^l + f^k \left(\frac{\partial g^l}{\partial t} + g^l{}_{;m} \dot{x}^m\right)$$

Expressions similar to (17.7) for higher-order tensors are easily obtained.

LEMMA 2. *The material derivatives of eulerian and lagrangian metric tensors and base vectors are zero,* e.g.,

$$\frac{Dg_{kl}}{Dt} = \frac{Dg^{kl}}{Dt} = \frac{D\mathbf{g}_k}{Dt} = \frac{D\mathbf{g}^k}{Dt} = 0 \tag{17.8}$$

PROOF. Consider

$$\frac{Dg_{kl}}{Dt} = \frac{\partial g_{kl}}{\partial t} + \frac{\delta g_{kl}}{\delta t} = \frac{\partial g_{kl}}{\partial t} + g_{kl;m} \dot{x}^m$$

We have $\partial g_{kl}/\partial t = 0$, since $g_{kl}$ is a function of $\mathbf{x}$ alone. Also from Ricci's theorem $g_{kl;m} = 0$; hence the proof for the first of (17.8). The proof of the rest of (17.8) follows the same line of reasoning.

The relations of the material derivative to the ordinary time derivative is given by the following theorem.

THEOREM 1. *The time rate of change of a spatial vector with material variables held constant has the material derivatives of the components of the vector as its components.*

$$\left.\frac{d}{dt}\mathbf{f}(\mathbf{x}, t)\right|_{\mathbf{X}=\text{const}} = \frac{Df^k}{Dt}\mathbf{g}_k \tag{17.9}$$

PROOF. Form the left side, i.e.,

$$\left.\frac{d}{dt}\mathbf{f}(\mathbf{x}, t)\right|_{\mathbf{X}=\text{const}} = \frac{\partial}{\partial t}(f^k \mathbf{g}_k) + \frac{\partial}{\partial x^l}(f^k \mathbf{g}_k)\dot{x}^l$$

Now $\partial \mathbf{g}_k/\partial t = 0$, since $\mathbf{g}_k$ is a function of $\mathbf{x}$ alone, and in the operation $\partial/\partial t$ spatial variables $\mathbf{x}$ are held constant. Moreover

$$\frac{\partial}{\partial x^l}(f^k \mathbf{g}_k) = f^k{}_{;l}\,\mathbf{g}_k$$

Hence

$$\frac{d}{dt}\mathbf{f}(\mathbf{x}, t)\bigg|_{\mathbf{X}=\text{const}} = \left(\frac{\partial f^k}{\partial t} + f^k{}_{;l}\,\dot{x}^l\right)\mathbf{g}_k = \frac{Df^k}{Dt}\mathbf{g}_k$$

DEFINITION. *Velocity is the time rate of change of position of a given particle*, i.e.,

$$\text{(17.10)} \qquad \mathbf{v}(\mathbf{x}, t) = \frac{d\mathbf{p}}{dt} \qquad \text{or} \qquad v^k \equiv \dot{x}^k \equiv \frac{\partial x^k}{\partial t} \equiv \frac{Dx^k}{Dt}$$

where $\mathbf{X}$ is held constant in the motion (17.1). Note that, in general, for arbitrary spatial vectors $\partial/\partial t \neq D/Dt$.

Since

$$\mathbf{p} = \mathbf{P} + \mathbf{u} - \mathbf{b}$$

where $\mathbf{P}$ is independent of time, we also have

$$\text{(17.11)} \qquad \mathbf{v} = \dot{\mathbf{u}} \qquad \text{or} \qquad v^k = \frac{Du^k}{Dt}$$

where $\mathbf{X}$ is held constant, and

$$\text{(17.12)} \qquad \mathbf{v} = \mathbf{v}(\mathbf{X}, t)$$

If we use (17.2) for $\mathbf{X}$, we may also write (17.12) as

$$\text{(17.13)} \qquad \mathbf{v} = \mathbf{v}[\mathbf{X}(\mathbf{x}, t), t] = \mathbf{v}(\mathbf{x}, t)$$

Hence there exist two different descriptions for the velocity vector: the material description (17.12) and the spatial description (17.13).

DEFINITION. *The acceleration vector* $\mathbf{a}$ *is defined as the time rate of change of the velocity vector for a given particle (i.e.,* $\mathbf{X}$ *held constant).*

$$\text{(17.14)} \qquad \mathbf{a}(\mathbf{x}, t) \equiv \frac{d\mathbf{v}}{dt} \qquad (\mathbf{X} = \text{const})$$

According to Theorem 1, for the contravariant components of the acceleration vector, we have

$$\text{(17.15)} \qquad a^k(\mathbf{x}, t) \equiv \frac{Dv^k}{Dt} \equiv \frac{\partial v^k}{\partial t} + \frac{\delta v^k}{\delta t} \equiv \frac{\partial v^k}{\partial t} + v^k{}_{;l}\,v^l$$

The terms $\delta v^k/\delta t = v^k{}_{;l}\,v^l$ are called *convective terms*. In the lagrangian representation, the material particle with a given velocity is identifiable. This scheme is an immediate extension of that of particle mechanics. The eulerian description, however, has no counterpart in mechanics.

Here at time $t$ the velocity vector associated with each spatial point is known, but the particle occupying the spatial point is not. As each particle moves through a spatial point, it acquires the velocity associated with that point at that instant. The foregoing picture is valid for all vector and tensor quantities used in each scheme.

Covariant components of velocity and acceleration vectors are obtained by lowering the indices, i.e.,

$$v_k(\mathbf{x}, t) = g_{kl} v^l \qquad a_k(\mathbf{x}, t) = g_{kl} a^l = \frac{Dv_k}{Dt} \tag{17.16}$$

A point where $\mathbf{v} = 0$ is called a *stagnation point*. If at a spatial point $x^k$ the velocity field does not change in time, we say that the motion at that point is *steady*. In this case we have

$$\mathbf{v} = \mathbf{v}(\mathbf{x}) \tag{17.17}$$

More generally, if a tensor field is a function of spatial coordinates alone, then the tensor field is steady.

If two of the velocity components are zero and the third depends on the corresponding space variable only, we have *lineal motion*, e.g.,

$$v^1 = v^1(x^1, t) \qquad v^2 = v^3 = 0 \tag{17.18}$$

If one velocity component is zero and the two others depend on two space variables corresponding to nonzero components, we have *plane motion*, e.g.,

$$v^1 = v^1(x^1, x^2, t) \qquad v^2 = v^2(x^1, x^2, t) \qquad v^3 \equiv 0 \tag{17.19}$$

Other special types of motions are easily constructed.

## 18. PATH LINES, STREAMLINES, AND STREAK LINES

A *path line* is a curve traversed by a particle $\mathbf{X}$ as time $t$ varies. Thus

$$x^k = x^k(X^K, t) \qquad X^K = \text{fixed} \tag{18.1}$$

is the equation of the path line of the particle initially located at $X^K$. Also the integral curve of the system

$$dx^k = v^k\, dt \tag{18.2}$$

that passes through $X^K$ at $t = 0$ gives the path line.

The *streamlines* at time $t$ are the curves that are tangent to the vectors of the velocity field. Hence the integral curves to

$$\mathbf{v} = k\, d\mathbf{p}$$

or

$$\frac{dx^1}{v^1} = \frac{dx^2}{v^2} = \frac{dx^3}{v^3} = \frac{1}{k} \tag{18.3}$$

are the streamlines.

*Streak lines* through a spatial point $\mathbf{x}$ at time $t$ are the locus of

$$\mathbf{x} = \mathbf{x}\,[\mathbf{X}\,(\mathbf{x}, t'), t] \qquad \text{as } t' \text{ varies} \tag{18.4}$$

Notice that to obtain streak lines, we put $\mathbf{X} = \mathbf{X}\,(\mathbf{x}, t')$ in the motion $\mathbf{x} = \mathbf{x}\,(\mathbf{X}, t)$ for fixed $t$.

At a spatial point $\mathbf{x}$ at time $t$, the path line of the particle occupying $\mathbf{x}$, the streamline, and the streak line through $\mathbf{x}$ all have a common tangent. When the motion is steady, all three types of lines coincide; in general, however, for an unsteady motion they are distinct.

Experimentally these lines are distinguished by dropping small visible floating objects into a fluid and taking photographs of the stream. A long time exposure of the fluid into which a single object is dropped will reveal a path line of a particle. A short time exposure of a fluid onto which many small visible particles have just been dropped will show the direction of the velocity field at all points containing the visible particles. Mentally joining the tangent lines, we trace the streamlines. An instantaneous exposure of a fluid onto which objects are being dropped continuously at one place will show a portion of the streak line through that place at that time.

*Stream sheets* and *stream tubes* are collections of streamlines that intersect an unclosed or closed curve. Since the material particles move in the direction of the velocity field, they cannot cross the stream sheets or tubes. Similar to the foregoing material vector lines, one defines other types of material lines by drawing curves tangent to vectors associated with spatial points at time $t$, e.g., *vortex lines*.[1] The sheets and tubes are similarly defined.

A manifold consisting of material particles is called a *material manifold*. A curve

$$X^\alpha = X^\alpha\,(S) \tag{18.5}$$

is a *material line*, where $S$ is a parameter. At time $t$ its *configuration* is given by

$$\mathbf{x}\,(S, t) = \mathbf{x}\,(\mathbf{X}\,(S), t) \tag{18.6}$$

where $\mathbf{x} = \mathbf{x}\,(\mathbf{X}, t)$ is the motion.

A *material surface* is defined by

$$X^\alpha = X^\alpha\,(L, M) \qquad \text{or} \qquad F\,(\mathbf{X}) = 0 \tag{18.7}$$

where $L$ and $M$ are parameters. The material-surface configuration at

[1] For the definition of vorticity see Art. 21, and for those of vortex lines, surfaces, or tubes see Art. 24.

time $t$ is given by

$$(18.8) \qquad \mathbf{x} = \mathbf{x}\,(\mathbf{X}\,(L, M), t) \qquad \text{or} \qquad \mathbf{F}\,(\mathbf{X}\,(\mathbf{x}, t)) = 0$$

A *material volume* is a region of material particles. We now give the criterion for material manifolds.

LAGRANGE'S CRITERION. *A necessary and sufficient condition for the surface $f\,(\mathbf{x}, t) = 0$ to be material is that*

$$(18.9) \qquad \dot{f} = \frac{\partial f}{\partial t} + f_{,k}\, v^k = 0$$

The proof of this theorem is as follows. Suppose that $f(\mathbf{x}, t) = 0$ is a material surface on which a typical point is moving with a velocity $\mathbf{v}$ which is not necessarily the velocity $\dot{\mathbf{x}}$ of the material point instantaneously occupying that point on the surface. The velocity $\mathbf{v}$ of this point on the surface may be obtained from

$$(18.10) \qquad \frac{\partial f}{\partial t} + f_{,k}\, v^k = 0$$

The normal component $v_{(\mathbf{n})}$ of $\mathbf{v}$ on the exterior normal to $f = 0$ is

$$(18.11) \qquad v_{(\mathbf{n})} = \frac{v^k f_{,k}}{\sqrt{g^{lm} f_{,l} f_{,m}}} = -\frac{\partial f/\partial t}{\sqrt{g^{lm} f_{,l} f_{,m}}}$$

The normal component $\dot{x}_{(\mathbf{n})}$ of the particle velocity is given by

$$(18.12) \qquad \dot{x}_{(\mathbf{n})} = \frac{\dot{x}^k f_{,k}}{\sqrt{g^{lm} f_{,l} f_{,m}}}$$

But now substitute $\partial f/\partial t$ from (18.11) and $\dot{x}^k f_{,k}$ from (18.12) into

$$\dot{f} = \frac{\partial f}{\partial t} + f_{,k}\, \dot{x}^k$$

Hence

$$(18.13) \qquad \dot{f} = (\dot{x}_{(\mathbf{n})} - v_{(\mathbf{n})}) \sqrt{g^{kl} f_{,k} f_{,l}}$$

This asserts that *at a point* $\mathbf{x}$ *on the surface $f = 0$, $\dot{f}$ is proportional to the normal speed, relative to the surface, of the particle situated instantaneously at* $\mathbf{x}$. Consequently, if the surface consists of the same material points, we must have $\dot{x}_{(\mathbf{n})} = v_{(\mathbf{n})}$ and $\dot{f} = 0$. This completes the proof for the necessary condition.

The proof of sufficiency—namely, if $\dot{f} = 0$, then the surface $f = 0$ consists of the same particles—is made as follows. Equation (18.9) is a first-order partial differential equation with the characteristic equations

$$(18.14) \qquad dt = \frac{dx^1}{v^1} = \frac{dx^2}{v^2} = \frac{dx^3}{v^3}$$

in which $x^k = x^k\,(X^K, t)$. These are the differential equations for the paths of particles. Integrals of these have the form

$$(18.15) \qquad x^k = x^k\,(X^K, t)$$

where $X^K$ are three arbitrary constants which identify the particle. Elimination of $X^K$ among (18.15) gives the general solution of (18.14):

$$f = \psi(X^1, X^2, X^3) \tag{18.16}$$

where $\psi$ is an arbitrary function. This shows that whenever $f = 0$, a particle once on the surface $f = 0$ remains on the surface throughout the motion.

Let us note that a *rigid boundary* surface $f = 0$ also satisfies (18.9).

HELMHOLTZ-ZORAWSKI CRITERION. *A necessary and sufficient condition for lines tangential to a vector field* $\mathbf{q}$ *to be material lines is that*

$$q^k \dot{q}^l - q^l \dot{q}^k - (q^k v^l{}_{,m} - q^l v^k{}_{,m})\, q^m = 0 \tag{18.17}$$

or

$$\mathbf{q} \times \left[\frac{\partial \mathbf{q}}{\partial t} + \operatorname{curl}(\mathbf{q} \times \mathbf{v}) + \mathbf{v} \operatorname{div} \mathbf{q}\right] = 0 \tag{18.18}$$

At time $t$ let $c$ be the curve tangent to the vector field $\mathbf{q}(\mathbf{x}, t)$. Suppose $\mathbf{x} = \mathbf{x}(S, t')$ is the material line $c'$ that coincides with $c$ at time $t$. At this instant $\mathbf{q}$ is tangent to this curve. Hence

$$\mathbf{q} \times \frac{\partial \mathbf{x}}{\partial S} = 0 \qquad \text{or} \qquad q^k \frac{\partial x^l}{\partial S} - q^l \frac{\partial x^k}{\partial S} = 0 \tag{18.19}$$

If this curve is to remain a material line, we must have the material derivative of the foregoing expression vanish.

$$\frac{D}{Dt}\left(q^k \frac{\partial x^l}{\partial S} - q^l \frac{\partial x^k}{\partial S}\right) = \dot{q}^k \frac{\partial x^l}{\partial S} - \dot{q}^l \frac{\partial x^k}{\partial S} + q^k \frac{\partial v^l}{\partial S} - q^l \frac{\partial v^k}{\partial S} = 0 \tag{18.20}$$

where we have used $D(\partial x^k/\partial S)/Dt = \partial \dot{x}^k/\partial S = \partial v^k/\partial S$. Equivalent to (18.19) is

$$\frac{\partial x^k}{\partial S} = a\, q^k \tag{18.21}$$

where $a$ is a nonzero factor, not necessarily a constant.

Combining (18.20) and (18.21), we get (18.17). Equation (18.18) is obtained by multiplying (18.17) by $e_{klm}\, q^m$ and summing over $k$ and $l$. This completes the proof of the necessary condition.

The sufficiency of the criterion is shown by remembering that when the criterion is satisfied, the quantity $\mathbf{q} \times \partial \mathbf{x}/\partial S$, which is zero initially, will have a zero material derivative always.

By taking $\mathbf{q} = \mathbf{v}$ in (18.18), we get

$$\mathbf{v} \times \frac{\partial \mathbf{v}}{\partial t} = 0 \tag{18.22}$$

or equivalently

$$\frac{\partial \mathbf{v}}{\partial t} = K(\mathbf{x}, t)\, \mathbf{v} \tag{18.23}$$

as the necessary and sufficient condition that the streamlines are material lines. This is the proof of the following theorem.

THEOREM 1. *The streamlines and the path lines coincide if and only if the motion is steady.*

## 19. MATERIAL DERIVATIVES OF THE ELEMENTS OF ARC LENGTH, SURFACE, AND VOLUME

In the theory of continuous media the expressions for time rates of line, surface, and volume integrals over the deforming body are often required. Here we give the theorems which not only provide the necessary apparatus for this purpose, but also introduce important new concepts essential in the study of motion of continuous media.

FUNDAMENTAL LEMMA. *The material derivative of displacement gradients is given by*

$$\frac{D}{Dt}(x^k{}_{,K}) = v^k{}_{;l}\, x^l{}_{,K} \qquad \frac{D}{Dt}(dx^k) = v^k{}_{;l}\, dx^l \tag{19.1}$$

To prove $(19.1)_1$, form the left side

$$\begin{aligned}
\frac{D}{Dt}(x^k{}_{,K}) &= \frac{\partial}{\partial t}(x^k{}_{,K}) + \frac{\delta}{\delta t}(x^k{}_{,K}) \\
&= \frac{\partial x^k{}_{,K}}{\partial t} + \left[ (x^k{}_{,K})_{,l} + \begin{Bmatrix} k \\ lm \end{Bmatrix} x^m{}_{,K} \right] \dot{x}^l \\
&= \frac{d}{dt}(x^k{}_{,K}) + \begin{Bmatrix} k \\ lm \end{Bmatrix} x^m{}_{,K}\, v^l \\
&= v^k{}_{,K} + \begin{Bmatrix} k \\ lm \end{Bmatrix} v^l\, x^m{}_{,K} \\
&= \left[ v^k{}_{,l} + \begin{Bmatrix} k \\ lm \end{Bmatrix} v^m \right] x^l{}_{,K} = v^k{}_{;l}\, x^l{}_{,K}
\end{aligned}$$

The third line on the right follows from the second by combining the first two terms, and the fourth line follows from this by interchanging the order of differentiation, i.e., $d(x^k{}_{,K})/dt = \partial(\dot{x}^k)/\partial X^K$. The last line is a result of the chain rule of partial differentiation and the definition of covariant partial differentiation.

To prove $(19.1)_2$, multiply $(19.1)_1$ by $dX^K$.

The following convention, which is used implicitly above, will be agreed upon throughout this book. In the calculation of derivatives with respect to $X^K$ (or $x^k$) the quantity before $,K$ (or $,k$) will be considered as a function of $X^K$ (or $x^k$). Thus, for example, $x^k{}_{,Kl}$ is calculated as follows: first we obtain $x^k{}_{,K} \equiv \partial x^k(\mathbf{X}, t)/\partial X^K$; next $x^k{}_{,K}$ is considered as a function of $\mathbf{x}$ and $t$ through $\mathbf{X} = \mathbf{X}(\mathbf{x}, t)$ so that

$$x^k{}_{,Kl} \equiv (\partial/\partial x^l)\,[x^k{}_{,K}(\mathbf{x}, t)]$$

A *corollary* to the fundamental lemma is

$$\frac{D}{Dt}(X^K{}_{,k}) = -X^K{}_{,l}\,v^l{}_{;k} \tag{19.2}$$

The proof of this follows from the differentiation of $x^k{}_{,K}\,X^K{}_{,l} = \delta^k{}_l$.

$$\left[\frac{D}{Dt}(x^k{}_{,K})\right] X^K{}_{,l} + x^k{}_{,K}\frac{D}{Dt}(X^K{}_{,l}) = 0$$

Now multiply both sides by $X^L{}_{,k}$ and use $(19.1)_1$ in the first term. Hence

$$\frac{D}{Dt}(X^K{}_{,k}) = -X^K{}_{,l}\,X^L{}_{,k}\,x^m{}_{,L}\,v^l{}_{;m} = -X^K{}_{,l}\,v^l{}_{;k}$$

THEOREM 1. *The material derivative of the square of the arc length is given by*

$$\frac{D}{Dt}(ds^2) = 2\,d_{kl}\,dx^k\,dx^l \tag{19.3}$$

where

$$d_{kl} \equiv v_{(k;l)} \equiv \tfrac{1}{2}(v_{k;l} + v_{l;k}) \tag{19.4}$$

is called the *deformation-rate tensor* of Euler.

To prove (19.3), we take the material derivative of $ds^2$:

$$\frac{D}{Dt}(ds^2) = \frac{D}{Dt}(g_{kl}\,dx^k\,dx^l) = g_{kl}\,dx^l\frac{D}{Dt}(dx^k) + g_{kl}\,dx^k\frac{D}{Dt}(dx^l)$$

where we have used (17.8). Now substitute $(19.1)_2$ for $\frac{D}{Dt}(dx^k)$. Hence

$$\begin{aligned}\frac{D}{Dt}(ds^2) &= g_{kl}\,v^k{}_{;m}\,dx^l\,dx^m + g_{kl}\,v^l{}_{;m}\,dx^k\,dx^m\\ &= v_{l;m}\,dx^l\,dx^m + v_{k;m}\,dx^k\,dx^m\end{aligned}$$

Replacing the dummy index $m$ by $k$ in the first term of the extreme right and by $l$ in the second term, we get (19.3). In the material description we can write

$$\begin{aligned}\frac{D}{Dt}(ds^2) &= 2\,d_{kl}\,x^k{}_{,K}\,x^l{}_{,L}\,dX^K\,dX^L\\ &= 2\,\dot{E}_{KL}\,dX^K\,dX^L\end{aligned} \tag{19.5}$$

where

$$\dot{E}_{KL} \equiv \frac{D}{Dt}(E_{KL}) = d_{kl}\, x^k{}_{,K}\, x^l{}_{,L} \tag{19.6}$$

which is shown in Art. 22 to be identical to the material derivative of the lagrangian strain tensor. Therefore we have not introduced a new symbol.

A vanishing deformation-rate tensor implies a vanishing rate of the square of the arc length. Consequently, the motion is a rigid-body motion. Conversely, when $D(ds^2)/Dt = 0$, for an arbitrary pair of points, we must have $d_{kl} = 0$. Hence we have *Killing's equation* in differential geometry, which states the theorem that follows.

THEOREM 2. *The necessary and sufficient condition for the motion of a body to be rigid is* $d_{kl} = 0$.

In the kinematics of surface and volume integrals we shall need the following lemma.

LEMMA. *The material derivative of the jacobian is given by*

$$\frac{DJ}{Dt} = J\, v^k{}_{;k} \tag{19.7}$$

To prove this, we differentiate the jacobian determinant $J = \sqrt{g/G}\, j$ and use (19.1)

$$\frac{DJ}{Dt} = \frac{D}{Dt}\left(\frac{\sqrt{g}}{\sqrt{G}}\, j\right) = \frac{\sqrt{g}}{\sqrt{G}} \frac{\partial j}{\partial(x^k{}_{,K})} \frac{D(x^k{}_{,K})}{Dt} = \frac{\sqrt{g}}{\sqrt{G}} \frac{\partial j}{\partial(x^k{}_{,K})}\, v^k{}_{;l}\, x^l{}_{,K}$$

But according to (4.6) we have

$$\frac{\partial j}{\partial(x^k{}_{,K})} = j\, X^K{}_{,k} \tag{19.8}$$

which upon substitution on the extreme right of the previous formula gives (19.7).

THEOREM 3. *The material derivative of the area element is given by*

$$\frac{D}{Dt}(da_k) = v^m{}_{;m}\, da_k - v^m{}_{;k}\, da_m \tag{19.9}$$

To prove this result, we calculate the material derivative of (12.5), i.e.,

$$\frac{D}{Dt}(da_k) = \frac{D}{Dt}(J\, X^K{}_{,k}\, dA_K) = \left[\frac{DJ}{Dt} X^K{}_{,k} + J \frac{D}{Dt}(X^K{}_{,k})\right] dA_K$$

Using (19.2) and (19.7) gives (19.9).

THEOREM 4. *The material derivative of the volume element is given by*

$$\frac{D}{Dt}(dv) = v^k{}_{;k}\, dv = \mathrm{I}_d\, dv \tag{19.10}$$

where $\mathrm{I}_d$ denotes the first deformation-rate invariant, i.e., $\mathrm{I}_d \equiv v^k{}_{;k} \equiv d^k{}_k$. From $(12.8)_1$ we have $dv = J\,dV$. Therefore

$$\frac{D}{Dt}(dv) = \frac{D}{Dt}(J\,dV) = \frac{DJ}{Dt}\,dV = v^k{}_{;k}\,dv$$

In the last step (19.7) is used.

Rivlin and Ericksen [1955] introduced higher-order rate tensors which play an important role in the constitutive theory of materials with memory (cf. Chap. 10). The *Rivlin-Ericksen* tensor of order $M$, $\mathbf{A}^{(M)}(\mathbf{x}, t)$ is generated by taking the $M$th material derivative of the square of arc length $ds^2$, i.e.,

$$\frac{D^M}{Dt^M}(ds^2) = A^{(M)}_{kl}\,dx^k\,dx^l \qquad (M = 1, 2, \ldots) \tag{19.11}$$

A recurrence relation for $\mathbf{A}^{(M)}$ is obtained as follows:

$$\frac{D^{M+1}}{Dt^{M+1}}(ds^2) = \frac{D}{Dt}\left[\frac{D^M}{Dt^M}(ds^2)\right] = \frac{D}{Dt}(A^{(M)}_{kl}\,dx^k\,dx^l)$$

$$= \frac{D}{Dt}(A^{(M)}_{kl})\,dx^k\,dx^l + A^{(M)}_{kl}\frac{D}{Dt}(dx^k)\,dx^l + A^{(M)}_{kl}\,dx^k\frac{D}{Dt}(dx^l)$$

Using (19.11) on the left and $(19.1)_2$ on the right, we obtain

$$A^{(M+1)}_{kl} = \frac{D}{Dt}(A^{(M)}_{kl}) + A^{(M)}_{km}\,v^m{}_{;l} + A^{(M)}_{ml}\,v^m{}_{;k} \tag{19.12}$$

An explicit expression for $\mathbf{A}^{(M)}$ can be found from

$$\frac{D^M}{Dt^M}(ds^2) = \frac{D^M}{Dt^M}(g_{kl}\,dx^k\,dx^l) = g_{kl}\frac{D^M}{Dt^M}(dx^k\,dx^l)$$

$$= g_{kl}\sum_{K=0}^{M}\binom{M}{K}\frac{D^{M-K}}{Dt^{M-K}}(dx^k)\frac{D^K}{Dt^K}(dx^l)$$

where $\binom{M}{K}$ is the binomial coefficient, i.e.,

$$\binom{M}{K} \equiv \frac{M!}{(M-K)!\,K!}$$

As in $(19.1)_1$, we can show that

$$\frac{D^M}{Dt^M}(dx^k) = v^{(M)k}{}_{;l}\,dx^l$$
$$v^{(M)k} \equiv \frac{D^M x^k}{Dt^M} \tag{19.13}$$

Using this and the definition (19.11), we therefore get

(19.14) $$A^{(M)}_{pq} = v^{(M)}_{p;q} + v^{(M)}_{q;p} + \sum_{K=1}^{M-1} \binom{M}{K} v^{(M-K)}_{k;p}\, v^{(K)k}{}_{;q}$$

But since

$$\frac{D^M}{Dt^M}(ds^2) = \frac{D^M}{Dt^M}(C_{KL}\,dX^K\,dX^L) = C^{(M)}_{KL}\,dX^K\,dX^L$$
$$= C^{(M)}_{KL}\,X^K{}_{,k}\,X^L{}_{,l}\,dx^k\,dx^l$$

we also have

(19.15) $$A^{(M)}_{kl} = C^{(M)}_{KL}\,X^K{}_{,k}\,X^L{}_{,l}$$

Therefore

(19.16) $$\mathbf{A}^{(M)} = \mathbf{C}^{(M)}\Big|_{t=0}$$

For a *rigid motion* $ds^2$ remains unchanged; hence $\mathbf{A}^{(M)}$ *vanish.*

## 20. KINEMATICS OF LINE, SURFACE, AND VOLUME INTEGRALS

LEMMA 1. *The material derivative of a line integral of any field* $\phi$ *over a material line* $\mathcal{C}$ *is calculated by*

(20.1) $$\frac{D}{Dt}\int_{\mathcal{C}} \phi\,dx^k = \int_{\mathcal{C}} (\dot{\phi}\,dx^k + \phi\,v^k{}_{;l}\,dx^l)$$

PROOF. Since a material line $\mathcal{C}$ has an equation $\mathbf{X} = \mathbf{X}(S)$, the integral on the left of (20.1) will have fixed limits in the material description. Thus

$$\frac{D}{Dt}\int_{\mathcal{C}} \phi\,dx^k = \int_{\mathcal{C}} \frac{D}{Dt}(\phi\,dx^k) = \int_{\mathcal{C}} \left[\dot{\phi}\,dx^k + \phi\,\frac{D}{Dt}(dx^k)\right]$$

Using $(19.1)_2$ on the extreme right, we get (20.1)

For a *fixed* spatial line $c$ in place of (20.1) we would have

(20.2) $$\frac{d}{dt}\int_c \phi\,dx^k = \frac{\partial}{\partial t}\int_c \phi\,dx^k = \int_c \frac{\partial\phi}{\partial t}\,dx^k$$

Expression (20.1) reduces to (20.2) when the line of integration of (20.1) is fixed in space. The difference arises from the motion of particles constituting $\mathcal{C}$.

LEMMA 2. *The material derivative of an integral of any field over a material surface* $\mathcal{S}$ *is given by*

(20.3) $$\frac{D}{Dt}\int_{\mathcal{S}} \phi\,da_k = \int_{\mathcal{S}} [\dot{\phi}\,da_k + \phi\,(-v^l{}_{;k}\,da_l + v^l{}_{;l}\,da_k)]$$

PROOF. Again in a material description of the surface, the limits are fixed. Hence

$$\frac{D}{Dt}\int_{\mathcal{S}} \phi \, da_k = \int_{\mathcal{S}} \frac{D}{Dt}(\phi \, da_k) = \int_{\mathcal{S}} \left[ \dot{\phi} \, da_k + \phi \frac{D}{Dt}(da_k) \right]$$

Substitution of (19.9) now gives (20.3).

For a *fixed* spatial surface $s$, (20.3) is replaced by

$$\frac{d}{dt}\int_{s} \phi \, da_k = \frac{\partial}{\partial t}\int_{s} \phi \, da_k = \int_{s} \frac{\partial \phi}{\partial t} da_k \tag{20.4}$$

The difference between (20.3) and (20.4) is again due to the motion of particles constituting the material surface $\mathcal{S}$. Expression (20.3) may be used to obtain the rate of change of the flux of the vector field $\mathbf{q}$. Thus replacing $\phi$ by $q^k$, we have

$$\frac{D}{Dt}\int_{\mathcal{S}} q^k \, da_k = \int_{\mathcal{S}} (\dot{q}^k - q^l v^k{}_{;l} + q^k v^l{}_{;l}) \, da_k \tag{20.5}$$

or

$$\frac{D}{Dt}\int_{\mathcal{S}} d\mathbf{a} \cdot \mathbf{q} = \int_{\mathcal{S}} d\mathbf{a} \cdot (\dot{\mathbf{q}} - \mathbf{q} \cdot \operatorname{grad} \mathbf{v} + \mathbf{q} \operatorname{div} \mathbf{v}) = \int_{\mathcal{S}} d\mathbf{a} \cdot \left[ \frac{\partial \mathbf{q}}{\partial t} + \operatorname{curl}(\mathbf{q} \times \mathbf{v}) + \mathbf{v} \operatorname{div} \mathbf{q} \right] \tag{20.6}$$

From this the following criterion results.

ZORAWSKI'S CRITERION. *For the flux of a vector* $\mathbf{q}$ *across every material surface to remain constant in time, it is necessary and sufficient that*

$$\dot{q}^k - q^l v^k{}_{;l} + q^k v^l{}_{;l} = 0 \tag{20.7}$$

or

$$\frac{\partial \mathbf{q}}{\partial t} + \operatorname{curl}(\mathbf{q} \times \mathbf{v}) + \mathbf{v} \operatorname{div} \mathbf{q} = 0 \tag{20.8}$$

LEMMA 3. *The material derivative of an integral taken over a material volume is given by*

$$\frac{D}{Dt}\int_{\mathcal{V}} \phi \, dv = \int_{\mathcal{V}} (\dot{\phi} + \phi v^k{}_{;k}) \, dv = \int_{\mathcal{V}} \left[ \frac{\partial \phi}{\partial t} + (\phi v^k)_{;k} \right] dv \tag{20.9}$$

The proof is immediately obtained by performing the operation $D/Dt$ inside the integral and using $(19.10)_1$. An alternative expression to (20.9) is

$$\frac{D}{Dt}\int_{\mathcal{V}} \phi \, dv = \int_{v} \frac{\partial \phi}{\partial t} dv + \int_{s} \phi v^k \, da_k \tag{20.10}$$

which is obtained from $(20.9)_2$ by taking the configuration of $\mathcal{V}$ instantaneously the same as a fixed volume $v$ and its surface $s$ and then using the Green-Gauss theorem. This form states that:

*The rate of change of total $\phi$ over a material volume is equal to the rate of creation of $\phi$ in a fixed volume $v$ instantaneously coinciding with $\mathcal{V}$ and the flux $\phi v^k$ through the bounding surface $s$ of $v$.*

## 21. DEFORMATION RATE, SPIN, VORTICITY

The deformation-rate tensor $d_{kl}$ has already been introduced in Art. 19. We define this and the *spin* tensor $w_{kl}$ below:

$$d_{kl} \equiv v_{(k;l)} \equiv \tfrac{1}{2}(v_{k;l} + v_{l;k}) \tag{21.1}$$

$$w_{kl} \equiv v_{[k;l]} \equiv \tfrac{1}{2}(v_{k;l} - v_{l;k}) \tag{21.2}$$

By adding (21.1) to (21.2), we get

$$v_{k;l} = d_{kl} + w_{kl} \tag{21.3}$$

The deformation-rate tensor is a symmetric tensor, while the spin tensor is a skew-symmetric tensor, i.e.,

$$d_{kl} = d_{lk} \qquad w_{kl} = -w_{lk} \tag{21.4}$$

In three dimensions, from a skew-symmetric tensor we can always build an axial vector. The *vorticity* vector $w^k$ is the axial vector associated with the spin tensor and is defined by

$$w^k = \epsilon^{klm} w_{ml} = \epsilon^{klm} v_{m;l} \qquad \text{or} \qquad \mathbf{w} = \operatorname{curl} \mathbf{v} \tag{21.5}$$

The associated covariant vector is obtained by lowering the index, i.e.,

$$w_k = g_{kl} w^l \tag{21.6}$$

We now proceed to show the physical significance of the deformation-rate and the spin tensors. The deformation-rate tensor $d_{kl}$ is a measure of the instantaneous rates of change of the length and angle of material elements. To see this, we calculate the *stretching* $d_{(\mathbf{n})}$ in the direction $\mathbf{n}$ by using (19.3)

$$d_{(\mathbf{n})} \equiv \frac{1}{ds}\frac{D(ds)}{Dt} = d_{kl}\, n^k n^l \qquad n^k \equiv \frac{dx^k}{ds} \tag{21.7}$$

where $n^k$ is the unit vector originating from the point $\mathbf{x}$. If, for example, $\mathbf{n}$ is taken along the $x^1$ axis of an orthogonal coordinate system, (21.7) gives

$$d_{(1)} = d^{(1)}{}_{(1)} \tag{21.8}$$

We therefore see that the normal physical components of the deformation-rate tensor are the stretchings along the coordinate curves. Similarly we may calculate the rate of angle change between two material elements $d\mathbf{x}_1$ and $d\mathbf{x}_2$ at $\mathbf{x}$ as follows:

$$\frac{D}{Dt}\cos\theta_{(\mathbf{n}_1,\mathbf{n}_2)} = \frac{D}{Dt}\left(g_{kl}\,\frac{dx^k{}_1}{ds_1}\,\frac{dx^l{}_2}{ds_2}\right)$$

$$= \frac{1}{ds_1\,ds_2}\,\frac{D}{Dt}\,(g_{kl}\,dx^k{}_1\,dx^l{}_2) - [d_{(\mathbf{n}_1)} + d_{(\mathbf{n}_2)}]\cos\theta_{(\mathbf{n}_1,\mathbf{n}_2)}$$

where $ds_1$ and $ds_2$ are the magnitudes of vectors $d\mathbf{x}_1$ and $d\mathbf{x}_2$, and $d_{(\mathbf{n}_1)}$ and $d_{(\mathbf{n}_2)}$ are the corresponding stretchings along these vectors. Using $(19.1)_2$, we see that

$$\frac{D}{Dt}\,(g_{kl}\,dx^k{}_1\,dx^l{}_2) = 2\,d_{kl}\,dx^k{}_1\,dx^l{}_2 \tag{21.9}$$

Hence we get

$$\frac{D}{Dt}\cos\theta_{(\mathbf{n}_1,\mathbf{n}_2)} = -\,\dot{\theta}_{(\mathbf{n}_1,\mathbf{n}_2)}\sin\theta_{(\mathbf{n}_1,\mathbf{n}_2)} \tag{21.10}$$

$$= 2\,d_{kl}\,n^k{}_1\,n^k{}_2 - [d_{(\mathbf{n}_1)} + d_{(\mathbf{n}_2)}]\cos\theta_{(\mathbf{n}_1,\mathbf{n}_2)}$$

Now consider the special case of two orthogonal material elements, i.e., $\theta_{(\mathbf{n}_1,\mathbf{n}_2)} = \pi/2$. Hence

$$-\,\dot{\theta}_{(\mathbf{n}_1,\mathbf{n}_2)} = 2\,d_{kl}\,n^k{}_1\,n^l{}_2 \tag{21.11}$$

If in addition $d\mathbf{x}_1$ and $d\mathbf{x}_2$ are tangential to the orthogonal coordinate curves $x^1$ and $x^2$ respectively, (21.11) reduces to

$$-\,\dot{\theta}_{(12)} = 2\,d^{(1)}{}_{(2)} \tag{21.12}$$

This shows that $d^{(1)}{}_{(2)}$ is one-half of the rate of shearing in the $x^1$ and $x^2$ directions. Hence we obtain the following theorem.

THEOREM 1. *The normal physical components of the deformation-rate tensor are the rates of stretch; the off-diagonal physical components are half the rates of shear in the orthogonal coordinate directions.*[1]

To understand the physical significance of the spin tensor, we consider the rate at which a material element along $d\mathbf{x}$ is rotating about a fixed direction $\boldsymbol{\nu}$. To this end we take the material derivative of

$$\cos\varphi \equiv \cos(d\mathbf{x}, \boldsymbol{\nu}) = g_{kl}\,\nu^l\,\frac{dx^k}{ds}$$

or

$$-\sin\varphi\,\dot{\varphi} = v_{l;k}\,n^k\,\nu^l - d_{(\mathbf{n})}\cos\varphi \qquad n^k \equiv \frac{dx^k}{ds} \tag{21.13}$$

[1] These results are due to Euler [1770, arts. 9–12]; for a modern version see Truesdell and Toupin [1960, art. 82].

When $\varphi = \pi/2$, this gives the relative spin of $d\mathbf{x}$ with respect to $\boldsymbol{\nu}$

$$-\dot{\varphi} = v_{l;k}\, n^k\, \nu^l \tag{21.14}$$

To see this, we select $\boldsymbol{\nu}$ along the tangent of the coordinate curve $x^l$ $(k \neq l)$ and write $\varphi_{lk} = v_{l;k}$ and $\dot{\varphi}^{(l)}{}_{(k)}$ for the physical components of $\varphi_{lk}$. Then

$$-\dot{\varphi}^{(l)}{}_{(k)} = \frac{v_{l;k}}{\sqrt{g_{\underline{ll}}\, g_{\underline{kk}}}} \tag{21.15}$$

Thus the physical component of $v_{l;k}$ $(k \neq l)$ *is the rate at which a material element along the* $x^k$ *axis of an orthogonal triad is rotating toward the* $x^l$ *axis*

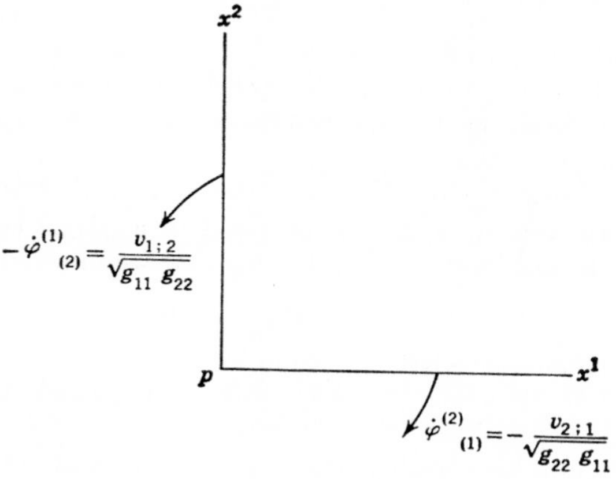


FIG. 21.1. Spin-tensor components.

*in a counterclockwise direction* (Fig. 21.1). The shearing in the $x^1$ and $x^2$ directions is the sum of these spins, since these axes are turning away from each other, i.e.,

$$-\dot{\theta}_{(12)} = -\dot{\varphi}_{12} - \dot{\varphi}_{21} = 2\, d_{12}$$

This is similar to (21.12), which was obtained earlier.

As may be seen in Fig. 21.1, the rate of relative rotation in the counterclockwise direction of a material element lying along the $x^1$ and $x^2$ coordinate curves is given by

$$\dot{\varphi}_{21} - \dot{\varphi}_{12} = v_{1;2} - v_{2;1} = 2\, w_{12}$$

Hence *half the difference of the relative spins (in the counterclockwise direction) gives the spin tensor of Cauchy.* In a rectangular frame of reference we have the same thing for the vorticity components, since

$$w_x = -2w_{yz} \qquad w_y = -2w_{zx} \qquad w_z = -w2_{xy}$$

According to *Killing's theorem*, the necessary and sufficient condition for a rigid motion is $d_{kl} = 0$. If this holds throughout a region, we have its general solution

$$v_k = \tilde{r}_{kl}\, p^l + \dot{b}_k \tag{21.16}$$

where $\dot{b}_k$ and $\tilde{r}_{kl}$ depend upon $t$ only; $\tilde{r}_{kl}$ is skew-symmetric; and $p^k{}_{;l} = \delta^k{}_l$. Thus $\mathbf{p}$ is the position vector of a material point with respect to an origin; $\dot{b}_k$ is a rigid velocity of translation of the origin; and $\tilde{r}_{kl}$ is the rotation tensor or $\tilde{r}^k = \epsilon^{klm}\,\tilde{r}_{ml}$ is the angular velocity about the origin. The origin of $\mathbf{p}$ can be arbitrary, and $\tilde{\mathbf{r}}$ is determined uniquely. From (21.16) we find that

$$w_{kl} = \tilde{\omega}_{kl} \tag{21.17}$$

Hence for rigid motion the spin tensor is the angular-velocity tensor.

An elegant theorem concerning the spin is the following.

THEOREM 2. *The spin is the angular velocity of the principal axes of the deformation-rate tensor.*[2]

PROOF. The proper values $d_\alpha$ and the proper directions $\mathbf{n}_\alpha$ of the deformation-rate tensor $d_{kl}$ are determined in a manner similar to the ones for the deformation tensors. In this case we must solve the system

$$(d^k{}_l - d_{(\mathrm{n})}\,\delta^k{}_l)\, n^l = 0 \tag{21.18}$$

The roots of the characteristic equation

$$|d^k{}_l - d_{(\mathrm{n})}\,\delta^k{}_l| = 0 \tag{21.19}$$

give the proper numbers (principal stretchings) $d_\alpha$, and in turn for each $d_\alpha$ through (21.18) we get a set of directions $\mathbf{n}_\alpha$. Since $d_{kl}$ is a symmetric tensor, everything that has been proved for the deformation tensor $c_{kl}$ has a dual for $d_{kl}$. Now take the material derivative of the unit vector $n^k = dx^k/ds$ tangent to one of the coordinate curves.

$$\dot{n}^k = \frac{D}{Dt}\left(\frac{dx^k}{ds}\right) = \frac{1}{ds}\,\frac{D}{Dt}\,(dx^k) - \frac{1}{ds^2}\,\frac{D}{Dt}\,(ds)\,dx^k$$

Using $(19.1)_2$ and (21.7) gives

$$\dot{n}^k = (d^k{}_l + w^k{}_l - d_{(\mathrm{n})}\,\delta^k{}_l)\, n^l \tag{21.20}$$

If now $\mathbf{n}$ is a proper direction for the deformation-rate tensor, then we have (21.18), which helps to simplify (21.20) to

$$\dot{n}^k = w^k{}_l\, n^l \tag{21.21}$$

This is the analytical statement of Theorem 2.

[2] An intuitive argument that the spin of a deforming body at each place and time can be regarded as the local angular velocity is due to Stokes [1845, art. 2]. The above theorem is due to Gosiewski [1890, art. 8]. See also Zorawski [1901, art. 2].

By lowering and raising the indices, from this we also get the expressions

(21.22) $$\dot{n}_k = w_{kl}\, n^l = w_k{}^l\, n_l = -w^l{}_k\, n_l$$

## 22. STRAIN RATE

*The lagrangian and eulerian strain rates are defined by*[1]

(22.1) $$\dot{E}_{KL}\,(\mathbf{X}, t) \equiv \frac{DE_{KL}}{Dt}$$

(22.2) $$\dot{e}_{kl}\,(\mathbf{x}, t) \equiv \frac{D\, e_{kl}}{Dt}$$

THEOREM 1. *The lagrangian and eulerian strain rates are given by*

(22.3) $$\dot{E}_{KL} = d_{kl}\, x^k{}_{,K}\, x^l{}_{,L}$$

(22.4) $$\dot{e}_{kl} = d_{kl} - (e^m{}_k\, v_{m;l} + e^m{}_l\, v_{m;k})$$

To prove (22.3), we calculate the material derivative of $ds^2$.

$$\frac{D}{Dt}\,(ds^2) = \frac{D\,C_{KL}}{Dt}\, dX^K\, dX^L = \frac{D}{Dt}\,(2\,E_{KL} + G_{KL})\, dX^K\, dX^L$$
$$= 2\,\frac{D\,E_{KL}}{Dt}\, dX^K\, dX^L$$

Comparing this with (19.5), we get (22.3).

To prove (22.4), we proceed as follows:

$$\frac{D}{Dt}\,(ds^2) = \frac{D}{Dt}\,(ds^2 - dS^2) = 2\,\frac{D}{Dt}\,(e_{kl}\, dx^k\, dx^l)$$

since $D(dS^2)/Dt = 0$. Now carry out the indicated differentiation and use $(19.1)_2$ in the process:

$$\frac{D}{Dt}\,(ds^2) = 2\,(\dot{e}_{kl} + e^m{}_k\, v_{m;l} + e^m{}_{;l}\, v_{m;k})\, dx^k\, dx^l$$

The left side of this is also given by (19.3). Thus for arbitrary $dx^k$ and symmetric strain tensor, this implies (22.4).

From the foregoing it is also clear that

(22.5) $$\dot{C}_{KL} = 2\,\dot{E}_{KL} \qquad \dot{c}_{kl} = -2\,\dot{e}_{kl} = -(c_{mk}\, v^m{}_{;l} + c_{ml}\, v^m{}_{;k})$$

Expressions (22.3) and (22.4) show that the strain rates in general are not the same as the deformation rates. At time $t = 0$ the medium is unstrained. Taking $x^k = X^K\, \delta^k{}_K$, we get

(22.6) $$\dot{E}_{KL}\,(\mathbf{X}, 0) = d_{kl}\, \delta^k{}_K\, \delta^l{}_L \qquad \dot{e}_{kl}\,(\mathbf{x}, 0) = d_{kl}$$

[1] Recently Naghdi and Wainwright [1961] have introduced a different definition of strain rate which makes the eulerian strain rate coincide with the deformation rate.

In the strained state, however, $d_{kl} = 0$ gives

$$\dot{E}_{KL} = 0 \qquad \dot{e}_{kl} = -(e^m{}_k v_{m;l} + e^m{}_l v_{m;k}) \tag{22.7}$$

Hence in an instantaneously rigid motion the lagrangian strain rate is zero; however, the eulerian strain rate is not. This latter situation stems from the fact that in a rigid motion of a strained material, the expression $ds^2 - dS^2 = 2\, e_{kl}\, dx^k\, dx^l$ remains constant. However, individual components $e_{kl}$ generally change. Thus, to an observer moving with a material particle, the spatial coordinates appear to rotate as the spatial points pass by.

For infinitesimal deformations the lagrangian strain rates are approximately the same as the deformation rates, i.e.,

$$\dot{E}_{KL} \cong d_{kl}\, \delta^k{}_K\, \delta^l{}_L$$

However,

$$\dot{e}_{kl} \cong d_{kl}$$

requires the further restriction that the spin $w_{kl}$ be of no greater order than the deformation rate, since in (22.4) the velocity gradients are expressible in terms of $d_{kl}$ and $w_{kl}$ [see (21.3)]. The simplest relation of the rate of rotation tensor and those of $\overset{-\frac{1}{2}}{\mathbf{c}}$ to the vorticity and the deformation rate was found by Noll [1955, art. 20]. It states that *the rate of rotation tensor* **R** *and those of* $\overset{-\frac{1}{2}}{\mathbf{c}}$ *at* $t = 0$ *are the same as the spin and the deformation rate at* $t = 0$, *i.e.,*

$$\dot{R}^k{}_l \Big|_{t=0} = w^k{}_l \qquad \frac{D}{Dt}\left(\overset{-\frac{1}{2}}{c}{}^k{}_l\right)\Big|_{t=0} = d^k{}_l \tag{22.8}$$

To this end we take the material derivative of $(10.21)_2$

$$\frac{D}{Dt}(x^k{}_{,M}) = v^k{}_{;r}\, x^r{}_{,M} = \frac{D}{Dt}(R^r{}_M)\, \overset{-\frac{1}{2}}{c}{}^k{}_r + R^r{}_M \frac{D}{Dt}\left(\overset{-\frac{1}{2}}{c}{}^k{}_r\right)$$

Multiply this by $X^M{}_{,l}$. Hence

$$v^k{}_{;l} = X^M{}_{,l}\left[\overset{-\frac{1}{2}}{c}{}^k{}_r\, \dot{R}^r{}_M + R^r{}_M \frac{D}{Dt}\left(\overset{-\frac{1}{2}}{c}{}^k{}_r\right)\right]$$

At the initial time $t = 0$, $X^M{}_{,l} \to \delta^M{}_l$ and $\mathbf{c} \to \mathbf{I}$. Furthermore, according to (10.21), $R^r{}_M = g^{Kr} R_{KM} \to \delta^r{}_M$. Consequently the preceding expression reduces to

$$v^k{}_{;l}\Big|_{t=0} = \dot{R}^k{}_l\Big|_{t=0} + \frac{D}{Dt}\left(\overset{-\frac{1}{2}}{c}{}^k{}_l\right)\Big|_{t=0}$$

Since $\overset{-\frac{1}{2}}{\mathbf{c}}$ is symmetric and **R** is orthogonal and $\dot{R}_{kl} = -\dot{R}_{lk}$, the skew-symmetric and symmetric parts of this equation give (22.8).

The calculation for the material derivatives of the proper numbers, and hence that of the principal stretches, can be obtained by multiplying (9.20) by $n^k$ and solving for $c_\alpha$, i.e.,

$$c_\alpha = c_{kl}\, n^k{}_\alpha\, n^l{}_\alpha \tag{22.9}$$

The material derivative of this is

$$\dot{c}_\alpha = \dot{c}_{kl}\, n^k{}_\alpha\, n^l{}_\alpha + c_{kl}\,(\dot{n}^k{}_\alpha\, n^l{}_\alpha + n^k{}_\alpha\, \dot{n}^l{}_\alpha)$$

Upon substituting $\dot{c}_{kl}$ from $(22.5)_2$ and $\dot{n}^k{}_\alpha$ from (21.21), we obtain

$$\dot{c}_\alpha = -2\, c^r{}_k\, d_{rl}\, n^k{}_\alpha\, n^l{}_\alpha \tag{22.10}$$

If we now substitute another form of (9.20), namely,

$$c^r{}_k\, n^k{}_\alpha = c_\alpha\, n^r{}_\alpha \tag{22.11}$$

into (22.10) and remember that $c_\alpha = 1/\lambda_\alpha{}^2$, we obtain the elegant formula

$$-\frac{\dot{c}_\alpha}{2\,c_\alpha} = \frac{\dot{\lambda}_\alpha}{\lambda_\alpha} = d_{kl}\, n^k{}_\alpha\, n^l{}_\alpha = d_{(\alpha)} \tag{22.12}$$

This states that *the material derivative of the logarithm of a principal stretch is the same as the normal stretching in that principal direction.*[2]

We may now calculate the material derivative of the $m$th power of the Cauchy deformation tensor by differentiating

$$\overset{m}{c}{}^k{}_l = \sum_\alpha (c_\alpha)^m\, n^k{}_\alpha\, n^\alpha{}_l \tag{22.13}$$

i.e.,

$$\frac{D}{Dt}(\overset{m}{c}{}^k{}_l) = \sum_\alpha [m\,(c_\alpha)^{m-1}\,\dot{c}_\alpha\, n^k{}_\alpha\, n^\alpha{}_l + (c_\alpha)^m\,(\dot{n}^k{}_\alpha\, n^\alpha{}_l + n^k{}_\alpha\, \dot{n}^\alpha{}_l)]$$

Now substitute $\dot{c}_\alpha$ from (22.12) and $\dot{n}^k{}_\alpha$ and $\dot{n}^\alpha{}_l$ from (21.21) and (21.22). Upon using (22.13), we get

$$\frac{D}{Dt}(\overset{m}{c}{}^k{}_l) = \overset{m}{c}{}^r{}_l\, w^k{}_r - \overset{m}{c}{}^k{}_r\, w^r{}_l - 2\,m\,\overset{m}{c}{}^k{}_s \sum_\alpha d_{(\alpha)}\, n^s{}_\alpha\, n^\alpha{}_l \tag{22.14}$$

which is valid for $m$ fractional.

To calculate the material derivative of the rotation tensor, we differentiate $(10.24)_2$, i.e.,

$$\frac{D}{Dt}(\overset{-1}{R}{}^K{}_k) = \frac{D}{Dt}(X^K{}_{,l})\,\overset{-\frac{1}{2}}{c}{}^l{}_k + X^K{}_{,l}\,\frac{D}{Dt}(\overset{-\frac{1}{2}}{c}{}^l{}_k)$$

[2] This and the results that follow appear to be new.

Using (19.2) and (22.14) gives

$$\text{(22.15)} \qquad \frac{D}{Dt}(\overset{-1}{R}{}^K{}_k) = -X^K{}_{,l}\,[d^l{}_r \overset{-\frac{1}{2}}{c}{}^r{}_k + w^r{}_k \overset{-\frac{1}{2}}{c}{}^l{}_r - \overset{-\frac{1}{2}}{c}{}^l{}_r \sum_\alpha d_{(\alpha)}\, n^r{}_\alpha\, n^\alpha{}_k]$$

From these results, by taking $X^K$ and $x^k$ identical at $t = 0$, one may deduce (22.8).

## 23. CIRCULATION

The line integral of the tangential component of the velocity vector along a curve $c$ is called the *circulation*. Thus

$$\Gamma = \oint_c v_k\, dx^k$$

is the circulation. According to Stokes' theorem, *the circulation around a closed circuit is equal to the flux of vorticity through any surface entirely bounded by the circuit, i.e.,*

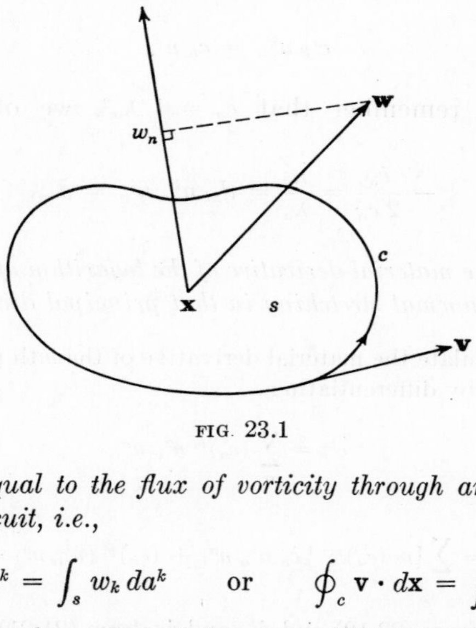


FIG. 23.1

$$\text{(23.1)} \qquad \oint_c v_k\, dx^k = \int_s w_k\, da^k \qquad \text{or} \qquad \oint_c \mathbf{v} \cdot d\mathbf{x} = \int_s \mathbf{w} \cdot d\mathbf{a}$$

The proof follows from *Stokes' theorem*, which for any vector $\mathbf{b}$ may be written as

$$\text{(23.2)} \qquad \oint_c \mathbf{b} \cdot d\mathbf{x} = \int_s (\text{curl}\, \mathbf{b}) \cdot d\mathbf{a}$$

Now take $\mathbf{b} = \mathbf{v}$ and remember that $\mathbf{w} = \text{curl}\, \mathbf{v}$.

A physical interpretation for vorticity is found as follows: Let $w_n$ be the projection of $\mathbf{w}$ upon the normal $\mathbf{n}$ to the surface at $\mathbf{x}$. If the area of the surface $s$ is denoted by $a$ (Fig. 23.1), then

$$\oint_c v_k\, dx^k = a\, w_n + 0\,(a^2)$$

or as $c$ shrinks down to the point $\mathbf{x}$, then

(23.3) $$w_n = \lim_{a \to 0} \frac{1}{a} \oint_c v_k \, dx^k$$

Thus *the ratio of the circulation around a closed circuit $c$ to the area enclosed by $c$ in the limit as $a \to 0$ is equal to the component of the vorticity in the direction of the normal to $s$ at $\mathbf{x}$.*

A motion is said to be *irrotational* if and only if the *spin*, and hence the vorticity, vanishes, i.e.,

(23.4) $$w_{kl} = 0$$

A motion is irrotational if and only if its velocity field is *lamellar;* i.e., the velocity field is derivable from a potential $\phi$ such that

(23.5) $$v_k = -\phi_{,k}$$

For an irrotational field we therefore have

(23.6) $$\int_{\mathbf{x}_1}^{\mathbf{x}_2} v_k \, dx^k = -\int_{\mathbf{x}_1}^{\mathbf{x}_2} d\phi = \phi(\mathbf{x}_1) - \phi(\mathbf{x}_2)$$

If the region is simply connected, upon setting $\mathbf{x}_1 = \mathbf{x}_2$, we find that the circulation is zero. Hence for simply connected regions we have the following theorem.

THEOREM 1. (*Kelvin*) *A motion is irrotational if and only if the circulation about every reducible circle is zero.*

The multiply connected regions may be made simply connected by the introduction of appropriate barriers. In forming circuits, the barriers must not be crossed. With this consideration for multiply connected regions, (23.6) is modified to

(23.7) $$-\int_{\mathbf{x}_1}^{\mathbf{x}_2} v_k \, dx^k = \phi(\mathbf{x}_2) - \phi(\mathbf{x}_1) + \sum_{k=1}^{r} n_k C_k$$

where $r$ is the number of barriers and $n_k$ are integers. Then $C_k$ are called the *cyclic constants* of the motion.

In an irrotational motion, from (23.5) and the definition of $d_{km}$ we have

(23.8) $$d_{km} = -\phi_{;km}$$

hence

(23.9) $$\mathrm{I}_d = -\phi_{;k}{}^{k} = -\nabla^2\phi$$

Therefore *an irrotational motion is isochoric if and only if*

(23.10) $$\nabla^2\phi = 0$$

Finally we give a theorem concerning a circulation-preserving motion.

THEOREM 2. *For a motion to be circulation-preserving, it is necessary and sufficient that the acceleration possess a potential.*

To prove this, we calculate the material time rate of the circulation over a material curve $\mathcal{C}$ which according to Stokes' theorem is

$$\frac{D\Gamma}{Dt} = \frac{D}{Dt}\oint_{\mathcal{C}} v_k\, dx^k = \frac{D}{Dt}\int_{\mathcal{S}} w_k\, da^k \tag{23.11}$$
$$= \int_{\mathcal{S}} d\mathbf{a} \cdot \left[\frac{\partial \mathbf{w}}{\partial t} + \operatorname{curl}(\mathbf{w} \times \mathbf{v})\right]$$

where the second line is obtained from (20.6) by taking $\mathbf{q} = \mathbf{w}$. Hence $D\Gamma/Dt = 0$ for every material surface $\mathcal{S}$ if and only if

$$\frac{\partial \mathbf{w}}{\partial t} + \operatorname{curl}(\mathbf{w} \times \mathbf{v}) \equiv \operatorname{curl} \dot{\mathbf{v}} = 0 \tag{23.12}$$

But this is satisfied if and only if the acceleration $\dot{\mathbf{v}}$ possesses a potential.

## 24. VORTICITY THEOREMS

The lines that are tangential to the vectors in a vorticity field are called *vortex lines.* The surfaces formed by the vortex lines are called *vortex surfaces,* and tubes are called *vortex tubes.*

Vortex lines are the integral curves of

$$\frac{dx_1}{w^1} = \frac{dx_2}{w^2} = \frac{dx_3}{w^3} \tag{24.1}$$

HELMHOLTZ'S FIRST THEOREM. *The total vorticity at a section of a vortex tube is the same as that of any other section of the tube.*

The proof follows from the Green-Gauss theorem applied to div $\mathbf{w}$, i.e.,

$$\int_v \operatorname{div} \mathbf{w}\, dv = \int_s \mathbf{w} \cdot \mathbf{n}\, da \tag{24.2}$$

We have $\operatorname{div} \mathbf{w} = \operatorname{div} \operatorname{curl} \mathbf{v} = 0$. Hence

$$\int_s \mathbf{w} \cdot \mathbf{n}\, da = 0 \tag{24.3}$$

By definition $\mathbf{w}$ is tangential to the surface of the tube (Fig. 24.1). Hence $\mathbf{w} \cdot \mathbf{n} = 0$ on the surface of the tube. Therefore (24.3) may be written as

$$\int_{s_1} \mathbf{w} \cdot \mathbf{n}_1\, da = -\int_{s_2} \mathbf{w} \cdot \mathbf{n}_2\, da \tag{24.4}$$

where $s_1$ and $s_2$ are any two sections of tube having exterior normals $\mathbf{n}_1$ and $\mathbf{n}_2$ respectively. Hence we have Kelvin's proof of Helmholtz's first theorem. The foregoing proof is valid even when the vorticity **w** is discontinuous; however, the velocity **v** must be continuous.

An important corollary of the foregoing theorem is that a vortex line cannot begin or end at any point in the interior of the fluid. Any vortex line must either close up or begin and end on the boundaries.

HELMHOLTZ'S SECOND THEOREM. *In a circulation-preserving motion the vortex lines are material lines.*

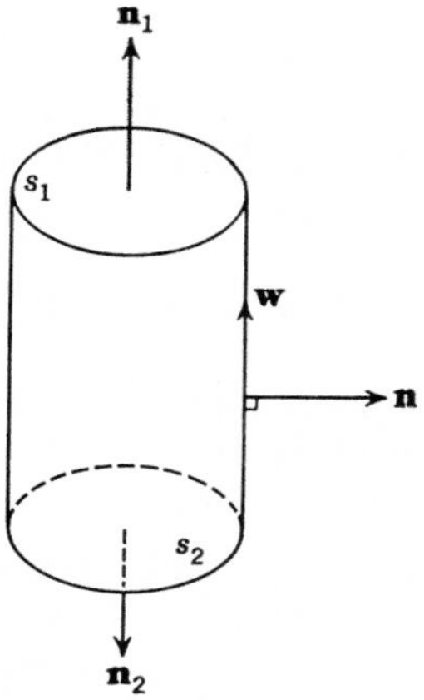


FIG. 24.1. Vortex tube.

According to the Helmholtz-Zorawski criterion (18.18), by taking $\mathbf{q} = \mathbf{w}$, we find that the necessary and sufficient condition for vortex lines to be material is

$$\mathbf{w} \times \left[\frac{\partial \mathbf{w}}{\partial t} + \operatorname{curl}(\mathbf{w} \times \mathbf{v})\right] = \mathbf{w} \times \operatorname{curl} \dot{\mathbf{v}} = 0 \tag{24.5}$$

since in a circulation-preserving motion we must have $\operatorname{curl} \dot{\mathbf{v}} = 0$ [see (23.12)]. Thus we have the proof.

HELMHOLTZ'S THIRD THEOREM. *If in a motion the vortex lines coincide with the material lines, then for the strengths of all vortex tubes to remain constant, it is necessary and sufficient that the motion be circulation-preserving.*

This follows by taking $\mathbf{q} = \mathbf{w}$ in the Zorawski criterion (20.8). Hence

$$\operatorname{curl} \dot{\mathbf{v}} = 0 \tag{24.6}$$

From the foregoing theorems it is clear that the circulation-preserving motions are distinctly separated from the other motions. The study of the manner by which the general motion departs from the circulation-preserving motion is an important objective of classical hydrodynamics.[1]

[1] For other related theorems see Lamb [1945, chap. VII] and Truesdell [1954].

## 25. MASS

In classical mechanics, with each body we associate a measure called *mass*. This measure has a new dimension $M$ independent of $L$ and $T$. *It is nonnegative and additive, and it is invariant under the motion.* If this measure is *absolutely continuous,* then there exists a density function $\rho$ called *mass density.* The total mass $\mathfrak{M}$ of the body is then found by

$$\mathfrak{M} = \int_{\mathcal{V}} \rho \, dv \qquad \dim \rho = \left[\frac{M}{L^3}\right] \tag{25.1}$$

If the mass is not continuous throughout $\mathcal{V}$, then instead of (25.1) we will have

$$\mathfrak{M} = \int_{\mathcal{V}_1} \rho \, dv + \sum_{\alpha} \mathfrak{M}_\alpha \tag{25.2}$$

where the summation is taken over the *discrete* masses and the integration over $\mathcal{V}_1$, where the mass is continuous.

The integration over the mass is defined as the *Lebesgue-Stieltjes* integral

$$\int_{\mathfrak{M}} f \, d\mathfrak{M} = \int_{\mathcal{V}_1} \rho f \, dv + \sum_{\alpha} \mathfrak{M}_\alpha f_\alpha \tag{25.3}$$

Since there is no particular difficulty in the interpretation of the continuous part of the integrals as summations whenever discrete masses exist, we shall henceforth assume that the mass is absolutely continuous and carry out the theorems only on *continuous mass media.*

A continuous mass medium is defined as one in which a volume of material particles has an assigned mass density. In this sense when the volume $\mathcal{V} \to 0$, then the total mass $\mathfrak{M} \to 0$. We thus have

$$0 \leq \rho < \infty \tag{25.4}$$

FUNDAMENTAL AXIOM 1. *Principle of Mass Conservation. The axiom of global mass conservation states that the total mass is invariant under the motion. Global mass conservation when applied to an infinitesimal neighborhood of a material point implies local mass conservation.*

Global mass conservation is expressed by

$$\int_V \rho_0 \, dV = \int_{\mathcal{V}} \rho \, dv \tag{25.5}$$

When the volume integrals are both expressed in terms of the lagrangian or eulerian descriptions, we write

$$\int_V (\rho_0 - \rho J) \, dV = 0 \qquad \text{or} \qquad \int_{\mathcal{V}} (\rho - \rho_0 J^{-1}) \, dv \tag{25.6}$$

One may also use (12.8), the expressions of the jacobian in terms of the strain invariants, i.e.,

$$J = \sqrt{\mathrm{III}_C} = \frac{1}{\sqrt{\mathrm{III}_c}} \tag{25.7}$$

The principle of *local* mass conservation follows from (25.6) as

$$\rho_0 = \rho J = \rho \sqrt{\mathrm{III}_C} \qquad \text{or} \qquad \rho = \rho_0 J^{-1} = \frac{\rho_0}{\sqrt{\mathrm{III}_C}} = \rho_0 \sqrt{\mathrm{III}_c} \tag{25.8}$$

These expressions are the *material equations of continuity*. The spatial description is obtained by expressing the global mass conservation as

$$\frac{D}{Dt} \int_{\mathcal{V}} \rho \, dv = 0$$

In (20.9) if we set $\phi = \rho$,

$$\int_{\mathcal{V}} \left[ \frac{\partial \rho}{\partial t} + (\rho v^k)_{;k} \right] dv = 0 \tag{25.9}$$

From this the local mass conservation follows:

$$\frac{\partial \rho}{\partial t} + (\rho v^k)_{;k} = 0 \tag{25.10}$$

This is the *spatial equation of continuity*.

Note that (25.8) and (25.10) are but different expressions of the same thing. In fact, (25.8) is the integral of (25.10). In solid mechanics (25.8) is generally more suitable for analysis, while in fluid mechanics (25.10) is.

## 26. MOMENTUM, MOMENT OF MOMENTUM, AND ENERGY

*Momentum* or *linear momentum* $\mathcal{P}$ *of the mass media contained in volume* $\mathcal{V}$ *is defined by*

$$\mathcal{P} \equiv \int_{\mathcal{V}} \mathbf{v} \, d\mathfrak{M} \tag{26.1}$$

*The moment of momentum or angular momentum of body* $\mathcal{V}$ *about the origin* $o$ *is defined by*

$$\underset{o}{\mathcal{H}} \equiv \int_{\mathcal{V}} \mathbf{p} \times \mathbf{v} \, d\mathfrak{M} \tag{26.2}$$

*The kinetic energy* $\mathcal{K}$ *of the body* $\mathcal{V}$ *is defined by*

$$\mathcal{K} \equiv \tfrac{1}{2} \int_{\mathcal{V}} v^2 \, d\mathfrak{M} = \tfrac{1}{2} \int_{\mathcal{V}} g_{kl} v^k v^l \, d\mathfrak{M} \tag{26.3}$$

In order to express the momentum and moment of momentum in component notation, we must translate all vectors acting in the element $d\mathfrak{M}$ to a common point $\mathbf{X}$ so that the sum (the integral) of these vectors may be made at that point. This is clear if we write $\mathcal{P}$ as

$$\mathcal{P} = \mathcal{P}^k \mathbf{g}_k = \int_{\mathcal{V}} v^k \mathbf{g}_k(\mathbf{x})\, d\mathfrak{M} \tag{26.4}$$

Now $\mathbf{g}_k(\mathbf{x})$ cannot be taken outside of the integral except in the special case of cartesian coordinates. We may, however take the scalar product of both sides by a vector $\mathbf{G}^K(\mathbf{X})$, thus obtaining the components of the momentum $\mathcal{P}^K$ in the coordinate system of $\mathbf{X}$.

$$\mathcal{P}^K(\mathbf{X}, t) = \int_{\mathcal{V}} g^K{}_k(\mathbf{X}, \mathbf{x})\, v^k(\mathbf{x}, t)\, d\mathfrak{M} \tag{26.5}$$

Similarly for the moment of momentum we have

$$\underset{o}{\mathcal{H}}{}^K = \int_{\mathcal{V}} g^K{}_k\, \epsilon^{klm} p_l v_m\, d\mathfrak{M} \tag{26.6}$$

A bivector representation of (26.6) is

$$\underset{o}{\mathcal{H}}{}^{KL} = \int_{\mathcal{V}} g^K{}_k\, g^L{}_l\, (p^k v^l - p^l v^k)\, d\mathfrak{M} \tag{26.7}$$

When the mass is continuous, in all these we put $d\mathfrak{M} = \rho\, dv$.

To the basic principles of mass conservation we add three other important axioms of mechanics.

FUNDAMENTAL AXIOM 2. *Principle of Balance of Momentum. The time rate of change of momentum is equal to the resultant force $\mathfrak{F}$ acting on the body*

$$\frac{d\mathcal{P}}{dt} = \mathfrak{F} \quad \text{or} \quad \frac{D}{Dt}\int_{\mathcal{V}} \rho\, g^K{}_k\, v^k\, dv = \mathfrak{F}^K \tag{26.8}$$

FUNDAMENTAL AXIOM 3. *Principle of Balance of Moment of Momentum. The time rate of change of moment of momentum about a fixed point o is equal to the resultant moment $\underset{o}{\mathfrak{M}}$ about o.*

$$\frac{d\underset{o}{\mathcal{H}}}{dt} = \underset{o}{\mathfrak{M}} \quad \text{or} \quad \frac{D}{Dt}\int_{\mathcal{V}} \rho\, g^K{}_k\, \epsilon^{klm} p_l v_m\, dv = \underset{o}{\mathfrak{M}}{}^K \tag{26.9}$$

In bivector notation the same thing reads

$$\frac{D}{Dt}\int_{\mathcal{V}} \rho\, g^K{}_k\, g^L{}_l\, (p^k v^l - p^l v^k)\, dv = \underset{o}{\mathfrak{M}}{}^{KL} \tag{26.10}$$

Equations (26.8) and (26.9) embodied in the foregoing two principles, Axioms 2 and 3, constitute *Euler's equations of motion* for a body. They may be considered as an extension of Newton's laws of motion for a particle.

FUNDAMENTAL AXIOM 4. *Principle of Conservation of Energy. Time rate of change of the kinetic plus internal energy is equal to the sum of the rate of work* $\mathcal{W}$ *of external forces and all other energies that enter or leave the body per unit time.*

$$\frac{D}{Dt}(\mathcal{K} + \mathcal{E}) = \mathcal{W} + \sum_{\alpha} \mathcal{U}_{\alpha} \tag{26.11}$$

where $\mathcal{E}$ and $\mathcal{W}$ represent respectively the *internal energy* and the *work* of the external forces per unit time, and $\mathcal{U}_\alpha$ represents the mechanical equivalent of the $\alpha$th kind of energy per unit time, e.g., heat energy, electrical energy, chemical energy, etc. Thus the energies are assumed to be *additive*. Equation (26.11), like (26.8) and (26.9), is a *balance* equation. In a given physical problem generally we have sufficiently clear ideas concerning $\mathcal{W}$, $\mathcal{U}_\alpha$, and of course the kinetic energy is well-defined. The remaining quantity, i.e., the internal energy $\mathcal{E}$, may be looked upon as the quantity that balances this equation. However, $\mathcal{E}$ has certain important characteristics that distinguish it from the rest. It is a *state function;* i.e., it is independent of the *process* followed in going from one state of the body to the next. It is a function of the *constitutive variables.* In *classical thermostatics* a large space is devoted to the study of this function. We shall return to this point in Chap. 4.

In terms of the *internal energy density per unit mass*, $\epsilon$, we can write

$$\mathcal{E} = \int_{\mathcal{V}} \epsilon \, d\mathfrak{M} = \int_{\mathcal{V}} \rho \epsilon \, dv \tag{26.12}$$

where $(26.12)_2$ is valid for continuous mass media.

The principle of energy conservation occurs as an integral of motion in very special situations in classical mechanics. In thermostatics in its special form, it is known as the *first principle of thermostatics.* The present formulation represents an extension of both that of classical mechanics and that of thermostatics. It is valid for dissipative and dynamical systems in which classical mechanics and thermostatics fail to apply.

The deep significance of the foregoing four basic principles of continuous media may be better appreciated after the development of the concept of stress.

## 27. AXIOM OF OBJECTIVITY

In the experimental determination of physical properties of materials, it is necessary to know how the motion of the observer will affect the measurements. It is evident that for those properties that are independent of the motion of the observer, measurements made in one frame of reference are sufficient to determine their values once and for all.

In the formulation of physical laws it is desirable to employ quantities which are independent of the observer or the frame of reference. Such quantities are called *objective*. For example, location of a point will appear different to observers located at different places, and therefore is not objective. Similarly the velocity of a point will appear to be different to observers moving with respect to each other. Hence again it is not objective. On the other hand, distances and angles are objective quantities since they are independent of the frame of reference.

Attempts to secure the invariance of the physical laws of motion from the observer have produced one of the great triumphs of twentieth-century physics. Newton's laws of motion have long been known to be valid only in a special reference frame (*galilean* frame of reference). Attempts to free the principles of classical mechanics from the motion of an observer were resolved by Einstein in his general theory of relativity by rejecting these principles altogether and denying an objective meaning for the concept of time and distance.

While we wish to stay in the domain of classical mechanics, we will find that in the description of materials and dynamical processes the axiom of objectivity plays a central role.[1] To formulate these physically evident facts, let us consider a point $\mathbf{x}$ in a reference frame $\mathfrak{F}$. In another frame of reference $\mathfrak{F}'$ this point will appear as $\mathbf{x}'$. The relation between $\mathbf{x}$ and $\mathbf{x}'$ must be such that the distance and the angle are preserved. The most general transformations of space and time that satisfy these conditions are of the form

$$\mathbf{x}' = \mathbf{Q}\,\mathbf{x} + \mathbf{b} \qquad t' = t - a \tag{27.1}$$

where $\mathbf{Q}(t)$ is an arbitrary real-valued nonsingular orthogonal transformation, $\mathbf{b}(t)$ is an arbitrary point, and $a$ is a constant. Both $\mathbf{Q}$ and $\mathbf{b}$ are continuously differentiable functions of time $t$ alone. The orthogonality condition for the matrix $\mathbf{Q}$ requires that

$$\mathbf{Q}\,\mathbf{Q}^T = \mathbf{Q}^T\,\mathbf{Q} = \mathbf{I} \tag{27.2}$$

where $\mathbf{Q}^T$ denotes the transposed $\mathbf{Q}$ and $\mathbf{I}$ is the unit matrix.

[1] Historically this problem arose from the concept of stress rate. Cauchy [1829] resolved this problem for a special case. Zaremba [1903*b*, 1937] gave a clearer representation. A general mathematical statement for purely mechanical theories was first presented by Noll [1955] in his discussions of "isotropy of space." Later works of Noll [1957, 1958, 1959] contain clear, rigorous statements and various important applications of the "principle of objectivity."

The principle of objectivity in another form which depends on convected coordinates was also given by Oldroyd [1950]. See also Lodge [1951]. A treatment similar to the one given here, but in a rectangular frame of reference, was given by Thomas [1955*a*, *b*]. See also Truesdell [1955*a*, *b*].

The transformation expressed by (27.1) and (27.2) has no simple and unambiguous coordinate representation and physical interpretation in curvilinear coordinates. However, in rectangular coordinates (27.1) and (27.2), read

$$x'^k = Q^k{}_l(t)\,x^l + b^k(t) \qquad t' = t - a$$
$$Q^k{}_l\,Q_m{}^l = Q_l{}^k\,Q^l{}_m = \delta^k{}_m \tag{27.3}$$

Since $\mathbf{Q}(t)$ is a function of $t$ only, by differentiating (27.3) with respect to $t$ we get

$$\dot{Q}^k{}_l\,Q_m{}^l = -Q^k{}_l\,\dot{Q}_m{}^l \qquad \dot{Q}_l{}^k\,Q^l{}_m = -Q_l{}^k\,\dot{Q}^l{}_m \tag{27.4}$$

If $\mathbf{v}$ is a vector in the original frame $\mathbf{x}$, it will appear in the new frame as

$$v'^k = Q^k{}_l\,v^l$$

Suppose $x^k = x^k(\mathbf{X}, t)$ represents the motion of the body $B$. Then through (27.3) we have

$$x'^k(\mathbf{X}, t') = Q^k{}_l(t)\,x^l(\mathbf{X}, t) + b^k(t)$$

which indicates that for $t' = t$ the two frames $\mathfrak{F}$ and $\mathfrak{F}'$ may move with respect to each other in an arbitrary *rigid motion.*

In rectangular coordinates, $Q^k{}_l(t)$ (for $\det Q^k{}_l = 1$) and $b^k(t)$ represent, respectively, the rotation and the translation of one frame with respect to the other. No such physical separation is possible for the general case (27.1).

In the ensuing analysis and throughout the book, for the sake of simplicity, the coordinate representation (27.3) is sometimes used. In such instances it is understood that the proofs are carried out in rectangular coordinates. However, through the tensorial character of quantities treated, the conclusions reached are valid in general curvilinear coordinates.

DEFINITION 1. *Two motions $x^k(\mathbf{X}, t)$ and $x'^k(\mathbf{X}, t')$ are called objectively equivalent (or, simply, equivalent) if*

$$x'^k(\mathbf{X}, t') = Q^k{}_l(t)\,x^l(\mathbf{X}, t) + b^k(t) \qquad t' = t - a \tag{27.5}$$

where $Q^k{}_l(t)$ satisfy $(27.3)_3$. Two equivalent motions differ only relative to the frame of reference. For a fixed frame the two motions may be made to coincide by the superposition of an arbitrary rigid motion on one.

DEFINITION 2. *Any tensorial quantity is said to be objective if in any two equivalent motions it obeys the appropriate tensor transformation law for all times.* Thus, for example, a vector $\mathbf{v}$ and a second-order tensor $\mathbf{s}$ are objective if their values in objectively equivalent motions are respectively given by

$$v'^k(\mathbf{X}, t') = Q^k{}_l(t)\, v^l(\mathbf{X}, t) \tag{27.6}$$

$$s'^k{}_l(\mathbf{X}, t') = Q^k{}_m(t)\, Q_l{}^n(t)\, s^m{}_n(\mathbf{X}, t) \tag{27.7}$$

Let us note that for quantities which are independent of time, objectivity does not come into play. For a vector which is time-independent under a coordinate transformation of the form $(27.5)_1$, the transformation law is precisely as given by (27.6). For time-dependent quantities, however, the situation is different. Consider, for example, the velocity vector $\mathbf{v} = \dot{\mathbf{x}}$.

From (27.5) we have

$$\frac{Dx'^k}{Dt'} = Q^k{}_l\, \dot{\mathbf{x}}^l + \dot{Q}^k{}_l\, x^l + \dot{b}^k$$

or

$$v'^k = Q^k{}_l\, v^l + \dot{Q}^k{}_l\, x^l + \dot{b}^k \tag{27.8}$$

Comparing this with (27.6), we see that the velocity vector is not objective. It is not difficult to show that the acceleration vector is not objective either. With the urge to find an example for an objective quantity, we proceed to a demonstration in the following theorem.

THEOREM 1. *The deformation rate tensor $d_{kl}$ is objective, but the spin tensor is not.* From (27.8), considering $v'^k = v'^k(\mathbf{x}', t')$, $v^k = v^k(\mathbf{x}, t)$, we will have

$$v'^k{}_{,l} = Q^k{}_m\, v^m{}_{,n} \frac{\partial x^n}{\partial x'^l} + \dot{Q}^k{}_m \frac{\partial x^m}{\partial x'^l}$$

To calculate $\partial x^n / \partial x'^l$, we solve for $x^l$ from $(27.3)_1$ by multiplying both sides by $Q_k{}^m$ and using $(27.3)_3$. Hence

$$x^k = Q_m{}^k\,(x'^m - b^m)$$

whence

$$\frac{\partial x^n}{\partial x'^l} = Q_l{}^n \tag{27.9}$$

Using this in the expression for $v'^k{}_{,l}$, we will have

$$v'^k{}_{,l} = Q^k{}_m\, Q_l{}^n\, v^m{}_{,n} + \dot{Q}^k{}_m\, Q_l{}^m \tag{27.10}$$

Similarly we find

$$v'_l{}^{,k} = Q^k{}_m\, Q_l{}^n\, v_n{}^{,m} + Q^k{}_m\, \dot{Q}_l{}^m \tag{27.11}$$

If we add (27.10) to (27.11) and note that the time rate of $(27.3)_3$ is zero, we get

$$d'^k{}_l = Q^k{}_m\, Q_l{}^n\, d^m{}_n \tag{27.12}$$

This proves that the deformation-rate tensor is objective.

If we subtract (27.11) from (27.10), we find

$$w'^k{}_l = Q^k{}_m \, Q_l{}^n \, w^m{}_n + \dot{Q}^k{}_m \, Q_l{}^m \tag{27.13}$$

Hence the spin tensor is *not* objective. The term

$$\Omega^k{}_l \equiv \dot{Q}^k{}_m \, Q_l{}^m \tag{27.14}$$

which is responsible for this is the relative angular velocity of the two frames.

By multiplying both sides of (27.13) by $Q^l{}_r$, we also find

$$\dot{Q}^k{}_l = Q^m{}_l \, w'^k{}_m - Q^k{}_m \, w^m{}_l \tag{27.15}$$

Two other expressions equivalent to this may be found as follows: multiply both sides of (27.10) by $Q^l{}_r$ and use $(27.3)_3$; replace the last term on the right of (27.10) by its equivalent $(27.4)_1$; afterwards multiply both sides by $Q_k{}^r$ and use (27.4). Hence

$$\begin{aligned} \dot{Q}^k{}_l &= Q^m{}_l \, v'^k{}_{,m} - Q^k{}_m \, v^m{}_{,l} = -Q^m{}_l \, v'_{m,}{}^k + Q^k{}_m \, v_{l,}{}^m \\ \dot{Q}_l{}^k &= -Q_m{}^k \, v'^m{}_{,l} + Q_l{}^m \, v^k{}_{,m} = Q_m{}^k \, v'_{l,}{}^m - Q_l{}^m \, v_{m,}{}^k \end{aligned} \tag{27.16}$$

Extreme rights of these expressions are found by a similar procedure applied to (27.11) and using $(27.4)_2$ instead of (27.10). These expressions may be used to evaluate higher-order time rates of $Q^k{}_l$ by successive substitutions.

# 3

# STRESS

## 28. SCOPE OF THE CHAPTER

This chapter deals with loads and the laws of the motion caused by them. The stress hypothesis is formulated in Art. 30, and the stress tensor and couple stress tensor are introduced in Art. 31. The principles of local balance of momenta leading to the basic dynamical equations of continuous media are given in Art. 32. A brief account of the stress quadric of Cauchy, which is an analogue of the strain quadric of Cauchy, may be found in Art. 33. Equations of motion are transformed to the reference state in Art. 34. The last article of the chapter gives an objective definition for *stress flux*.

## 29. EXTERNAL AND INTERNAL LOADS

A material body under the influence of external and internal forces undergoes a deformation. These forces may be mechanical, electrical, chemical, or of some other origin. In the newtonian mechanics of a particle the forces acting on a particle are assumed to be a function of the position vector **p**, velocity vector **v**, and the time. When a continuum is looked upon as a collection of material particles, however, we may find that the forces may depend on various-order spatial gradients, higher-order time rates, time and spatial integrals, and chemical and electromagnetic variables. Although a statistical mechanical description throws more light onto the nature of forces, an adequate characterization of the forces does not exist presently. As in classical mechanics, forces are not defined. The force $\mathfrak{F}$ and the couple $\mathfrak{M}$ acting on a body are vector quantities given by

$$\mathfrak{F} = \int_{\mathcal{V}} d\mathfrak{F} \qquad \mathfrak{M} = \int_{\mathcal{V}} (\mathbf{p} \times d\mathfrak{F} + d\mathfrak{M}) \tag{29.1}$$

These quantities are known a priori. The first of (29.1) indicates that the resultant force $\mathfrak{F}$ consists of the vector sum of all forces acting on the body. The second of (29.1) is the resultant moment about an origin $O$ which is the sum of the *total moment* $\int_{\mathcal{V}} \mathbf{p} \times d\mathfrak{F}$ of the individual forces about $O$ and the sum of all *concentrated* couples $d\mathfrak{M}$.

From a continuum viewpoint, whatever the origin may be, the forces and couples may be divided into three categories.

1. *Extrinsic Body Loads.* These are the forces and couples that arise from external effects. They act on the mass points of the body. A load density per unit mass is assumed to exist so that the total body force is obtained by integrating the load per unit mass over the volume of the body. The extrinsic body force per unit volume is sometimes called the *volume force.* The existence of a *body moment* per unit mass or per unit volume in continuum mechanics is questioned on physical grounds. For the sake of generality, however, we will include these couples in our analysis. Examples of body forces are gravity and electrostatic forces.

Extrinsic body forces are *not* objective. The transformation of these forces is deduced from the principles of momenta [Art. 26, (26.8)].

2. *Extrinsic Surface Loads (Contact Loads).* These loads arise from the action of one body on another through the bounding surface. They are sometimes called *contact loads.* The extrinsic surface force per unit area is assumed to exist and is called the *surface traction.* The existence of the surface couple per unit area, the *couple stress,* is also questioned in continuum mechanics, as is that of the body moment. For the purpose of generality we include these couples in our analysis. The surface tractions and the surface couples depend on the orientation of the surface on which they act. The hydrostatic pressure acting on the surface of a submerged body and surface tractions produced by an electrostatic field are examples of extrinsic surface loads.

Contact loads are assumed to be *objective.*

3. *Internal Loads (Mutual Loads).* These are the result of the mutual action of pairs of particles that are located in the interior of the media. According to Newton's third law, the action of one particle on the other of a pair is equal in magnitude and opposite in direction to the reaction created by the second particle on the first. *Therefore the resultant internal force is zero.*

Mutual loads are *objective.*

The interparticle forces appear as a surface traction on the bounding surface of a part of the body isolated from the rest. This concept gives rise to the *stress hypothesis*, which is treated in the following article.

Let $\mathbf{f}$ be the body force per unit mass and $\mathbf{t}_{(\mathbf{n})}$ be the surface traction acting at a point on the surface whose exterior normal is $\mathbf{n}$. Suppose that at isolated points $\mathbf{p}_\alpha$ there act *concentrated forces* $\mathfrak{F}_\alpha$. Then the resultant force acting on the body is given by

$$\mathfrak{F} = \oint_{\mathbb{S}} \mathbf{t}_{(\mathbf{n})}\, da + \int_{\mathcal{V}} \mathbf{f}\, d\mathfrak{M} + \sum_{\alpha} \mathfrak{F}_\alpha \tag{29.2}$$

If $\mathbf{l}$, $\mathbf{m}_{(\mathbf{n})}$, and $\mathfrak{M}_\alpha$ represent respectively the body moment per unit mass, the surface couple, and the concentrated couple at the position $\mathbf{p}_\alpha$, then the resultant moment about the origin $O$ is given by

$$\mathfrak{M} = \oint_{\mathbb{S}} [\mathbf{m}_{(\mathbf{n})} + \mathbf{p} \times \mathbf{t}_{(\mathbf{n})}]\, da + \int_{\mathcal{V}} (\mathbf{l} + \mathbf{p} \times \mathbf{f})\, d\mathfrak{M} + \sum_{\alpha} (\mathfrak{M}_\alpha + \mathbf{p}_\alpha \times \mathfrak{F}_\alpha) \tag{29.3}$$

Concentrated loads are often imagined as resulting from a limiting process in which the surface loads (body loads) become infinite while the area (the volume) in which they act becomes zero, such that the resultant load remains finite. Such limiting processes often lead to ambiguities requiring care in their interpretation. The limiting process in this general form is not well-defined. Further clarification requires a uniqueness theorem.

By interpreting the volume and surface integrals in a Lebesgue-Stieltjes sense, one can avoid writing the summation in (29.2) and (29.3). To avoid the difficulties in theorems concerning *local* situations, e.g., infinities in the stress distribution in the neighborhood of a concentrated load, the *local* theorems will be assumed to apply to the points where no concentrated load acts. For *global* theorems there is no need for such an assumption. With this caution we have

$$\begin{aligned} \mathfrak{F} &= \oint_{\mathbb{S}} \mathbf{t}_{(\mathbf{n})}\, da + \int \mathbf{f}\, d\mathfrak{M} \\ \mathfrak{M} &= \oint_{\mathbb{S}} (\mathbf{m}_{(\mathbf{n})} + \mathbf{p} \times \mathbf{t}_{(\mathbf{n})})\, da + \int_{\mathcal{V}} (\mathbf{l} + \mathbf{p} \times \mathbf{f})\, d\mathfrak{M} \end{aligned} \tag{29.4}$$

Principles of balance of global momentum and global moment of momentum now read

$$\begin{aligned} \frac{d}{dt} \int_{\mathcal{V}} \mathbf{v}\, d\mathfrak{M} &= \oint_{\mathbb{S}} \mathbf{t}_{(\mathbf{n})}\, da + \int_{\mathcal{V}} \mathbf{f}\, d\mathfrak{M} \\ \frac{d}{dt} \int_{\mathcal{V}} \mathbf{p} \times \mathbf{v}\, d\mathfrak{M} &= \oint_{\mathbb{S}} (\mathbf{m}_{(\mathbf{n})} + \mathbf{p} \times \mathbf{t}_{(\mathbf{n})})\, da + \int_{\mathcal{V}} (\mathbf{l} + \mathbf{p} \times \mathbf{f})\, d\mathfrak{M} \end{aligned} \tag{29.5}$$

These equations constitute Euler's equations of motion. Since the internal forces are in equilibrium among themselves, they do not appear in these equations.

Since the extrinsic body loads are not objective, Euler's equations of motion (29.5) are *not* objective. These equations, in fact, give the laws of transformation for the extrinsic body loads, since the transformation of momentum, moment of momentum, and contact loads in objectively equivalent motions are known. The urge to replace the equations of the particle dynamics (Newton's equations of motion ) by an objective set led to Einstein's discovery of the general theory of relativity. The relativity correction is found to be very small for most dynamical problems. Only for very large astronomical distances and for speeds close to that of light does this correction play an important role. Thus, for the sake of simplicity, it is desirable to remain in the domain of classical mechanics.

## 30. INTERNAL LOADS, STRESS HYPOTHESIS

The state of internal loads and the connection of these to the surface loads may be understood by applying the global momentum principle to regions fully and partially contained in the body. First consider a small volume $v$ bounded by a closed surface $s$ such that $v + s$ is fully contained in the body (Fig. 30.1). At a point $p$ of $s$ the interaction of $v$ and $\mathcal{V} - v$ is *equipollent* to a system of surface forces $\mathbf{t}_{(\mathbf{n})}$ called *stress vectors* and surface couples $\mathbf{m}_{(\mathbf{n})}$ called *couple stresses. Both stress vectors and couple stresses are objective.*

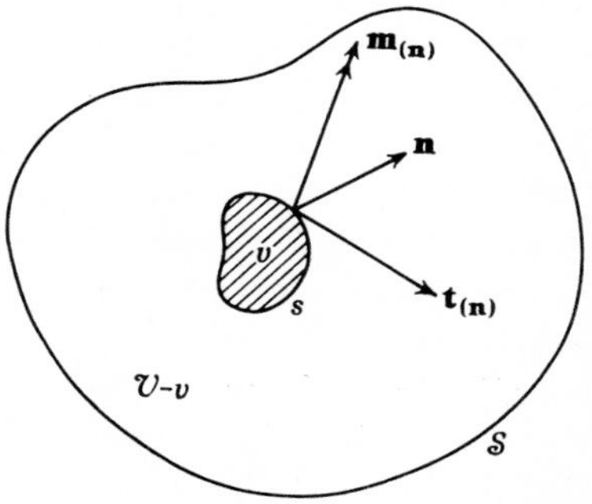


FIG. 30.1. Stress vector and couple stress.

These loads depend not only on the position vector $\mathbf{p}$ of the point on $s$ under consideration and the time, but also on the *exterior normal* $\mathbf{n}$ to $s$ at the point. For different surfaces through the same point at the same time, in general, the loads have different directions and intensities. On the external surface of the body $\mathcal{S}$ they become external surface tractions already analyzed in Art. 29. We have therefore kept the same notation, since no confusion will arise from this duality. The momentum principles applied to $v + s$ are identical in form to (29.5) except that the volume integrals are now taken over $v$ and the surface integrals over $s$.

The dependence of the stress vector and the couple stress on the exterior normal can be found by applying the principle of linear momentum to a small tetrahedron with its vertex $\mathbf{p}$ in the interior of $v$ and having three of its faces the coordinate surfaces and the fourth face on $s$ (Fig. 30.2). The stress vectors[1] on the coordinate surfaces are denoted by $-\mathbf{t}_{(k)}$. We now apply the principle of linear momentum $(29.5)_1$ to the above

[1] Since the exterior normal of a coordinate surface makes an angle larger than 90° with a coordinate direction not in the coordinate surface, without loss in generality, we take the stress vector acting on the surface as $-\mathbf{t}_{(k)}$ rather than $\mathbf{t}_{(k)}$.

tetrahedron. Using the mean-value theorem, we can estimate the volume and surface integrals stated in (29.5). Thus

$$\frac{d}{dt}(\rho\,\mathbf{v}^*\,\Delta v) = \mathbf{t}^*_{(\mathrm{n})}\,\Delta a - \mathbf{t}^*_{(k)}\,\Delta a^{(k)} + \rho\,\mathbf{f}^*\,\Delta v$$

where $\mathbf{v}^*$ and $\mathbf{f}^*$ are the velocity vector and the body force respectively, at a point within the volume $\Delta v$ of the tetrahedron; $\mathbf{t}^*_{(\mathrm{n})}$ is the stress vector at some point of the surface $\Delta a$; and $\mathbf{t}^*_{(k)}$ are those on areas $\Delta a^{(k)}$ of the

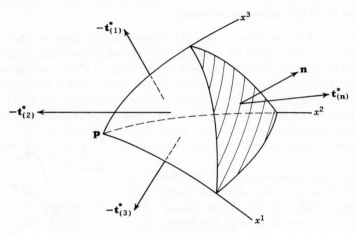

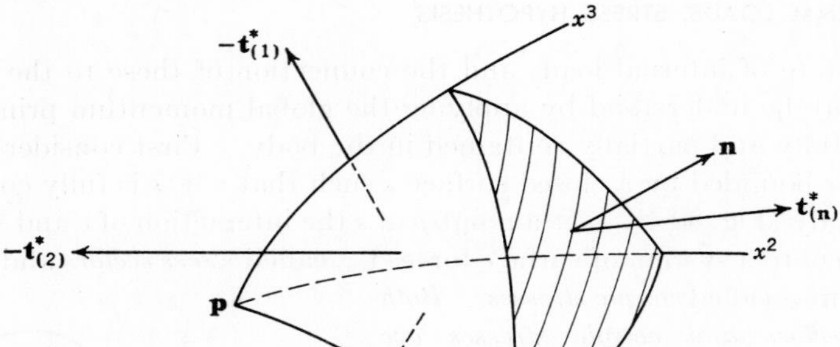


FIG. 30.2. Tetrahedron.

coordinate surfaces of the tetrahedron. Mass is assumed to be continuous so that the mass density $\rho$ exists. Upon dividing both sides of the above equation by $\Delta a$ and letting $\Delta a \to 0$ so that point $p$ approaches the surface $s$ of $v$ from the interior, we will have $\Delta v/\Delta a \to 0$. Hence

(30.1) $$\mathbf{t}_{(\mathrm{n})}\,da = \mathbf{t}_{(k)}\,da^{(k)}$$

The four surfaces of the tetrahedron form a closed surface. Therefore in the limit the vector sum of the areas on the coordinate surfaces must add up to the area vector $d\mathbf{a}$, i.e.,

(30.2) $$d\mathbf{a} = \mathbf{n}\,da = \sum_k da^{(k)}\,\frac{\mathbf{g}_k}{\sqrt{g_{kk}}} = da^k\,\mathbf{g}_k$$

From this we get

(30.3) $$da^{(k)}/\sqrt{g_{\underline{kk}}} = da^k = n^k\,da$$

Substituting this into (30.1), we get

(30.4) $$\mathbf{t}_{(\mathrm{n})} = \sum_k \mathbf{t}_{(k)}\sqrt{g_{kk}}\,n^k = \mathbf{t}_{(k)}\,n^{(k)} = \mathbf{t}_k\,n^k = \mathbf{t}^k\,n_k$$

where $n^{(k)}$ are the physical components of the exterior normal $\mathbf{n}$ and

$$\mathbf{t}_k = \mathbf{t}_{(k)} \sqrt{\underline{g_{kk}}} \qquad \mathbf{t}^k = g^{kl}\,\mathbf{t}_l$$
$$n^{(k)} = n^k \sqrt{\underline{g_{kk}}} \tag{30.5}$$

We have therefore proved the following theorem.

THEOREM 1. *The stress vector at a point of a surface with an exterior unit normal* $\mathbf{n}$ *is a linear function of the stress vectors acting on coordinate surfaces through the same point, the coefficients being the physical components of the cosine directors of* $\mathbf{n}$.

Stress vectors $\mathbf{t}_{(k)}$, by definition, are independent of $\mathbf{n}$. *Assuming that* $\mathbf{t}_{(\mathbf{n})}$ *is a continuous function of* $\mathbf{n}$, if we change the sign of $\mathbf{n}$ in (30.4), we find that the stress vector changes sign, i.e.,

$$\mathbf{t}_{(-\mathbf{n})} = -\mathbf{t}_{(\mathbf{n})} \tag{30.6}$$

Hence the proof of the following corollary.

COROLLARY. *The stress vectors acting on the opposite sides of the same surface at a given point are equal in magnitude and opposite in sign.*[2]

Application of a similar argument to couple stresses by use of $(29.5)_2$ leads to

$$\mathbf{m}_{(\mathbf{n})} = \sum_k \mathbf{m}_{(k)} \sqrt{g_{kk}}\, n^k = \mathbf{m}_{(k)}\, n^{(k)} = \mathbf{m}_k\, n^k = \mathbf{m}^k\, n_k \tag{30.7}$$

$$\mathbf{m}_{(-\mathbf{n})} = -\mathbf{m}_{(\mathbf{n})} \tag{30.8}$$

We may again mention that the existence of couple stresses, surface couples, and body couples is often rejected in continuum mechanics, with the following argument. A couple in classical mechanics is pictured as a pair of parallel forces of equal magnitude and opposite sense, separated by a moment arm. It is assumed that the forces are *bounded*. If we let the moment arm approach zero, keeping the forces bounded, the moment of the couple vanishes.

Inclusion of the unbounded forces in mechanics must await experimental verifications. For the sake of generality, however, we have included surface couples, body couples, and couple stresses in some of the developments.

## 31. STRESS TENSOR

*The stress tensor* $t_{kl}$ *is the lth component of the stress vector* $\mathbf{t}_k$ *acting on the positive side of the kth coordinate surface. The stress tensor is objective.*

$$\mathbf{t}_k = t_{kl}\,\mathbf{g}^l \tag{31.1}$$

[2] For an alternative proof of this based on the use of the principle of objectivity, see Noll [1957, p. 20].

The first index in $t_{kl}$ indicates the coordinate surface on which $\mathbf{t}_k$ acts and the second index the direction of the component. For example, $t_{23}$ is the $x^3$ component of $\mathbf{t}_2$, acting on the coordinate surface $x^2 = \text{const}$. If the exterior normal of the coordinate surface $x^k = \text{const}$ makes an acute angle with the positive coordinate curve $x^k$, then the positive directions of the stress components $t_{kl}$ acting on this surface are by convention in the positive coordinate directions of $x^l$. If the exterior normal makes an

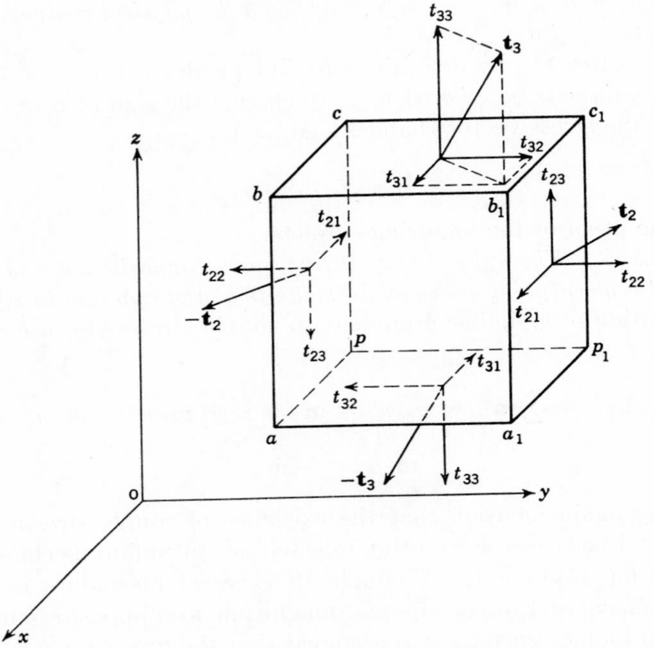


FIG. 31.1. Stress tensor.

angle more than 90° with the positive $x^k$ coordinate curve, then the positive directions of $t_{kl}$ on this surface are in the directions of the negative coordinate curves $x^l$. The positive stress components are shown in Fig. 31.1 for a rectangular coordinate system. Positive stress components on the surface $p_1a_1b_1c_1$ are oriented in the positive directions of the $x$, $y$, and $z$ axes, since the exterior normal of this plane is in the direction of the $y > 0$ axis. On the plane $pabc$, on the other hand, positive stress components are oriented in the direction of the negative coordinate axes, for on this plane the exterior normal is in the direction of the $y < 0$ axis. Similar conventions apply to the stress components acting on the faces $x = \text{const}$ and $z = \text{const}$. In order not to crowd the figure, the stress components acting on the $x = \text{const}$ planes are omitted. The sign convention given above is not unique. It is, however, generally accepted in the literature. *The components $t_{11}$, $t_{22}$, and $t_{33}$ are called the normal stresses, and the mixed components such as $t_{12}$, $t_{23}$, etc., are called the shearing stresses.*

Substituting (31.1) into (30.4), we get

$$\text{(31.2)} \qquad \mathbf{t}_{(\mathrm{n})} = t_{kl}\, n^k\, \mathbf{g}^l \qquad \text{or} \qquad t_{(\mathrm{n})l} = t_{kl}\, n^k$$

which is the proof of the following theorem.

FUNDAMENTAL THEOREM. *The stress vector acting on any plane through a point is fully characterized as a linear function of the stress tensor at the point.*

The tensorial character of $t_{kl}$ may be seen by using the quotient rule in $(31.2)_2$. Since $t_{(\mathrm{n})l}$ and $n^k$ are covariant and contravariant vectors, $t_{kl}$ is a covariant tensor of second order.

By raising the indices, we also obtain mixed and contravariant components of the stress tensor, i.e.,

$$\text{(31.3)} \qquad \begin{aligned} t^k{}_l &= g^{km}\, t_{ml} \qquad & t^{kl} &= g^{ln}\, t^k{}_n = g^{km}\, g^{ln}\, t_{mn} \\ t_l{}^k &= g^{km}\, t_{lm} \qquad & t^{kl} &= g^{km}\, t_m{}^l \end{aligned}$$

Equivalent to (31.2) we therefore have

$$\text{(31.4)} \qquad \begin{aligned} \mathbf{t}_{(\mathrm{n})} &= t^k{}_l\, n_k\, \mathbf{g}^l = t_l{}^k\, n^l\, \mathbf{g}_k = t^{lk}\, n_l\, \mathbf{g}_k = \cdots \\ t^l{}_{(\mathrm{n})} &= t_k{}^l\, n^k = t^{kl}\, n_k = \cdots \\ t_{(\mathrm{n})k} &= t_{lk}\, n^l = t^l{}_k\, n_l = \cdots \end{aligned}$$

Note also through $(30.5)_2$ and (31.1) that

$$\text{(31.5)} \qquad \mathbf{t}^k = t^k{}_l\, \mathbf{g}^l = t^{kl}\, \mathbf{g}_l$$

Parallel to the foregoing, the couple stress $\mathbf{m}_k$ may be expressed in terms of its components $m_{kl}$, the *couple stress tensor*, by

$$\text{(31.6)} \qquad \mathbf{m}_k = m_{kl}\, \mathbf{g}^l \qquad \text{or} \qquad \mathbf{m}^k = m^k{}_l\, \mathbf{g}^l = m^{kl}\, \mathbf{g}_l$$

*The couple stress tensor is objective.* The sign convention for $m_{kl}$ is the same as $t_{kl}$, since $\mathbf{m}_k$ is to be treated as an axial vector. Through (30.7) we now write

$$\text{(31.7)} \qquad \mathbf{m}_{(\mathrm{n})} = m_{kl}\, n^k\, \mathbf{g}^l \qquad \text{or} \qquad m_{(\mathrm{n})l} = m_{kl}\, n^k = m^k{}_l\, n_k$$

Equivalent to the axial vector $m_{(\mathrm{n})l}$ is the bivector defined by

$$\text{(31.8)} \qquad 2\, m^{kl}_{(\mathrm{n})} = \epsilon^{klr}\, m_{(\mathrm{n})r} \qquad m_{(\mathrm{n})k} = \epsilon_{kpr}\, m^{pr}_{(\mathrm{n})}$$

and equivalent to the couple stress tensor is the *objective* third-order tensor

$$\text{(31.9)} \qquad 2\, m^{kpr} = \epsilon^{lpr}\, m^k{}_l \qquad \text{or} \qquad m^k{}_l = \epsilon_{lpr}\, m^{kpr}$$

Now introduce $(31.8)_2$ and $(31.9)_2$ into $(31.7)_2$, i.e.,

$$m_{(\mathrm{n})l} = \epsilon_{lpr}\, m^{pr}_{(\mathrm{n})} = \epsilon_{lpr}\, m^{kpr}\, n_k$$

from which it follows that

$$m^{pr}_{(\mathrm{n})} = m^{kpr}\, n_k \qquad m^{kpr} = -m^{krp} \tag{31.10}$$

The foregoing analysis is applicable without change to any point on the surface $s$ of the body whenever the tangent plane is continuous there. Thus, if the loading is prescribed on the surface, we have the following *boundary conditions* on tractions and couples

$$t^l_{(\mathrm{n})} = t^{kl}\, n_k = s^l \qquad m^l_{(\mathrm{n})} = m^{kl}\, n_k = q^l \tag{31.11}$$

where $s^l$ and $q^l$ are respectively the prescribed surface traction and the surface couple on $s$. The boundary conditions on couples may be written equivalently in terms of $m^{klr}$ as

$$m^{pr}_{(\mathrm{n})} = m^{kpr}\, n_k = q^{pr} \tag{31.12}$$

where $q^{pr}$ is a bivector equivalent to $q_k$ acting on the surface $s$ of the body, i.e.,

$$2\, q^{pr} = \epsilon^{kpr}\, q_k \tag{31.13}$$

Physical components of the stress tensor are obtained from $(31.2)_1$ by using $(30.5)_3$ to express $n^k$ in terms of its physical component $n^{(k)}$ and writing $\mathbf{e}_{(k)} = \mathbf{g}_k/\sqrt{g_{\underline{kk}}}$. Hence

$$\mathbf{t}_{(\mathrm{n})} = \sum_{k,l} t_l{}^k \frac{\sqrt{g_{kk}}}{\sqrt{g_{ll}}}\, n^{(l)}\, \mathbf{e}_{(k)} = t_{(l)}{}^{(k)}\, n^{(l)}\, \mathbf{e}_{(k)} \tag{31.14}$$

where

$$t_{(l)}{}^{(k)} = t_l{}^k \frac{\sqrt{g_{\underline{kk}}}}{\sqrt{g_{\underline{ll}}}} \tag{31.15}$$

are the *left physical components* of the stress tensor.[1] Similarly for the left physical components of the couple stress $m_l{}^k$ we have

$$m_{(l)}{}^{(k)} = m_l{}^k \frac{\sqrt{g_{\underline{kk}}}}{\sqrt{g_{\underline{ll}}}} \tag{31.16}$$

From the definitions of the body force $\mathbf{f}$, the surface traction $\mathbf{t}_{(\mathrm{n})}$, the surface couple $\mathbf{m}_{(\mathrm{n})}$, the stress tensor $t_l{}^k$, and the couple stress $m_l{}^k$, we see that these quantities have the physical dimensions

[1] For a discussion of physical components of tensors see Appendix, Art. A3.

$$[\mathbf{f}] = \frac{L}{T^2} = \frac{\text{force}}{\text{mass}} \qquad [\mathbf{t}_{(\mathbf{n})}] = \frac{M}{L\,T^2} = \frac{\text{force}}{\text{area}}$$

$$[\mathbf{m}_{(\mathbf{n})}] = \frac{M}{T^2} = \frac{\text{force} \times \text{distance}}{\text{area}} \tag{31.17}$$

$$[t_{(l)}{}^{(k)}] = \frac{M}{L\,T^2} = \frac{\text{force}}{\text{area}} \qquad [m_{(l)}{}^{(k)}] = \frac{M}{T^2} = \frac{\text{force} \times \text{distance}}{\text{area}}$$

where brackets [ ] indicate the dimension. Here $M$ denotes mass, $L$ length, and $T$ time. In the CGS system force is measured in dynes, length in centimeters, and time in seconds. Therefore in this system $\mathbf{t}_{(\mathbf{n})}$ and $t_{(l)}{}^{(k)}$ are measured in dynes per square centimeter. In the English practical units they are measured in pounds per square inch.

Finally we give a short list of various notations used for the stress tensor by various writers.

| | |
|---|---|
| Eringen, Clebsch, Truesdell | $t_{11}$ $t_{22}$ $t_{33}$ $t_{23}$ $t_{31}$ $t_{12}$ |
| Cauchy (early work) | $A$ $B$ $C$ $D$ $E$ $F$ |
| Cauchy (later work), St. Venant, Maxwell | $p_{xx}$ $p_{yy}$ $p_{zz}$ $p_{yz}$ $p_{zx}$ $p_{xy}$ |
| F. Neumann, Kirchhoff, Love | $X_x$ $Y_y$ $Z_z$ $Y_z$ $Z_x$ $X_y$ |
| K. Pearson | $\widehat{xx}$ $\widehat{yy}$ $\widehat{zz}$ $\widehat{yz}$ $\widehat{zx}$ $\widehat{xy}$ |
| Kelvin | $P$ $Q$ $R$ $S$ $T$ $V$ |
| Karman, Timoshenko | $\sigma_x$ $\sigma_y$ $\sigma_z$ $\tau_{yz}$ $\tau_{zx}$ $\tau_{xy}$ |
| Russian and German writers, Green, and Zerna | $\tau_{11}$ $\tau_{22}$ $\tau_{33}$ $\tau_{23}$ $\tau_{31}$ $\tau_{12}$ |
| Some English and American writers and others | $\sigma_{11}$ $\sigma_{22}$ $\sigma_{33}$ $\sigma_{23}$ $\sigma_{31}$ $\sigma_{12}$ <br> $\sigma_{xx}$ $\sigma_{yy}$ $\sigma_{zz}$ $\sigma_{yz}$ $\sigma_{zx}$ $\sigma_{xy}$ |

## 32. PRINCIPLES OF BALANCE OF LOCAL MOMENTA

If we carry out the indicated differentiation on the left of (29.5) and use the principle of local mass conservation $D(d\mathfrak{M})/Dt = 0$, we can express (29.5) in the forms

$$\int_{\mathcal{V}} \mathbf{a}\, d\mathfrak{M} = \oint_{\mathcal{S}} \mathbf{t}_{(\mathbf{n})}\, da + \int_{\mathcal{V}} \mathbf{f}\, d\mathfrak{M} \tag{32.1}$$

$$\int_{\mathcal{V}} \mathbf{p} \times \mathbf{a}\, d\mathfrak{M} = \oint_{\mathcal{S}} [\mathbf{m}_{(\mathbf{n})} + \mathbf{p} \times \mathbf{t}_{(\mathbf{n})}]\, da + \int_{\mathcal{V}} (\mathbf{l} + \mathbf{p} \times \mathbf{f})\, d\mathfrak{M} \tag{32.2}$$

where $\mathbf{a} \equiv \dot{\mathbf{v}}$ is the acceleration vector. These are but another form of the balance of global momentum and global moment of momentum. We now take $\mathcal{V} + \mathcal{S}$ as a small internal portion of the body having continuous mass distribution and, upon using $(30.4)_4$ and $(30.7)_4$, write

$$\int_v \rho\, \mathbf{a}\, dv = \oint_s \mathbf{t}^k n_k\, da + \int_v \rho\, \mathbf{f}\, dv \tag{32.3}$$

$$\int_v \rho\, \mathbf{p} \times \mathbf{a}\, dv = \oint_s (\mathbf{m}^k + \mathbf{p} \times \mathbf{t}^k)\, n_k\, da + \int_v \rho\, (\mathbf{l} + \mathbf{p} \times \mathbf{f})\, dv \tag{32.4}$$

Applying the Green-Gauss theorem to convert the surface integrals into volume integrals, we get

$$\int_v \left[\frac{1}{\sqrt{g}}\frac{\partial}{\partial x^k}(\sqrt{g}\,\mathbf{t}^k) + \rho\,(\mathbf{f} - \mathbf{a})\right] dv = 0 \tag{32.5}$$

$$\int_v \left\{\frac{1}{\sqrt{g}}\frac{\partial}{\partial x^k}(\sqrt{g}\,\mathbf{m}^k) + \rho\,\mathbf{l} + \mathbf{g}_k \times \mathbf{t}^k + \mathbf{p} \times \left[\frac{1}{\sqrt{g}}\frac{\partial}{\partial x^k}(\sqrt{g}\,\mathbf{t}^k) + \rho\,(\mathbf{f} - \mathbf{a})\right]\right\} dv = 0 \tag{32.6}$$

These are the mathematical expressions of the *principles of the balance of global momentum* and *global moment of momentum.* For these to be valid for any arbitrary volume $v$, the necessary and sufficient condition is the vanishing of the integrands. Hence

$$\frac{1}{\sqrt{g}}\frac{\partial}{\partial x^k}(\sqrt{g}\,\mathbf{t}^k) + \rho\,(\mathbf{f} - \mathbf{a}) = 0 \tag{32.7}$$

$$\frac{1}{\sqrt{g}}\frac{\partial}{\partial x^k}(\sqrt{g}\,\mathbf{m}^k) + \rho\,\mathbf{l} + \mathbf{g}_k \times \mathbf{t}^k = 0 \tag{32.8}$$

Note that to obtain (32.8), we have used (32.7) and have dropped the bracketed expression in the integrand of (32.6) for *local* balance. To obtain the equivalent form of (32.7) and (32.8) in component notation, we replace $\mathbf{t}^k$ by $(31.5)_2$ and $\mathbf{m}^k$ by $(31.6)_3$ and employ the relations

$$\frac{1}{\sqrt{g}}\frac{\partial\sqrt{g}}{\partial x^k} = \left\{\begin{matrix} r \\ rk \end{matrix}\right\} \qquad \frac{\partial \mathbf{g}_r}{\partial x^k} = \left\{\begin{matrix} n \\ rk \end{matrix}\right\}\mathbf{g}_n \tag{32.9}$$

Hence

$$t^{jk}{}_{;j} + \rho\,(f^k - a^k) = 0 \tag{32.10}$$

$$m^{ji}{}_{;j} + \rho l^i + \epsilon^{ijk}\,t_{jk} = 0 \tag{32.11}$$

These are respectively the *first and second laws of motion of Cauchy* and the proofs of the following theorems.[1]

THEOREM 1. *A necessary and sufficient condition for the local balance of momentum is* (32.7) *or* (32.10).

THEOREM 2. *A necessary and sufficient condition for the local balance of moment of momentum, when the linear momentum is locally balanced, is the satisfaction of the second law of motion of Cauchy* [*either* (32.8) *or* (32.11)].

*Both laws of motion of Cauchy are not objective.*

The bivector representation of Cauchy's second law (32.11) is

$$m^{kij}{}_{;k} + \rho\,l^{ij} + t^{[ij]} = 0 \tag{32.12}$$

[1] Cauchy [1827*a*, *b*, 1828]. The second law was discovered by Fresnel [1868] in 1822, but was not published until 1868.

where $l^{ij}$ is the bivector equivalent of $l_k$, i.e.,

$$2\, l^{ij} = \epsilon^{ijk}\, l_k \qquad l_i = \epsilon_{ijk}\, l^{jk}$$

By eliminating the skew-symmetric part of the stress tensor from (32.10), by use of (32.12) we get

$$t^{(jk)}{}_{;j} - m^{(ij)k}{}_{;ij} + \rho\,(f^k - l^{jk}{}_{;j} - a^k) = 0 \tag{32.13}$$

When there are no body couples and couple stresses, (32.12) reduces to

$$t^{ij} = t^{ji} \tag{32.14}$$

which is the proof of the corollary that follows.

COROLLARY. *When there are no body couples and couple stresses and when the local linear momentum is balanced, the necessary and sufficient condition for the balance of local moment of momentum is the symmetry of the stress tensor.*

For a mechanical medium the existence of body or surface couples is often rejected. Therefore in such a medium we have only six independent stress components: namely, $t^{11}$, $t^{22}$, $t^{33}$, $t^{23} = t^{32}$, $t^{31} = t^{13}$, and $t^{12} = t^{21}$. Consequently the order of the two indices at the same level is unimportant, and also the left and right mixed components of the stress tensor are the same, i.e.,

$$t^{kl} = t^{lk} \qquad t^k{}_l = t_l{}^k \tag{32.15}$$

We may therefore freely write (32.10) as

$$t^{kl}{}_{;l} + \rho\,(f^k - a^k) = 0 \tag{32.16}$$

By lowering the indices, we get the equivalent equations

$$t^l{}_{k;l} + \rho\,(f_k - a_k) = 0 \qquad t_{lk;}{}^l + \rho\,(f_k - a_k) = 0 \tag{32.17}$$

Finally we express Cauchy's first law of motion in terms of the physical components of vectors and tensors involved. To do this, we expand $(32.17)_1$ to the form

$$t^l{}_{k,l} + \begin{Bmatrix} l \\ rl \end{Bmatrix} t^r{}_k - \begin{Bmatrix} r \\ kl \end{Bmatrix} t^l{}_r + \rho\, g_{kl}\,(f^l - a^l) = 0 \tag{32.18}$$

Vectors $f^l$ and $a^l$ are related to their physical components $f^{(l)}$ and $a^{(l)}$ by expressions of the form $(30.5)_3$, while $t^k{}_l = t_l{}^k$ is related to its physical components $t_{(l)}{}^{(k)}$ by (31.15). Using also the identity

$$\begin{Bmatrix} l \\ rl \end{Bmatrix} = \frac{\partial}{\partial x^r} \log \sqrt{g} \qquad g = \det |g_{kl}| \tag{32.19}$$

Eq. (32.18) may be written as

$$\sum_{l=1}^{3}\left\{\frac{\partial}{\partial x^l}\left[t_{(k)}{}^{(l)}\frac{\sqrt{g_{\underline{kk}}}}{\sqrt{g_{ll}}}\right]+t_{(k)}{}^{(l)}\frac{\sqrt{g_{\underline{kk}}}}{\sqrt{g_{ll}}}\frac{\partial}{\partial x^l}(\log\sqrt{g})\right.$$
$$\left.-\sum_{m=1}^{3}\left[\left\{{l \atop km}\right\}t_{(l)}{}^{(m)}\frac{\sqrt{g_{ll}}}{\sqrt{g_{mm}}}\right]+\rho\frac{g_{kl}}{\sqrt{g_{ll}}}[f^{(l)}-a^{(l)}]\right\}=0 \tag{32.20}$$

which is valid in any coordinate system and for the case where the stress tensor is symmetric. A great deal of simplification is achieved when the coordinates are orthogonal. In this case $g_{kl} = 0$ for $k \neq l$ and $g^{kk} = 1/g_{kk}$, and the left and right components of the stress tensor are the same,[2] i.e., $t^{(k)}{}_{(l)} = t_{(l)}{}^{(k)}$ (even for a nonsymmetric stress tensor). Thus

$$\sum_{l=1}^{3}\left\{\frac{1}{\sqrt{g}}\frac{\partial}{\partial x^l}\left[t^{(l)}{}_{(k)}\frac{\sqrt{g}}{\sqrt{g_{ll}}}\right]+\frac{1}{\sqrt{g_{\underline{kk}}\,g_{ll}}}\frac{\partial\sqrt{g_{\underline{kk}}}}{\partial x^l}t^{(l)}{}_{(k)}\right.$$
$$\left.-\frac{1}{\sqrt{g_{\underline{kk}}\,g_{ll}}}\frac{\partial\sqrt{g_{ll}}}{\partial x^k}t^{(l)}{}_{(l)}\right\}+\rho\,[f^{(k)}-a^{(k)}]=0 \tag{32.21}$$

There is no particular difficulty in finding the expression corresponding to (32.11) in terms of physical components of the vectors and tensors involved.

## 33. STRESS QUADRIC OF CAUCHY AND STRESS INVARIANTS

The normal component $N$ of the stress vector $\mathbf{t}_{(\mathbf{n})}$ acting at point $p$ of surface $s$ with exterior normal $\mathbf{n}$ (Fig. 33.1) is calculated by

$$N = \mathbf{t}_{(\mathbf{n})} \cdot \mathbf{n} \tag{33.1}$$

Upon substituting the expression for $\mathbf{t}_{(\mathbf{n})}$ from $(31.2)_1$, we get

$$N = t_{kl}\, n^k\, n^l \tag{33.2}$$

For a fixed $N$, upon changing the orientation of the surface at $p$, we see that the stress components $t_{kl}$ change, satisfying (33.2). The quadric surface represented by (33.2) is called the *stress quadric of Cauchy*. The variables $n^k$ of (33.2) are subject to the condition that $\mathbf{n}$ is a unit normal, i.e.,

$$g_{kl}\, n^k\, n^l = 1 \tag{33.3}$$

[2] Cf. Appendix, Art. A3.

For vanishing body couples and couple stresses the stress tensor is a symmetric tensor. Consequently for the *nonpolar* case we have a complete correspondence between the stress quadric of Cauchy and the strain quadric of Cauchy. To translate the results of Arts. 8 and 9, all we need is to notice the one-to-one correspondence between $t_{kl}$ and $e_{kl}$ or $c_{kl}$ and between $n^k$ and $\frac{dx^k}{ds}$. With this understanding we have the following lemmas.

1. There exist at least three and generally three *principal directions* of stress.

2. There are three principal stresses $t_\alpha$ ($\alpha = 1, 2, 3$) which act on the principal planes.

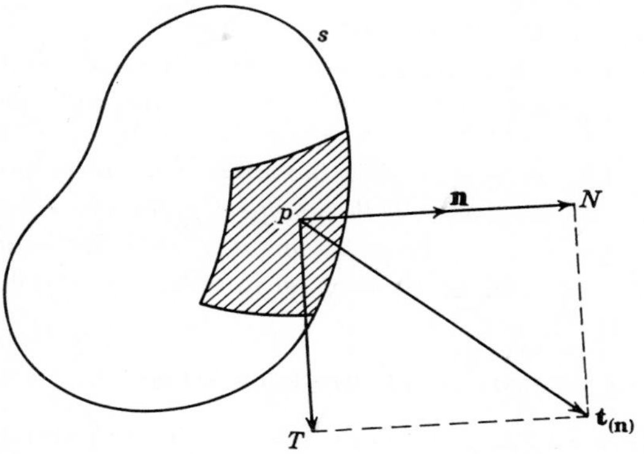


FIG. 33.1. Normal and tangential tractions.

3. On the principal planes the shearing stresses vanish and the normal stresses take the stationary values $t_\alpha$.

4. In general there are three independent *stress invariants* $\mathrm{I}_t$, $\mathrm{II}_t$, and $\mathrm{III}_t$ whose expressions are identical in form to (9.9) and (9.10) of the strain invariants except that everywhere $C^K{}_L$ and $C_\alpha$ must be replaced by $t^k{}_l$ and $t_\alpha$.

Special types of stress conditions also have one-to-one correspondence with those of strain. For example, if two of the principal stresses are zero, the state of stress is called *simple tension* or *uniaxial stress;* when one of the principal stresses vanishes, it is called *plane* or *biaxial;* and if no principal stress vanishes, the state of stress is *triaxial.*

In a plane stress, if the two principal stresses are equal and opposite in sign, with reference to the rectangular coordinates bisecting the two principal axes in the plane, all normal stresses vanish. The state of stress for this case is therefore called *pure shearing stress.*

For pure shearing stress we therefore have a stress matrix of the form

$$\|t_{kl}\| = \begin{bmatrix} 0 & t_{xy} & 0 \\ t_{xy} & 0 & 0 \\ 0 & 0 & 0 \end{bmatrix} \qquad t_{xy} \neq 0 \tag{33.4}$$

An invariant condition for pure shear is

$$\mathrm{I}_t = 0 \qquad \mathrm{III}_t = 0 \tag{33.5}$$

Hence

$$t_{xy} = t_1 = -t_2 = \sqrt{-\mathrm{II}_t} \tag{33.6}$$

Various geometrical constructions, such as Mohr's circle, for the determination of the principal planes and principal stresses are identical to their counterparts for the strain.

Finally we give the following theorem which concerns the stationary values of the shearing stresses and has found application in failure theories.

THEOREM 1. *The maximum shearing stress acts on the plane that bisects the angle between the greatest and the smallest principal stresses. Its value is one-half the difference between the greatest and the smallest principal stresses.* Proof of this theorem may be found in textbooks on elasticity (cf. Sokolnikoff [1956, art. 18]).

## 34. EQUATIONS OF MOTION IN THE REFERENCE STATE

The stress tensor $t^{kl}$ and the body force $f^k$ defined above are functions of the spatial point $x^k$ and time $t$. Cauchy's laws of motion are eulerian descriptions. Through the equations of motion (2.1) we can express these quantities and the equations of motion in the reference state.

We introduce the stress vector $\mathbf{T}^K$ at point $\mathbf{x}$ referred to the undeformed area $dA_K$ at $\mathbf{X} = \mathbf{X}(\mathbf{x}, t)$ by

$$\mathbf{t}_{(\mathbf{n})}\, da = \mathbf{t}^k\, da_k = \mathbf{T}^K\, dA_K \tag{34.1}$$

But according to (12.5) we have

$$da_k = J\, X^K{}_{,k}\, dA_K \tag{34.2}$$

Substituting this into (34.1),

$$\mathbf{t}^k = J^{-1}\, x^k{}_{,K}\, \mathbf{T}^K \qquad \mathbf{T}^K = J\, X^K{}_{,k}\, \mathbf{t}^k \tag{34.3}$$

Clearly

$$\frac{1}{\sqrt{g}}(\sqrt{g}\,\mathbf{t}^k)_{,k} = \frac{1}{\sqrt{g}}(\sqrt{g}\,J^{-1}\,x^k{}_{,K}\,\mathbf{T}^K)_{,k} = \frac{1}{\sqrt{g}}(j^{-1}\,x^k{}_{,K}\sqrt{G}\,\mathbf{T}^K)_{,k}$$

$$= \sqrt{G}\left(\frac{\sqrt{g}}{\sqrt{G}}\,J^{-1}\,X^k{}_{,K}\,\mathbf{T}^K\right)_{,k} = \frac{1}{j\sqrt{g}}(\sqrt{G}\,\mathbf{T}^K)_{,k}\,x^k{}_{,K}$$

since $j = \sqrt{G/g}\,J$ and $(j^{-1}\,x^k{}_{,K})_{,k} = 0$. Regarding $\mathbf{T}^K = \mathbf{T}^K(\mathbf{X}, t)$, this becomes

$$\frac{1}{\sqrt{g}}(\sqrt{g}\,\mathbf{t}^k)_{,k} = \frac{1}{J\sqrt{G}}(\sqrt{G}\,\mathbf{T}^K)_{,K}$$

The introduction of this into (32.7) gives the expression of Cauchy's first law expressed in the reference state.

$$\text{(34.4)} \qquad \frac{1}{\sqrt{G}}(\sqrt{G}\,\mathbf{T}^K)_{,K} + \rho_0 J\,(\mathbf{f} - \mathbf{a}) = 0$$

This result also follows by expressing the equation of global balance of linear momentum (32.1) in material coordinates.

Piola introduced the pseudostresses $T^{Kl}$ and $T^{KL}$ by[1]

$$\text{(34.5)} \qquad \mathbf{T}^K = T^{Kl}\,\mathbf{g}_l \equiv T^{KL}\,x^l{}_{,L}\,\mathbf{g}_l$$

Through $(34.3)_2$ and $(31.5)_2$

$$\text{(34.6)} \qquad T^{Kl} = J X^K{}_{,k}\,t^{kl}$$

$$\text{(34.7)} \qquad T^{KL} = T^{Kl}\,X^L{}_{,l} = J\,X^K{}_{,k}\,X^L{}_{,l}\,t^{kl}$$

From (34.1) and (34.5) it may be seen that $\|T^{Kl}\|$ gives the stress at $\mathbf{x}$ measured per unit area at $\mathbf{X}$. In terms of the components $T^{Kl}$(34.4) reads

$$T^{Kk}{}_{,K} + T^{Km}\begin{Bmatrix} k \\ ml \end{Bmatrix} x^l{}_{,K} + T^{Kk}\begin{Bmatrix} L \\ LK \end{Bmatrix} + \rho_0\,(f^k - a^k) = 0$$

We may express this in a more concise form

$$\text{(34.8)} \qquad T^{Kk}{}_{:K} + \rho_0\,(f^k - a^k) = 0$$

by introducing the concept of *total covariant differentiation* of any *two-point tensor field* $A^{Kk}(\mathbf{X}, \mathbf{x})$ as defined in Appendix A6.

$$A^{Kk}{}_{:L} \equiv A^{Kk}{}_{,L} + \begin{Bmatrix} K \\ ML \end{Bmatrix} A^{Mk} + \left(A^{Kk}{}_{,l} + \begin{Bmatrix} k \\ ml \end{Bmatrix} A^{Km}\right) x^l{}_{,L}$$

Note that in (34.8) $T^{Kk} = T^{Kk}(\mathbf{X})$.

Cauchy's second law for zero body couples and couple stresses (nonpolar case) takes the complicated form

$$\text{(34.9)} \qquad T^{Kk}\,x^m{}_{,K} = T^{Km}\,x^k{}_{,K}$$

[1] [1833; 1836; 1848, secs. 34–38]. See also Kirchhoff [1852, 763–764], E. and F. Cosserat [1896, sec. 15], Trefftz [1931], and Brillouin [1925, sec. 7; 1928, 11].

Cauchy's laws in terms of $T^{KL}$ become

$$(34.10)\quad (T^{KL}\, x^k{}_{,L})_{,K} + \left(\begin{Bmatrix} k \\ ml \end{Bmatrix} x^m{}_{,L}\, x^l{}_{,K} + \begin{Bmatrix} M \\ MK \end{Bmatrix} x^k{}_{,L}\right) T^{KL} + \rho_0\,(f^k - a^k) = 0$$

$$T^{KL} = T^{LK}$$

For theories of small deformations (34.8) and (34.10) may be used to obtain approximate equations of simpler character in the reference state. Since during the deformation the surface of the body is changing, the boundary conditions on the deforming surface of the body constitute a nonlinear set that depends on the unknown dependent variable, the displacement vector **u**. When the boundary-value problem is formulated in the reference state, since the surface of the body is known, this difficulty does not arise. However, Cauchy's laws now take more complicated forms. It is not difficult to see that[2] for the linear theory (theory of infinitesimal deformations) *the difference between Cauchy's laws expressed in the reference state and those in eulerian forms disappears.*

## 35. STRESS FLUX

Experiments indicate that it is quite common for the dynamical behavior of materials to depend on the time rate of change of stress. The stress rate, in a fashion similar to strain rate, may be defined by

$$(35.1)\qquad \dot{t}^k{}_l \equiv \frac{Dt^k{}_l}{Dt}$$

The material properties, however, cannot depend on the stress rate defined by (35.1), for the stress rate so defined is not *objective.* We should now like to find an objective tensor that can replace (35.1). This tensor will be called *stress flux.*

According to the axiom of objectivity defined in Art. 27, a properly defined stress flux $\hat{t}^k{}_l$ in objectively equivalent motions must transform as[1]

$$(35.2)\qquad \hat{t}'^k{}_l = Q^k{}_m\, Q_l{}^n\, \hat{t}^m{}_n \qquad \text{or} \qquad \hat{\mathbf{t}}' = \mathbf{Q}\,\mathbf{t}\,\mathbf{Q}^T$$

Now the stress tensor $t^k{}_l$ is objective. Hence its values in equivalent motions (27.5) are related to each other by

$$(35.3)\qquad t'^k{}_l = Q^k{}_m\, Q_l{}^n\, t^m{}_n$$

If we take the material derivative of both sides of (35.3), we find

$$(35.4)\qquad \dot{t}'^k{}_l = \dot{t}^m{}_n\, Q^k{}_m\, Q_l{}^n + t^m{}_n\, \dot{Q}^k{}_m\, Q_l{}^n + t^m{}_n\, Q^k{}_m\, \dot{Q}_l{}^n$$

[2] Eringen [1963].

[1] The coordinate form $(35.2)_1$ refers to rectangular coordinates (see Art. 27 for a discussion of this restriction).

From this by use of (27.15) we eliminate $\dot{\mathbf{Q}}$. Hence

$$\dot{t}'^k{}_l + t'^k{}_m w'^m{}_l - t'^m{}_l w'^k{}_m = (\dot{t}^m{}_n + t^m{}_r w^r{}_n - t^r{}_n w^m{}_r) Q^k{}_m Q_l{}^n$$

This shows that (35.2) is satisfied if we define the stress flux as

$$\hat{t}^k{}_l \equiv \dot{t}^k{}_l + t^k{}_m w^m{}_l - t^m{}_l w^k{}_m \tag{35.5}$$

This definition is *not* unique. It is possible to find other expressions that satisfy the principle of objectivity. For example, four other possible expressions for the stress flux, that are objective, are obtained by replacing $\dot{\mathbf{Q}}$ in (35.4) by its various expressions given by (27.16)

$$\begin{aligned}
\hat{t}^k{}_l &= \dot{t}^k{}_l + t^m{}_l v_{m;}{}^k + t^k{}_m v^m{}_{;l} \\
\hat{t}^k{}_l &= \dot{t}^k{}_l - t^m{}_l v^k{}_{;m} - t^k{}_m v_{l;}{}^m \\
\hat{t}^k{}_l &= \dot{t}^k{}_l - t^m{}_l v^k{}_{;m} + t^k{}_m v^m{}_{;l} \\
\hat{t}^k{}_l &= \dot{t}^k{}_l + t^m{}_l v_{m;}{}^k - t^k{}_m v_{l;}{}^m
\end{aligned} \tag{35.6}$$

All of these satisfy (35.2). Still other permissible expressions different from those given above can be found.[2]

[2] For additional discussion and references see Arts. 27 and 72. For higher-order stress flux see Art. 93.

# 4

# ENERGY AND ENTROPY

## 36. SCOPE OF THE CHAPTER

The present chapter is devoted to the concepts of energy and entropy. The principle of conservation of energy treated in Art. 37 constitutes a fundamental postulate of physics. It generalizes the first law of thermostatics to include dynamical and dissipative systems. The discoveries in modern physics (e.g., theory of relativity) have shown that this axiom is not violated even though the principles of classical mechanics are violated. For example, the conservation of mass at extreme velocities near the speed of light is violated, but the energy conservation is not. Potential energy and strain energy are defined in Art. 38, and the transition from the energy principle to the more restricted first law of classical thermodynamics is shown.

The concept of entropy is fundamentally akin to the concepts of heat and temperature. Continuum mechanics is always darkened with thermal clouds. While an adequate theory of thermodynamics for the treatment of large thermal changes does not exist, nevertheless the problems and difficulties that it brings to mechanical systems cannot be avoided. Article 39 is devoted to such concepts accompanying the entropy as thermodynamic states, temperature, thermodynamic tensions, thermodynamic paths, specific heat, etc. Irreversible thermodynamics has recently found new applications to the foundations through the concept of entropy production. Thermodynamic stress, dissipative stress, the principle of inadmissibility of decreasing entropy, and the Clausius-Duhem inequality are to be found in Art. 40. In the last article we give the concept of thermodynamic and mechanical equilibrium and show how the principle of virtual work together with the condition of thermal equilibrium can lead to a special form of Cauchy's first law and to the boundary condition. In nondissipative systems this approach often finds a convenient and unified method of formulation (cf. Chap. 11).

## 37. PRINCIPLE OF CONSERVATION OF ENERGY

Global conservation of energy has already been formulated in Art. 26. According to this the time rate of change of kinetic energy $\mathcal{K}$ and internal energy $\mathcal{E}$ is equal to the sum of work $\mathcal{W}$ done upon the body by the external forces per unit time and the sum of other energies $\mathcal{U}_\alpha$ per unit time. This is expressed by (26.12), i.e.,

$$\dot{\mathcal{K}} + \dot{\mathcal{E}} = \mathcal{W} + \sum_\alpha \mathcal{U}_\alpha \tag{37.1}$$

Among the various types of energies we may cite *heat energy, chemical energy, electrical energy,* etc. To simplify the treatment here, we consider only heat energy.

*Interconvertibility* of heat $Q$ and mechanical energy was known to Carnot [1824–1832] and was formulated clearly by Joule [1843]. In thermodynamics the global balance of energy

$$\dot{\mathcal{K}} + \dot{\mathcal{E}} = \mathcal{W} + Q \tag{37.2}$$

is known as the *first law* of thermodynamics.

The heat input $Q$ in (37.2) is measured in mechanical units and has the same dimension as the mechanical power $\mathcal{W}$, namely,

$$[Q] = [\mathcal{W}] = \frac{\text{force} \times \text{distance}}{\text{time}} = \frac{ML^2}{T^3}$$

where $M$ is the mass unit, $L$ is the distance, and $T$ is the time. In CGS units the measure of mechanical power is erg/sec = dyne cm/sec. In English units lb ft/sec is in common use.

For a continuous mass medium $\mathcal{V} + \mathcal{S}$ for the kinetic and internal energies, we write

$$\mathcal{K} = \tfrac{1}{2} \int_{\mathcal{V}} \rho\, v_p v^p \, dv \qquad \mathcal{E} = \int_{\mathcal{V}} \rho\, \epsilon \, dv \tag{37.3}$$

where $\epsilon$ is the *internal energy density* per unit mass, $\mathbf{v}$ is the velocity vector, and $\rho$ is the mass density. The mechanical power consists of the work done by the surface tractions, surface couples, the body force, and body couples, i.e.,

$$\mathcal{W} = \oint_{\mathcal{S}} (t^{rp} v_p - m^{rpq} w_{pq})\, da_r + \int_{\mathcal{V}} \rho\, (f^p v_p - l^{pq} w_{pq})\, dv \tag{37.4}$$

The stress tensor $t^{rp}$ and the couple stress $m^{rpq}$ were defined in Art. 31, and the body couple $l^{pq}$ was introduced in Art. 32. Also $f^p$ is the body force and $w_{pq}$ is the spin tensor defined in Art. 21. The heat input consists of a *flux of heat* $q^p$ through the surface $\mathcal{S}$ into $\mathcal{V}$ and the *supply of energy* per unit mass, $h$, created by distributed energy sources in the body.

Hence

$$Q = \oint_{\mathcal{S}} q^p \, da_p + \int_{\mathcal{V}} \rho h \, dv \tag{37.5}$$

We now calculate each term of (37.2). For this we carry out the operation $D/Dt$ inside the integrals of $\mathcal{K}$ and $\mathcal{E}$ and convert the surface integrals of $\mathcal{W}$ and $Q$ into volume integrals by use of the Green-Gauss theorem. Hence

$$\begin{aligned}
\dot{\mathcal{K}} &= \int_{\mathcal{V}} \left[ \rho \, a^p v_p \, dv + \tfrac{1}{2} v^p v_p \frac{D}{Dt} (\rho \, dv) \right] \\
\dot{\mathcal{E}} &= \int_{\mathcal{V}} \left[ \rho \, \dot{\epsilon} \, dv + \epsilon \frac{D}{Dt} (\rho \, dv) \right] \\
\mathcal{W} &= \int_{\mathcal{V}} [t^{rp}{}_{;r} v_p + t^{rp} v_{p;r} - m^{rpq}{}_{;r} w_{pq} - m^{rpq} w_{pq;r} \\
&\qquad + \rho (f^p v_p - l^{pq} w_{pq})] \, dv \\
Q &= \int (q^p{}_{;p} + \rho h) \, dv
\end{aligned} \tag{37.6}$$

Now write $v_{p;r} = d_{pr} + w_{pr}$ in the expression $\mathcal{W}$. Hence

$$\begin{aligned}
\mathcal{W} = \int_{\mathcal{V}} [(t^{rp}{}_{;r} + \rho f^p) v_p - (t^{[pq]} + m^{rpq}{}_{;r} + \rho \, l^{pq}) w_{pq} \\
+ (t^{(rp)} d_{pr} - m^{rpq} w_{pq;r})] \, dv
\end{aligned} \tag{37.7}$$

Upon carrying these expressions into (37.2) and rearranging terms, we get

$$\begin{aligned}
&\int_{\mathcal{V}} [\rho \, \dot{\epsilon} - t^{(pr)} d_{rp} + m^{rpq} w_{pq;r} - q^p{}_{;p} - \rho h] \, dv \\
&= \int_{\mathcal{V}} (-\tfrac{1}{2} v^p v_p - \epsilon) \frac{D}{Dt} (\rho \, dv) + \int_{\mathcal{V}} v_p (t^{rp}{}_{;r} + \rho f^p - \rho a^p) \, dv \\
&\qquad - \int_{\mathcal{V}} w_{pq} (t^{[pq]} + m^{rpq}{}_{;r} + \rho \, l^{pq}) \, dv
\end{aligned} \tag{37.8}$$

This is the final expression of the global conservation of energy. When the energy is balanced for arbitrarily small volume elements, we have the *local* conservation of energy. In this case the integrals of (37.8) may be dropped. Note also that the integrand of each integral on the right vanishes on account of local conservation of mass, balance of momentum and moment of momentum, thus reducing (37.8) to

$$\rho \, \dot{\epsilon} = t^{(pq)} d_{pq} - m^{rpq} w_{pq;r} + q^p{}_{;p} + \rho h \tag{37.9}$$

This is the differential equation of the *local energy balance.*[1] For the

[1] Surface distribution of energy is not incorporated here. For this another flux term similar to $q^p{}_{;p}$ may be added to (37.9).

npolar case (vanishing couple stress and body couple) (37.9) further luces to

'.10) $$\rho\,\dot{\epsilon} = t^{pq}\,d_{pq} + q^{p}{}_{;p} + \rho\,h$$

ce in this case we have $t^{(pq)} = t^{pq}$. Hence the mechanical energy

'.11) $$\phi = t^{pq}\,d_{pq}$$

ılso called the *stress power.*

POTENTIAL ENERGY, STRAIN ENERGY

Global conservation of energy may be put into a more familiar form a special case when the external forces $f_p$ are steady and derivable m a potential $U\,(\mathbf{x})$, i.e.,

.1) $$f_p = -U_{,p}$$

r simplicity consider the nonpolar case. Upon substituting this into '.4), we get

.2) $$\mathcal{W} = \oint_{\mathcal{S}} t^{rp}\,v_p\,da_r - \int_{\mathcal{V}} \rho\,U_{,p}\,v^p\,dv$$

we set

.3) $$\mathcal{U} = \int_{\mathcal{V}} \rho\,U\,dv$$

n clearly

$$\dot{\mathcal{U}} = \frac{D}{Dt}\int_{\mathcal{V}} \rho\,U\,dv = \int_{\mathcal{V}} \rho\,\dot{U}\,dv = \int_{\mathcal{V}} \rho\,U_{,p}\,v^p\,dv$$

nsequently (38.2) may also be written as

.4) $$\mathcal{W} = \oint_{\mathcal{S}} t^{rp}\,v_p\,da_r - \dot{\mathcal{U}}$$

uation (37.2) may therefore be written as

.5) $$\dot{\mathcal{K}} + \dot{\mathcal{E}} + \dot{\mathcal{U}} = \oint_{\mathcal{S}} t^{rp}\,v_p\,da_r + Q$$

ıen the right side of this equation is zero, we get a *theorem of mechanical rgy conservation; namely, the sum of global kinetic, internal, and potential rgies is constant,* i.e.,

$$\mathcal{K} + \mathcal{E} + \mathcal{U} = \text{const}$$

Among many possibilities we see that this is valid when

1. *The body is insulated,* i.e., $Q = 0$; and
2. *Either surface tractions or surface velocities are zero* (*more general when they are orthogonal to each other*).

This, of course, is a special situation.

Consider now the general case of global energy conservation (37.
It is reasonable to assume that the stress tensor is divisible into two par

$$\mathbf{t} = {}_E\mathbf{t} + {}_D\mathbf{t} \tag{38.6}$$

of which ${}_E\mathbf{t}$ is the *reversible* part of the stress, which will be called t *hyperelastic stress,* and ${}_D\mathbf{t}$ is the *irreversible* or *dissipative* part. Hen ${}_E\mathbf{t}$ is defined as being derivable from a potential called the *strain ener function* $\tau\,(x^k{}_{,K})$ so that

$$\rho\,\dot{\tau} = {}_E t^{pq}\,d_{pq} \tag{38.7}$$

We now substitute (38.6) and (38.7) into (37.10) and integrate it ov the volume. Hence

$$\int_{\mathcal{V}} \rho\,\dot{\epsilon}\,dv = \int_{\mathcal{V}} \rho\,\dot{\tau}\,dv + \int_{\mathcal{V}} {}_D t^{pq}\,d_{pq}\,dv + \int_{\mathcal{V}} (q^p{}_{;p} + \rho\,h)\,dv$$

This may also be written as

$$\dot{\mathcal{E}} = \dot{\mathfrak{I}} + \mathfrak{D} + Q \tag{38.8}$$

where $\mathcal{E}$ and $Q$ are the total internal energy and the heat energy, anc and $\mathfrak{D}$ are the *total strain energy* and the *total dissipative power* defined

$$\mathfrak{I} \equiv \int_{\mathcal{V}} \rho\,\tau\,dv \qquad \mathfrak{D} \equiv \int_{\mathcal{V}} {}_D t^{pq}\,d_{pq}\,dv \tag{38.9}$$

Equation (38.8) states that *the time rate of strain energy, the dissipat power, and the heat energy produce the change in the internal energy.* Th is but another form of the statement of the axiom of global conservati of energy.

It is not difficult to show that Piola's stress ${}_E T^K{}_k$ given by

$${}_E T^K{}_k = \rho_0\,\frac{\partial \tau}{\partial x^k{}_{,K}} \tag{38.10}$$

satisfies (38.7). To see this, we recall (34.6), from which we solve for

$$t^{kl} = \frac{\rho}{\rho_0}\,T^{Kl}\,x^k{}_{,K} \tag{38.11}$$

since $J = \rho_0/\rho$. Now

$${}_E t^{kl}\,d_{lk} = {}_E t^{kl}\,v_{l;k} = \frac{\rho}{\rho_0}\,{}_E T^{Kl}\,x^k{}_{,K}\,v_{l;k} = \frac{\rho}{\rho_0}\,{}_E T^K{}_l\,\frac{D}{Dt}\,(x^l{}_{,K})$$

here we used $(19.1)_1$. Upon substituting (38.10) into this, we get 8.7). Through (38.10) and (38.11) we also write

8.12) $$_E t^k{}_l = \rho\, x^k{}_{,K} \frac{\partial \tau}{\partial x^l{}_{,K}}$$

A special case for the strain energy is

8.13) $$\tau = \tau(J) = \tau\left(\frac{\rho_0}{\rho}\right)$$

or this case, using the dual of (19.8) for $J$ in

$$_E t^k{}_l = \rho\, x^k{}_{,K} \frac{\partial \tau}{\partial J} \frac{\partial J}{\partial x^l{}_{,K}} = \rho\, x^k{}_{,K} \frac{\partial \tau}{\partial J} J\, X^K{}_{,l}$$

get

8.14) $$_E t^k{}_l = -\pi\, \delta^k{}_l$$

here

8.15) $$\pi(J) \equiv -\rho_0 \frac{\partial \tau}{\partial J}$$

the elastic *hydrostatic* pressure. Conversely (38.14) implies (38.13). this particular case (38.7) reduces to

8.16) $$\rho\, \dot{\tau} = -\pi\, v^k{}_{;k}$$

sing $(19.10)_1$, we see that

8.17) $$\dot{\mathfrak{Z}} = -\int_{\mathfrak{V}} \pi \frac{D}{Dt}(dv)$$

In the general case the stress tensor may be divided into a pressure $\bar{p}$ d a deviatoric part $\bar{t}^{kl}$, i.e.,

8.18) $$t^k{}_l = -\bar{p}\, \delta^k{}_l + \bar{t}^k{}_l$$

here

8.19) $$\bar{p} = -\frac{I_t}{3} \qquad \bar{t}^k{}_k = 0$$

he stress power now becomes

$$\phi = t^{kl} d_{lk} = -\bar{p}\, v^k{}_{;k} + \bar{t}^{kl} d_{lk}$$

hen the deviatoric part vanishes, for the case of $\bar{p} = \pi$, we see that $= \rho\, \dot{\tau}$.

Finally we may deduce the first principle of thermostatics from the regoing results. Classical thermostatics deals with homogeneous systems. It assumes that the stress consists of a purely hydrostat pressure $p$ that is constant. We may generally take $\pi = p(t)$ to be function of time so that more general processes can be included. Fro (38.17) it now follows that

$$d\mathfrak{I} = -p\,dv \tag{38.20}$$

In classical thermostatics the dissipative energy $\mathfrak{D} = 0$. Multiplyin both sides of (38.8) by $dt$, we get

$$d\mathcal{E} = -p\,dv + \delta\mathfrak{Q} \tag{38.21}$$

where we have written

$$d\mathcal{E} = \dot{\mathcal{E}}\,dt \qquad \delta\mathfrak{Q} \equiv Q\,dt \tag{38.22}$$

with the interpretations that all variations are considered time-ind pendent and that they are changes between neighboring states.

Equation (38.21) is the well-known expression of the first principle thermostatics. Its limitation is now clear from the fact that

1. The dissipative part of stress is neglected.
2. The nondissipative part of stress consists of hydrostatic pressure
3. The system is uniform and time-independent. This last restrictio is the most critical one.

If we try to incorporate the dissipative stress power into (38.21), w may be forced into considering the effect of dynamical forces, since the give rise to dissipative power. Let us multiply (37.2) by $dt$ and write a equation of the form (38.21). The result involves an extra term, how ever, the change of kinetic energy, which is definitely out of the realm classical thermostatics.

## 39. ENTROPY

The introduction of the concept of entropy into thermostatics stem from a desire to write $\delta\mathfrak{Q}$ as a differential so that (38.21) may take differential form

$$d\mathcal{E} = -p\,dv + \theta\,dH \tag{39.1}$$

where $H$ is called *total entropy* and $\theta$ is the *absolute temperature*. Thus on searches for the conditions under which we are allowed to write

$$\frac{\delta\mathfrak{Q}}{\theta} = dH \tag{39.2}$$

[1] This is not essential, and a more general case of elastic stress may be incorporate by replacing (38.21) by $d\mathcal{E} = \delta\mathfrak{W} + \delta\mathfrak{Q}$.

ıat is, for what types of changes does an integration factor $1/\theta$ exist so at $\frac{\delta \mathfrak{Q}}{\theta}$ may be written as a total differential? This question was ·gantly answered by a theorem due to Caratheodory [1909, 1925].[1] ıratheodory derived the concept of temperature and entropy by using e concept of *thermal equilibrium* and the assumption that for any state ere is an arbitrarily near state that the system cannot reach without pending work. For nonequilibrium processes, which are natural ther than being exceptional, all attempts to define entropy immediately ce great difficulties. A careful reflection will immediately show that e primary complications stem from trying to define a state function lled entropy from its limiting value at the state of equilibrium. Matheıtically it is clear that properties of a function at its limit point are dom adequate for its complete description. If, on the other hand, the nction is known by a linearization process, its behavior near its limit int may be obtained clearly. Presently there is no adequate theory of *·eversible* thermodynamics which yields the indicated linearizations.[2] ·cause of these difficulties some writers start with the concept of entropy the primitive and build the thermodynamics from this premise.[3] For e present treatment we find this approach safer than the traditional one ually found in textbooks on thermodynamics.

*Thermodynamic States.* The total of $n + 1$ independent parameters $\nu_\alpha$ $(\alpha = 1, 2, \ldots, n)$ that influence the internal energy density $\epsilon$ at a ıce and time is called the *thermodynamic state.* The parameters $\nu_\alpha$ have e dimension of mechanical and electrical units, and the dimension of $\eta$ *independent* of those of $\nu_\alpha$ and has the dimension of *energy per unit nperature per unit mass.* The parameter $\eta$ so singled out is called the *ecific entropy* or *entropy density* (entropy per unit mass).

The basic assumption of thermodynamics is that the thermodynamic ıte, $\eta$ and $\nu_\alpha$, is sufficient to determine $\epsilon$, independent of time, place,

[1] In this connection see also Born [1921], Ehrenfest-Afanassjewa [1925], Mimura 31], and Whaples [1952].

[2] A large class of recent studies in irreversible thermodynamics is concerned with linear constitutive relations between forces and fluxes. The coefficients appearing these relations are assumed to be symmetric tensors (Onsager relations). By use the classical Gibbs equation one then calculates the "entropy production." The ɜrature on the subject is extensive. For a clear physical treatment of discrete stems see De Groot [1952] and Prigogine [1947]. A comprehensive early treatment continuum physics is due to Jaumann [1911] and Lohr [1917]. For more recent rks see Biot [1955] and Eringen [1960]. For a discussion of discrete and continuum ɜories see Eringen [1963].

[3] See, for instance, Gibbs [1873, p. 31], Hilbert [1907, pp. 435–438], Eckart [1940], d Meixner [1941, art. 3; 1943, art. 2]. The present article follows the essential ideas pressed in Truesdell and Toupin [1960, chap. E II]. For an axiomatic approach thermostatics see Coleman and Noll [1959*a*].

motion, and stress. This is expressed by

$$\epsilon = \epsilon\,(\eta, \mathbf{v}, \mathbf{X}) \tag{39.3}$$

The parameters $\eta$ and $\nu_\alpha$ may depend on time and place or motion, i.e

$$\eta = \eta\,(\mathbf{x}, t) \qquad \mathbf{v} = \mathbf{v}\,(\mathbf{x}, t) \tag{39.4}$$

Therefore for a given motion $\mathbf{x} = \mathbf{x}\,(\mathbf{X}, t)$ we will, in general, hav $\epsilon = \epsilon\,(\mathbf{X}, t)$. However, $\epsilon$ according to functional form (39.3) is completel characterized without regard to motion and time. Note that, so far, th only distinct character of $\eta$ is its *dimensional independence* from $\mathbf{v}$. I other words, mechanical and electrical parameters are not sufficient characterize completely the internal energy density $\epsilon$. Hence th additional parameter is introduced to complete the specification. Th functional form of (39.3) depends on the given substance. A system said to be thermodynamically *homogeneous* if $\epsilon$ is independent of $\mathbf{X}$.

*Temperature and Thermodynamic Tensions. Temperature* $\theta$ ar *thermodynamic tensions* $\tau_\alpha$ are defined by

$$\theta \equiv \frac{\partial \epsilon}{\partial \eta} \qquad \tau^\alpha \equiv \frac{\partial \epsilon}{\partial \nu_\alpha} \tag{39.5}$$

Hence for any arbitrary change of thermodynamic state of a give particle $\mathbf{X}$, we have

$$d\epsilon = \theta\, d\eta + \tau^\alpha\, d\nu_\alpha \tag{39.6}$$

This is known as the Gibbs equation, obtained by Gibbs [1873] for a speci system. When $\nu_1 = 1/\rho$ is the specific volume, then $-\tau^1$ is the *therm dynamic pressure.* For a mixture, if $\nu_2, \nu_3, \ldots$ are taken as the co centrations of the constituents of the mixture, the corresponding tensio $\tau^\alpha$ are called *chemical potentials.*

For a fixed particle, $\mathbf{X}$ = fixed, from (39.6) we also have

$$\dot{\epsilon} = \theta\,\dot{\eta} + \tau^\alpha\,\dot{\nu}_\alpha \tag{39.7}$$

From the definitions (39.5) it immediately follows that

$$\theta = \theta\,(\eta, \mathbf{v}, \mathbf{X}) \qquad \tau^\alpha = \tau^\alpha\,(\eta, \mathbf{v}, \mathbf{X}) \tag{39.8}$$

It is possible to select $\theta$ as a new state variable to replace $\eta$, i.e.,

$$\eta = \eta\,(\theta, \mathbf{v}, \mathbf{X}) \tag{39.9}$$

Substitution of this into (39.3) gives

$$\epsilon = \epsilon\,(\theta, \mathbf{v}, \mathbf{X}) \tag{39.10}$$

d substitution into $(39.8)_2$ gives

$$\tau^\alpha = \tau^\alpha(\theta, \mathbf{v}, \mathbf{X}) \qquad \text{or} \qquad \nu_\alpha = \nu_\alpha(\theta, \boldsymbol{\tau}, \mathbf{X}) \tag{39.11}$$

quations (39.11) are known as the *thermal equations of state.* The ange of variables of this type and the interrelations obtained among the ferentials of various state variables occupy the whole body of classical ermodynamics.

*Thermodynamic Path.* For a given particle $\mathbf{X}$, $\eta = \eta(\lambda)$, $\mathbf{v} = \mathbf{v}(\lambda)$ fine a *thermodynamic path* in the space of thermodynamic state $\eta$, $\mathbf{v}$. e paths on which $\eta = \text{const}$ are called *isentropic,* and those with $=$ const are called *isothermal.*

*Specific heat* $\kappa$ and *latent heats* $\lambda_\alpha$ and $\mu_\alpha$ for a given particle $\mathbf{X}$ are spectively defined by

$$\kappa \equiv \frac{\delta q}{d\theta} = \frac{1}{\dot\theta}(\dot\epsilon - \tau^\beta \dot\nu_\beta) \tag{39.12}$$

$$\lambda_\alpha \equiv \frac{\delta q}{d\tau^\alpha} = \frac{1}{\dot\tau^\alpha}(\dot\epsilon - \tau^\beta \dot\nu_\beta) \tag{39.13}$$

$$\mu_\alpha \equiv \frac{\delta q}{d\nu_\alpha} = \frac{1}{\dot\nu_\alpha}(\dot\epsilon - \tau^\beta \dot\nu_\beta) \tag{39.14}$$

Since $\mathbf{X}$ is fixed, by writing $\lambda = \lambda(t)$ on a thermodynamic path $P$, we ay also write

$$\kappa = \frac{1}{d\theta_P}(d\epsilon_P - \tau^\beta\, d\nu_{\beta P}) = \theta\frac{d\eta_P}{d\theta_P} \tag{39.15}$$

$$\lambda_\alpha = \frac{1}{d\tau^\alpha_P}(d\epsilon_P - \tau^\beta\, d\nu_{\beta P}) = \theta\frac{d\eta_P}{d\tau^\alpha_P} \tag{39.16}$$

$$\mu_\alpha = \frac{1}{d\nu_{\alpha P}}(d\epsilon_P - \tau^\beta\, d\nu_{\beta P}) = \theta\frac{d\eta_P}{d\nu_{\alpha P}} \tag{39.17}$$

here we used (39.6) to get the extreme right of these expressions. For easurement purposes it is convenient to keep $\mathbf{v} = \text{const}$ or $\boldsymbol{\tau} = \text{const}$. hus the specific heat at constant *substate* $\mathbf{v}$ follows from

$$\kappa_\nu = \left(\frac{\partial\epsilon}{\partial\theta}\right)_{\mathbf{v}} \tag{39.18}$$

o determine the specific heat at constant tension $\kappa_\tau$, we regard $\epsilon$ as a nction of $\theta$ and $\nu$. Hence through (39.18) we write

$$\kappa = \frac{1}{d\theta_P}\left\{\left(\frac{\partial\epsilon}{\partial\theta}\right)_{\mathbf{v}} d\theta_P + \left[\left(\frac{\partial\epsilon}{\partial\nu_\beta}\right)_{\theta,\nu_\alpha} d\nu_{\beta P} - \tau^\beta\, d\nu_{\beta P}\right]\right\} \qquad (\alpha \neq \beta) \tag{39.19}$$

here a subscript attached to a partial derivative indicates that the quantity represented by the subscript is held constant, i.e.,

$$(\partial\epsilon/\partial\theta)_{\mathbf{v}} \equiv (\partial\epsilon/\partial\theta)_{\mathbf{v}=\text{const}}$$

If in (39.19) we hold tensions $\boldsymbol{\tau}$ constant, we get

$$\kappa_\tau - \kappa_\nu = \left[\left(\frac{\partial\epsilon}{\partial\nu_\beta}\right)_{\theta,\nu_\alpha} - \tau^\beta\right]\left(\frac{\partial\nu_\beta}{\partial\theta}\right)_{\boldsymbol{\tau}} \qquad (\alpha \neq \beta) \tag{39.20}$$

where $\mathbf{v}$ is regarded as given by $(39.11)_2$. In the literature the ratio specific heats

$$\gamma \equiv \frac{\kappa_\tau}{\kappa_\nu} \tag{39.21}$$

finds important applications. A more general definition of specific he and latent heat was given by Brillouin.[4]

## 40. ENTROPY PRODUCTION

A differential equation for the specific entropy is obtained if we elin nate $\dot{\epsilon}$ between (37.9) and (39.7).

$$\rho\,\theta\,\dot{\eta} = t^{(pq)}\,d_{pq} - m^{rpq}\,w_{pq;r} + q^p{}_{;p} + \rho\,h - \rho\,\tau^\alpha\,\dot{\nu}_\alpha \tag{40.1}$$

This may also be expressed as

$$\rho\,\theta\,\dot{\eta} = g_{pr}\,t^{(pq)}\,v^r{}_{;q} + m^{rp}{}_q\,v^q{}_{;pr} + q^p{}_{;p} + \rho\,h - \rho\,\tau^\alpha\,\dot{\nu}_\alpha \tag{40.2}$$

where we have used (21.1), (21.2), and $(31.10)_2$. From $(19.1)_1$ we ha

$$v^r{}_{;q} = X^K{}_{,q}\,\frac{D}{Dt}\,(x^r{}_{,K})$$

Using this, we may also derive an expression for $v^q{}_{;pr}$:

$$\begin{aligned} v^q{}_{;pr} &= \left[\frac{D}{Dt}\,(x^q{}_{,K})\,X^K{}_{,p}\right]_{;r} \\ &= \left[\frac{D}{Dt}\,(x^q{}_{,K})\right]_{;r} X^K{}_{,p} + \frac{D}{Dt}\,(x^q{}_{,K})\,X^K{}_{;pr} \\ &= \frac{D}{Dt}\,[(x^q{}_{,K})_{;m}\,x^m{}_{,L}]\,X^L{}_{,r}\,X^K{}_{,p} + \frac{D}{Dt}\,(x^q{}_{,K})\,X^K{}_{;pr} \end{aligned}$$

where the equivalence of the third line to the second line can be shown b expanding the first term in the third line and using $(19.1)_1$ and th commutation rule

$$\frac{D}{Dt}\,[(x^q{}_{,K})_{;m}] - \left[\frac{D(x^q{}_{,K})}{Dt}\right]_{;m} = -\,(x^q{}_{,K})_{;l}\,\dot{x}^l{}_{;m}$$

[4] [1888, art. 3, pp. 8–9]. A recent discussion of specific heat of an elastic solid given by Bordoni [1955].

We may thus write

$$(40.3)\qquad v^q{}_{;pr} = \frac{D}{Dt}(x^q{}_{:KL})\, X^K{}_{,p}\, X^L{}_{,r} + X^K{}_{;pr}\frac{D}{Dt}(x^q{}_{,K})$$

where

$$(40.4)\qquad x^q{}_{:KL} \equiv (x^q{}_{,K})_{;m}\, x^m{}_{,L}$$

is the total covariant derivative of $x^q{}_{,K}$ (**X**) [cf. (A6.7)]. By using $(19.1)_1$ and (40.3), Eq. (40.2) can be expressed as

$$(40.5)\qquad \rho\,\theta\,\dot{\eta} = [g_{qr}\, t^{(rk)}\, X^K{}_{,k} + m^{rp}{}_q\, X^K{}_{;pr}]\frac{D}{Dt}(x^q{}_{,K}) + m^{rp}{}_q\, X^K{}_{,p}\, X^L{}_{,r}\frac{D}{Dt}(x^q{}_{:KL}) + q^p{}_{;p} + \rho\, h - \rho\,\tau^\alpha\,\dot{\nu}_\alpha$$

So far the state variables $\nu_\alpha$ have been left unspecified. The form of (40.5) suggests that we may select the first nine parameters $\nu_\alpha$ as $x^p{}_{,K}$ and the next eighteen parameters as $x^p{}_{:KL}$ in some order. This implies that the equation of state is of the form

$$(40.6)\qquad \epsilon = \epsilon\,(\eta, x^p{}_{,K}, x^p{}_{:KL}, \nu_\gamma) \qquad (\gamma = 28, \ldots, n)$$

The corresponding first nine $\tau^\alpha$ will be labeled $\tau_p{}^K$ and the next eighteen $\tau_p{}^{KL}$ so that according to $(39.5)_2$ we have

$$(40.7)\qquad \tau_p{}^K \equiv \frac{\partial\epsilon}{\partial(x^p{}_{,K})} \qquad \tau_p{}^{KL} \equiv \frac{\partial\epsilon}{\partial(x^p{}_{:KL})} \qquad \tau^\gamma \equiv \frac{\partial\epsilon}{\partial\nu_\gamma}$$

Equation (40.5) can now be simplified to

$$(40.8)\qquad \theta\,\dot{\eta} = {}_D\tau_q{}^K\frac{D}{Dt}(x^q{}_{,K}) + {}_D\tau_q{}^{KL}\frac{D}{Dt}(x^q{}_{:KL}) + \frac{1}{\rho}\, q^p{}_{;p} + h - \sum_{\gamma=28}^{n}\tau^\gamma\,\dot{\nu}_\gamma$$

where

$$(40.9)\qquad \begin{aligned} \rho\,{}_D\tau_q{}^K &\equiv g_{qr}\, t^{(rk)}\, X^K{}_{,k} + m^{rp}{}_q\, X^K{}_{;pr} - \rho\,\tau_q{}^K \\ \rho\,{}_D\tau_q{}^{KL} &\equiv m^{rp}{}_q\, X^K{}_{,p}\, X^L{}_{,r} - \rho\,\tau_q{}^{KL} \end{aligned}$$

From the first of these we solve for $t^{(pq)}$ and from the second[1] $m^{(rp)}{}_q$:

$$(40.10)\qquad \begin{aligned} t^{(pq)} &= \rho\, g^{pk}\left(\tau_k{}^K - \frac{1}{\rho}\, m^{sr}{}_k\, X^K{}_{;rs} + {}_D\tau_k{}^K\right) x^q{}_{,K} \\ m^{(rp)}{}_q &= \rho\,(\tau_q{}^{KL} + {}_D\tau_q{}^{KL})\, x^p{}_{,K}\, x^r{}_{,L} \end{aligned}$$

[1] Note that we cannot determine $m^{[rp]}{}_q$ since the coefficient of $m^{rp}{}_q$ is symmetric in indices $p$ and $r$, an important point that apparently has not been noted before. Further discussion follows.

If we now substitute the second of these into the first, upon using the identity

$$X^K{}_{;rs} \equiv -x^k{}_{:LM}\, X^K{}_{,k}\, X^L{}_{,r}\, X^M{}_{,s}$$

which is obtained by taking the covariant derivative of the identity $x^k{}_{,K}\, X^K{}_{,r} = \delta^k{}_r$ and upon using (40.4), we find that (40.10) reduces to the form[2]

$$\begin{aligned} t^{(pq)} &= {}_Dt^{(pq)} + \rho\, g^{rp}\left(\frac{\partial\epsilon}{\partial x^r{}_{,K}}\, x^q{}_{,K} + \frac{\partial\epsilon}{\partial x^r{}_{:KL}}\, x^q{}_{:KL}\right) \\ m^{(rp)}{}_q &= {}_Dm^{(rp)}{}_q + \rho\, \frac{\partial\epsilon}{\partial x^q{}_{:KL}}\, x^p{}_{,K}\, x^r{}_{,L} \end{aligned} \tag{40.11}$$

where

$$\begin{aligned} {}_Dt^{(pq)} &\equiv \rho\, g^{rp}\, ({}_D\tau_r{}^K\, x^q{}_{,K} + {}_D\tau_r{}^{KL}\, x^q{}_{:KL}) \\ {}_Dm^{(rp)}{}_q &= \rho\, {}_D\tau_q{}^{KL}\, x^p{}_{,K}\, x^r{}_{,L} \end{aligned} \tag{40.12}$$

are the *dissipative parts* ${}_D\mathbf{t}$ and ${}_D\mathbf{m}$ of the stress $\mathbf{t}$ and couple stress $\mathbf{m}$. Thus the stress tensor and the couple stress each have a dissipative part and a recoverable part. *The recoverable parts are derivable from a potential, i.e., the internal energy density* $\epsilon$.

We may now express the differential equation of the entropy in the form

$$\rho\,\theta\,\dot\eta = {}_Dt^{(pq)}\, d_{qp} + {}_Dm^{(rq)p}\, w_{pq;r} + q^p{}_{;p} + \rho\, h - \rho \sum_{\alpha=28}^{n} \tau^\alpha\, \dot\nu_\alpha \tag{40.13}$$

which shows that *only the dissipative parts of the stress and couple stress contribute to the entropy.*

We now proceed to show the *indeterminacy of couple stress.* Referring to (32.13), we see that only the symmetric part of the stress $t^{(jk)}$ and that of the couple stress $m^{(ij)k}$ provided by the constitutive equations (40.11) enter into the equation of motion. Therefore the solution of (32.13) under appropriate boundary and initial conditions can only provide $t^{(jk)}$ and $m^{(ij)k}$. Now through (32.12) we can calculate

$$t^{[jk]} = -m^{ijk}{}_{;i} - \rho l^{jk} = -m^{(ij)k}{}_{;i} - m^{[ij]k}{}_{;i} - \rho l^{jk}$$

Therefore unless the skew-symmetric part $m^{[ij]k}$ is given, we cannot determine $t^{[ij]}$. Conversely the determination of $m^{[ij]k}$ requires the knowledge of $t^{[ij]}$. No other constitutive equations are available for either. Thus the couple stress is *not* fully determinate. Note, however, that the skew-symmetric parts of stress and couple stress are not essential in the determination of the displacement field.

[2] This result, which generalizes the work of E. and F. Cosserat [1909, arts. 53–55], in essence was obtained by Hellinger [1914, art. 7b]. An analysis based on irreversible thermodynamics was given by Eringen [1960].

The situation is further clarified if we list the *eight* independent components of $m^{(rp)q}$ given by (40.11). They are

$$\begin{matrix} m^{112} & m^{221} & m^{331} & m^{(23)1} \\ m^{113} & m^{223} & m^{332} & m^{(13)2} \end{matrix}$$

Since there are *nine* $m^{pqr}$ and no corresponding equation, the couple stress is not fully determinate. It is consistent with the concept of couple stress to introduce into mechanics a skew-symmetric second-order tensor, which may be called *intrinsic angular momentum* $\rho\boldsymbol{\sigma}$ or *spin inertia* $\rho\dot{\boldsymbol{\sigma}}$, such that Cauchy's second law (32.12) is modified as

$$m^{kij}{}_{;k} + \rho l^{ij} + t^{[ij]} = \rho\dot{\sigma}^{ij}$$

Now by using the gradients of $\boldsymbol{\sigma}$ in place of $x^k{}_{:KL}$ in $\epsilon$, we should obtain nine constitutive equations for $m$ in place of $(40.11)_1$. This latter viewpoint must at present be considered as a conjecture, awaiting future developments.

The following special cases are interesting to consider separately.

*The Nonpolar Case.* In this case we have the couple stress zero. Hence

$$t^{(pq)} = \rho\, g^{rp} \frac{\partial \epsilon}{\partial x^r{}_{,K}}\, x^q{}_{,K} + {}_Dt^{(pq)} \tag{40.14}$$

$$\rho\,\theta\,\dot{\eta} = {}_Dt^{(pq)}\, d_{pq} + q^p{}_{;p} + \rho\, h - \rho \sum_{\alpha=28}^{n} \tau^\alpha\, \dot{\nu}_\alpha \tag{40.15}$$

When the recoverable part of the stress is purely hydrostatic, we write

$$t^p{}_q = -\pi\,\delta^p{}_q + {}_Dt^p{}_q \qquad \pi \equiv -\left(\frac{\partial\epsilon}{\partial\nu}\right)_\eta \tag{40.16}$$

where $\nu = 1/\rho$ is the specific volume and $\pi$ is the corresponding *thermodynamic pressure.* The stress tensor may be expressed as

$$t^p{}_q = -\bar{p}\delta^p{}_q + \bar{t}^p{}_q \tag{40.17}$$

where $\bar{p}$ is the *mechanical pressure* and $\bar{t}$ is the *deviatoric stress,* i.e.,

$$\bar{p} = -\tfrac{1}{3}\, t^p{}_p \qquad \bar{t}^p{}_p = 0 \tag{40.18}$$

Substitution of (40.17) into (40.16) gives

$${}_Dt^p{}_q = -(\bar{p} - \pi)\,\delta^p{}_q + \bar{t}^p{}_q \tag{40.19}$$

which shows that *the excess of pressure over the thermodynamic pressure will contribute to the dissipation.* In the literature the thermodynamic and mechanical pressures are often assumed to be the same. This in the theory of stokesian fluids is known as the "Stokes assumption." The validity of this is questioned on experimental grounds (cf. Art. 48).

*Nondissipative Case.* In this case ${}_D\mathbf{t} = {}_D\mathbf{m} = 0$. Hence the stress and couple stress are given by

$$(40.20)\qquad \begin{aligned} t^{(pq)} &= \rho\, g^{rp} \left( \frac{\partial \epsilon}{\partial x^r{}_{,K}}\, x^q{}_{,K} + \frac{\partial \epsilon}{\partial x^r{}_{:KL}}\, x^q{}_{:KL} \right) \\ m^{(rp)}{}_q &= \rho\, \frac{\partial \epsilon}{\partial x^q{}_{:KL}}\, x^p{}_{,K}\, x^r{}_{,L} \end{aligned}$$

If, further, $\epsilon$ is independent of $x^p{}_{:KL}$, we get the nonpolar case, i.e.,

$$(40.21)\qquad t^{pq} = \rho\, g^{rp} \frac{\partial \epsilon}{\partial x^r{}_{,K}}\, x^q{}_{,K} \qquad m^{rp}{}_q = 0$$

According to (34.6) and since $\rho J = \rho_0$, Piola's stress is found to be

$$(40.22)\qquad T_q{}^K = \rho_0 \left( \frac{\partial \epsilon}{\partial x^q{}_{,K}} \right)_\eta$$

Thus for the nondissipative case a stress potential $\Sigma$ exists and is given by[3] $\Sigma = \rho_0\, \epsilon$. Relations of the form (40.22) are known as stress-strain relations.

*Global Entropy Production.* The global entropy production is obtained from the local entropy production (40.13) by integrating $\rho\, \dot{\eta}$ over the volume and by writing

$$\int_{\mathcal{V}} \rho\, \dot{\eta}\, dv = \frac{D}{Dt} \int_{\mathcal{V}} \rho\, \eta\, dv = \dot{H}$$

$$\int_{\mathcal{V}} \frac{1}{\theta}\, q^p{}_{;p}\, dv = \int_{\mathcal{V}} \left[ \left( \frac{q^p}{\theta} \right)_{;p} + \frac{q^p \theta_{,p}}{\theta^2} \right] dv = \oint_{\mathcal{S}} \frac{1}{\theta}\, q^p\, da_p + \int_{\mathcal{V}} \frac{q^p \theta_{,p}}{\theta^2}\, dv$$

where in the first expressions the equation of mass conservation is employed and in the second the Green-Gauss theorem is used. The global entropy production is therefore given by

$$(40.23)\qquad \dot{H} - \oint_{\mathcal{S}} \frac{q^p}{\theta}\, da_p = \int_{\mathcal{V}} \left( \Delta + \frac{\rho h}{\theta} \right) dv$$

where

$$(40.24)\qquad \theta\, \Delta \equiv {}_D t^{(pq)}\, d_{qp} + {}_D m^{(rq)p}\, w_{pq;r} + q^p (\log \theta)_{,p} - \rho \sum_{\alpha=28}^{n} \tau^\alpha\, \dot{\nu}_\alpha$$

Equation (40.23) shows that the global entropy change is due to an influx of entropy $q^p/\theta$ and to *entropy production* $(\Delta/\rho) + (h/\theta)$ created within the body. The entropy created within the body is *nonnegative;* this can be seen as follows.

[3] The existence of the stress potential for the isothermal case $\theta$ = const is usually argued by writing $\psi = \epsilon - \theta\, \eta$ in (39.7) after which equation (40.1) is written in terms of $\psi$, which for $\theta$ = const, $q^p{}_{;p} \equiv \rho\, h \equiv 0$ leads to a stress potential. For a discussion of these other cases see Eringen [1964, chap. VI].

It is an experimental fact that a system at a uniform temperature and free of heat sources will consume mechanical work; that is, the non-recoverable part of the work is *lost*, not created. This means $\theta \Delta > 0$ for $\theta = \text{const}$. Similarly for a system at rest the heat flows from hot to cold, i.e., $-q^p \theta_{,p} \leq 0$ for the body at rest. Hence

$$(40.25) \qquad \begin{aligned} &{}_Dt^{(pq)} d_{qp} + {}_Dm^{(rq)p} w_{pq;r} - \rho \sum_{\alpha=28}^{n} \tau^\alpha \dot{\nu}_\alpha \geq 0 \quad (q = 0 \text{ or } \theta = \text{const}) \\ &q^p \theta_{,p} \geq 0 \qquad \text{for } v^p \equiv 0 \qquad \text{(body at rest)} \end{aligned}$$

or in any case

$$(40.26) \qquad \theta \Delta \geq 0$$

This principle is often used as a starting point for the linear irreversible thermodynamics.[4] From (40.23), when $\theta > 0$ ($\theta$ is taken as the *absolute temperature*), upon using (40.24), there results the well-known Clausius-Duhem[5] inequality

$$(40.27) \qquad \dot{H} - \oint_{\mathcal{S}} \frac{q^p}{\theta} da_p \geq \int_{\mathcal{V}} \frac{\rho h}{\theta} dv$$

This is the expression of the *second principle* of thermostatics. It is a postulate of irreversibility which gives the trend that the physical system must follow. For the *adiabatic process* $q \equiv h \equiv 0$. This gives $\dot{H} \geq 0$, which states that *in an adiabatic process the global entropy cannot decrease.*

## 41. THERMODYNAMIC AND MECHANICAL EQUILIBRIA

A system is in *mechanical equilibrium* if in any inertial system the acceleration vanishes. In this case Cauchy's first law becomes

$$(41.1) \qquad t^{lk}{}_{;l} + \rho f^k = 0$$

and Cauchy's second law remains unchanged, i.e.,

$$(41.2) \qquad m^{rk}{}_{;r} + l^k + \epsilon^{krs} t_{rs} = 0$$

No special thermodynamical consequences result from these laws.

A system is in global (local) *thermal equilibrium* if the global (local) entropy production is zero, i.e.,

$$(41.3) \qquad \dot{H} = 0 \qquad \text{(global equilibrium)}$$

$$(41.4) \qquad \rho \dot{\eta} = 0 \qquad \text{(local equilibrium)}$$

Since the local entropy production is nonnegative, this implies that individual dissipative energies vanish separately. Hence the stress

[4] See, for instance, De Groot [1952], Biot [1955], and Eringen [1960].

[5] Clausius [1854, p. 152; 1862, art. 1; 1865, art. 1, pp. 14–17] gave the case $q = h = 0$; Duhem [1901, chap. 1, art. 6] gave the surface integral.

tensor, couple stress, and all thermodynamic tensions are *dissipation-free.* In this case according to (40.20) a stress potential $\Sigma \equiv \rho_0 \epsilon$ exists such that the stress tensor and couple stress are given by (40.20), i.e.,

$$t^{(pq)} = \frac{\rho}{\rho_0} g^{rp} \left( \frac{\partial \Sigma}{\partial x^r{}_{,K}} x^q{}_{,K} + \frac{\partial \Sigma}{\partial x^r{}_{:KL}} x^q{}_{:KL} \right) \tag{41.5}$$

$$m^{(rq)}{}_p = \frac{\rho}{\rho_0} \frac{\partial \Sigma}{\partial x^p{}_{:KL}} x^q{}_{,K} x^r{}_{,L} \tag{41.6}$$

We should like to show that for static deformations of a nondissipative medium a *principle of virtual work* may be used to derive Cauchy's first law of motion as a special case of a general criterion of equilibrium.

Consider a family of deformations $\mathbf{x} = \mathbf{x}(\mathbf{X}, \lambda)$, where $\lambda$ is a parameter. Assume that for a fixed value of $\lambda$, say $\lambda = 0$, the deformation $\mathbf{x} = \mathbf{x}(\mathbf{X}, 0)$ is given. The first variation of deformation $\delta\mathbf{x}$ is defined by

$$\delta \mathbf{x} \equiv \left. \frac{\partial \mathbf{x}}{\partial \lambda} \right|_{\lambda = 0,\ \mathbf{X} = \text{const}} d\lambda \tag{41.7}$$

For a function $f = f(x^k, x^k{}_{,K}, x^k{}_{:KL}, \ldots)$ the first variation of $f$ is defined by

$$\delta f \equiv \left. \frac{\partial f}{\partial \lambda} \right|_{\lambda = 0,\ \mathbf{X} = \text{const}} d\lambda \tag{41.8}$$

The variation symbol $\delta$ commutes with the partial derivative $\partial/\partial X^k$.

$$\delta(f_{,K}) = (\delta f)_{,K} \tag{41.9}$$

From the definition of variation it is clear that $\delta(\ )/d\lambda$ is similar to material differentiation with $\lambda$ replacing the time $t$.

We now postulate the general criterion of equilibrium as the union of the principle of virtual work and thermodynamic equilibrium.[1]

$$\delta \int_{\mathcal{V}} \rho \epsilon \, dv = \int_{\mathcal{S}} t_{(\mathbf{n})k} \, \delta x^k \, da + \int_{\mathcal{V}} \rho f_k \, \delta x^k \, dv \tag{41.10}$$

$$\delta \int_{\mathcal{V}} \rho \eta \, dv = 0 \tag{41.11}$$

subject to the condition that all variations satisfy the principle of conservation of mass.

$$\delta(\rho \, dv) = 0 \tag{41.12}$$

Physically, the left of (41.10) is the variation of the total internal energy, and the right is the work (virtual work) done by the body and surface forces in a virtual displacement $\delta\mathbf{x}$. Equation (41.11) is the expression of variation of the total entropy of the body. Now we have

[1] Here we treat the nonpolar case. There is no particular difficulty in extending this to the polar case.

$\epsilon = \epsilon(\eta, \nu_\alpha)$, so that (41.10) may be written as

$$\int_{\mathcal{V}} (\rho\,\theta\,\delta\eta + \rho\tau^\alpha\,\delta\nu_\alpha)\,dv = \oint_{\mathcal{S}} t_{(n)k}\,\delta x^k\,da + \int_{\mathcal{V}} \rho f_k\,\delta x^k\,dv \tag{41.13}$$

$$\int_{\mathcal{V}} \rho\,\delta\eta\,dv = 0$$

where (41.12) has been used. The second condition gives $\eta$ = const. In this case or in the case $\theta$ = const, (41.13) reduces to

$$\int_{\mathcal{V}} \rho\,\tau^\alpha\,\delta\nu_\alpha\,dv = \oint_{\mathcal{S}} t_{(n)k}\,\delta x^k\,da + \int_{\mathcal{V}} \rho f_k\,\delta x^k\,dv \tag{41.14}$$

When $\delta\nu_\alpha$ and $\delta x^k$ are treated as independent variations, this gives

$$\tau^\alpha = 0 \qquad t_{(n)k} = 0 \qquad f_k = 0 \tag{41.15}$$

If, however, we choose $x^k{}_{,K}$ for $\nu_\alpha$, then $\tau^\alpha$ becomes $\partial\epsilon/\partial x^k{}_{,K}$ so that (41.14) reads

$$\int_{\mathcal{V}} \rho\,\frac{\partial\epsilon}{\partial x^k{}_{,K}}\,\delta x^k{}_{,K}\,dv = \oint_{\mathcal{S}} t_{(n)k}\,\delta x^k\,da + \int_{\mathcal{V}} \rho f_k\,\delta x^k\,dv \tag{41.16}$$

By a method similar to (19.1), we can show that

$$\delta x^k{}_{,K} = (\delta x^k)_{;l}\,x^l{}_{,K} \tag{41.17}$$

Now write

$$\rho\,\frac{\partial\epsilon}{\partial x^k{}_{,K}}\,\delta x^k{}_{,K} = \left(\rho\,\frac{\partial\epsilon}{\partial x^k{}_{,K}}\,x^l{}_{,K}\,\delta x^k\right)_{;l} - \left(\rho\,\frac{\partial\epsilon}{\partial x^k{}_{,K}}\,x^l{}_{,K}\right)_{;l}\delta x^k$$

on the left of (41.16), and by using the Green-Gauss theorem, convert the first term into a surface integral. Hence

$$\int_{\mathcal{S}} \left(t_{(n)k} - \rho\,\frac{\partial\epsilon}{\partial x^k{}_{,K}}\,x^l{}_{,K}\,n_l\right)\delta x^k\,da + \int_{\mathcal{V}} \left[\left(\rho\,\frac{\partial\epsilon}{\partial x^k{}_{,K}}\,x^l{}_{,K}\right)_{;l} + \rho f_k\right]\delta x^k\,dv = 0 \tag{41.18}$$

If there are no kinematical constraints, the local condition of equilibrium follows from this:

$$\left(\rho\,\frac{\partial\epsilon}{\partial x^k{}_{,K}}\,x^l{}_{,K}\right)_{;l} + \rho f_k = 0 \qquad \text{in } \mathcal{V} \tag{41.19}$$

$$\rho\,\frac{\partial\epsilon}{\partial x^k{}_{,K}}\,x^l{}_{,K}\,n_l = t_{(n)k} \qquad \text{on } \mathcal{S} \tag{41.20}$$

Remembering the thermodynamic stresses defined by $(40.21)_1$, we may also write

$$t^l{}_{k;l} + \rho f_k = 0 \qquad \text{in } \mathcal{V} \tag{41.21}$$

$$t^l{}_k\,n_l = t_{(n)k} \qquad \text{on } \mathcal{S} \tag{41.22}$$

It is now clear that it is not inconsistent with the principles of mechanics to set

$$\rho \frac{\partial \epsilon}{\partial x^k{}_{,K}} x^l{}_{,K} = t^l{}_k \tag{41.23}$$

where $t^l{}_k$ is the stress tensor.

While the thermodynamic equilibrium with the aid of the concept of the principle of virtual work produces Cauchy's first law and boundary conditions in an elegant fashion, its limitation must not be forgotten. First of all it applies to a static situation. Second, Cauchy's second law cannot be derived by such methods. In fact, symmetry of the stress tensor requires additional considerations. Following E. and F. Cosserat [1909, art. 51] and Toupin [1956, art. 10], we can show that the *moment equation is satisfied identically if the internal energy function is invariant under a rigid rotation of the deformed body.* This constitutes a requirement of objectivity which is not included in the general thermodynamic equilibrium stated above. The proof of this theorem is given below. Suppose $\epsilon(\nu_1{}^k, \nu_2{}^k, \ldots, \nu_n{}^k)$ is a function of vector components $\nu_\Gamma{}^k$ $(\Gamma = 1, 2, \ldots, n)$, which is invariant under the substitution

$$\nu_\Gamma{}^k \to Q^k{}_l \, \nu_\Gamma{}^l$$

where $Q^k{}_l$ is an arbitrary rotation satisfying $(27.3)_2$ with

$$\det Q^k{}_l = 1$$

An infinitesimal rotation has the form $Q^k{}_l = \epsilon^k{}_l + \delta^k{}_l$, where $\epsilon^k{}_l$ is an arbitrary antisymmetric tensor. Since $\epsilon$ is to be invariant under this substitution, we must have

$$\epsilon(\nu_1{}^k, \ldots, \nu_n{}^k) = \epsilon(Q^k{}_l \, \nu_1{}^l, \ldots, Q^k{}_l \, \nu_n{}^l) = \epsilon(\bar{\nu}_1{}^k, \ldots, \bar{\nu}_n{}^k)$$

The necessary condition for this invariance is

$$d\epsilon = \frac{\partial \epsilon}{\partial \bar{\nu}_\Gamma{}^k} \frac{\partial \bar{\nu}_\Gamma{}^k}{\partial Q^m{}_n} dQ^m{}_n = 0$$

For an infinitesimal rotation this reads

$$\frac{\partial \epsilon}{\partial \nu_\Gamma{}^k} \nu_\Gamma{}^l \, \epsilon^k{}_l = 0$$

This implies that the coefficient of the antisymmetric tensor $\epsilon^k{}_l$ must be symmetric or

$$\sum_\Gamma \frac{\partial \epsilon}{\partial \nu_{\Gamma[k}} \nu_\Gamma{}^{l]} = 0 \tag{41.24}$$

It can also be shown that this condition is sufficient to ensure that $\epsilon$ is invariant to *finite* rotation. If we now recognize $\nu_\Gamma{}^k$ as $x^k{}_{,K}$, we obtain

$$\frac{\partial \epsilon}{\partial x^{[k}{}_{,K}} x^{l]}{}_{,K} = 0 \tag{41.25}$$

or since

$$t^{kl} = \rho\, g^{rk} \frac{\partial \epsilon}{\partial x^r{}_{,K}} x^l{}_{,K} = \frac{\rho}{\rho_0} g^{rk}\, T_r{}^K x^l{}_{,K}$$

we have

$$t^{kl} = t^{lk}$$

which is the proof of the theorem.

Extension of this theorem to more general cases in which couple stress exists does not present any essential difficulty. Indeed in this case

$$\epsilon = \epsilon\,(x^p{}_{,K}, x^p{}_{:KL})$$

so that (41.25) must be replaced by

$$\frac{\partial \epsilon}{\partial x^{[p}{}_{,K}} x^{q]}{}_{,K} + \frac{\partial \epsilon}{\partial x^{[p}{}_{:KL}} x^{q]}{}_{:KL} = 0 \tag{41.26}$$

As noted before, constitutive equations $(40.20)_2$ for the couple stress provide eight equations for $m^{(rp)q}$. The remaining *ten* components of $(40.20)_2$ provide additional restrictions on $\epsilon$. These are:

$$\frac{\partial \epsilon}{\partial x^k{}_{:KL}} g^{kq}\, x^{(p}{}_{,K}\, x^{r)}{}_{,L} + \frac{\partial \epsilon}{\partial x^k{}_{:KL}} g^{kr}\, x^{(q}{}_{,K}\, x^{p)}{}_{,L} + \frac{\partial \epsilon}{\partial x^k{}_{:KL}} g^{kp}\, x^{(r}{}_{,K}\, x^{q)}{}_{,L} = 0 \tag{41.27}$$

In spite of all this, we still have reservations concerning the thermodynamical approach to continuum. Cauchy's laws apply to all kinds of media under dynamical conditions. Dissipative phenomena are not excluded from the domain of applications of the principles of momentum balance. On the other hand, the concept of thermodynamic equilibrium is applicable to static situations. While an additional principle such as the Euler-D'Alembert principle may be used to drag in the inertia forces, the inclusion of viscous stresses cannot be made without additional fundamental assumptions.

The concept of thermodynamic equilibrium and the concept of energetics in the master hands of Gibbs [1875, pp. 184–190], Duhem [1911], Jaumann [1911, 1918], Lohr [1917], and others have achieved perfection and elegance to perhaps an almost undeserved degree.

Finally we refer the reader to more extensive and generalized forms of variational principles as collected by Hellinger [1914], Truesdell and Toupin [1960, chap. D.V.], and Eringen [1963].

# 5

# CONSTITUTIVE EQUATIONS

## 42. SCOPE OF THE CHAPTER

The entire content of previous chapters is applicable to any continuous medium.

Material bodies of the same mass and geometry respond to the same external effects in different ways. Internal constitution of matter is responsible for these differences. From a continuum point of view we may develop equations which reflect the gross effects of structural differences in materials. Since instruments measuring global phenomena automatically read the statistical averages, the continuum theory of constitutive equations makes sense physically. Although the science presently is far from providing a complete theory of constitutive equations that encompasses all known phenomena, various serious attempts for special types of media have already gained some acceptance by theoreticians and a small amount of successful verification by experimentalists. The general methods available for the beginning steps of a universal theory are collected in Art. 43. Invariance requirements are basic in the continuum viewpoint; a set of requirements and rules is to be found in Art. 44. The axioms of this article are used to arrive at constitutive equations for simple media, namely, elastic solids and stokesian fluids. The constitutive equations for an ideally elastic solid that possesses a stress potential are developed in Art. 45. This special elastic solid with no dissipation is called a *hyperelastic solid.* Elastic solids of more general type not possessing a stress potential constitute a large class whose constitutive equations cannot be arrived at by the approach of Green used in Art. 45. For these solids we have the method of Cauchy in Art. 46. We devote Art. 47 to isotropic bodies of both types because they play an important role in the development of the theory of elasticity. The conditions for an elastic body to become hyperelastic are given in this article [Eq. (47.34)].

To illustrate properly the methods of Art. 44, we felt the need for another example of a continuous medium. The stokesian fluids have been chosen for this. The constitutive equations, the thermodynamical and/or mechanical demands made on them, and the various types of pressures (e.g., thermodynamical, mechanical) are studied in Art. 48. Article 49 is devoted to polynomial approximations of constitutive equations. We have left to later chapters the study of constitutive equations of various other types of continuous media that are more complicated in nature. Hypoelasticity, plasticity, viscoelastic materials, and the elastic dielectric are treated in Chaps. 8 to 11.

## 43. METHODS AVAILABLE

The basic principles of conservation of mass, balance of momenta, conservation of energy, and the inadmissibility of decreasing entropy, which were laid down at the end of Chap. 2 and studied in Chaps. 3 and 4, are not sufficient to determine uniquely the unknowns involved. A counting of equations and unknowns will show that we have eight equations (one equation for conservation of mass, three for balance of linear momentum, three for balance of moment of momentum, and one for conservation of energy). These are collected below.

Conservation of mass:

$$\frac{\partial \rho}{\partial t} + (\rho\, v^i)_{;i} = 0 \tag{43.1}$$

Balance of linear momentum:

$$t^{jk}{}_{;j} + \rho\,(f^k - a^k) = 0 \tag{43.2}$$

Balance of moment of momentum:

$$m^{kij}{}_{;k} + \rho l^{ij} = -t^{[ij]} \tag{43.3}$$

Conservation of energy:

$$\rho\,\dot{\epsilon} = t^{(jk)}\, d_{kj} - m^{ljk}\, w_{jk;l} + q^k{}_{;k} + \rho\, h \tag{43.4}$$

The unknowns $\rho$, $v^i$, $t^{jk}$, $m^{ljk} = -m^{lkj}$, $q^k$ are twenty-five in number; $a^k$ and $w_{jk}$ are expressible in terms of $v^i$; and $f^k$, $l^{ij}$, $h$, and $\epsilon$ are supposed to be given, the first three being the external agents imposed on the body and $\epsilon$ determining the character of the medium. Clearly the foregoing eight equations are in general inadequate for a *unique* determination of the twenty-five unknowns involved. When electrical and chemical variables are brought into play, the situation becomes much worse. Excluding some special situations, e.g., rigid motion, the foregoing equations must be supplemented by additional equations. The need for more equations is clear from the following physical considerations also. The above basic equations are valid for any type of mechanical media. No differentiation has so far been made between various types of media, e.g., solids, liquids, and gases. Two different material bodies having the same geometry and mass distribution and subjected to identical external agents respond differently. Therefore the material properties of the medium under consideration must be brought into the mathematical scheme in some satisfactory manner. There are many possible approaches to this problem.

*The Statistical Mechanical Approach.* This approach is based on the concept that all materials are made of atomic and molecular units attached to each other by intermolecular ties. Newtonian mechanics, wave mechanics, or relativistic mechanics, and electromagnetic theory describe the behavior of these elements. The methods of statistical mechanics may therefore be employed to obtain the phenomenological behavior of materials.

This pregnant idea has given birth to such important fields as kinetic theory, transport theory, statistical mechanics, and solid-state physics. The nature of the molecular forces, however, excluding a few ideal situations, has turned out to be so complicated, and the collision mechanism of the molecular elements and their motions so intricate, that present advances in the statistical theories are primarily confined to dilute gases and the electrical properties of solids. A molecular theory for rubberlike materials has also been developed recently.[1]

A continuum theory even in these most advanced areas provides the essential guidance. The mechanical properties of materials stand as an unceasing challenge to statistical mechanics. In a continuum theory it is a natural desire to construct all fundamental equations with the basic unified philosophy appropriate to the theory.

*A Purely Mathematical Approach.* Such an approach is possible, based on the idea already expressed above; namely, that the complete set of equations should predict a *unique* outcome for the physical phenomena. This approach very quickly leads to a dead end. On the one hand, the mathematical conditions (e.g., boundary and initial equations) approximating the given physical phenomena cannot be predicted with reason-

[1] For molecular theory of gases and liquids see Chapman and Cowling [1952], Green [1952], Hirschfelder, Curtiss, and Bird [1954], and Grad [1958]; on solid state the works of Seitz [1940], Kittel [1956], and Born and Huang [1954]. An account of various aspects of the theory, including an adequate bibliography of the statistical theory of rubber elasticity, is given in the books by Treloar [1958] and Mason and Wookey [1958].

ble certainty without logical guidance from the physical formulation. On the other hand, the requirement for a unique outcome does not lead to a unique formulation. At present even for very simple situations the existence and uniqueness theorems have not been proved. The existence and uniqueness proofs should therefore be postponed until the basic field equations are well-established. Afterwards with the use of such theorems, f they exist, we can distinguish the boundary and initial conditions that yield unique solutions.

*Guidance from Thermodynamics.* Whenever temperature and heat are nvolved, the mechanical principles must be supplemented by the thermodynamical principles to provide a rational treatment for the concept of neat. The present status of thermodynamics is inadequate for treating grossly nonlinear and highly dissipative phenomena. Linear irreversible thermodynamics will probably acquire the desired rigor for explaining the inear irreversible phenomena.[2] For the treatment of finite deformation and irreversibility, however, there presently exist no thermodynamical tools. Therefore for an exact continuum theory we must revert to other channels of continuum physics. In the end, however, we must see that he principle of entropy is satisfied. Thermodynamics provides us with certain prohibitions that the outcome phenomena must satisfy. For equilibrium processes, thermodynamics may be used to obtain constitutive equations.

*Continuum Physics.* In continuum physics help and guidance must be drawn from all of the foregoing disciplines. It is not possible to develop general constitutive relations which encompass all possible special situations and materials, although some fairly general classes of materials may be brought under one set of constitutive equations. Such wide generalizations, however, often cloud the fundamental physical and mathematical deas without making any essential contribution. Unifications and generalizations carry great temptations which we must overcome for the purpose of clarity in the fundamental ideas. We shall therefore pursue the modest approach of building more complicated general cases gradually after certain ideal cases have been constructed. Thus, for example, the deally elastic body and the stokesian fluid will be treated before hypoelasticity, solids having fluid characteristics, and materials with memory are presented.

## 44. INVARIANCE REQUIREMENTS

A constitutive equation defines an *ideal material.* For the ideal material to represent a physical material adequately, certain physical principles

[2] "Theory of Continuous Media," by the present writer [1964], is written with the viewpoint of making use of the principles of linear irreversible thermodynamics in determining the phenomenological relations.

must be satisfied at the outset. We divide these principles into s
categories:

1. *Principles of exclusion*
2. *Coordinate invariance requirements*
3. *Spatial invariance requirements*
4. *Material invariance requirements*
5. *Dimensional invariance*
6. *Requirements of consistency*

1. *Principles of Exclusion.* The general rules that may be introduc for the selection of constitutive variables can neither define the entire s of independent constitutive variables nor the functional forms th acquire. They at most provide an exclusion principle by which certa variables may be disregarded. Below we enumerate a few of the principles.

1*a*. *The Principle of Heredity. The behavior of materials at time t specified in terms of the past experience of the body up to time t.* Let immediately remark that the principle of heredity is contrary to t principle of classical mechanics; for in newtonian mechanics, given t initial conditions at $t = 0$ and under very general continuity requiremen for the forces (the Lipschitz conditions), the future as well as the pa experience of the body is completely determined.

The principle of heredity provides an exclusion principle for t dependence of constitutive equations on *functionals* in the future range time. Thus, for example, we may write a functional relation between t stress and strain in the form

$$t_{ij}(\mathbf{x}, t) = f_{ij}[\epsilon_{ij}(\mathbf{x}', t')] \tag{44.1}$$

where

$$\mathbf{x}' = \mathbf{g}(\mathbf{X}, t') \qquad \mathbf{x} = \mathbf{g}(\mathbf{X}, t) \qquad (t' \leq t) \tag{44.2}$$

Accordingly it is indicated that $t_{ij}$ at the point $\mathbf{x}$ at time $t$ depends on t entire history of strain at all time $t' \leq t$ (cf. Art. 94).

1*b*. *Principle of Neighborhood. The behavior of a material point occupying the spatial point* $\mathbf{x}$ *at time t is specified in terms of the behavior an arbitrarily small neighborhood of* $\mathbf{X}$. This principle, together wi the principle of heredity, provides an exclusion principle for the depen ence on the particles that are situated far away from $\mathbf{X}$ at all times pri to $t$. These two principles may be combined into a third princip which follows.

*Principle of Determinism. The behavior of a material point* $\mathbf{X}$ *occupyi* $\mathbf{x}$ *at time t is determined by the past history of the motion of an arbitrar small neighborhood of* **X**.[1] According to this principle we may generalize (44.1) into

$$t_{ij}(\mathbf{x}, t) = f_{ij}[\mathbf{x}'(\mathbf{Z}, t'), t'] \qquad (t' \leq t)$$

where **Z** is a neighborhood of **X**, and $\mathbf{x}'(\mathbf{Z}, t')$ represents the motion of the neighborhood of **X** prior to time $t$. According to the principle of determinism, therefore, the stress at a material point **X** at time $t$ is determined once the motion of an arbitrary small neighborhood of **X** prior to time $t$ is known. Consequently *if any two motions coincide in some neighborhood* $N(\mathbf{X})$ *for all times* $t' \leq t$, *the stresses at* **X** *for these two motions are the same.*

The principle of determinism is very general in scope and certainly provides a broad principle for the mechanical constitutive equations. It is not difficult, however, to show again that it gives no clue concerning constitutive variables of nonmechanical origin, e.g., electromagnetic variables. Clearly two bodies having the same geometry, mass distribution, and identical motion of a neighborhood of a material point **X** at time $t$ may be subjected to different stresses on account of different electromagnetic properties of its neighborhood. The same applies even in the mechanical case when the body is constrained internally. For example, the body may be *rigid* or *incompressible*. In the former case the motions that are permitted are rigid motions for which, for example, the stress is completely indeterminate. For incompressible bodies only isochoric motions are admitted. This latter objection can be eliminated by applying the foregoing principles only for a class of *admissible motions.* This condition leaves a part of the stress (e.g., pressure) indeterminate. We must, however, supply additional principles for the exclusion of the electromagnetic variables. For this we propose the following principle.

1c. *Principle of Electromagnetic Constitution. The behavior of a material point* **X** *occupying a spatial point* **x** *at the time t is influenced by the history of the electromagnetic field prior to the time t.* Notice that in electromagnetism every point at time $t$ is influenced by the field present at all other points prior to the time $t$.

This point distinguishes the electromagnetic field from the mechanical field. Here the so-called concept of "far field," or effect at a distance, carries just as much responsibility for the physical behavior of a material point as do its neighboring points. Rigorous investigations of electromechanical constitutive equations are as yet to appear. An example of this area is provided in Chap. 11 on electroelasticity.

In order to keep account of all variables that enter a constitutive equation, Truesdell and Toupin [1960, art. 293] have introduced the following principle.

1d. *Principle of Equipresence. A variable present in one constitutive*

[1] Noll and Truesdell introduced this principle for stress (private communication).

*equation should be present in all.* This principle states that all constitutive equations of the same material must contain the same independent variables. For example, if in a thermoelastic solid the stress is a function of the strain and of the temperature gradient, then the heat-flux vector must be a function of the same variables, i.e., $\mathbf{t} = \mathbf{f}(\mathbf{e}, \text{grad } \theta)$ implies $\mathbf{q} = \mathbf{g}(\mathbf{e}, \text{grad } \theta)$. The different tensorial characters of $\mathbf{t}$ and $\mathbf{q}$, combined with other principles, may affect the nature of the dependence of $\mathbf{t}$ and $\mathbf{q}$ on variables $\mathbf{e}$ and grad $\theta$. For special materials and/or for approximate theories, dependence on one or the other variable may even disappear.

In an attempt to provide a unified constitutive theory for all materials we introduce the following principle.

1e. *Principle of Unification. Different constitutive variables that characterize particular materials should be present in the constitutive equations of all materials.* This principle should be interpreted as allowing the inclusion of constitutive variables, which may be present in special situations, into the general scheme. It does not provide means for separating theories for various cases in which the constitutive variables may form groups with weak or no ties. To illustrate the point, consider the elastic solid and stokesian fluids which are respectively defined by constitutive equations of the form $\mathbf{t} = \mathbf{f}(\mathbf{e})$ and $\mathbf{t} = \mathbf{f}(\mathbf{d})$. For any solid we may, in accordance with the principle of unification, write $\mathbf{t} = \mathbf{f}(\mathbf{e}, \mathbf{d})$. When we find other media in which stress is expressed as a function of some other variables, these variables will also have to be incorporated into the function $\mathbf{f}$.

The foregoing general principles do not provide us with quick rules in writing functional equations for the constitutive variables. Often for simple nonhereditary systems the field quantities explicitly appearing in the equation of energy have been taken as the fundamental constitutive variables. We prefer to make the following proposal.

1*f*. *Dissipative Constitutive Variables. The field quantities explicitly present in the equation of entropy production constitute the basic dissipative constitutive variables of a simple dissipative system.* Consider, for example the equation of entropy production (40.24), e.g.,

$$(44.3) \qquad \theta \Delta = {}_Dt^{(pq)} d_{qp} + {}_Dm^{(rq)p} w_{pq;r} + q^p (\log \theta)_{,p} - \rho \sum_{\alpha=28}^{n} \tau^\alpha \dot{\nu}_\alpha$$

In this equation one set from each of the pairs $({}_Dt^{pq}, d_{qp})$, $({}_Dm^{(rq)p}, w_{pq;r})$ $(\rho \tau^\alpha, \dot{\nu}_\alpha)$, and $(q^p, \theta_{,p}/\theta)$ may be expressed as a tensor function of the remaining variables, e.g.,

$$(44.4) \qquad {}_Dt^{(pq)} = f^{(pq)} \left( d_{qp}, w_{pq;r}, \dot{\nu}_\alpha, \frac{\theta_{,p}}{\theta} \right)$$

since the nondissipative part of the stress $t^{(pq)} - {}_Dt^{(pq)}$ has already been determined from the equation of state for $\epsilon$ [see Eq. $(40.11)_1$]. This method supplies just an adequate number of constitutive equations in terms of a minimum number of constitutive variables. The variables so paired in the linear theory of irreversible processes are called *forces* and *fluxes.* While there is no unique way of separation of forces and fluxes, one can distinguish forces from fluxes by physical reasoning or by the use of the *extensive property* (the additiveness) of forces. By considering $f^{(pq)}$ as a functional of its variables at all times prior to $t$ and including in the argument of $f^{(pq)}$ the history of the variables of neighboring points, we can generalize (44.4) to larger classes of problems. We find the present method more definitive than suggested by the previous principles.

In constitutive equations of the form (44.4) such variables as stress rates do not appear explicitly; however, if $f^{(pq)}$ is regarded as a functional of its arguments, it is not difficult to arrive at the stress rate by differentiation with respect to time.

The foregoing proposal for theories of finite deformations is new and as yet undeveloped.

2. *Coordinate Invariance. Coordinate invariance requires that the constitutive functions be absolute tensor point functions of their variables.* Such functions are invariant with respect to coordinate transformations. Otherwise a change of description would produce a different response in the same material subjected to the same disturbances.

The coordinate invariance is achieved by writing the equations in tensorial forms.

3. *Spatial Invariance (Material Objectivity). Constitutive equations are invariant to rigid motion of the spatial coordinates.* Physically it is evident that the constitutive equations are independent of the observer. Therefore rigid motion of the spatial frame should leave the constitutive equations invariant. This invariance requirement places certain restrictions on the constitutive equations and variables. Thus, for example, in two objectively equivalent motions

$$\mathbf{x}' = \mathbf{x}'(\mathbf{X}, t') \qquad \mathbf{x} = \mathbf{x}(\mathbf{X}, t) \tag{44.5}$$

where

$$\begin{gathered} x'^k = Q^k{}_l(t)\, x^l + b^k(t) \\ Q^k{}_r\, Q_l{}^r = Q^r{}_l\, Q_r{}^k = \delta^k{}_l \qquad t' = t - a \end{gathered} \tag{44.6}$$

the constitutive relation

$$t_{kl} = f_{kl}(\mathbf{x}, t) \tag{44.7}$$

should remain invariant, i.e.,

$$t'_{kl} = f_{kl}(\mathbf{x}', t') \tag{44.8}$$

where $t'_{kl}$ is referred to coordinates $x'^k$ at time $t'$. In other words, the function $f_{kl}$ that appears in (44.8) is the same function that appears in (44.7). This requirement is responsible for eliminating such terms as $g^K{}_k \, x^k{}_{,K}$ from the constitutive equations. The deep significance of the material objectivity will become clear in the specific examples that are given below (cf. Arts. 46 and 48).

4. *Material Invariance (Material Isomorphism). Constitutive equations invariant with respect to a group of transformations of the material coordinates which is a subgroup of a full orthogonal group, are said to have a material symmetry characterized by the subgroup.* Let $S^K{}_L$ be a transformation (rigid rotation and/or reflection) of the natural state so that $X^K$ is changed into $X'^K$ by

$$X'^K = S^K{}_L \, X^L$$

where

$$G_{KL} \, S^K{}_M \, S^L{}_N = G_{MN}$$

The determinant of $S^K{}_L$ need not be 1. In general we have $\det S^K{}_L = \pm 1$. For example, we may be allowed to go from coordinates $(X^1, X^2, X^3)$ to $(X'^1 = X^1, X'^2 = X^2, X'^3 = -X^3)$ (the reflection of the $X^3$ axis). Invariance of the constitutive equations to rigid rotations-reflections such as $S^K{}_L$ characterizes the material symmetry in the initial state. Physically, for a given material, the material symmetry will be known at the outset. For example, the elastic properties of a solid at a given point in two perpendicular directions may be the same. In this case a number of equivalent coordinate systems exist such that, referred to these frames, the stress-strain relations remain unchanged (e.g., we may have $(X, Y)$ or $(Y, Z)$ or $(Z, X)$ axes coincide with these directions). The material symmetry determines the rigid-rotation-reflection group $S^K{}_L$.

If there exists no preferred direction with respect to a certain constitutive property of the material, we say that the material is *isotropic* with respect to that property.[2] Otherwise the material is said to be *aeolotropic* or *anisotropic*. A material that is isotropic with respect to one property need not be isotropic with respect to other properties. For example, a solid may be isotropic in stress and strain without being isotropic in electric displacement.

5. *Dimensional Invariance. Constitutive equations depend on the number of dimensionally invariant moduli or material constants.* This dependence cannot be stated without the knowledge of the functional form of the constitutive equations. However, requirements placed upon the number of dimensionally independent moduli place restrictions on the constitutive equations (cf. Chaps. 9 and 10).

[2] For a rigorous definition of isotropy see Art. 46.

6. *Requirements of Consistency. All constitutive equations must be consistent with the basic principles of mass, momentum, energy, and electromagnetism.*

A constitutive functional should therefore satisfy all of the foregoing invariance requirements.

## 45. CONSTITUTIVE EQUATIONS OF HYPERELASTIC BODIES: GREEN'S METHOD

An ideally elastic body is distinguished from other material systems by its property that the stress depends upon the state of deformation only. More specifically, (1) upon the application of external loads no electrical, chemical or thermal phenomena take place and (2) the solid possesses a distinguished state called the *natural state.* In its natural state the body is assumed to have *uniform conditions;* i.e., it is *unstressed* and has a constant uniform temperature and other constant fields. Upon the application of external loads the body deforms, subsequently reaching different stressed states into which its motion carries it. According to (1) the initial constant temperature and other uniform fields (e.g., electromagnetic fields) are not disturbed. We may therefore assume that they are not present at all. When the external loads are released, the natural-state assumption requires that the body resume its natural state again. Thus the minimum energy required to produce a given deformation is available for full recovery. The initial-state assumption may therefore be interpreted as the *zero dissipation.* Consequently the constitutive equations must be derivable from an *internal energy* function. This is the method of Green,[1] according to which the internal energy is assumed to be a function of the strain. Such solids are sometimes called *hyperelastic.*

An alternative method due to Cauchy[2] is based on the assumption that in an ideally elastic body *the stress is a function of strain.* This method will be presented in Art. 46. For the infinitesimal strain these two approaches lead to the same result. For theories of finite deformations, however, Cauchy's method is more general and additional assumptions are needed to bring Cauchy's theory into the more definitive form of Green's theory.

DEFINITION. *A solid is said to be hyperelastic if it possesses a strain*

[1] Green [1839, p. 249; 1841, pp. 275–296] obtained the stress-strain relations for the infinitesimal deformations. For theories of finite deformations we find the excellent work of Finger [1894*b*], E. and F. Cosserat [1896, 1909] and Brillouin [1925, 1928]. Murnaghan's [1937] treatment produced the final form. A critical appraisal of the theory up to 1952 is found in Truesdell [1952, pp. 173–182]. For other presentations see Doyle and Ericksen [1956] and Smith and Rivlin [1958].

[2] [1823, 1828, 1829]. Cauchy's method for theories of infinitesimal deformations produces thirty-six independent elastic constants while Green's produces only twenty-one constants. The positive-definite character of the strain energy is responsible for reducing the number of constants in Green's theory from thirty-six to twenty-one.

*energy* $\Sigma \equiv \rho_0 \epsilon$ *of the form*

$$\Sigma = \Sigma\,(X^K, x^k, g^k{}_K, \rho, \mathbf{G}_K, x^k{}_{,K}) \tag{45.1}$$

*such that*

$$\frac{\rho}{\rho_0}\,\dot{\Sigma} = t^k{}_l\, d^l{}_k \tag{45.2}$$

In (45.1) $X^K$, $x^k$ are respectively the material and spatial coordinates and $\mathbf{G}_K$ is the base vector in $X^K$, which we shall also refer to as the *material descriptor* in its connection with the characterization of the directional dependence of the energy $\epsilon$ in the natural state. As we shall see, the dependence of $\Sigma$ on the base vector $\mathbf{G}_K$ is responsible for the anisotropy, while dependence on $\mathbf{X}$ is responsible for the inhomogeneity. Let us note that (45.2) is the energy equation for non-heat-conducting media having no couple stresses. The form of (45.1) indicates that $\Sigma$ depends only on the local configuration at time $t$, not on the entire past history. The elastic materials may therefore be called simple materials with no memory other than of the natural state. The principle of neighborhood is introduced by the displacement gradients $x^k{}_{,K}$. In this form there exist no dissipative and electromagnetic variables.

By use of the requirement of consistency we eliminate $\rho$ in the following manner. Through the continuity equation we have

$$\frac{\rho_0}{\rho} = \frac{1}{6}\,(\det g^K{}_k)\, e_{klm}\, e^{KLM}\, x^k{}_{,K}\, x^l{}_{,L}\, x^m{}_{,M} \tag{45.3}$$

We therefore see that by substituting $\rho$ from (45.3) into (45.1), we may express (45.1) in terms of the remaining variables; i.e., without loss in generality we may take

$$\Sigma = \Sigma\,(X^K, x^k, g^k{}_K, \mathbf{G}_K, x^k{}_{,K}) \tag{45.4}$$

Next we must see that the principle of objectivity (category 3 in Art. 44) is satisfied.

According to the principle of objectivity, $\Sigma$ should be invariant in objectively equivalent motions; i.e., if we change the spatial coordinate rigidly,

$$\begin{aligned} x'^k\,(\mathbf{X}, t') &= Q^k{}_l\,(t)\, x^l\,(\mathbf{X}, t) + b^k\,(t) \\ t' = t - a \qquad & Q^k{}_l\, Q_m{}^l = Q^l{}_m\, Q_l{}^k = \delta^k{}_m \end{aligned} \tag{45.5}$$

the strain energy should remain invariant. We now consider three special cases.

1. *The Rigid Translation of the Spatial Frame.* In this case we have

$$Q^k{}_l \equiv \delta^k{}_l \qquad b^k \equiv -x^k \qquad a \equiv 0 \tag{45.6}$$

If in this choice of coordinates the particle **X** remains at the origin, we have

$$\mathbf{x}' = \mathbf{x} - \mathbf{x} = 0 \tag{45.7}$$

All derivatives of **x** remain unchanged under this transformation. Therefore dependence of $\Sigma$ on $x^k$ cannot occur unless the system is *spatially inhomogeneous;* i.e., strain energy changes with the translation of the spatial frame. This, of course, is not acceptable. Hence

$$\Sigma = \Sigma\,(X^K, g^k{}_K, \mathbf{G}_K, x^k{}_{,K}) \tag{45.8}$$

2. *Translation with Respect to Time.* In this case we have

$$Q^k{}_l \equiv \delta^k{}_l \qquad b^k \equiv 0 \qquad a \equiv t \tag{45.9}$$

and this gives

$$\mathbf{x}' = \mathbf{x} \qquad t' = 0 \tag{45.10}$$

This means that $\Sigma$ cannot depend on time $t$ explicitly, but only on the history up to time $t$. The choice of the arguments of (45.1) satisfies this automatically, since we included neither time $t$ nor the history of various tensors in (45.1). In more general constitutive relations this condition, as an analogue of case 1, imposes nontrivial conditions.

3. *Rigid Rotatory Motion of the Spatial Frame.* In this case we have $b^k \equiv 0$, $a \equiv 0$, and $Q^k{}_l$ is arbitrary. Under this rigid rotation of the spatial frame of reference, various tensors take new values. Thus

$$x^k{}_{,K} \to x^l{}_{,K}\, Q^k{}_l \qquad g^k{}_K \to Q^k{}_l\, g^l{}_K$$

Therefore (45.8) is valid for arbitrary $Q^k{}_l$, i.e.,

$$\Sigma = \Sigma\,(X^K, Q^k{}_l\, g^l{}_K, \mathbf{G}_K, Q^k{}_l\, x^l{}_{,K}) \tag{45.11}$$

Next we make use of an important theorem of Cauchy [1850] on invariant functions of several vectors. *If $F\,(V^k{}_1, V^k{}_2, \ldots, V^k{}_n)$ is a single-valued function of a system of $n$ vectors which is invariant to rigid rotations, then $F$ must reduce to a function of the length of vectors, the scalar products $I_{\Gamma\Delta} = g_{kl}\, V^k{}_\Gamma\, V^l{}_\Delta$, and the determinants of the components of the vectors taken three at a time, $D_{\Gamma\Delta\Upsilon} = \epsilon_{klm}\, V^k{}_\Gamma\, V^l{}_\Delta\, V^m{}_\Upsilon$.*

For our purpose it is sufficiently general to assume that the function $F$ is a polynomial in its arguments. This ensures the single-valuedness of the result. For a proof of this theorem see Weyl [1946, p. 53]. In terms of the arguments of (45.11), $\Sigma$ must be a function of

$$\begin{aligned} C_{KL} &= \delta_{kl}\, x^k{}_{,K}\, x^l{}_{,L} \\ J &= \tfrac{1}{6}\,(\det g^K{}_k)\, e_{klm}\, e^{KLM}\, x^k{}_{,K}\, x^l{}_{,L}\, x^m{}_{,M} \\ G_{KL} &= \delta_{kl}\, Q^k{}_r\, Q^l{}_s\, g^r{}_K\, g^s{}_L \qquad g^k{}_K \end{aligned} \tag{45.12}$$

Since we have

$$\det (C^K{}_L) = J^2$$

dependence on $C_{KL}$ implies dependence on $J$, and dependence on $g^k{}_K$ implies dependence on $G_{KL}$. Therefore we eliminate $J$ and $G_{KL}$ from our list

$$\Sigma = \Sigma (X^K, g^k{}_K, \mathbf{G}_K, C_{KL}) \tag{45.13}$$

Further (45.13) must be independent with respect to an arbitrary transformation of either set of coordinates $x^k$ or $X^K$ (*coordinate invariance*, category 2 in Art. 44). Under the transformation of coordinates $x^k$ all quantities behave like absolute scalars except $g^k{}_K$. The only absolute scalar that can be formed from this tensor is $G_{KL}$. Therefore (45.13) now reduces to

$$\Sigma = \Sigma (X^K, G_{KL}, \mathbf{G}_K, C_{KL}) = \Sigma (X^K, \mathbf{G}_K, C_{KL}) \tag{45.14}$$

since $G_{KL} = \mathbf{G}_K \cdot \mathbf{G}_L$.

According to a well-known theorem of algebra,[3] by a transformation of coordinates $X^K$ both the metric tensor $G_{KL}$ and the matrix $C_{KL}$ can be reduced to diagonal form. If $C_1$, $C_2$, and $C_3$ are the diagonal entries of the diagonalized form of $C_{KL}$ in this *special* coordinate system, (45.14) can be written as

$$\Sigma = \Sigma (X^K, \mathbf{G}_K, C_1, C_2, C_3) \tag{45.15}$$

This completes the coordinate invariance.

Next we turn to *material invariance* (category 4 in Art. 44) in the natural state. This requires invariance of $\Sigma$ with respect to a group of transformations determined by material symmetry. If the material is *homogeneous* in the natural state, dependence on $X^K$ drops out

$$\Sigma = \Sigma (\mathbf{G}_K, C_{KL}) \qquad \text{(homogeneous media)} \tag{45.16}$$

If the material is isotropic, then the directional independence in the natural state requires that $\Sigma$ be independent of the material descriptor $\mathbf{G}_K$. Hence

$$\Sigma = \Sigma (X^K, C_{KL}) \qquad \text{(isotropic media)} \tag{45.17}$$

If the material has a certain rectilinear *aeolotropy*, by the invariance of the material coordinates with respect to a subgroup of a full orthogonal group, we obtain conditions to be imposed on (45.16). Thirty-two different kinds of crystal symmetry may be shown to exist.[4]

[3] Cf. Bôcher [1952, chap. XIII].

[4] See, for instance, Love [1944 chap. VI], Voigt [1900], and Schouten [1951]. For recent contributions see Smith and Rivlin [1957, 1958] and Pipkin and Rivlin [1959]. An account of the Smith-Rivlin theory is presented in the recent book by Green and Adkins [1960, chap. 1].

For a general anisotropic solid we have shown that by transforming material coordinates $X^K$ in a special coordinate system, we may express $\Sigma$ as given by (45.15). For an isotropic solid the dependence of $\Sigma$ on material descriptors $\mathbf{G}_K$ drops out, thus reducing it to

$$\Sigma = \Sigma\,(X^K, C_1, C_2, C_3) \tag{45.18}$$

Since $C_\alpha$ are functions of the invariants $\mathrm{I}_C$, $\mathrm{II}_C$, and $\mathrm{III}_C$, we replace (45.18) by its equivalent

$$\Sigma = \Sigma\,(X^K, \mathrm{I}_C, \mathrm{II}_C, \mathrm{III}_C) \qquad \text{(isotropic media)} \tag{45.19}$$

where

$$\begin{aligned} \mathrm{I}_C &= \delta^K{}_L\, C^L{}_K = C_1 + C_2 + C_3 \\ \mathrm{II}_C &= \frac{1}{2!}\,\delta^K{}_M{}^L{}_N\, C^M{}_K\, C^N{}_L = C_1 C_2 + C_2 C_3 + C_3 C_1 \\ \mathrm{III}_C &= \frac{1}{3!}\,\delta^K{}_P{}^L{}_Q{}^M{}_R\, C^P{}_K\, C^Q{}_L\, C^R{}_M = \det\,(C^K{}_L) = C_1 C_2 C_3 \end{aligned} \tag{45.20}$$

But now through (9.22), (9.23), (9.28), and (9.29) we may express one set of invariants in terms of other sets. Consequently for an isotropic solid we may equally well write

$$\Sigma = \Sigma\,(X^K, \mathrm{I}_c, \mathrm{II}_c, \mathrm{III}_c) = \Sigma\,(X^K, \mathrm{I}_e, \mathrm{II}_e, \mathrm{III}_e) = \cdots \tag{45.21}$$

Thus *an isotropic ideally elastic solid may be described by a strain-energy function $\Sigma$ which is a single-valued function of material coordinates and any one of the material or spatial variables $C_{KL}$, $E_{KL}$, $c_{kl}$, $e_{kl}$, $\overset{-1}{c}_{kl}$, . . . .*

$$\Sigma = \Sigma\,(\mathbf{X}, \mathbf{C}) = \Sigma\,(\mathbf{X}, \mathbf{c}) = \Sigma\,(\mathbf{X}, \mathbf{e}) = \Sigma\,(\mathbf{X}, \overset{-1}{\mathbf{c}}) = \cdots \tag{45.22}$$

Various forms of the stress-strain relations may be derived by using (45.22) in (45.2).

*Boussinesq's Form.* In this case $C_{KL}$ or $E_{KL}$ are taken as the argument in $\Sigma$. Hence

$$t^{kl}\,d_{kl} = \frac{\rho}{\rho_0}\,\frac{\partial \Sigma}{\partial C_{KL}}\,\dot{C}_{KL} = 2\,\frac{\rho}{\rho_0}\,\frac{\partial \Sigma}{\partial C_{KL}}\,x^k{}_{,K}\,x^l{}_{,L}\,d_{kl} \tag{45.23}$$

If this relation is to hold for arbitrary $d_{kl}$, we must have

$$t^{kl} = 2\,\frac{\rho}{\rho_0}\,\frac{\partial \Sigma}{\partial C_{KL}}\,x^k{}_{,K}\,x^l{}_{,L} = \frac{\rho}{\rho_0}\,\frac{\partial \Sigma}{\partial E_{KL}}\,x^k{}_{,K}\,x^l{}_{,L} \tag{45.24}$$

This form is attributed to Boussinesq [1870, 1872].[5]

[5] See also Murnaghan [1937] and Truesdell [1952, p. 176].

*Kelvin-Cosserat Form.* If we recall the pseudostress of Piola introduced by (34.6) and (34.7), from (45.24) we can obtain other forms:

$$T^{Kl} = \frac{\partial \Sigma}{\partial E_{KN}} x^l{}_{,N} \tag{45.25}$$

$$T^{KL} = \frac{\partial \Sigma}{\partial E_{KL}} \tag{45.26}$$

which may be attributed to Kelvin [1863] and the Cosserats [1896, art. 24].

*C. Neumann-Kirchhoff Form.* We may revert to the use of $x^k{}_{,K}$ as the independent variable in $\Sigma$. To this end let us note that

$$\frac{\partial \Sigma}{\partial x^k{}_{,M}} = \frac{\partial \Sigma}{\partial E_{KL}} \frac{\partial E_{KL}}{\partial x^k{}_{,M}}$$

but

$$\frac{\partial E_{KL}}{\partial x^k{}_{,M}} = \frac{1}{2} \frac{\partial}{\partial x^k{}_{,M}} (g_{mn}\, x^m{}_{,K}\, x^n{}_{,L} - G_{KL})$$

or

$$\frac{\partial E_{KL}}{\partial x^k{}_{,M}} = \frac{1}{2} (\delta^M{}_K\, x_{k,L} + \delta^M{}_L\, x_{k,K}) \tag{45.27}$$

Consequently

$$\frac{\partial \Sigma}{\partial x^k{}_{,M}} = \frac{1}{2} \left( \frac{\partial \Sigma}{\partial E_{KM}} + \frac{\partial \Sigma}{\partial E_{MK}} \right) x_{k,K} \tag{45.28}$$

But from (45.24) we have

$$t^k{}_l = \frac{\rho}{2\,\rho_0} \left( \frac{\partial \Sigma}{\partial E_{KL}} + \frac{\partial \Sigma}{\partial E_{LK}} \right) x^k{}_{,K}\, x_{l,L}$$

Upon using (45.28), we may write

$$t^k{}_l = \frac{\rho}{\rho_0} \frac{\partial \Sigma}{\partial x^l{}_{,K}} x^k{}_{,K} \tag{45.29}$$

This is C. Neumann's form of the stress-strain relations.[6] In terms of Piola's stress we obtain Kirchhoff's form.[7]

$$T^K{}_l = \frac{\partial \Sigma}{\partial x^l{}_{,K}} \tag{45.30}$$

The foregoing forms of the stress-strain relations are valid in a compressible medium. For an incompressible medium the deformation is

[6] [1860, eq. (21)]. See also Finger [1894*b*], E. and F. Cosserat [1896, art. 24], and Rivlin [1948*a*, *b*, *c*; 1960*a*, eq. (2.12)].

[7] [1852]. See also Gibbs [1875], E. and F. Cosserat [1909, art. 54], and Brillouin [1925].

ochoric (i.e., $I_d = 0$ or $J = 1$). Hence we may add to the foregoing pressions a pressure term without affecting the energy balance. Thus, r example, (45.29) can be modified for incompressible solids to Poincaré's 892, art. 33] equation

$$t^k{}_l = -p\,\delta^k{}_l + \frac{\partial \Sigma}{\partial x^l{}_{,K}}\, x^k{}_{,K} \tag{45.31}$$

*Hamel's Spatial Form.* It is not difficult to pass from the foregoing aterial forms of the stress-strain relations to spatial forms by considering as a function of $X^K{}_{,k}$ or $\overset{-1}{\mathbf{C}}$. Thus we may write (45.2) as

$$t^k{}_l\, v^l{}_{;k} = \frac{\rho}{\rho_0} \frac{\partial \Sigma}{\partial X^K{}_{,k}} \frac{D}{Dt} (X^K{}_{,k})$$

sing (19.2), we obtain

$$t^k{}_l\, v^l{}_{;k} = -\frac{\rho}{\rho_0} \frac{\partial \Sigma}{\partial X^K{}_{,k}} X^K{}_{,l}\, v^l{}_{;k}$$

nce this must be valid for arbitrary $v^l{}_{;k}$, we must have

$$t^k{}_l = -\frac{\rho}{\rho_0} \frac{\partial \Sigma}{\partial X^K{}_{,k}} X^K{}_{,l} \tag{45.32}$$

his is Hamel's [1912, art. 369] form of the stress-strain relations.

*Murnaghan's Spatial Form.* Murnaghan [1937] assumed that $\Sigma$ is a nction of $\overset{-1}{\mathbf{C}}$. Hence

$$t^{kl} = -\frac{\rho}{\rho_0} \frac{\partial \Sigma}{\partial \overset{-1}{C}{}^{KM}} \frac{\partial \overset{-1}{C}{}^{KM}}{\partial X^L{}_{,l}} X^{L,k}$$

ut

$$\frac{\partial \overset{-1}{C}{}^{KM}}{\partial X^L{}_{,l}} = \frac{\partial}{\partial X^L{}_{,l}} (g^{km} X^K{}_{,k} X^M{}_{,m}) = \delta^K{}_L X^{M,l} + \delta^M{}_L X^{K,l} \tag{45.33}$$

Ience follows Murnaghan's spatial form

$$t^{kl} = -2 \frac{\rho}{\rho_0} \frac{\partial \Sigma}{\partial \overset{-1}{C}{}^{KL}} X^{K,k} X^{L,l} \tag{45.34}$$

Another spatial form due to Murnaghan can be obtained from (45.32) y considering $\Sigma = \Sigma(\mathbf{X}, \mathbf{c}) = \Sigma(\mathbf{X}, \mathbf{e})$. Thus

$$t^k{}_l = -\frac{\rho}{\rho_0} \frac{\partial \Sigma}{\partial c_{mn}} \frac{\partial c_{mn}}{\partial X^K{}_{,k}} X^K{}_{,l}$$

but

$$X^K{}_{,l} \frac{\partial c_{mn}}{\partial X^K{}_{,k}} = X^K{}_{,l} \frac{\partial}{\partial X^K{}_{,k}} (G_{MN} X^M{}_{,m} X^N{}_{,n})$$
$$= G_{KN} \delta^k{}_m X^N{}_{,n} X^K{}_{,l} + G_{MK} \delta^k{}_n X^M{}_{,m} X^K{}_{,l}$$
$$= \delta^k{}_m c_{nl} + \delta^k{}_n c_{ml}$$

Hence

$$(45.35) \qquad t^k{}_l = -\frac{2\rho}{\rho_0} c_{lm} \frac{\partial \Sigma}{\partial c_{km}} = -\frac{2\rho}{\rho_0} c^k{}_m \frac{\partial \Sigma}{\partial c^l{}_m}$$
$$= \frac{\rho}{\rho_0} (\delta^k{}_m - 2 e^k{}_m) \frac{\partial \Sigma}{\partial e^l{}_m}$$

All of the foregoing forms of the constitutive equations are valid f[or] anisotropic inhomogeneous ideally elastic solids, provided that $\Sigma$ [is] understood to depend on $\mathbf{G}_K$. For isotropic solids further simplificatic[ons] can be achieved. These are left to Art. 47.

## 46. CONSTITUTIVE EQUATIONS OF ELASTIC BODIES: CAUCHY'S METHOD

In this article we proceed to give Cauchy's method of determinin[g] stress-strain relations for an ideally elastic solid. This method is ver[y] general and finds application in dissipative systems when the method [of] Green fails. To make the method clear, we start with the simplest ty[pe] of constitutive assumptions. This extension to more complicated cas[es] pursues the same line of reasoning as we shall see in later chapters (c[f.] Chaps. 8 to 10).

Consider the class of materials for which each of the stress componen[ts] is a single-valued function of the deformation gradients $x^m{}_{,K}$, i.e.,

$$(46.1) \qquad t^{kl} = f^{kl} (x^m{}_{,K})$$

Clearly for the nine functions $f^{kl}$ not all general forms are admissibl[e]. We have $t^{kl} = t^{lk}$ (nonpolar case), which implies that $f^{kl} = f^{lk}$. Th[is] reduces the number of functions from nine to six. Next we must conside[r] invariance requirements studied in Art. 44.

Consider first spatial invariance. A rigid motion

$$(46.2) \qquad \begin{aligned} x'^k &= Q^k{}_l (t) x^l + b^k (t) \\ Q^k{}_l Q_m{}^l &= Q^l{}_m Q_l{}^k = \delta^k{}_m \end{aligned}$$

of the spatial frame should not change in the constitutive equation (46.1[).] Let us calculate the stress $t'^{kl}$ in the coordinates $x'^k$. We have

$$(46.3) \qquad t'^{kl} = t^{rs} Q^k{}_r (t) Q^l{}_s (t) \qquad x'^m{}_{,K} = x^n{}_{,K} Q^m{}_n (t)$$

The constitutive relations in the new frame are

$$(46.4) \qquad t'^{kl} = f^{kl} (x'^m{}_{,K})$$

Substituting (46.3) into (46.4) gives

$$t^{rs} Q^k{}_r(t) Q^l{}_s(t) = f^{kl}[Q^m{}_n(t)\, x^n{}_{,K}] \tag{46.5}$$

From this we solve for $t^{rs}$

$$t^{rs} = Q_k{}^r(t) Q_l{}^s(t) f^{kl}[Q^m{}_n(t)\, x^n{}_{,K}] = f^{rs}(x^m{}_{,K}) \tag{46.6}$$

which imposes conditions on the six functions $f^{rs}$ since $Q^k{}_l$ is an arbitrary nonsingular orthogonal matrix. Thus (46.6) must be valid for every rigid motion of the spatial frame. Functions satisfying such conditions as (46.6) are called *hemitropic* functions of their arguments.

Every *form-invariant* function $f^{kl}$ must satisfy (46.6). From the classical theory of invariants a complete table of basic invariants of the orthogonal group is available. We have the following theorem (see Weyl [1946, p. 53]).

THEOREM 1. *Every even orthogonal polynomial invariant depending on three vectors (having components $x^1{}_{,K}, x^2{}_{,K}, x^3{}_{,K}$) in three-dimensional vector space is expressible as a polynomial in terms of six scalar products $C_{KL} = g_{kl}\, x^k{}_{,K}\, x^l{}_{,L}$. Every odd invariant is expressible as a sum of scalar triple products $f\, \epsilon_{klm}\, x^k{}_{,K}\, x^l{}_{,L}\, x^m{}_{,M}$ with coefficient $f$ being an even invariant.*

The basic invariants are therefore

$$C_{KL} = g_{kl}\, x^k{}_{,K}\, x^l{}_{,L} \qquad \epsilon_{KLM}\sqrt{C} \tag{46.7}$$

where $C \equiv \det C_{KL}$, $\epsilon_{KLM} = e_{KLM}\sqrt{G}$, and $G \equiv \det G_{KL}$. Thus

$$f^{kl} = f^{kl}(C_{KL}, \sqrt{C})$$

Since $C$ is expressible as a function of $C_{KL}$, we may finally write

$$f^{kl} = f^{kl}(C_{KL}) \tag{46.8}$$

where $f^{kl}(\mathbf{C})$ is no longer a polynomial in $\mathbf{C}$; however it can always be approximated by a polynomial to any desired degree of accuracy whenever $\mathbf{f}$ is continuously differentiable.

Upon bringing (46.8) into (46.6), for the general case, we obtain

$$t^{rs}(t) = Q_k{}^r(t) Q_l{}^s(t) f^{kl}[C_{KL}(t)] \tag{46.9}$$

or simply

$$t^{rs} = Q_k{}^r Q_l{}^s f^{kl}(C_{KL}) \qquad \text{or} \qquad t_{rs} = Q^k{}_r Q^l{}_s f_{kl}(C_{KL}) \tag{46.10}$$

Further reduction can be achieved by identifying $Q^k{}_r$ with the rotation tensor $\overset{-1}{R}{}^k{}_r$; i.e., we choose

$$Q^k{}_r = \overset{-1}{R}{}^k{}_r = g^k{}_M \overset{\frac{1}{2}}{C}{}^M{}_K\, x^K{}_{,k} \tag{46.11}$$

where the last expression follows from $(10.22)_2$. Substitution of this into $(46.10)_2$ gives

$$t_{rs} = F_{RS}\, X^R{}_{,r}\, X^S{}_{,s} \tag{46.12}$$

where

$$F_{RS}(\mathbf{C}) \equiv g^k{}_M\, g^l{}_N\, \overset{\frac{1}{2}}{C}{}^M{}_R\, \overset{\frac{1}{2}}{C}{}^N{}_S\, f_{kl}(\mathbf{C}) \tag{46.13}$$

is a symmetric material tensor whose components are referred to the material coordinate system.[1]

For materials that possess direction-dependent material properties, $F_{RS}$ is also a function of the base vectors (*material descriptors*) $\mathbf{G}_K$, i.e.,

$$F_{RS} = F_{RS}(C_{KL}, \mathbf{G}_K) \tag{46.14}$$

For inhomogeneous materials an additional independent variable $X^K$ must be included.

It should be noted that with the foregoing choice of $Q^k{}_r$ not only does the stress tensor remain spatially objective, but also the requirements of coordinate invariance both in material and in spatial coordinates are satisfied. Thus requirements 1, 2, and 3 of Art. 44 are satisfied.

It is possible, by transforming the coordinates $X^K$ into a special coordinate system in which $C_{KL}$ is diagonalized, to have

$$F_{RS} = F_{RS}(C_1, C_2, C_3, \mathbf{G}_K) \tag{46.15}$$

Since the $C_\alpha$ are expressible as functions of the invariants, we may express (46.15) also as

$$F_{RS} = F_{RS}(\mathrm{I}_C, \mathrm{II}_C, \mathrm{III}_C, \mathbf{G}_K) \tag{46.16}$$

For an incompressible material, the phenomenological relations (46.12) must be modified, since in this case $t_{rs}$ is undetermined to the extent of a hydrostatic pressure $p$. In this case we replace $t_{rs}$ by $t_{rs} + p\, g_{rs}$, thus modifying (46.12) to

$$t_{rs} = -p\, g_{rs} + F_{RS}\, X^R{}_{,r}\, X^S{}_{,s} \tag{46.17}$$

The response function $F_{RS}$ must now be redefined. Since $\det C^R{}_S = 1$, i.e., $\mathrm{III}_C = 1$, we have

$$F_{RS} = F_{RS}(\mathrm{I}_C, \mathrm{II}_C, \mathbf{G}_K) \tag{46.18}$$

Constitutive equations (46.12) may be replaced by other equivalent forms which employ Finger's deformation tensor $\overset{-1}{\mathbf{c}}$. For this purpose

[1] Two alternative derivations of (46.12) for materials having hereditary characteristics were given by Green and Rivlin [1957] and Noll and Truesdell (privately).

we make the substitution $Q_k{}^r = R_k{}^r = g^r{}_K R_k{}^K$ in $(46.10)_1$. Thus

$$t^{rs} = g^r{}_K g^s{}_L R_k{}^K R_l{}^L f^{kl}(C_{KL}) = g^r{}_R g^s{}_S f^{RS}(C_{KL} R_k{}^K R_l{}^L) \tag{46.19}$$

where the last step follows from the hemitropic character of $f^{kl}$ as expressed by (46.6). But from Finger's lemma (10.18) and $(10.16)_2$ we have

$$\overset{-1}{c}_{kl} = C_{KL} R_k{}^K R_l{}^L \tag{46.20}$$

Thus we obtain constitutive equations of another type

$$t^{rs} = f^{rs}(\overset{-1}{c}_{kl}, \mathbf{G}_K) \tag{46.21}$$

where the dependence on $\mathbf{G}_K$ is explicitly shown to take into account possible anisotropy. Equations (46.21) take the place of (46.12). Other forms equivalent to (46.12) and (46.21) are possible.[2]

The foregoing constitutive equations are valid for anisotropic ideally elastic solids. When the material possesses certain directional symmetry in its natural state, we must employ the principle of material isomorphism (category 4 in Art. 44) to determine further restrictions that must be imposed on the response functions $F_{RS}$ and $f^{rs}$. Here, for the purpose of illustration, we shall consider only the isotropic materials.

*An elastic material is said to be isotropic in its natural state if the constitutive equation* (46.12) *is form-invariant with respect to a full orthogonal group of transformations of the natural state.*[3]

To determine the mathematical restrictions implied by isotropy on the response functions $F_{RS}$ and $f^{rs}$, we subject the body in its undeformed configuration to a rigid rotation, i.e.,

$$X'^K = S^K{}_R X^R \tag{46.22}$$

where

$$S^K{}_R S_L{}^R = S_R{}^K S^R{}_L = \delta^K{}_L \tag{46.23}$$

We now permit $\det S^K{}_R = \pm 1$, thus allowing the mirror image of $X^K$ (the right- and left-hand systems) to be included in the transformation group describing the material symmetry. Such situations arise, for example, when the material possesses a plane of symmetry. Constitutive relations (46.12) in the new coordinates $X'^K$ must have the same

[2] Cf. references cited in preceding footnote.

[3] Such materials are sometimes called isotropic materials with center of symmetry, or *holohedral*. If the orthogonal group is proper (reflection is not allowed), then they are named isotropic materials with no center of symmetry, or *hemihedral*.

form, i.e.,

$$F_{RS}(\mathbf{C})\, X^R{}_{,r}\, X^S{}_{,s} = F'_{KL}(\mathbf{C}')\, X'^K{}_{,r}\, X'^L{}_{,s} \tag{46.24}$$

where $F'_{RS}$ and $C'_{KL}$ are respectively the response function and th deformation tensor of the rotated medium. They obey the tenso transformations

$$F'_{KL} = F_{MN} \frac{\partial X^M}{\partial X'^K} \frac{\partial X^N}{\partial X'^L} \qquad C'_{KL} = C_{MN} \frac{\partial X^M}{\partial X'^K} \frac{\partial X^N}{\partial X'^L}$$

i.e.,

$$F'_{KL} = F_{MN}\, S_K{}^M\, S_L{}^N \qquad C'_{KL} = C_{MN}\, S_K{}^M\, S_L{}^N \tag{46.25}$$

From (46.22) we have

$$\frac{\partial X'^K}{\partial x^r} = S^K{}_R\, X^R{}_{,r}$$

Substituting this into (46.24), we get

$$F_{RS}(\mathbf{C})\, X^R{}_{,r}\, X^S{}_{,s} = F'_{KL}(\mathbf{C}')\, S^K{}_R\, S^L{}_S\, X^R{}_{,r}\, X^S{}_{,s}$$

This may also be written as

$$[F_{RS}(\mathbf{C}) - F'_{KL}(C')\, S^K{}_R\, S^L{}_S]\, X^R{}_{,r}\, X^S{}_{,s} = 0$$

Since this is valid for arbitrary gradients $X^R{}_{,r}$, and owing to the symmetrie in indices $R$, $S$, etc., we have

$$F_{RS}(\mathbf{C}) = F'_{KL}(\mathbf{C}')\, S^K{}_R\, S^L{}_S \tag{46.26}$$

Substituting $(46.25)_1$ into this equation we find

$$F_{RS}(\mathbf{C}) = F_{RS}(\mathbf{C}') \tag{46.27}$$

We have thus proved *that the constitutive equations in the original an rotated systems* $\mathbf{X}$ and $\mathbf{X}'$ *will be form-invariant if and only if the response function is form-invariant*, i.e.,

$$f_{rs}(\mathbf{C}) = f_{rs}(\mathbf{C}') \text{ implies } F_{RS}(\mathbf{C}) = F_{RS}(\mathbf{C}')$$

or more explicitly

$$F_{RS}(C_{KL}) = F_{RS}(C_{MN}\, S_K{}^M\, S_L{}^N) \tag{46.28}$$

This is the mathematical restriction that must be imposed on the response function due to material symmetries as defined by the rotation group $S^K{}_L$. For an isotropic medium the rotation group is the full orthogonal group.

An elegant form of (46.28) results if we indicate explicit dependence of $F_{RS}$ on the base vectors $\mathbf{G}_K$ and then rotate our coordinate system $X^K$ by the same amount as the body. Upon this rotation the body and the coordinate system take configurations identical to their initial state before the rotation. Thus

$$C'_{KL} \to C_{KL} \qquad F'_{RS} \to F_{RS}$$

but $\mathbf{G}_K$, which were the base vectors in $X^K$, change into

$$\mathbf{G}'_K = \mathbf{G}_L S_K{}^L$$

Consequently (46.27) or (46.28) is equivalent to

$$F_{RS}\,(C_{KL}, \mathbf{G}_K) = F_{RS}\,(C_{KL}, \mathbf{G}_L S_K{}^L) \tag{46.29}$$

This result clearly indicates the role of $\mathbf{G}_K$ as a material descriptor. The material symmetry group $S_K{}^L$ through (46.29) can determine the response function for various types of anisotropic media.

For the isotropic solid, (46.29) must be valid for all orthogonal $S_K{}^L$. This implies that the values of $F_{RS}$ can only depend on the orthogonal invariants of the vectors $\mathbf{G}_K$, i.e., on the inner products $G_{KL} = \mathbf{G}_K \cdot \mathbf{G}_L$. Thus for isotropic materials the response functions will have the functional form

$$F_{RS} = F_{RS}\,(C_{KL}, G_{KL}) \qquad \text{(isotropic medium)} \tag{46.30}$$

The constitutive equations for the isotropic elastic solid are therefore given by

$$t_{rs} = F_{RS}\,(C_{KL}, G_{KL})\, X^R{}_{,r}\, X^S{}_{,s} \tag{46.31}$$

Let us recall a well-known theorem of algebra, already used in this article: namely, that by a coordinate transformation it is possible to diagonalize simultaneously two matrices $C_{KL}$ and $G_{KL}$. If the diagonal entries of $C_{KL}$ are $C_1$, $C_2$, and $C_3$, we can write (46.30) also as

$$\begin{aligned} F_{RS} &= F_{RS}\,(C_1, C_2, C_3) \\ &= F_{RS}\,(\mathrm{I}_C, \mathrm{II}_C, \mathrm{III}_C) \qquad \text{(isotropic medium)} \end{aligned} \tag{46.32}$$

where $\mathrm{I}_C$, $\mathrm{II}_C$, and $\mathrm{III}_C$ are the invariants of $C_{KL}$. It is now clear that *the transition from anisotropic media to isotropic media is made by omitting the dependence of the response function* (46.16) *of the anisotropic solid on the material descriptor* $\mathbf{G}_K$.

Since the same thing is valid for the incompressible solid, the constitutive equation (46.17) remains valid for the incompressible solid under the provision that

$$F_{RS} = F_{RS}\,(\mathrm{I}_C, \mathrm{II}_C) \qquad \text{(incompressible isotropic medium)} \tag{46.33}$$

The foregoing considerations are valid, without change, for the response function $f^{rs}(\overset{-1}{c}_{kl}, \mathbf{G}_K)$. Thus for the isotropic solid we have the constitutive relations

$$t^{rs} = f^{rs}(\overset{-1}{c}_{kl}, G_{KL}) \tag{46.34}$$

where the form of $f^{rs}$ does not depend on the choice of the coordinate system.

## 47. CONSTITUTIVE EQUATIONS OF ISOTROPIC IDEALLY ELASTIC SOLIDS

*Green's Method.* In Art. 45, by use of Green's energy method, we deduced that for an isotropic ideally elastic solid we have an elastic stress potential

$$\Sigma = \Sigma(X^K, \mathrm{I}, \mathrm{II}, \mathrm{III}) \tag{47.1}$$

where I, II, and III may be chosen as the invariants of any one of the material or spatial strain measures $\mathbf{C}$, $\mathbf{c}$, $\overset{-1}{\mathbf{c}}$, $\mathbf{E}$, . . . ; whereas for the anisotropic solid it is required that $\Sigma$ in addition be a function of the material descriptors $\mathbf{G}_k$. According to $(45.35)_2$ we have

$$t^k{}_l = -\frac{2\rho}{\rho_0} c^k{}_m \frac{\partial \Sigma}{\partial c^l{}_m} \tag{47.2}$$

But now

$$\frac{\partial \Sigma}{\partial c^l{}_m} = \frac{\partial \Sigma}{\partial \mathrm{I}} \frac{\partial \mathrm{I}}{\partial c^l{}_m} + \frac{\partial \Sigma}{\partial \mathrm{II}} \frac{\partial \mathrm{II}}{\partial c^l{}_m} + \frac{\partial \Sigma}{\partial \mathrm{III}} \frac{\partial \mathrm{III}}{\partial c^l{}_m}$$

Using expressions equivalent to (9.9) for the invariants of $\mathbf{c}$, we calculate

$$\begin{gathered} \frac{\partial \mathrm{I}_c}{\partial c^l{}_m} = \delta^m{}_l \qquad \frac{\partial \mathrm{II}_c}{\partial c^l{}_m} = \mathrm{I}_c\, \delta^m{}_l - c^m{}_l \\ \frac{\partial \mathrm{III}_c}{\partial c^l{}_m} = c^m{}_n\, c^n{}_l - \mathrm{I}_c\, c^m{}_l + \mathrm{II}_c\, \delta^m{}_l \end{gathered} \tag{47.3}$$

Consequently

$$\frac{\partial \Sigma}{\partial c^l{}_m} = \frac{\partial \Sigma}{\partial \mathrm{I}_c} \delta^m{}_l + \frac{\partial \Sigma}{\partial \mathrm{II}_c} (\mathrm{I}_c\, \delta^m{}_l - c^m{}_l) + \frac{\partial \Sigma}{\partial \mathrm{III}_c} (c^m{}_n\, c^n{}_l - \mathrm{I}_c\, c^m{}_l + \mathrm{II}_c\, \delta^m{}_l) \tag{47.4}$$

Substitution of this and (25.8) into (47.2) now gives

$$t^k{}_l = a_0\, \delta^k{}_l + a_1\, c^k{}_l + a_2\, c^k{}_m\, c^m{}_l \tag{47.5}$$

here

$$a_0\,(\mathbf{X}, \mathrm{I}_c, \mathrm{II}_c, \mathrm{III}_c) = -2\,\mathrm{III}_c^{\frac{3}{2}}\,\frac{\partial\Sigma}{\partial \mathrm{III}_c}$$

7.6)
$$a_1\,(\mathbf{X}, \mathrm{I}_c, \mathrm{II}_c, \mathrm{III}_c) = -2\,\sqrt{\mathrm{III}_c}\left(\frac{\partial\Sigma}{\partial \mathrm{I}_c} + \mathrm{I}_c\,\frac{\partial\Sigma}{\partial \mathrm{II}_c}\right)$$

$$a_2\,(\mathbf{X}, \mathrm{I}_c, \mathrm{II}_c, \mathrm{III}_c) = 2\,\sqrt{\mathrm{III}_c}\,\frac{\partial\Sigma}{\partial \mathrm{II}_c}$$

order to reduce triple products such as $c^k{}_m\, c^m{}_n\, c^n{}_l$ appearing in $t^k{}_l$, we ive also used in (47.5) the Cayley-Hamilton theorem for the matrix $^k{}_l\|$. According to this theorem a matrix satisfies its characteristic uation, i.e.,

7.7)
$$\mathbf{c}^3 - \mathrm{I}_c\,\mathbf{c}^2 + \mathrm{II}_c\,\mathbf{c} - \mathrm{III}_c\,\mathbf{I} = 0$$

in component notation

7.8)
$$c^k{}_m\, c^m{}_n\, c^n{}_l - \mathrm{I}_c\, c^k{}_m\, c^m{}_l + \mathrm{II}_c\, c^k{}_l - \mathrm{III}_c\, \delta^k{}_l = 0$$

pon multiplying (47.8) by $\overset{-1}{c}{}^l{}_r$, we get

7.9)
$$c^k{}_m\, c^m{}_l = \mathrm{I}_c\, c^k{}_l - \mathrm{II}_c\, \delta^k{}_l + \mathrm{III}_c\, \overset{-1}{c}{}^k{}_l$$

hen this is used in (47.5) to eliminate $c^k{}_m\, c^m{}_l$, there result the elegant ress-strain relations of Finger [1894a]:

47.10)
$$t^k{}_l = b_{-1}\, \overset{-1}{c}{}^k{}_l + b_0\, \delta^k{}_l + b_1\, c^k{}_l$$

here

$$b_{-1} = 2\,\mathrm{III}_c^{\frac{3}{2}}\,\frac{\partial\Sigma}{\partial \mathrm{II}_c} = \frac{2}{\sqrt{\mathrm{III}_{\overset{-1}{c}}}}\,\frac{\partial\Sigma}{\partial \mathrm{I}_{\overset{-1}{c}}}$$

47.11)
$$\begin{aligned} b_0 &= -2\,\sqrt{\mathrm{III}_c}\left(\mathrm{II}_c\,\frac{\partial\Sigma}{\partial \mathrm{II}_c} + \mathrm{III}_c\,\frac{\partial\Sigma}{\partial \mathrm{III}_c}\right) \\ &= \frac{2}{\sqrt{\mathrm{III}_{\overset{-1}{c}}}}\left(\mathrm{II}_{\overset{-1}{c}}\,\frac{\partial\Sigma}{\partial \mathrm{II}_{\overset{-1}{c}}} + \mathrm{III}_{\overset{-1}{c}}\,\frac{\partial\Sigma}{\partial \mathrm{III}_{\overset{-1}{c}}}\right) \end{aligned}$$

$$b_1 = -2\,\sqrt{\mathrm{III}_c}\,\frac{\partial\Sigma}{\partial \mathrm{I}_c} = -2\,\sqrt{\mathrm{III}_{\overset{-1}{c}}}\,\frac{\partial\Sigma}{\partial \mathrm{II}_{\overset{-1}{c}}}$$

here the extreme rights of (47.11) are obtained from the middle parts y using (9.22) and (9.23).

The stress-strain relations for incompressible media are obtained from 47.10) by setting $\mathrm{III}_{\overset{-1}{c}} = 1$ and adding a term involving the hydrostatic pressure. Thus

$$t^k{}_l = -p\,\delta^k{}_l + 2\frac{\partial\Sigma}{\partial \underset{c}{\mathrm{I}_{-1}}}\overset{-1}{c}{}^k{}_l - 2\frac{\partial\Sigma}{\partial \underset{c}{\mathrm{II}_{-1}}}c^k{}_l \tag{47.12}$$

as derived by Ariano [1930] and Rivlin [1948c].

Another form of stress-strain relations that is used frequently employ the convected coordinates. In these coordinates, components of $G_{KL}$ an $c_{kl}$ coincide. Thus, writing $G_{kl} = c_{kl}$, (47.10) and (47.12) may be pu into the form used by Green and Zerna [1954, eq. (2.8.8)]

$$t^{kl} = \phi\, c^{kl} + \psi\, B^{kl} + p\, g^{kl} \tag{47.13}$$

where

$$\phi = \frac{2}{\sqrt{\mathrm{III}}}\frac{\partial\Sigma}{\partial\mathrm{I}} \qquad \psi = \frac{2}{\sqrt{\mathrm{III}}}\frac{\partial\Sigma}{\partial\mathrm{II}} \qquad p = 2\sqrt{\mathrm{III}}\,\frac{\partial\Sigma}{\partial\mathrm{III}}$$
$$B^{kl} = \mathrm{I}\, c^{kl} - g_{mn}\, c^{km}\, c^{ln} \tag{47.14}$$

where invariants I, II, and III defined by

$$\mathrm{I} = g_{kl}\, c^{kl} \qquad \mathrm{II} = \tfrac{1}{2}(\mathrm{I}^2 - g_{kl}\, g_{mn}\, c^{km}\, c^{ln}) = g^{rs}\, c_{rs}\,\mathrm{III}$$
$$\mathrm{III} = \frac{g}{G} \tag{47.15}$$

are the values of $\underset{c}{\mathrm{I}_{-1}}$, $\underset{c}{\mathrm{II}_{-1}}$, and $\underset{c}{\mathrm{III}_{-1}}$ in convected coordinates. When th body is incompressible, we have $\mathrm{III} = 1$; hence $\Sigma = \Sigma(\mathrm{I}, \mathrm{II})$ so that $p$ i undefined. The form (47.13) of the stress-strain relations remair unchanged except that now

$$\phi = 2\frac{\partial\Sigma}{\partial\mathrm{I}} \qquad \psi = 2\frac{\partial\Sigma}{\partial\mathrm{II}} \tag{47.16}$$

*Other Restrictions on Constitutive Equations.* In the natural state th medium is unstressed and undeformed, i.e., $t^k{}_l = 0$, $c^k{}_l = \overset{-1}{c}{}^k{}_l = \delta^k$ Upon substituting these into (47.10) and writing $\underset{c}{\mathrm{I}_{-1}} = \underset{c}{\mathrm{II}_{-1}} = 3$ $\underset{c}{\mathrm{III}_{-1}} = 1$, we obtain

$$\left(\frac{\partial\Sigma}{\partial \underset{c}{\mathrm{I}_{-1}}}\right)_0 + 2\left(\frac{\partial\Sigma}{\partial \underset{c}{\mathrm{II}_{-1}}}\right)_0 + \left(\frac{\partial\Sigma}{\partial \underset{c}{\mathrm{III}_{-1}}}\right)_0 = 0 \tag{47.17}$$

where subscript 0 indicates evaluation at the natural state. Equatio (47.17) is a condition that must be imposed on $\Sigma$.

Thermodynamical considerations will in general bring addition demands upon the stored-energy function $\Sigma$. Such developments, how ever, are not in a satisfactory state for the theories of finite deformation ruesdell [1952, art. 41] and Baker and Ericksen [1954] have discovered ertain inequalities for which experimental as well as theoretically sound erifications exist.

In terms of principal stretches $\lambda_\alpha$ and principal stresses $t_\alpha$, (47.10) reads

$$t_\alpha = b_{-1}\lambda_\alpha^2 + b_0 + b_1\lambda_\alpha^{-2} \tag{47.18}$$

It is reasonable to assume that in an isotropic body the greatest (least) ension occurs in the direction corresponding to the greatest (least) tretch, i.e., analytically

$$t_\alpha > t_\beta \qquad \text{whenever } \lambda_\alpha > \lambda_\beta \tag{47.19}$$

From (47.18) we get

$$t_\alpha - t_\beta = (\lambda_\alpha^2 - \lambda_\beta^2)\left(b_{-1} - \frac{b_1}{\lambda_\alpha^2\lambda_\beta^2}\right)$$

Therefore a necessary and sufficient condition for $\lambda_\alpha > \lambda_\beta$ to imply $t_\alpha > t_\beta$ is that

$$b_{-1} > \frac{b_1}{\lambda_\alpha^2\lambda_\beta^2} \tag{47.20}$$

ince this is unaltered when $\lambda_\alpha$ and $\lambda_\beta$ are interchanged, this inequality ıust hold unless $\lambda_\alpha = \lambda_\beta$ $(\alpha \neq \beta)$, in which case we should also consider he possibility of the vanishing of the coefficient of $\lambda_\alpha{}^2 - \lambda_\beta{}^2$. Thus

$$b_{-1} \geq \frac{b_1}{\lambda_\alpha^4} \tag{47.21}$$

he invariants contained in $b_{-1}$, $b_0$, and $b_1$ are expressed in terms of $\lambda_\alpha$ by 9.22). Since $\mathrm{III}_{\underset{c}{-1}} = \mathrm{III}_C = \lambda_1{}^2\lambda_2{}^2\lambda_3{}^2 > 0$, using (47.11), (47.20) and 47.21) take the explicit forms:

$$\begin{aligned} &\frac{\partial\Sigma}{\partial \mathrm{I}_{\underset{c}{-1}}} + \lambda_\alpha^2 \frac{\partial\Sigma}{\partial \mathrm{II}_{\underset{c}{-1}}} > 0 \qquad \text{if } \lambda_\beta \neq \lambda_\gamma \qquad (\alpha, \beta, \gamma \neq) \\ &\frac{\partial\Sigma}{\partial \mathrm{I}_{\underset{c}{-1}}} + \lambda_\alpha^2 \frac{\partial\Sigma}{\partial \mathrm{II}_{\underset{c}{-1}}} \geq 0 \qquad \text{if } \lambda_\beta = \lambda_\gamma \qquad (\alpha, \beta, \gamma \neq) \end{aligned} \tag{47.22}$$

he same procedure applied to incompressible materials (47.12) also ives (47.22).

A number of experimental results on rubber show that

$$\frac{\partial\Sigma}{\partial \mathrm{I}_{\underset{c}{-1}}} > 0 \qquad \frac{\partial\Sigma}{\partial \mathrm{II}_{\underset{c}{-1}}} > 0 \tag{47.23}$$

holds for a wide range of values of $\underset{c}{\mathrm{I}}_{-1}$ and $\underset{c}{\mathrm{II}}_{-1}$ so that $(47.22)_1$ certainly holds in this case.[1] It must also be noted that for the classical theory of elasticity, if one uses $\mathbf{t} = \lambda_e \mathrm{I}_{\tilde{e}} \mathbf{I} + 2\,\mu_e\, \tilde{\mathbf{e}}$ in place of (47.10), one obtains the condition $\mu_e > 0$, which is known to be valid for all materials adequately described by this theory.[2]

*Cauchy's Method.* It is possible to arrive at the stress-strain relation for isotropic solids by employing the results obtained in Art. 46. We may use either of the forms (46.31) and (46.34) as the starting point, i.e.

$$t^{rs} = F^{RS}\,(C_{KL}, G_{KL})\, X^R{}_{,r}\, X^S{}_{,s} \tag{47.24}$$

$$t^{rs} = f^{rs}\,(\overset{-1}{c}_{kl}, G_{KL}) \tag{47.25}$$

The response functions $F^{RS}$ and $f^{rs}$ are symmetric *isotropic functions*. For an isotropic analytic function $\mathbf{b} = \mathbf{f}\,(\mathbf{a})$, where $\mathbf{b}$ and $\mathbf{a}$ are matrices $b^k{}_l$ and $a^k{}_l$, we have

$$\mathbf{b} = k_\alpha\, \mathbf{a}^\alpha \tag{47.26}$$

where $k_\alpha$ are scalar functions of $\mathbf{a}$. Any analytic scalar function of a 3 by 3 matrix $\mathbf{a}$ is a function of three principal invariants $\mathrm{I}_a$, $\mathrm{II}_a$, and $\mathrm{III}_a$. Therefore $k_\alpha$ are functions of these three invariants only. According to the Cayley-Hamilton theorem we have

$$\mathbf{a}^3 = \mathrm{III}_a \mathbf{I} - \mathrm{II}_a\, \mathbf{a} + \mathrm{I}_a\, \mathbf{a}^2 \tag{47.27}$$

Therefore $\mathbf{a}^3$ and all higher powers of $\mathbf{a}$ in (47.26) may be expressed in terms of $\mathbf{I}$, $\mathbf{a}$, and $\mathbf{a}^2$ and the invariants. Thus $\mathbf{b}$ is an *analytic isotropic function of* $\mathbf{a}$ *if and only if it can be expressed as*

$$\mathbf{b} = g_0 \mathbf{I} + g_1\, \mathbf{a} + g_2\, \mathbf{a}^2 \tag{47.28}$$

or in index notation

$$b^k{}_l = g_0\, \delta^k{}_l + g_1\, a^k{}_l + g_2\, a^k{}_m\, a^m{}_l \tag{47.29}$$

where $g_0$, $g_1$, and $g_2$ are functions of the three invariants only.

Applying this theorem to $\mathbf{t}$ in (47.25), we therefore write

$$t^k{}_l = g_0\, \delta^k{}_l + g_1\, \overset{-1}{c}{}^k{}_l + g_2\, \overset{-1}{c}{}^k{}_m\, \overset{-1}{c}{}^m{}_l \tag{47.30}$$

where $g_\alpha = g_\alpha\,(\underset{c}{\mathrm{I}}_{-1}, \underset{c}{\mathrm{II}}_{-1}, \underset{c}{\mathrm{III}}_{-1})$.

[1] In the experiments they performed on rubber, Rivlin and Saunders [1951] have not observed any case where the equality in $(47.22)_2$ holds.

[2] For a number of other theoretical implications of (47.22) see Ericksen [1955]. See also Arts. 54 and 58. Coleman and Noll [1959*a*], basing their work on thermostatic considerations, recently gave a theorem leading to the above results. They point out, however, that the results due to Baker and Ericksen are not necessarily valid for principal stresses measured per unit area of the deformed body unless all these stresses are positive. They make reference to work of Barta [1957] for related inequalities.

By putting $\mathbf{a} = \overset{-1}{\mathbf{c}}$ in the Cayley-Hamilton theorem (47.27) and ıultiplying both sides by $\mathbf{c}$, we get

$$\text{17.31)} \qquad \overset{-1}{c}{}^{k}{}_{m}\, \overset{-1}{c}{}^{m}{}_{l} = \mathrm{III}_{\underset{c}{-1}}\, c^{k}{}_{l} - \mathrm{II}_{\underset{c}{-1}}\, \delta^{k}{}_{l} + \mathrm{I}_{\underset{c}{-1}}\, \overset{-1}{c}{}^{k}{}_{l}$$

pon using this in (47.30), we may write it also as

$$\text{17.32)} \qquad t^{k}{}_{l} = h_{-1}\, \overset{-1}{c}{}^{k}{}_{l} + h_0\, \delta^{k}{}_{l} + h_1\, c^{k}{}_{l}$$

here

$$\text{17.33)} \quad h_{-1} = g_1 + g_2\, \mathrm{I}_{\underset{c}{-1}} \qquad h_0 = g_0 - g_2\, \mathrm{II}_{\underset{c}{-1}} \qquad h_1 = g_2\, \mathrm{III}_{\underset{c}{-1}}$$

his is of the form found by Green's method [see (47.10)] if we recognize $_\alpha$ as $b_\alpha$.

It is now clear that both Green's method and Cauchy's method for the otropic material lead to the same form for stress-strain relations. Iotice, however, that the elastic constants $b_\alpha$ appearing in Green's ıethod are derived from a potential function $\Sigma$, whereas the relation of 'auchy's elastic constants $h_\alpha$ to a strain-energy function $\Sigma$ is not clear. ı fact, the existence of such a potential function clearly imposes restric-.ons on $h_\alpha$. To show this, we solve for $\partial\Sigma/\partial\mathrm{I}_c$, $\partial\Sigma/\partial\mathrm{II}_c$, and $\partial\Sigma/\partial\mathrm{III}_c$ om (47.11). Upon cross differentiation we obtain the necessary and ıfficient conditions for $h_\alpha$ to accept a representation of this form in rms of a single function $\Sigma$.[3]

$$\text{17.34)} \qquad \begin{gathered} \frac{\partial h_{-1}}{\partial \mathrm{I}} = -\mathrm{III}\,\frac{\partial h_1}{\partial \mathrm{II}} \qquad \frac{h_1}{2} + \mathrm{III}\,\frac{\partial h_1}{\partial \mathrm{III}} = \frac{\partial h_0}{\partial \mathrm{I}} + \frac{\mathrm{II}}{\mathrm{III}}\,\frac{\partial h_{-1}}{\partial \mathrm{I}} \\ \frac{h_{-1}}{2} - \mathrm{III}\,\frac{\partial h_{-1}}{\partial \mathrm{III}} = h_{-1} + \mathrm{II}\,\frac{\partial h_{-1}}{\partial \mathrm{II}} + \mathrm{III}\,\frac{\partial h_0}{\partial \mathrm{II}} \end{gathered}$$

When these conditions are satisfied, then a strain-energy function $\Sigma$ xists so that (47.32) reduces to (47.10) obtained by Green's method.

These results clearly indicate the restricted nature of Green's method. 'or an anisotropic solid the difference between the results of the two heories stands clearly at the outset. For the infinitesimal strain approxi-ıation the fact that Cauchy's method gives thirty-six elastic constants hile Green's method gives twenty-one is well-known. The required reduc-ion of the number of constants by fifteen employs the positive-definite haracter of the strain-energy function as an additional requirement to 'auchy's method.

[3] Caprioli [1955] has shown that the existence of a strain-energy function is a con-equence of the following two assumptions: (1) stress is a function of strain tensor nly and (2) the work required to deform the body from the natural state to any other ate is nonnegative.

The foregoing analysis clearly applies to stress-strain relations (47.24)

Finally it is important to note that the principal axes of $\mathbf{a}^\alpha$ are th same as those of $\mathbf{a}$. Hence (47.26) indicates that the principal axes of t and $\mathbf{a}$ coincide. The same being applicable to (47.30), we have th theorem that follows.

THEOREM 1. *In an isotropic medium any principal axis of strain in th deformed state is also a principal axis of the stress.*

*Transition to the Linear Theory.* Constitutive equations (47.10) ar suitable for the solution of problems in finite deformations. The transi tion to linear theory, however, requires substitution of the polynomia expansion of $\Sigma$ in terms of strain invariants (cf. Art. 60). A quicl conversion may be made by substitutions

$$\underset{c}{\mathrm{I}_{-1}} \cong 3 + 2\,\mathrm{I}_{\tilde{e}} \qquad \underset{c}{\mathrm{II}_{-1}} \cong 3 + 4\,\mathrm{I}_{\tilde{e}} \qquad \underset{c}{\mathrm{III}_{-1}} \cong 1 + 2\,\mathrm{I}_{\tilde{e}}$$

$$(47.35) \qquad \frac{\partial \Sigma}{\partial \underset{c}{\mathrm{I}_{-1}}} \cong \mu_e + \frac{\lambda_e + 2\,\mu_e}{2}\,\mathrm{I}_{\tilde{e}} \qquad \frac{\partial \Sigma}{\partial \underset{c}{\mathrm{II}_{-1}}} \cong -\frac{\mu_e}{2} \qquad \frac{\partial \Sigma}{\partial \underset{c}{\mathrm{III}_{-1}}} \cong 0$$

where $\lambda_e$ and $\mu_e$ are the Lamé constants of the classical theory of elasticity

It may be verified that when (47.35) and

$$(47.36) \qquad c^k{}_l \cong \delta^k{}_l - 2\,\tilde{e}^k{}_l \qquad \overset{-1}{c}{}^k{}_l \cong \delta^k{}_l + 2\,\tilde{e}^k{}_l$$

are substituted into (47.10) and only the linear terms in $\tilde{\mathbf{e}}$ are retained we obtain Hooke's law of the classical linear theory of elasticity, i.e.,

$$(47.37) \qquad t^k{}_l = \lambda\,\mathrm{I}_{\tilde{e}}\,\delta^k{}_l + 2\,\mu_e\,\tilde{e}^k{}_l$$

In terms of the constitutive coefficients $b_\alpha$ the foregoing substitution are equivalent to

$$(47.38) \qquad b_{-1} \cong 2\,\mu_e + \lambda_e\,\mathrm{I}_{\tilde{e}} \qquad b_0 \cong -\mu_e\,(3 + \mathrm{I}_{\tilde{e}}) \qquad b_1 \cong \mu_e\,(1 + \mathrm{I}_{\tilde{e}})$$

The replacements for the constitutive coefficients $h_{-1}$, $h_0$, and $h_1$ ar identical to (47.38).

## 48. STOKESIAN FLUIDS

The notion of fluidity was expressed by Stokes [1845] in his remarkabl paper which he gave at the age of twenty-six. Stokes states that "th difference between the pressure on a plane in a given direction passin through any point $P$ of a fluid in motion and the pressure which woul exist in all directions about $P$ if the fluid in its neighborhood were in a state of relative equilibrium depends only on the relative motion of th fluid immediately about $P$; and that the relative motion due to an motion of rotation may be eliminated without affecting the difference o the pressures above-mentioned." This somewhat vague idea contains the essential ingredients of fluidity which is postulated below.

DEFINITION 1. (*Stokesian Fluid*) *A stokesian fluid is a continuous medium such that* (1) *it admits a constitutive equation*

$$\mathbf{t} = \mathbf{f}(\mathbf{d}) \tag{48.1}$$

*where* $\mathbf{t}$ *and* $\mathbf{d}$ *are the stress tensor and the deformation rate tensor respectively;* (2) $\mathbf{t}$ *does not explicitly depend on the position* $\mathbf{x}$ *(spatial homogeneity);* (3) *the response function* $\mathbf{f}$ *is independent of the orientation of axes (material objectivity); and* (4) *when* $\mathbf{d} = 0$, (48.1) *reduces to*

$$\mathbf{t} = -\pi \mathbf{I} \tag{48.2}$$

*where* $\pi$ *is a scalar called the thermodynamic pressure or simply pressure defined by* $(40.16)_2$.

Let us note that the fluid medium so defined is but one example of a large class of materials that possess more general constitutive equations. Fluid media having constitutive equations of the form

$$\mathbf{t} + \pi \mathbf{I} = \mathbf{f}(\mathbf{d}, \mathbf{w}) \qquad \mathbf{f}(0, \mathbf{w}) = 0 \tag{48.3}$$

were introduced early by Boussinesq [1868]; fluids involving higher gradients of $\mathbf{v}$ of the form

$$t^k{}_l + \pi\, \delta^k{}_l = f^k{}_l\,(v^{r_1}{}_{,s_1}, v^{r_1}{}_{,s_1s_2}, v^{r_1}{}_{,s_1s_2s_3}, \ldots) \tag{48.4}$$

by Lévy [1869]; and other more general fluids by Reiner [1945], Rivlin [1947*a*], Truesdell [1949*a*, *b*,], and later by Noll [1955]. A critical review of the subject matter up to 1952 may be found in Truesdell [1952, chap. V].

In order to follow a development parallel to the ideally elastic solid, we shall postulate the stokesian fluid as follows and subsequently prove that this definition is equivalent to the one given above.

DEFINITION 2. (*Stokesian Fluid*) *Stokesian fluids admit a constitutive equation*

$$t^k{}_l = f^k{}_l\,(x^m, v^n, v^r{}_{,s}) \tag{48.5}$$

*subject to spatial and material objectivity, and*

$$t^k{}_l = -\pi\, \delta^k{}_l \qquad \text{when} \qquad d_{rs} = 0 \tag{48.6}$$

*where* $t^k{}_l$ *and* $d_{rs}$ *are the stress tensor and deformation-rate tensor and* $x^m$ *and* $v^n$ *are the position and velocity vectors.*

We now should like to present two theorems.

THEOREM 1. *Definition* 2 *is equivalent to Definition* 1.

According to spatial objectivity, $f^k{}_l$ should be form-invariant in objectively equivalent motions. Thus, if we change the rectangular spatial frame of reference rigidly

$$x'^k = Q^k{}_l(t)\, x^l + b^k(t) \tag{48.7}$$
$$t' = t - a \qquad Q^k{}_l\, Q_m{}^l = Q^l{}_m\, Q_l{}^k = \delta^k{}_m$$

then we should have

$$t'^k{}_l = f^k{}_l(x'^m, v'^m, v'^r{}_{,s}) \tag{48.8}$$

Applying a rigid translation in a special form,

$$Q^k{}_l = \delta^k{}_l \qquad b^k = -x^k \qquad a = 0$$

we obtain $\mathbf{x}' = \mathbf{x} - \mathbf{x} = 0$. Thus $t^k{}_l$ cannot depend on $\mathbf{x}$.

Next we apply a constant-velocity motion

$$Q^k{}_l = \delta^k{}_l \qquad x'^k = x^k - v^k t \qquad (v^k = \text{const})$$

which shows that $\mathbf{f}$ cannot depend on $\mathbf{v}$. Thus we may write

$$t'^k{}_l = f^k{}_l(v'^r{}_{,s}) \tag{48.9}$$

Now consider the general rigid rotation (48.7). According to (46.3) and (27.10) $t^k{}_l$ and $v^r{}_{,s}$ change as

$$t'^k{}_l = t^r{}_s\, Q^k{}_r\, Q_l{}^s \qquad v'^r{}_{,s} = Q^r{}_m\, Q_s{}^k\, v^m{}_{,k} + \dot{Q}^r{}_m\, Q_s{}^m \tag{48.10}$$

Substitution of (48.10) into (48.9) gives

$$t^r{}_s\, Q^k{}_r\, Q_l{}^s = f^k{}_l(Q^r{}_m\, v^m{}_{,n}\, Q_s{}^n + \dot{Q}^r{}_m\, Q_s{}^m) \tag{48.11}$$

We can always select $Q^k{}_r = -\delta^k{}_r$ and $\dot{Q}^k{}_r$ equal to any antisymmetric transformation given a priori. Thus, choosing

$$Q^k{}_r = -\delta^k{}_r \qquad \dot{Q}^k{}_r = w^k{}_r$$

where $w^k{}_r$ is the spin tensor, (48.11) gives

$$t^k{}_l = f^k{}_l(v^r{}_{,s} - w^r{}_s) = f^k{}_l(d^r{}_s)$$

since $2\,w^r{}_s = v^r{}_{,s} - v_{s,}{}^r$ and $2\,d^r{}_s = v^r{}_{,s} + v_{s,}{}^r$ in rectangular coordinates. Since $\mathbf{t}$ and $\mathbf{d}$ are tensors, this result is valid in any general coordinate system. Hence, the proof of the theorem.

THEOREM 2. *Constitutive relations for stokesian fluids are equivalent to*

$$t^k{}_l = (-\pi + \alpha_0)\,\delta^k{}_l + \alpha_1\, d^k{}_l + \alpha_2\, d^k{}_r\, d^r{}_l \tag{48.12}$$

*where*

$$\alpha_\kappa = \alpha_\kappa(\mathrm{I}_d, \mathrm{II}_d, \mathrm{III}_d) \qquad \alpha_0(0, 0, 0) = 0 \tag{48.13}$$

In an objectively equivalent motion we have

$$t^k{}_l = f^k{}_l\,(d^r{}_s) \qquad t'^k{}_l = f^k{}_l\,(Q^r{}_m\,d^m{}_n\,Q_s{}^n)$$

Substituting $(48.10)_1$ into the second part of the above, we have

$$t^r{}_s\,Q^k{}_r\,Q_l{}^s = f^k{}_l\,(Q^r{}_m\,d^m{}_n\,Q_s{}^n) \tag{48.14}$$

or

$$t^r{}_s = Q_k{}^r\,Q^l{}_s\,f^k{}_l\,(Q^r{}_m\,d^m{}_n\,Q_s{}^n) = f^r{}_s\,(d^m{}_n)$$

Hence

$$Q^k{}_r\,Q_l{}^s\,f^r{}_s\,(d^m{}_n) = f^k{}_l\,(Q^r{}_m\,Q_s{}^n\,d^m{}_n) \tag{48.15}$$

This implies that $f^r{}_s$ is spatially isotropic. Therefore, in the same way as in Art. 47, we can express $f^k{}_l$ as

$$f^k{}_l = \alpha\,\delta^k{}_l + \alpha_1\,d^k{}_l + \alpha_2\,d^k{}_m\,d^m{}_l \tag{48.16}$$

where $\alpha$, $\alpha_1$, and $\alpha_2$ are functions of deformation-rate invariants $\mathrm{I}_d$, $\mathrm{II}_d$, and $\mathrm{III}_d$. Now according to (48.6) for $d^k{}_l = 0$ we must have

$$f^k{}_l\,(0) = \alpha\,(0,0,0)\,\delta^k{}_l = -\pi\,\delta^k{}_l$$

Thus, defining

$$\alpha_0\,(\mathrm{I}_d, \mathrm{II}_d, \mathrm{III}_d) \equiv \alpha\,(\mathrm{I}_d, \mathrm{II}_d, \mathrm{III}_d) + \pi$$

we may put (48.16) into the form

$$t^k{}_l = (-\pi + \alpha_0)\,\delta^k{}_l + \alpha_1\,d^k{}_l + \alpha_2\,d^k{}_m\,d^m{}_l$$

where $\alpha_0\,(0,0,0) = 0$. Hence the proof of the theorem. It is clear from (48.12) that the stokesian fluids as defined above are isotropic. Recently a theory on anisotropic fluids was developed by Ericksen [1960*a*, *b*, *c*, *d*].

For an *incompressible fluid* we have

$$\mathrm{I}_d = 0 \tag{48.17}$$

and $\pi$ is undefined. Since $\pi$ enters the constitutive equations only in the combination $-\pi + \alpha_0$, we may without loss in generality take

$$-p \equiv -\pi + \alpha_0$$

as a basic unknown instead of $\pi$. Thus the constitutive equations for an incompressible fluid may be expressed as

$$t^k{}_l = -p\,\delta^k{}_l + \alpha_1\,(\mathrm{II}_d, \mathrm{III}_d)\,d^k{}_l + \alpha_2\,(\mathrm{II}_d, \mathrm{III}_d)\,d^k{}_m\,d^m{}_l \tag{48.18}$$

*Inequalities Restricting Constitutive Equations.* The thermodynamical pressure $\pi$, according to $(40.16)_2$, is a well-defined quantity for the static conditions of the fluid. The phenomenological functions must be determined from the experiments. A question arises as to whether other physical restrictions have to be imposed on the forms of these functions. At this point we need to resort to irreversible thermodynamics. According to the constitutive relations (48.12) the stress tensor consists of two parts: a *nondissipative* part

$$-\pi\, \delta^k{}_l$$

and a *dissipative* part

$$(48.19)\qquad {}_Dt^k{}_l = \alpha_0\, \delta^k{}_l + \alpha_1\, d^k{}_l + \alpha_2\, d^k{}_r\, d^r{}_l$$

since ${}_D\mathbf{t} = 0$ whenever $\mathbf{d} = 0$. Thus we may write

$$(48.20)\qquad t^k{}_l = -\pi\, \delta^k{}_l + {}_Dt^k{}_l$$

If we associate ${}_Dt^k{}_l$ with the thermodynamic dissipative stress for the nonpolar case and all other thermodynamic variables $\nu_\alpha$ are taken to be zero for a *nonnegative* entropy production, according to (40.22) we must have

$$(48.21)\qquad \theta\,\Delta \equiv {}_Dt^k{}_l\, d^l{}_k \geq 0$$

where $\theta\,\Delta$ is the so-called *dissipation function.* Upon substituting (48.19) into this, we obtain

$$\alpha_0\, d^k{}_k + \alpha_1\, d^k{}_l\, d^l{}_k + \alpha_2\, d^k{}_r\, d^r{}_l\, d^l{}_k \geq 0$$

According to the defining equations of invariants we have

$$(48.22)\qquad \begin{aligned} d^k{}_k &= \mathrm{I}_d \qquad d^k{}_l\, d^l{}_k = \mathrm{I}_d{}^2 - 2\,\mathrm{II}_d \\ d^k{}_r\, d^r{}_l\, d^l{}_k &= \mathrm{I}_d{}^3 - 3\,\mathrm{I}_d\,\mathrm{II}_d + 3\,\mathrm{III}_d \end{aligned}$$

Consequently *nonnegative dissipation requires that*

$$(48.23)\qquad \alpha_0\,\mathrm{I}_d + \alpha_1\,(\mathrm{I}_d{}^2 - 2\,\mathrm{II}_d) + \alpha_2\,(\mathrm{I}_d{}^3 - 3\,\mathrm{I}_d\,\mathrm{II}_d + 3\,\mathrm{III}_d) \geq 0$$

*for any physically possible motion.* When the phenomenological coefficients accept power series expansions

$$(48.24)\qquad \alpha_\kappa = \sum_{r,s,t} A_{\kappa rst}\,\mathrm{I}_d{}^r\,\mathrm{II}_d{}^s\,\mathrm{III}_d{}^t \qquad (\kappa = 1, 2, 3)$$

where $A_{\kappa rst}$ are constants, then (48.23) will impose certain restrictions on these coefficients. It is not obvious how one finds a general inequality that $A_{\kappa rst}$ must satisfy for arbitrary ranges of $r$, $s$, and $t$.

When the constitutive equations are linear in $\mathbf{d}$, we have

$$(48.25)\qquad \alpha_0 = A_{0100}\,\mathrm{I}_d \qquad \alpha_1 = A_{1000} \qquad \alpha_2 = 0$$

and (48.23) in this case can be seen to imply

$$(48.26)\qquad A_{1000} \geq 0 \qquad 3\,A_{0100} + A_{1000} \geq 0$$

The implications of these will be made clear below. For higher-order polynomial approximations in **d** of the constitutive equations, the conditions appear to be very complex. Further elaboration of this approach is made in Art. 49.

An alternative nonthermodynamical approach, similar to the one given in Art. 47 that leads to certain inequalities that must be imposed on constitutive coefficients, is due to Baker and Ericksen [1954] and Ericksen [1955]. A heuristic argument based on physical considerations is that tension exerted across a plane is greatest (least) whenever the stretching in the direction of the normal to this plane is greatest (least). Mathematically

(48.27) $$t_\alpha > t_\beta \qquad \text{whenever } d_\alpha > d_\beta$$

where $t_\alpha$ and $d_\alpha$ are respectively the tension and stretching. Now write constitutive equations (48.12) as

(48.28) $$t_\alpha = -\pi + \alpha_0 + \alpha_1 d_\alpha + \alpha_2 d_\alpha{}^2$$

From this, by forming $t_\alpha - t_\beta$, we see that for a compressible material (48.27) is satisfied if and only if

(48.29) $$\begin{aligned} \alpha_1 + \alpha_2 (d_\alpha + d_\beta) > 0 \qquad & \text{if } d_\alpha \neq d_\beta \\ \alpha_1 + \alpha_2 (d_\alpha + d_\beta) \geq 0 \qquad & \text{if } d_\alpha = d_\beta \qquad (\alpha \neq \beta) \end{aligned}$$

For the *incompressible* material we have $d_1 + d_2 + d_3 = 0$. Hence

(48.30) $$\begin{aligned} \alpha_1 - \alpha_2 d_\alpha > 0 \qquad & \text{if } d_\beta \neq d_\gamma \qquad (\alpha, \beta, \gamma \neq) \\ \alpha_1 - \alpha_2 d_\alpha \geq 0 \qquad & \text{if } d_\beta = d_\gamma \qquad (\alpha, \beta, \gamma \neq) \end{aligned}$$

For a *plane* motion of an *incompressible* fluid $d_3 = 0$ and $d_2 = -d_1$. Thus

(48.31) $$\begin{aligned} & \alpha_1 > 0 \qquad \alpha_1 > \alpha_2 d_1 \qquad \alpha_1 > -\alpha_2 d_1 \qquad && \text{if } d_1 \neq 0 \\ & \alpha_1 \geq 0 && \text{if } d_1 = 0 \end{aligned}$$

From this there follows

(48.32) $$\left| \frac{\alpha_1}{\alpha_2 d_1} \right| > 0$$

except perhaps when $d_1 = 0$, in which case $d_2 = d_3 = 0$, so that the motion is instantaneously rigid and the left may be indeterminate. For the classical theory we have $\alpha_2 \equiv 0$, $\alpha_1 \equiv 2\mu_v > 0$, and (48.30) holds.

The rate at which the stresses do work in distorting the fluid is defined by

(48.33) $$W_d = \tfrac{1}{2} t^p{}_q \bar{d}^q{}_p$$

where

$$\bar{d}^q{}_p = d^q{}_p - \tfrac{1}{3}\,\mathrm{I}_d\,\delta^q{}_p \tag{48.34}$$

is the deviatoric rate of deformation. Referred to principal directions of stress which are also principal directions of deformation rate, (48.33) reads

$$W_d = \tfrac{1}{2}\,t_\alpha\,\bar{d}_\alpha = \tfrac{1}{6}\,[(t_1 - t_2)\,(d_1 - d_2) + (t_2 - t_3)\,(d_2 - d_3) + (t_3 - t_1)\,(d_3 - d_1)] \tag{48.35}$$

It is now clear that axiom (48.27) implies

$$W_d \geq 0 \tag{48.36}$$

A counterexample can be constructed to show that (48.36) does not necessarily imply (48.27). Even though we found a close tie between the axiom (48.27) and the distortion energy, this does not readily imply that the entropy production $\theta\,\Delta$ is nonnegative. Since

$$\theta\,\Delta = {}_Dt^p{}_q\,d^q{}_p = W_d + \tfrac{1}{6}\,\mathrm{I}_d\,\mathrm{I}_t$$

we see that for $\theta\,\Delta \geq 0$ we must have $W_d + \tfrac{1}{6}\,\mathrm{I}_d\,\mathrm{I}_t \geq 0$. For incompressible fluids $\mathrm{I}_d = 0$; hence $\theta\,\Delta > 0$ if and only if $W_d \geq 0$, so that in this case there exists a relation between the thermodynamical requirement of entropy production and (48.27).

*Thermodynamic and Mechanical Pressure.* We now show the relation of thermodynamic pressure $\pi$ to the *mechanical pressure* $\bar{p}$ defined by

$$\bar{p} = -\tfrac{1}{3}\,t^k{}_k = -\tfrac{1}{3}\,\mathrm{I}_t \tag{48.37}$$

Introducing *deviatoric* stress $\bar{t}^k{}_l$ by

$$t^k{}_l = -\bar{p}\,\delta^k{}_l + \bar{t}^k{}_l \qquad \bar{t}^k{}_k = 0 \tag{48.38}$$

from (48.20) we get

$${}_Dt^k{}_l = (\pi - \bar{p})\,\delta^k{}_l + \bar{t}^k{}_l \tag{48.39}$$

If we set $k = l$ and use (48.19) and (48.22), this becomes

$$3\,(\pi - \bar{p}) = 3\,\alpha_0 + \alpha_1\,\mathrm{I}_d + \alpha_2\,(\mathrm{I}_d{}^2 - 2\,\mathrm{II}_d) \tag{48.40}$$

It is now clear that the thermodynamic pressure is in general not the same as the mechanical pressure when the fluid is in motion. For *the static case* $\mathrm{I}_d = \mathrm{II}_d = \mathrm{III}_d = \alpha_0\,(0, 0, 0) = 0$ and $\pi = \bar{p}$.

If we use the power series expansion (48.24) in (48.40), we find that *the necessary and the sufficient condition for* $\pi = \bar{p}$ *in every motion is that*

$$3\,A_{0rst} + A_{1,\,r-1,\,s,t} + A_{2,\,r-2,\,s,t} - 2\,A_{2,\,r,\,s-1,\,t} = 0 \tag{48.41}$$

*for all r, s, t.* There seem to be no physical grounds for $\pi = \bar{p}$, for the fluid in motion.

Setting $k = l$ in (48.18) and using (48.22), (48.37), and (48.17), for the incompressible fluids we now obtain

$$3\,(p - \bar{p}) = -2\,\alpha_2\,(\mathrm{II}_d, \mathrm{III}_d)\,\mathrm{II}_d \tag{48.42}$$

Thus *the necessary and sufficient condition for* $p = \bar{p}$ *in an isotropic incompressible fluid is that the constitutive equations are quasi-linear* in $d^k{}_l$, i.e.,

$$\alpha_2\,(\mathrm{II}_d, \mathrm{III}_d) = 0 \tag{48.43}$$

The general constitutive equations (48.18) for an incompressible fluid contain three phenomenological functions: namely, $p$, $\alpha_1$, and $\alpha_2$. Of these $\alpha_1$ and $\alpha_2$ are to be determined through experimental measurements. The pressure $p$ here is left undefined. Determination of $p$ will be effected through the boundary conditions.

Let us note that the term "pressure" here is used for three different quantities: the thermodynamic pressure $\pi$, which is well-defined by $(40.16)_2$ whenever the fluid is in thermodynamic equilibrium and compressible; the mechanical pressure $\bar{p}$, which is also well-defined through (48.37) and is shown in general to be different from the thermodynamic pressure unless certain conditions (48.41) among the phenomenological constants are accidentally satisfied; finally the pressure $p$, introduced in (48.18) for the incompressible fluids, which is left undefined. The pressure measured in an experiment depends on the measuring instrument and in general is a particular component of the stress tensor. In a deforming fluid, identification of pressure with the quantities called pressure in the theory is in general not valid.

Let us further remark that the phenomenological coefficients $\alpha_\kappa$ may in addition to deformation invariants depend on thermodynamic variables, pressure, and temperature. Truesdell [1949*a*, *b*; 1952, p. 232] has shown that the phenomenological coefficients in a stokesian fluid must depend on nondimensional pressure $\pi/\bar{\pi}$ and nondimensional temperature $\theta/\bar{\theta}$, where $\bar{\pi}$ and $\bar{\theta}$ may respectively be taken as the critical pressure and boiling temperature. There exist other fluids, e.g., *Reiner-Rivlin* fluid, in which the response function may also contain a *time constant.* In order to account properly for the presence of the thermodynamic variables and the physical restrictions that accompany them, the thermodynamics of irreversible processes must properly be used together with the mechanical principles which have been the fundamental tool of the foregoing developments. At present, while an adequate linear theory exists,[1] the nonlinear

[1] Cf. Eringen [1960]. For the detailed applications of the linear irreversible thermodynamics to continuum mechanics, see also Eringen [1964] and the references therein.

theory remains untouched. We therefore choose not to cloud the rigorous mechanical foundations with the vague and inadequate theories of irreversible thermodynamics at its present stage.

## 49. POLYNOMIAL APPROXIMATIONS

The constitutive equations (48.12) for compressible fluids and (48.18) for incompressible fluids are too complicated for the solution of all but a few nontrivial problems (cf. Chap. 7). Generally polynomial approximations of various degrees in $\mathbf{d}$ are used in the treatment of problems in fluid flow.

THEOREM 1. *The phenomenological coefficients* $\alpha_\kappa\,(\mathrm{I}_d, \mathrm{II}_d, \mathrm{III}_d)$ *of the most general constitutive equation*

$$t^k{}_l = (-\pi + \alpha_0)\,\delta^k{}_l + \alpha_1\,d^k{}_l + \alpha_2\,d^k{}_r\,d^r{}_l \tag{49.1}$$

*of degree N in* $\mathbf{d}$ *are polynomials in* $\mathrm{I}_d$, $\mathrm{II}_d$, and $\mathrm{III}_d$ *of degree* $N - \kappa$. *For a compressible fluid* $\alpha_0$ *vanishes with* $\mathbf{d}$, *and for an incompressible fluid we put* $\pi - \alpha_0 \equiv p$.

Now the degrees of $\mathrm{I}_d$, $\mathrm{II}_d$, and $\mathrm{III}_d$ in $\mathbf{d}$ are 1, 2, 3 respectively. Thus for $t^k{}_l$ to be of degree $N$ in $\mathbf{d}$, the coefficients $\alpha_0$, $\alpha_1$, and $\alpha_2$ can at most be of degrees $N$, $N - 1$, and $N - 2$ respectively. The vanishing of $\alpha_0$ with $\mathbf{d}$ and the fact that for incompressible flow $-\pi + \alpha_0 \equiv p$ have already been shown to be the case. Therefore we have the following.

1. *Zeroth Approximation.* The order $N \equiv 0$, i.e.,

$$\alpha_0 = \alpha_1 = \alpha_2 = 0 \tag{49.2}$$

Hence

$$t^k{}_l = -\pi\,\delta^k{}_l \tag{49.3}$$

This is the case of *inviscid fluids*. Here $\pi$ may be a function of the thermodynamic variables, density $\rho$ and temperature $\theta$, i.e.,

$$\pi = \pi\,(\rho, \theta) \tag{49.4}$$

Fluids in which $\pi = \pi\,(\rho)$ are called *barotropic*. When the fluid is incompressible, $\pi =$ const and we have the so-called *ideal fluids*. Clearly for *the zeroth approximation the dissipation vanishes.*

2. *First-order Theory.* In this case we have

$$\alpha_0 = \lambda_v\,\mathrm{I}_d \qquad \alpha_1 = 2\,\mu_v \qquad \alpha_2 = 0 \tag{49.5}$$

where $\lambda_v$ and $\mu_v$ are functions of thermodynamic variables $\rho$, $\theta$. We have

$$\begin{aligned} t^k{}_l &= (-\pi + \lambda_v\,\mathrm{I}_d)\,\delta^k{}_l + 2\,\mu_v\,d^k{}_l && \text{(compressible)} \\ t^k{}_l &= -\pi\,\delta^k{}_l + 2\,\mu_v\,d^k{}_l && \text{(incompressible)} \end{aligned} \tag{49.6}$$

This is the *Cauchy-Poisson* law of the classical *Navier-Stokes* theory of viscous flow.

The dissipation function is

(49.7)
$$\theta\,\Delta = {}_D t^k{}_l\, d^l{}_k = \lambda_v\, \mathrm{I}_d^2 + 2\,\mu_v\, d^k{}_l\, d^l{}_k = (\lambda_v + 2\,\mu_v)\,\mathrm{I}_d^2 - 4\,\mu_v\,\mathrm{II}_d$$

where we used (48.22). The dissipation function must be nonnegative. Introducing the expressions of invariants in terms of principal deformation rates $d_\alpha$, i.e.,

(49.8)
$$\mathrm{I}_d = d_1 + d_2 + d_3 \qquad \mathrm{II}_d = d_1\,d_2 + d_2\,d_3 + d_3\,d_1 \qquad \mathrm{III}_d = d_1\,d_2\,d_3$$

the dissipation function $\theta\,\Delta$ may be expressed as

(49.9)
$$3\,\theta\,\Delta = (3\,\lambda_v + 2\,\mu_v)\,\mathrm{I}_d^2 + 2\,\mu_v\,J_2$$

where

(49.10)
$$J_2 \equiv (d_1 - d_2)^2 + (d_2 - d_3)^2 + (d_3 - d_1)^2 = 2\,\mathrm{I}_d^2 - 6\,\mathrm{II}_d$$

Since both $\mathrm{I}_d^2$ and $J_2$ are nonnegative, we have:

THEOREM 2. *The necessary and sufficient condition for the dissipation function of a first-order compressible fluid to be nonnegative is that*

(49.11)
$$3\,\lambda_v + 2\,\mu_v \geq 0 \qquad \mu_v \geq 0$$

For an incompressible fluid $\mathrm{I}_d = 0$ and (49.9) is nonnegative whenever $\mu_v \geq 0$. This result would also follow from the general inequality (48.23).

The phenomenological coefficients $\lambda_v$ and $\mu_v$ are called *dilatational* and *shear viscosity coefficients* respectively.

It is of interest to see under what conditions the thermodynamic and mechanical pressures coincide. From (48.40) and (49.5) we get

(49.12)
$$3\,(\pi - \bar{p}) = (3\,\lambda_v + 2\,\mu_v)\,\mathrm{I}_d$$

We therefore see that whenever either $\mathrm{I}_d = 0$ or $3\,\lambda_v + 2\,\mu_v = 0$, we have $\pi = \bar{p}$. Now the first case is the case of an incompressible fluid. Recalling the general case (48.42), we see that *it is only an accident of the linear theory that for incompressible fluids* $\pi = \bar{p}$. For the general case this is not valid.

The requirement $3\,\lambda_v + 2\,\mu_v = 0$ is known as the *Stokes condition*. Experimental facts are seen to contradict this condition.[1]

The use of the Stokes condition, however, does not lead to great discrepancies in the calculations for most problems unless the problem is so

[1] See the excellent discussion given by Truesdell [1952, p. 228].

chosen as to eliminate the effect of $2\mu_v$ as compared to $\lambda_v$, e.g., spherically symmetric sound-wave propagation.

3. *Second-order Theory.* In a second-order theory

$$(49.13) \qquad \alpha_0 = \lambda_v \mathrm{I}_d + \lambda_1 \mathrm{I}_d^2 + \lambda_2 \mathrm{II}_d \qquad \alpha_1 = 2\mu_v + 2\mu_1 \mathrm{I}_d \qquad \alpha_2 = 4\nu_v$$

where $\lambda_v$, $\lambda_1$, $\lambda_2$, $\mu_v$, $\mu_1$, and $\nu_v$ are functions of thermodynamic variables. The constitutive equations read

$$(49.14) \qquad t^k{}_l = (-\pi + \lambda_v \mathrm{I}_d + \lambda_1 \mathrm{I}_d^2 + \lambda_2 \mathrm{II}_d)\, \delta^k{}_l + (2\mu_v + 2\mu_1 \mathrm{I}_d)\, d^k{}_l + 4\nu_v\, d^k{}_r\, d^r{}_l \qquad \text{(compressible)}$$

$$(49.15) \qquad t^k{}_l = -p\,\delta^k{}_l + 2\mu_v\, d^k{}_l + 4\nu_v\, d^k{}_r\, d^r{}_l \qquad \text{(incompressible)}$$

The dissipation function for the compressible case is

$$(49.16) \qquad \theta\Delta = (\lambda_v + 2\mu_v)\,\mathrm{I}_d^2 - 4\mu_v \mathrm{II}_d + (\lambda_1 + 2\mu_1 + 4\nu_v)\,\mathrm{I}_d^3 + (\lambda_2 - 4\mu_1 - 12\nu_v)\,\mathrm{I}_d \mathrm{II}_d + 12\nu_v \mathrm{III}_d$$

where we used (48.22). First we should like to examine the case of incompressible fluids. In this case $\mathrm{I}_d = 0$ and we have

$$(49.17) \qquad \theta\Delta = -4\mu_v \mathrm{II}_d + 12\nu_v \mathrm{III}_d \qquad \text{(incompressible)}$$

Now in terms of the principal values $d_\alpha$ of $\mathbf{d}$ we have

$$\mathrm{II}_d = d_1 d_2 + d_2 d_3 + d_3 d_1 = -(d_1{}^2 + d_2{}^2 + d_1 d_2)$$
$$\mathrm{III}_d = d_1 d_2 d_3 = -d_1 d_2{}^2 - d_2 d_1{}^2$$

since $\mathrm{I}_d = d_1 + d_2 + d_3 = 0$. Substituting these into (49.17), we obtain

$$\theta\Delta = 4\mu_v d_1{}^2 \left[\xi^2 + \left(1 - 3\frac{\nu_v}{\mu_v} d_2\right)(\xi + 1)\right] \qquad \xi \equiv \frac{d_2}{d_1}$$

The discriminant of the bracketed quadratic expression is

$$-3\left(1 + \frac{\nu_v}{\mu_v} d_2\right)\left(1 - 3\frac{\nu_v}{\mu_v} d_2\right)$$

which cannot be made either nonpositive or nonnegative for all real values of $d_2$ and material constants unless $\nu_v = 0$. Therefore we have the following theorem.

THEOREM 3. *For the dissipation function of an incompressible fluid of second order to be nonnegative, it is necessary and sufficient that we have* $\nu_v \equiv 0$ *and* $\mu_v \geq 0$. This shows that *there exist no incompressible fluids of second order*,[2] since now (49.15) with $\nu_v \equiv 0$ reduces to $(49.6)_2$.

Based on this by the necessity of continuous transition from compressible fluid to incompressible fluid set $\nu_v = 0$ in (49.16), which shows that *the most general second-order compressible fluid is a quasi-linear fluid.*

[2] This and the following results appear to be new.

To determine the restriction that the nonnegative dissipation imposes upon the phenomenological coefficients of a second-order compressible fluid, we examine (49.16) with $\nu_v \equiv 0$. Introducing the expressions of $\mathrm{I}_d$, $\mathrm{II}_d$, and $\mathrm{III}_d$ in terms of $d_1$, $d_2$, and $d_3$, we may put this expression into the form

$$(49.18)\quad 3\,\theta\,\Delta = (3\,\lambda_v + 2\,\mu_v)\,\mathrm{I}_d^2 + 2\,\mu_v\,J_2 + \mathrm{I}_d\,[(3\,\lambda_1 + 2\,\mu_1 + \lambda_2)\,\mathrm{I}_d^2 - \tfrac{1}{2}\,(\lambda_2 - 4\,\mu_1)\,J_2]$$

where $J_2$ is as defined in (49.10). The first two terms which are nonnegative are the contributions of the first-order theory. The last two terms contain cubic terms in $d_\alpha$. Hence they must be made nonnegative independent of the first two terms in every possible motion. But no matter what the coefficients are, by taking $\mathrm{I}_d$ positive or negative we can change the sign of these terms, except when the coefficients are zero. Hence

$$(49.19)\qquad \lambda_1 = -2\,\mu_1 \qquad \lambda_2 = 4\,\mu_1$$

and we therefore have the following theorem.

THEOREM 4. *The second-order theory introduces only one more phenomenological coefficient into the theory and the constitutive equations are quasi-linear,* i.e.,

$$(49.20)\quad t^k{}_l = (-\pi + \lambda_v\,\mathrm{I}_d - 2\,\mu_1\,\mathrm{I}_d^2 + 4\,\mu_1\,\mathrm{II}_d)\,\delta^k{}_l + (2\,\mu_v + 2\,\mu_1\,\mathrm{I}_d)\,d^k{}_l$$

*Moreover the dissipative function of a second-order theory is identical to that of the first-order theory,* i.e., (49.7) or (49.9).

From (49.20), by setting $k = l$, we get

$$(49.21)\quad 3\,(\pi - \bar{p}) = (3\,\lambda_v + 2\,\mu_v)\,\mathrm{I}_d - 4\,\mu_1\,\mathrm{I}_d^2 + 12\,\mu_1\,\mathrm{II}_d$$

*Even for the incompressible fluid* (i.e., $\mathrm{I}_d = 0$) *we see that the thermodynamic and mechanical pressures for all motions are no longer the same unless* $\mu_1 = 0$. *For the compressible fluid, we must have in addition,* $3\,\lambda_v + 2\,\mu_v = 0$ *to make* $\bar{p} = \pi$.

# 6

# THEORY OF ELASTICITY

## 50. SCOPE OF THE CHAPTER

Fundamental field equations and boundary and initial conditions of the theory of finite elasticity are presented in Art. 51. Article 52 deals with homogeneous strain and its special forms, pure homogeneous strain, simple extension, and simple shear. Torsion of a circular cylinder, expansion and eversion of a thick spherical shell, and bending of a block are presented in Arts. 53, 54, and 55, respectively. These illustrative problems of the theory of finite deformation employ inverse methods: namely, given a special class of deformations that are physically reasonable, specific functional forms satisfying the basic field equations are determined. The boundary tractions to sustain these particular deformations are then calculated. Some of these problems have no counterpart in the linear theory (e.g., the eversion of spherical shell), and most of them exhibit special effects (e.g., Poynting effect, Kelvin effect) that are not encountered in the linear theory. Finite plane strain is formulated in Art. 56, and it is applied in Art. 57 to the solution of the flexure of an initially curved cuboid. A final illustrative example given in Art. 58 is concerned with finite elastic waves. In Art. 59 we have a short list of other recent works in finite elasticity. Article 60 deals briefly with various approximate theories. The last article of this chapter contains a description of several experimental investigations concerned, in general, with the constitutive relations for elastic materials and, in particular, with the form of the strain-energy function for such materials.

## 51. FUNDAMENTAL EQUATIONS

Basic field equations of the theory of hyperelasticity consist of the following three kinds.

1. *Equation of Conservation of Mass* (25.8):

$$\frac{\rho}{\rho_0} = \sqrt{\mathrm{III}_c} = \frac{1}{\sqrt{\mathrm{III}_{\overset{-1}{c}}}} \tag{51.1}$$

2. *Equations of Balance of Momenta* (nonpolar case) (32.16) and (32.15):

$$t^{kl}{}_{;l} + \rho\,(f^k - a^k) = 0 \qquad t^{kl} = t^{lk} \tag{51.2}$$

3. *Constitutive Equations* (isotropic media) (47.10):

$$t^k{}_l = b_{-1}\,\overset{-1}{c}{}^k{}_l + b_0\,\delta^k{}_l + b_1\,c^k{}_l \qquad \text{(compressible)} \tag{51.3}$$

where

$$b_{-1} = \frac{2}{\sqrt{\mathrm{III}}}\frac{\partial\Sigma}{\partial\mathrm{I}} \qquad b_0 = \frac{2}{\sqrt{\mathrm{III}}}\left(\mathrm{II}\,\frac{\partial\Sigma}{\partial\mathrm{II}} + \mathrm{III}\,\frac{\partial\Sigma}{\partial\mathrm{III}}\right)$$
$$b_1 = -2\sqrt{\mathrm{III}}\,\frac{\partial\Sigma}{\partial\mathrm{II}} \tag{51.4}$$

and

$$t^k{}_l = -p\,\delta^k{}_l + 2\,\frac{\partial\Sigma}{\partial\mathrm{I}}\,\overset{-1}{c}{}^k{}_l - 2\,\frac{\partial\Sigma}{\partial\mathrm{II}}\,c^k{}_l \qquad \text{(incompressible)} \tag{51.5}$$

After the solution of problems in finite deformation, the transition to the linear theory may be made by the procedure outlined at the end of Art. 47, i.e., by putting

$$\mathrm{I} \cong 3 + 2\,\mathrm{I}_{\tilde e} \qquad \mathrm{II} \cong 3 + 4\,\mathrm{I}_{\tilde e} \qquad \mathrm{III} \cong 1 + 2\,\mathrm{I}_{\tilde e}$$
$$\frac{\partial\Sigma}{\partial\mathrm{I}} \cong \mu_e + \frac{\lambda_e + 2\,\mu_e}{2}\,\mathrm{I}_{\tilde e} \qquad \frac{\partial\Sigma}{\partial\mathrm{II}} \cong -\frac{\mu_e}{2} \qquad \frac{\partial\Sigma}{\partial\mathrm{III}} = 0 \tag{51.6}$$

in the solution obtained. We note that for the incompressible case $\mathrm{III} = 1$ and $\partial\Sigma/\partial\mathrm{III}$ is indeterminate.

The constitutive equations are subject to restrictions (47.20) and (47.21) or (47.22), i.e.,

$$\frac{\partial\Sigma}{\partial\mathrm{I}} + \lambda_\alpha^2\,\frac{\partial\Sigma}{\partial\mathrm{II}} > 0 \qquad \text{if } \lambda_\beta \neq \lambda_\gamma \qquad (\alpha, \beta, \gamma \neq)$$
$$\frac{\partial\Sigma}{\partial\mathrm{I}} + \lambda_\alpha^2\,\frac{\partial\Sigma}{\partial\mathrm{II}} \geq 0 \qquad \text{if } \lambda_\beta = \lambda_\gamma \qquad (\alpha, \beta, \gamma \neq) \tag{51.7}$$

In addition to these equations we have the following relations.

4. *Geometrical and Kinematical Relations.* From (4.8) and (4.15) for the deformation tensors we have

$$c_{kl} = G_{KL}\,X^K{}_{,k}\,X^L{}_{,l} \qquad \overset{-1}{c}{}^{kl} = G^{KL}\,x^k{}_{,K}\,x^l{}_{,L} \tag{51.8}$$

From $(17.10)_2$ and (17.15) for the velocity $v^k$ and acceleration vector $a^k$ we have

$$v^k = \frac{\partial x^k}{\partial t} \qquad a^k = \frac{Dv^k}{Dt} = \frac{\partial v^k}{\partial t} + v^k{}_{;l}\,v^l \tag{51.9}$$

In the foregoing equations the density $\rho_0$ of the body at the natural state, the body force $f^k$, and either the phenomenological coefficients $b_{-1}$, $b_0$ and $b_1$ or the functional form of the stress potential $\Sigma$ (I, II, III) are to be given subject to restrictions (51.7). In general we shall not be concerned with particular forms[1] of $\Sigma$. For rubberlike incompressible materials Mooney's [1940] expression

$$\Sigma = A_1 (\mathrm{I} - 3) + A_2 (\mathrm{II} - 3) \tag{51.10}$$

where $A_1 \geq 0$, $A_2 \geq 0$, appears to provide a simple approximate representation in fair agreement with experiments for a wide range of deformation.

5. *Boundary and Initial Conditions.* When tractions $t^k{}_{(\mathrm{n})}$ are prescribed on the surface $\mathcal{S}$ of the body, we have from (31.2)

$$t^k{}_{(\mathrm{n})} = t^{lk} n_l = s^k \qquad \text{on } \mathcal{S} \tag{51.11}$$

When the surface displacements are prescribed, then we may prescribe either $u^k$ or $x^k$ on $\mathcal{S}$.

The initial conditions require that we prescribe

$$x^k (\mathbf{X}, 0) = x_0{}^k \qquad \dot{x}^k (\mathbf{X}, 0) = v_0{}^k \qquad \text{in } \mathcal{V} \text{ at } t = 0 \tag{51.12}$$

More complicated boundary conditions may involve specification of surface tractions on a part $\mathcal{S}_t$ of the boundary and displacements on the remaining part $\mathcal{S}_u = \mathcal{S} - \mathcal{S}_t$ of the boundary surface. Such problems are known as *mixed boundary-value problems.* In other problems some components of surface tractions [say $t^1{}_{(\mathrm{n})}$, $t^2{}_{(\mathrm{n})}$] and the other component ($u^3$ or $x^3$) of the displacement vector may be prescribed on $\mathcal{S}$. These are known as the *mixed-mixed boundary-value problems.* Since only very simple problems in the theory of finite elasticity have been dealt with, we shall, of course, not undertake problems involving complicated boundary conditions.[2] It must be noted, however, that the correct boundary and initial conditions must not violate the uniqueness theorem for the solution.

## 52. HOMOGENEOUS STRAIN[1]

Homogeneous strain encompasses one of the simplest classes of problems in elasticity. Referred to the same rectangular coordinates, the deformation for the homogeneous strain is expressed by

$$z^k = A^k{}_K Z^K \tag{52.1}$$

[1] For a discussion of some special forms of $\Sigma$ see Green and Adkins [1960].

[2] These problems play a central role in linear continuum mechanics. For these we refer the reader to Eringen [1964].

[1] These problems were first treated by Rivlin [1948*c*] and Rivlin and Saunders [1951]. See also Green and Zerna [1954, chap. 3].

where $\|A^k{}_K\|$ is a constant nonsingular matrix. Using (51.8), we have

(52.2)
$$\overset{-1}{c}{}^{kl} = \delta^{KL}\, x^k{}_{,K}\, x^l{}_{,L} = \delta^{KL}\, A^k{}_K\, A^l{}_L$$
$$c_{kl} = \delta_{KL}\, \overset{-1}{A}{}_k{}^K\, \overset{-1}{A}{}_l{}^L$$

where $\overset{-1}{A}{}_k{}^K$ is the inverse matrix to $A^k{}_K$, i.e.,

(52.3)
$$A^k{}_K\, \overset{-1}{A}{}_l{}^K = \delta^k{}_l \qquad \text{or} \qquad \overset{-1}{A}{}_l{}^K = \frac{\text{cofactor } (A^l{}_K)}{\det\, (A^l{}_K)}$$

According to (51.1) we have

(52.4)
$$\frac{\rho}{\rho_0} = \sqrt{\text{III}_c} = \sqrt{\det\, (c^k{}_l)} = \det\, (\overset{-1}{A}{}_k{}^K)$$

Therefore the deformation is isochoric if and only if $\det\, (\overset{-1}{A}{}_k{}^K) = 1$. The stress-strain relations follow from (51.3) and (51.5):

(52.5)
$$t^k{}_l = b_{-1}\, \delta^{KL}\, A^k{}_K\, A_{lL} + b_0\, \delta^k{}_l + b_1\, \delta_{KL}\, \overset{-1}{A}{}^{Kk}\, \overset{-1}{A}{}^L{}_l$$

where $A^l{}_L = A_{lL}$, $\overset{-1}{A}{}^{Kk} = \overset{-1}{A}{}^K{}_k$, and the phenomenological coefficients $b_{-1}$, $b_0$, and $b_1$ are constants; the latter are given by (51.4).

For incompressible media (51.5) must be used to obtain the stress tensor

(52.6)
$$t^k{}_l = -p\, \delta^k{}_l + 2\, \frac{\partial \Sigma}{\partial \text{I}}\, \delta^{KL}\, A^k{}_K\, A_{lL} - 2\, \frac{\partial \Sigma}{\partial \text{II}}\, \delta_{KL}\, \overset{-1}{A}{}^{kK}\, \overset{-1}{A}{}_l{}^L$$

The equations of equilibrium [(51.2) with $\mathbf{f} = \mathbf{a} = 0$] are satisfied automatically for the compressible solid, and for the incompressible solid they are satisfied if and only if $p = \text{const}$. Below we give a few special cases.

1. *Pure Homogeneous Strain.* In this case we have

(52.7)
$$A^1{}_1 = \lambda_1 = 1 + e_1 \qquad A^2{}_2 = \lambda_2 = 1 + e_2$$
$$A^3{}_3 = \lambda_3 = 1 + e_3 \qquad A^k{}_L = 0\ (k \neq L)$$

where $e_\alpha$ are extensions as defined by (7.3). Therefore the deformation is expressed by

(52.8)
$$x^1 = x = \lambda_1 X \qquad x^2 = y = \lambda_2 Y \qquad x^3 = z = \lambda_3 Z$$

Hence we have

(52.9)
$$\|A^k{}_K\| = \begin{bmatrix} \lambda_1 & 0 & 0 \\ 0 & \lambda_2 & 0 \\ 0 & 0 & \lambda_3 \end{bmatrix} \qquad \|\overset{-1}{A}{}^K{}_k\| = \begin{bmatrix} 1/\lambda_1 & 0 & 0 \\ 0 & 1/\lambda_2 & 0 \\ 0 & 0 & 1/\lambda_3 \end{bmatrix}$$

From (52.2) and this we get

$$(52.10)\quad \|\overset{-1}{c}{}^{kl}\| = \begin{bmatrix} \lambda_1^2 & 0 & 0 \\ 0 & \lambda_2^2 & 0 \\ 0 & 0 & \lambda_3^2 \end{bmatrix} \qquad \|c_{kl}\| = \begin{bmatrix} 1/\lambda_1^2 & 0 & 0 \\ 0 & 1/\lambda_2^2 & 0 \\ 0 & 0 & 1/\lambda_3^2 \end{bmatrix}$$

Invariants are

$$(52.11)\quad \mathrm{I} = \lambda_1^2 + \lambda_2^2 + \lambda_3^2 \qquad \mathrm{II} = \lambda_1^2\lambda_2^2 + \lambda_2^2\lambda_3^2 + \lambda_3^2\lambda_1^2 \qquad \mathrm{III} = \lambda_1^2\lambda_2^2\lambda_3^2$$

Stress-strain relations (52.5) for compressible media now read

$$(52.12)\quad \begin{aligned} t_{11} &= 2\,\lambda_1 \left\{ \frac{1}{\lambda_2\lambda_3} \left[ \frac{\partial\Sigma}{\partial \mathrm{I}} + (\lambda_2^2 + \lambda_3^2)\frac{\partial\Sigma}{\partial \mathrm{II}} \right] + \lambda_2\lambda_3 \frac{\partial\Sigma}{\partial \mathrm{III}} \right\} \\ t_{22} &= 2\,\lambda_2 \left\{ \frac{1}{\lambda_3\lambda_1} \left[ \frac{\partial\Sigma}{\partial \mathrm{I}} + (\lambda_3^2 + \lambda_1^2)\frac{\partial\Sigma}{\partial \mathrm{II}} \right] + \lambda_3\lambda_1 \frac{\partial\Sigma}{\partial \mathrm{III}} \right\} \\ t_{33} &= 2\,\lambda_3 \left\{ \frac{1}{\lambda_1\lambda_2} \left[ \frac{\partial\Sigma}{\partial \mathrm{I}} + (\lambda_1^2 + \lambda_2^2)\frac{\partial\Sigma}{\partial \mathrm{II}} \right] + \lambda_1\lambda_2 \frac{\partial\Sigma}{\partial \mathrm{III}} \right\} \\ t_{kl} &= 0 \qquad (k \neq l) \end{aligned}$$

For the incompressible media we have $\lambda_1\lambda_2\lambda_3 = 1$. Through (51.5) we now get

$$(52.13)\quad t_{kk} = -p + 2\,\lambda_k^2 \frac{\partial\Sigma}{\partial \mathrm{I}} - \frac{2}{\lambda_k^2}\frac{\partial\Sigma}{\partial \mathrm{II}} \qquad \text{(not summed on } k\text{)}$$

2. *Simple Extension.* For the particular case of simple extension under a force parallel to the $x$ axis, $\lambda_2 = \lambda_3$, $t_{22} = t_{33} = 0$ and hence

$$(52.14)\quad \begin{aligned} t_{11} &= 2\,\lambda_1 \left( \frac{1}{\lambda_2^2}\frac{\partial\Sigma}{\partial \mathrm{I}} + 2\frac{\partial\Sigma}{\partial \mathrm{II}} + \lambda_2^2 \frac{\partial\Sigma}{\partial \mathrm{III}} \right) \\ 0 &= \frac{1}{\lambda_1\lambda_2}\frac{\partial\Sigma}{\partial \mathrm{I}} + \left( \frac{\lambda_1}{\lambda_2} + \frac{\lambda_2}{\lambda_1} \right)\frac{\partial\Sigma}{\partial \mathrm{II}} + \lambda_1\lambda_2 \frac{\partial\Sigma}{\partial \mathrm{III}} \end{aligned}$$

The second equation is a transcendental equation relating $\lambda_1$ to $\lambda_2$. Neither the *existence* nor the *uniqueness* of a real solution of this equation leading to $\lambda_2 = f(\lambda_1)$ is indicated. Thus the problem of *stability* needs to be investigated. It may be possible to have more than one such solution so that the equilibrium may depend on the way the load is applied. For the theory of infinitesimal deformations we have shown that [cf. (51.6)]

$$(52.15)\quad \frac{\partial\Sigma}{\partial \mathrm{I}} \cong \mu_e + \tfrac{1}{2}(\lambda_e + 2\,\mu_e)\,\mathrm{I}_{\tilde{e}} \qquad \frac{\partial\Sigma}{\partial \mathrm{II}} \cong -\tfrac{1}{2}\mu_e \qquad \frac{\partial\Sigma}{\partial \mathrm{III}} \cong 0$$

When these are substituted into $(52.14)_2$ and second-order terms in $e_{a}$

are neglected, we get

$$-e_2/e_1 = \lambda_e/2\,(\lambda_e + \mu_e) = \nu \tag{52.16}$$

where $\lambda_e$ and $\mu_e$ are the *Lamé constants* and $\nu$ is *Poisson's ratio.* It is therefore clear that $(52.14)_2$ is an equation determining the contraction ratio $\nu$ for a compressible medium. For a nonlinear material its existence and uniqueness need further investigation. For a given compressible material to produce a given extension, we may perhaps need surface loading.

For an incompressible material, by setting $t_{22} = t_{33} = 0$ in (52.13), we determine the unknown function $p$

$$p = \frac{2}{\lambda_1}\frac{\partial \Sigma}{\partial \mathrm{I}} - 2\,\lambda_1 \frac{\partial \Sigma}{\partial \mathrm{II}} \tag{52.17}$$

Incompressibility requires that $\lambda_1 \lambda_2^2 = 1$. Consequently

$$t_{11} = 2\left(\lambda_1^2 - \frac{1}{\lambda_1}\right)\left(\frac{\partial \Sigma}{\partial \mathrm{I}} + \frac{1}{\lambda_1}\frac{\partial \Sigma}{\partial \mathrm{II}}\right) \tag{52.18}$$

Thus *in an incompressible body a simple extension of any magnitude may be produced by a purely tensile load.*

3. *Hydrostatic Pressure.* For this case we have $\lambda_\alpha = K$, $\mathbf{t} = -p\,\mathbf{I}$. Therefore (52.12) reduces to

$$p = -2\left(\frac{1}{K}\frac{\partial \Sigma}{\partial \mathrm{I}} + 2\,K\frac{\partial \Sigma}{\partial \mathrm{II}} + K^3\frac{\partial \Sigma}{\partial \mathrm{III}}\right) \tag{52.19}$$

Since $K = (\rho/\rho_0)^{-\frac{1}{3}}$, it follows that we have an equation of state of the general form $p = p\,(\rho)$.

4. *Simple Shear.* The deformation of simple shear has already been studied in Art. 15 (2*c*). In a simple shear an aggregate of parallel planes moves, remaining parallel to their original direction in an amount proportional to their distance from one of these planes. Thus a rectangular cross section $Z$ = const ($OACB$) of a cuboid after deformation becomes a parallelogram ($OAcb$) (Fig. 52.1; see also Fig. 15.2).

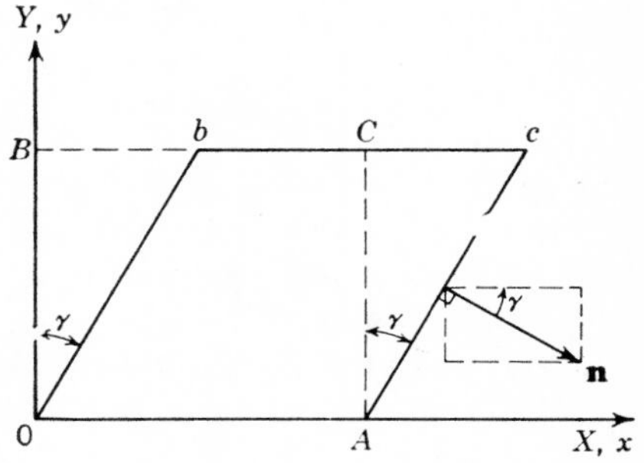

FIG. 52.1. Simple shear.

Referred to the same rectangular coordinates, we have

$$x = X + K\,Y \qquad y = Y \qquad z = Z \tag{52.20}$$

Comparing this with (52.1), we see that a simple shear is a homogeneous strain with a deformation matrix

$$(52.21)\qquad \|A^l{}_L\| = \begin{bmatrix} 1 & K & 0 \\ 0 & 1 & 0 \\ 0 & 0 & 1 \end{bmatrix} \qquad \|\overset{-1}{A}{}_l{}^L\| = \begin{bmatrix} 1 & -K & 0 \\ 0 & 1 & 0 \\ 0 & 0 & 1 \end{bmatrix}$$

According to (52.2) we have

$$(52.22)\qquad \|\overset{-1}{c}{}^{kl}\| = \begin{bmatrix} 1+K^2 & K & 0 \\ K & 1 & 0 \\ 0 & 0 & 1 \end{bmatrix} \qquad \|c_{kl}\| = \begin{bmatrix} 1 & -K & 0 \\ -K & 1+K^2 & 0 \\ 0 & 0 & 1 \end{bmatrix}$$

Invariants are

$$(52.23)\qquad \mathrm{I} = \mathrm{II} = 3 + K^2 \qquad \mathrm{III} = 1$$

Therefore the deformation is isochoric.

Stress-strain relations (52.5) now give

$$(52.24)\qquad \begin{aligned} t_{11} &= 2\,(1+K^2)\frac{\partial\Sigma}{\partial \mathrm{I}} + 2\,(2+K^2)\frac{\partial\Sigma}{\partial \mathrm{II}} + 2\,\frac{\partial\Sigma}{\partial \mathrm{III}} \\ t_{22} &= 2\,\frac{\partial\Sigma}{\partial \mathrm{I}} + 4\,\frac{\partial\Sigma}{\partial \mathrm{II}} + 2\,\frac{\partial\Sigma}{\partial \mathrm{III}} \\ t_{33} &= 2\,\frac{\partial\Sigma}{\partial \mathrm{I}} + 2\,(2+K^2)\frac{\partial\Sigma}{\partial \mathrm{II}} + 2\,\frac{\partial\Sigma}{\partial \mathrm{III}} \\ t_{12} &= 2\,K\left(\frac{\partial\Sigma}{\partial \mathrm{I}} + \frac{\partial\Sigma}{\partial \mathrm{II}}\right) \qquad t_{23} = t_{31} = 0 \end{aligned}$$

The unit normal of the deformed face $Ac$ is given by

$$(52.25)\qquad n_1 = \cos\gamma = (1+K^2)^{-\frac{1}{2}} \qquad n_2 = -K\,(1+K^2)^{-\frac{1}{2}} \qquad n_3 = 0$$

The surface tractions on this surface are given by (51.11), i.e.,

$$(52.26)\qquad \begin{aligned} t^1{}_{(1)} &= 2\,(1+K^2)^{-\frac{1}{2}}\left(\frac{\partial\Sigma}{\partial \mathrm{I}} + 2\,\frac{\partial\Sigma}{\partial \mathrm{II}} + \frac{\partial\Sigma}{\partial \mathrm{III}}\right) \\ t^2{}_{(1)} &= -2\,K\,(1+K^2)^{-\frac{1}{2}}\left(\frac{\partial\Sigma}{\partial \mathrm{II}} + \frac{\partial\Sigma}{\partial \mathrm{III}}\right) \\ t^3{}_{(1)} &= 0 \end{aligned}$$

Normal and tangential tractions $N$ and $T$ on $Ac$ are therefore given by

$$(52.27)\qquad \begin{aligned} N &= t^1{}_{(1)}\,n_1 + t^2{}_{(1)}\,n_2 = 2\,(1+K^2)^{-1}\left[\frac{\partial\Sigma}{\partial \mathrm{I}} + (2+K^2)\frac{\partial\Sigma}{\partial \mathrm{II}} \right. \\ &\qquad\qquad \left. + (1+K^2)\frac{\partial\Sigma}{\partial \mathrm{III}}\right] \\ T &= t^1{}_{(1)}\,n_2 - t^2{}_{(1)}\,n_1 = -2\,K\,(1+K^2)^{-1}\left(\frac{\partial\Sigma}{\partial \mathrm{I}} + \frac{\partial\Sigma}{\partial \mathrm{II}}\right) \end{aligned}$$

ormal and tangential components of the tractions acting on the = const and $Z$ = const surfaces may be read from (52.24).

It is clear from (52.27) that *the simple shear defined by* (52.20) *cannot be aintained by shearing surface loads alone. It also is necessary to impose itable normal tractions on the surfaces of the block.* This result is contrary the case of linear elasticity theory. Indeed by using (52.15), we see at for the theory of infinitesimal deformations (52.27) reduces to

2.28)
$$N = (1 + K^2)^{-1}[(\lambda_e + \mu_e)\, \mathrm{I}_{\bar{e}} - K^2 \mu_e] = 0\,(K^2)$$
$$T = -K\,(1 + K^2)^{-1}[\mu_e + (\lambda_e + 2\,\mu_e)\,\mathrm{I}_{\bar{e}}] = 0\,(K)$$

is shows that $N \to 0$ as $K^2$ and $T$ as $K$. Hence in this limit $N$ may be iored as compared with $T$. For a theory of finite deformations *we need supply not only a hydrostatic tension of amount $t_{33}$ in order to prohibit ume change, but also a normal traction to keep the proportions of the ly.* The hydrostatic tension so required is said to be due to the *Kelvin ect,* and the necessity of the normal tractions is a "cross effect" known the *Poynting effect.* The signs of these effects depend on the phenomelogical coefficients. The Kelvin and Poynting effects are the results of finite deformations and are not present in the linear theory.

For the incompressible solid, through (51.5) and (52.23) we get

2.29)
$$t_{11} = -p + 2\,K^2 \frac{\partial \Sigma}{\partial \mathrm{I}} \qquad t_{22} = -p - 2\,K^2 \frac{\partial \Sigma}{\partial \mathrm{II}}$$
$$t_{12} = 2\,K \left( \frac{\partial \Sigma}{\partial \mathrm{I}} + \frac{\partial \Sigma}{\partial \mathrm{II}} \right) \qquad t_{33} = -p \qquad t_{31} = t_{32} = 0$$

selecting $p$ appropriately, we may clear one pair of parallel faces from rmal traction. If we take $p = 0$, then the $Z$ = const surfaces will be e of tractions. In this case on the face $X$ = const we have

2.30)
$$N = -2\,K^2\,(1 + K^2)^{-1} \left[ \frac{\partial \Sigma}{\partial \mathrm{I}} + (2 + K^2)\,\frac{\partial \Sigma}{\partial \mathrm{II}} \right]$$

the requirement (51.7) is imposed, we see that the bracket on the right nonnegative; hence the normal force $N$ is a *pressure.* Without this ssure the specimen will tend to broaden, and since it is incompressible, will also *shorten.* This is the Poynting effect for the incompressible id. The Kelvin effect is no longer present.

Another interesting result that follows from (52.24) or (52.29) is that

2.31)
$$t_{11} - t_{22} = K\, t_{12}$$

both compressible and incompressible solids and is independent of the terial properties.

## 53. TORSION OF A CIRCULAR CYLINDER[1]

The deformation accompanying a uniform twist of a circular cylin represented by

$$(53.1) \qquad r = R \qquad \theta = \Theta + K\,Z \qquad z = Z$$

was studied in Art. 15 (3*a*). Here $r$, $\theta$, $z$ and $R$, $\Theta$, $Z$ are the cylindri coordinates for the spatial coordinates $x^k$ and the material coordina $X^K$ (Fig. 15.4). The constant $K$ is the twist per unit length. For t metric tensor $G_{KL}$ and $g_{kl}$ we have

$$(53.2) \qquad \|G_{KL}\| = \begin{bmatrix} 1 & 0 & 0 \\ 0 & R^2 & 0 \\ 0 & 0 & 1 \end{bmatrix} \qquad \|g_{kl}\| = \begin{bmatrix} 1 & 0 & 0 \\ 0 & r^2 & 0 \\ 0 & 0 & 1 \end{bmatrix}$$

From (51.8) we get

$$(53.3) \qquad \|\overset{-1}{c}{}^k{}_l\| = \begin{bmatrix} 1 & 0 & 0 \\ 0 & 1 + K^2\,r^2 & K \\ 0 & K\,r^2 & 1 \end{bmatrix} \qquad \|c^k{}_l\| = \begin{bmatrix} 1 & 0 & 0 \\ 0 & 1 & -K \\ 0 & -K\,r^2 & K^2\,r^2 + \end{bmatrix}$$

Hence

$$(53.4) \qquad \mathrm{I} = \mathrm{II} = 3 + K^2\,r^2 \qquad \mathrm{III} = 1$$

Thus it follows that phenomenological coefficients $b_{-1}$, $b_0$, and $b_1$ functions of $r$ alone. We treat the problem as an incompressible c since the incompressibility condition is automatically satisfied.

From (51.5), by raising indices with $g^{kl}$, we obtain the stress systen

$$(53.5) \qquad \begin{aligned} t^{11} &= -p + 2\,\frac{\partial\Sigma}{\partial \mathrm{I}} - 2\,\frac{\partial\Sigma}{\partial \mathrm{II}} \\ r^2\,t^{22} &= -p + 2\,(1 + K^2\,r^2)\,\frac{\partial\Sigma}{\partial \mathrm{I}} - 2\,\frac{\partial\Sigma}{\partial \mathrm{II}} \\ t^{33} &= -p + 2\,\frac{\partial\Sigma}{\partial \mathrm{I}} - 2\,(K^2\,r^2 + 1)\,\frac{\partial\Sigma}{\partial \mathrm{II}} \\ t^{23} &= 2\,K\left(\frac{\partial\Sigma}{\partial \mathrm{I}} + \frac{\partial\Sigma}{\partial \mathrm{II}}\right) \qquad t^{31} = t^{12} = 0 \end{aligned}$$

For a vanishing body force the equilibrium equations read

$$(53.6) \qquad t^{rk}{}_{,r} + \begin{Bmatrix} s \\ sr \end{Bmatrix} t^{rk} + \begin{Bmatrix} k \\ rs \end{Bmatrix} t^{rs} = 0$$

[1] This problem was treated by Rivlin [1948*c*, 1949*b*] and by Green and Shield [19 See also Green and Zerna [1954, art. 3.3] and Reiner [1951]. For an analysis of r circular bars see Goodier and Shaw [1957].

hristoffel symbols in the $(r, \theta, z)$ system are

$$\left\{ {1 \atop 22} \right\} = -r \qquad \left\{ {2 \atop 12} \right\} = \left\{ {2 \atop 21} \right\} = \frac{1}{r} \qquad \text{all other } \left\{ {k \atop lm} \right\} = 0 \tag{3.7)}$$

onsequently (53.6) takes the explicit form

$$\begin{gathered} \frac{\partial}{\partial r}\left(-p + 2\frac{\partial \Sigma}{\partial \mathrm{I}} - 2\frac{\partial \Sigma}{\partial \mathrm{II}}\right) - 2K^2 r \frac{\partial \Sigma}{\partial \mathrm{I}} = 0 \\ \frac{\partial p}{\partial \theta} = 0 \qquad \frac{\partial p}{\partial z} = 0 \end{gathered} \tag{3.8)}$$

ence $p$ is a function of $r$ alone, and it may be determined by integrating 3.8)$_1$, i.e.,

$$p = 2\left(\frac{\partial \Sigma}{\partial \mathrm{I}} - \frac{\partial \Sigma}{\partial \mathrm{II}} - K^2 \int^r r \frac{\partial \Sigma}{\partial \mathrm{I}}\, dr\right) + C_1$$

the cylindrical surface $r = a$ is to be free of tractions, we must have $= 0$ since $t^{31} = t^{32} = 0$. This gives

$$C_1 = 2K^2 \int^a r \frac{\partial \Sigma}{\partial \mathrm{I}}\, dr$$

onsequently

$$\begin{aligned} t^{11} &= t^{(1)}{}_{(1)} = -2K^2 \int_r^a r \frac{\partial \Sigma}{\partial \mathrm{I}}\, dr \\ t^{22} &= \frac{t^{(2)}{}_{(2)}}{r^2} = 2K^2 \left(r^2 \frac{\partial \Sigma}{\partial \mathrm{I}} - \int_r^a r \frac{\partial \Sigma}{\partial \mathrm{I}}\, dr\right) \\ t^{33} &= t^{(3)}{}_{(3)} = -2K^2 \left(r^2 \frac{\partial \Sigma}{\partial \mathrm{II}} + \int_r^a r \frac{\partial \Sigma}{\partial \mathrm{I}}\, dr\right) \\ t^{23} &= \frac{t^{(2)}{}_{(3)}}{r} = 2K\left(\frac{\partial \Sigma}{\partial \mathrm{I}} + \frac{\partial \Sigma}{\partial \mathrm{II}}\right) \qquad t^{31} = t^{12} = 0 \end{aligned} \tag{3.9)}$$

here $t^{(k)}{}_{(l)} = t^k{}_l \sqrt{g_{\underline{kk}}/g_{\underline{ll}}}$ are the physical components of the stress nsor.

Since there is no other integration constant available, the tractions at e ends $z = 0$ and $z = l$ of the cylinder can no longer be controlled. t $z = l$ we have for the normal $n_1 = n_2 = 0$, $n_3 = 1$. Therefore the actions are

$$t^1{}_{(1)} = t^{k1} n_k = 0 \qquad t^2{}_{(1)} = t^{k2} n_k = t^{23} \qquad t^3{}_{(1)} = t^{k3} n_k = t^{33}$$

'e therefore see that there is no radial traction. There are, however, xial and tangential tractions to any circle $r = \text{const.}$ *The Poynting fect thus appears as a normal traction $t^3{}_3$ which must be supplied to the end ctions in order to maintain the surface $r = a$ of the cylinder free of tractions.*

The surface tractions $(0, r\, t^{23}, t^{33})$ distributed at the end section a equipollent to a twisting moment $M$ and an axial force $N$ given by

$$\text{(53.10)}\qquad \begin{aligned} M &= 2\pi \int_0^a r^3\, t^{23}\, dr = \frac{2\pi}{K}\left(a^2\, \Sigma \Big|_{r=a} - \int_0^{a^2} \Sigma\, d\xi\right) \\ N &= 2\pi \int_0^a r\, t^{33}\, dr = -\pi K^2 \int_0^{a^2} \xi \left(\frac{\partial \Sigma}{\partial \mathrm{I}} + 2\,\frac{\partial \Sigma}{\partial \mathrm{II}}\right) d\xi \end{aligned}$$

where $\xi \equiv r^2$. In accordance with (47.23), if we assume that $\partial\Sigma/\partial\mathrm{I}$ a $\partial\Sigma/\partial\mathrm{II}$ are nonnegative, we see that the axial force is compressive. this force is not supplied, upon twisting, the cylinder will tend to elonga The Poynting effect can be seen to disappear for the linear theory, f upon using (52.15) in transition to the linear theory, we see that

$$(t^{11}, t^{22}, t^{33}) = 0\,(K^2) \qquad t^{23} = \mu_e K = 0\,(K)$$

Hence the axial force is $0\,(K^2)$, which is negligibly small for small twist

## 54. EXPANSION AND EVERSION OF A THICK SPHERICAL SHELL

A problem that is not encountered in the linear theory is concern with turning a spherical shell inside out. The solution of this proble was first treated by Armanni [1915], using a special stress potential

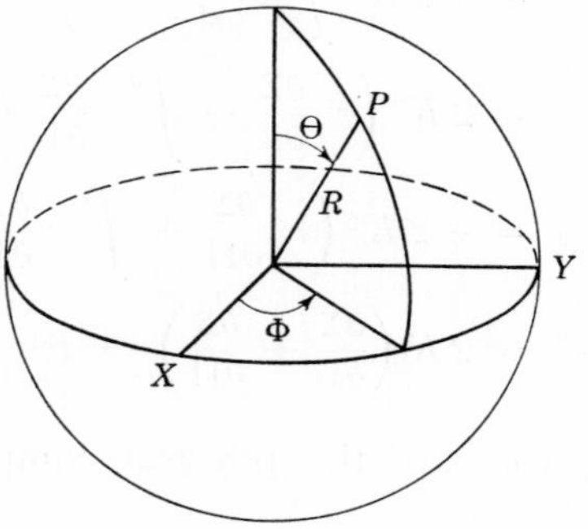


FIG. 54.1. Spherical coordinates.

The problem was treated more generally by Green[1] [1955]. We give solution of this problem alongside the inflation of a shell subjected internal pressure.

We take $X^K$ and $x^k$ as the same spherical coordinates and write

$$X^1 = R \qquad X^2 = \Theta \qquad X^3 = \Phi \qquad\qquad x^1 = r \qquad x^2 = \theta \qquad x^3 = \phi$$

Here $R$ and $r$ are radial distances from the origin (the center of the sphere $\theta$ and $\Theta$ are latitudes, and $\phi$ and $\Phi$ are the longitudes (Fig. 54.1). Co

[1] See also Doyle and Ericksen [1956, VIII, art. 4].

der the deformation appropriate to a uniform expansion:

4.1) $$r = r(R) \qquad \theta = \Theta \qquad \phi = \Phi$$

here $r(R)$ is a monotone-increasing function.

The metric tensors are

4.2) $$\|G_{KL}\| = \begin{bmatrix} 1 & 0 & 0 \\ 0 & R^2 & 0 \\ 0 & 0 & R^2 \sin^2 \Theta \end{bmatrix} \qquad \|g_{kl}\| = \begin{bmatrix} 1 & 0 & 0 \\ 0 & r^2 & 0 \\ 0 & 0 & r^2 \sin^2 \theta \end{bmatrix}$$

The deformation tensors follow from (51.8) and (54.1) by raising and wering indices.

4.3) $$\|\overset{-1}{c}{}^k{}_l\| = \begin{bmatrix} (r')^2 & 0 & 0 \\ 0 & r^2/R^2 & 0 \\ 0 & 0 & r^2/R^2 \end{bmatrix} \qquad \|c^k{}_l\| = \begin{bmatrix} 1/(r')^2 & 0 & 0 \\ 0 & R^2/r^2 & 0 \\ 0 & 0 & R^2/r^2 \end{bmatrix}$$

ence the invariants are given by

4.4) $$\mathrm{I} = (r')^2 + 2\frac{r^2}{R^2} \qquad \mathrm{II} = 2\left(\frac{r'\,r}{R}\right)^2 + \left(\frac{r}{R}\right)^4 \qquad \mathrm{III} = \left(\frac{r'\,r^2}{R^2}\right)^2$$

Here we should like to treat the case of an incompressible medium. or this we set III $= 1$, which gives

$$r'\,r^2 = \pm R^2$$

pon integration we find

4.5) $$r = (A \pm R^3)^{\frac{1}{3}}$$

here $A$ is a constant which should be taken as positive for expansion, $> R$. The plus sign in front of $R^3$ is for expansion, and the minus sign for taking the inside of the shell out (eversion). The eversion may be ade by slicing the undeformed sphere, turning it inside out, and rejoin- g the cut so that particles which were contiguous before the cut was ade are so after it is rejoined. The deformation for eversion is pre- ribed by

$$r = r(R) \qquad \theta = \pi - \Theta \qquad \phi = \Phi$$

here $r$ now is a monotone-decreasing function. The bounding surfaces e interchanged upon eversion.

For both expansion and eversion, by using (54.5), (54.3), and (54.4), e obtain

$$\|\overset{-1}{c}{}^k{}_l\| = \begin{bmatrix} R^4/r^4 & 0 & 0 \\ 0 & r^2/R^2 & 0 \\ 0 & 0 & r^2/R^2 \end{bmatrix} \qquad \|c^k{}_l\| = \begin{bmatrix} r^4/R^4 & 0 & 0 \\ 0 & R^2/r^2 & 0 \\ 0 & 0 & R^2/r^2 \end{bmatrix}$$

4.6) $$\mathrm{I} = \left(\frac{R}{r}\right)^4 + 2\left(\frac{r}{R}\right)^2 \qquad \mathrm{II} = \left(\frac{r}{R}\right)^4 + 2\left(\frac{R}{r}\right)^2 \qquad \mathrm{III} = 1$$

Hence $\Sigma = \Sigma(\text{I}, \text{II}) = \Sigma(r) = \Sigma(R)$. Using (51.5) for the stress com ponents, we find

$$
(54.7)\quad
\begin{aligned}
t^1{}_1 &= t^{(1)}{}_{(1)} = -p + 2\frac{\partial\Sigma}{\partial \text{I}}\frac{R^4}{r^4} - 2\frac{\partial\Sigma}{\partial \text{II}}\frac{r^4}{R^4}\\
t^2{}_2 &= t^3{}_3 = t^{(2)}{}_{(2)} = t^{(3)}{}_{(3)} = -p + 2\frac{\partial\Sigma}{\partial \text{I}}\frac{r^2}{R^2} - 2\frac{\partial\Sigma}{\partial \text{II}}\frac{R^2}{r^2}\\
&= t^1{}_1 + \left(\frac{\epsilon\, r\, R^3}{2\,A}\right)\frac{\partial\Sigma}{\partial r}
\end{aligned}
$$

All other $t^k{}_l = 0$. The last line for $t^2{}_2$ is obtained by using

$$
\frac{\partial \text{I}}{\partial r} = \frac{R^2}{r^2}\frac{\partial \text{II}}{\partial r} = 4\left(\frac{r^2}{R^2} - \frac{R^4}{r^4}\right)\left(\frac{1}{r} - \frac{R'}{R}\right) = \epsilon\, 4\left(\frac{r^2}{R^2} - \frac{R^4}{r^4}\right)\frac{A}{r\,R^3}
$$

where $\epsilon = 1$ for eversion and $\epsilon = -1$ for expansion and $R' \equiv dR/d$
Hence

$$
(54.8)\quad \frac{\partial\Sigma}{\partial r} = \left(\frac{\partial\Sigma}{\partial \text{I}} + \frac{r^2}{R^2}\frac{\partial\Sigma}{\partial \text{II}}\right)\frac{\partial \text{I}}{\partial r}
$$

is used to obtain the last expression of $t^2{}_2$ in (54.7). Through the equ librium equations with $\mathbf{f} = 0$ we find that

$$
(54.9)\quad \frac{dt^{(1)}{}_{(1)}}{dr} = \frac{2}{r}\left[t^{(2)}{}_{(2)} - t^{(1)}{}_{(1)}\right] = \left(\frac{\epsilon\, R^3}{A}\right)\frac{\partial\Sigma}{\partial r}
$$

Integration gives

$$
(54.10)\quad
\begin{aligned}
t^{(1)}{}_{(1)} &= \epsilon\int\left(\frac{R^3}{A}\right)d\Sigma + C_1\\
t^{(2)}{}_{(2)} &= \epsilon\int\left(\frac{R^3}{A}\right)d\Sigma + \left(\frac{\epsilon\, r\, R^3}{2\,A}\right)\frac{d\Sigma}{dr} + C_1
\end{aligned}
$$

By proper selection of $C_1$ we may make $t^{(1)}{}_{(1)}$ zero and thus clear th exterior surface of the deformed shell. If $R = a$ and $R = b > a$ are th interior and the exterior surfaces of the undeformed shell, then th interior and the exterior surfaces of the deformed shell are respectivel given by

$$
(54.11)\quad
\begin{aligned}
r &= (A + a^3)^{\frac{1}{3}} \qquad r = (A + b^3)^{\frac{1}{3}} \qquad \text{(expansion)}\\
r &= (A - b^3)^{\frac{1}{3}} \qquad r = (A - a^3)^{\frac{1}{3}} \qquad \text{(eversion)}
\end{aligned}
$$

where we must also choose $A > b^3$. Thus to clear the exterior surface the expanding shell, we set $t^{(1)}{}_{(1)} = 0$ at $r = (A + b^3)^{\frac{1}{3}}$, which results

$$
C_1 = \int^{(A+b^3)^{\frac{1}{3}}}\left(\frac{R^3}{A}\right)\frac{d\Sigma}{dr}\,dr
$$

nce in the expansion we find

4.12)

$$t^{(1)}{}_{(1)} = \int_r^{(A+b^3)^{\frac{1}{3}}} \left(\frac{R^3}{A}\right) \frac{d\Sigma}{dr}\, dr$$

$$t^{(2)}{}_{(2)} = t^{(3)}{}_{(3)} = \int_r^{(A+b^3)^{\frac{1}{3}}} \left(\frac{R^3}{A}\right) \frac{d\Sigma}{dr}\, dr - \left(\frac{r\,R^3}{2\,A}\right) \frac{d\Sigma}{dr}$$

e constant $A$ is determined by setting $t^{(1)}{}_{(1)} = -p_0$ at the inner face $r = (A + a^3)^{\frac{1}{3}}$. Hence

4.13)

$$\frac{1}{A} \int_{(A+a^3)^{\frac{1}{3}}}^{(A+b^3)^{\frac{1}{3}}} R^3 \frac{d\Sigma}{dr}\, dr = -p_0$$

termines $A$.

In a similar fashion for the eversion we find

4.14)

$$t^{(1)}{}_{(1)} = -\int_r^{(A-a^3)^{\frac{1}{3}}} \left(\frac{R^3}{A}\right) \frac{d\Sigma}{dr}\, dr$$

$$t^{(2)}{}_{(2)} = t^{(3)}{}_{(3)} = -\int_r^{(A-a^3)^{\frac{1}{3}}} \left(\frac{R^3}{A}\right) \frac{d\Sigma}{dr}\, dr + \left(\frac{r\,R^3}{2\,A}\right) \frac{d\Sigma}{dr}$$

ere $A$ may be determined similarly from the boundary condition at e inner surface. Inequalities (51.7) now become

$$\frac{d\Sigma}{d\mathrm{I}} + \left(\frac{r}{R}\right)^2 \frac{\partial\Sigma}{\partial\mathrm{II}} > 0 \qquad \frac{\partial\Sigma}{\partial\mathrm{I}} + \left(\frac{R}{r}\right)^4 \frac{\partial\Sigma}{\partial\mathrm{II}} \geq 0$$

us using (54.8), we find that $\epsilon\, d\Sigma/dr$ and

$$\left(\frac{r}{R}\right)^2 - \left(\frac{R}{r}\right)^4 = \frac{(r^3 + R^3)\,(r^3 - R^3)}{r^4\,R^2}$$

ust be of the same sign. In expansion $r > R$ so that $d\Sigma/dr < 0$. onsequently, according to $(54.12)_1$, $t^{(1)}{}_{(1)}$ increases monotonically with $r$. r the eversion $d\Sigma/dr$ is positive or negative according as

$$r^3 - R^3 = A - 2\,R^3$$

positive or negative. If the sphere $R^3 = A/2$ on which $c^k{}_l = \delta^k{}_l$ lies tween the inner and outer surfaces, it is then possible that $\int R^3\, d\Sigma$ may nish. If we take $t^{(1)}{}_{(1)} = 0$ on both boundaries, we then obtain a case which the interior of a simply connected body is strained, but on the rface of the body no external loads act. Since at least in the form of $\Sigma$ tained for spherically symmetric problems this is possible, we see that e uniqueness theorem of the theory of linear elasticity does not carry er to the theory of finite elasticity.

## 55. BENDING OF A BLOCK[1]

Let $x^k$ be referred to cylindrical coordinates $r$, $\theta$, $z$ and $X^K$ to rectangul coordinates $X$, $Y$, $Z$. The metric tensors are

$$G_{KL} = G^{KL} = \delta_{KL} \qquad \|g_{kl}\| = \begin{bmatrix} 1 & 0 & 0 \\ 0 & r^2 & 0 \\ 0 & 0 & 1 \end{bmatrix} \tag{55.1}$$

Consider the deformation prescribed by

$$r = f(X) \qquad \theta = g(Y) \qquad z = h(Z) \tag{55.2}$$

The deformation tensors were found in Art. 15 [Eq. $(15.36)_1$]. Sin $\mathrm{III} = (f f' g' h')^2$, we see that for the deformation to be isochoric, w must have $f f' = A$, $g' = C$, $h' = (A\,C)^{-1} = D$, where $A$, $C$, and $D$ a constants. Consequently after setting two integration constants equ to zero, to center the deformed block with respect to the spatial coord nates, we will have[2]

$$r = (2\,A\,X + B)^{\frac{1}{2}} \qquad \theta = C\,Y \qquad z = D\,Z \tag{55.3}$$

Deformation tensors and invariants are

$$\|\overset{-1}{c}{}^k{}_l\| = \begin{bmatrix} A^2/r^2 & 0 & 0 \\ 0 & C^2\,r^2 & 0 \\ 0 & 0 & D^2 \end{bmatrix} \qquad \|c^k{}_l\| = \begin{bmatrix} r^2/A^2 & 0 & 0 \\ 0 & 1/C^2\,r^2 & 0 \\ 0 & 0 & 1/D^2 \end{bmatrix} \tag{55.4}$$

$$\mathrm{I} = \frac{A^2}{r^2} + C^2\,r^2 + D^2 \qquad \mathrm{II} = \frac{r^2}{A^2} + \frac{1}{C^2\,r^2} + \frac{1}{D^2} \qquad \mathrm{III} = 1 \tag{55.5}$$

Therefore $\Sigma = \Sigma(r)$. Suppose that the undeformed surface of the bloc $X = -a$ goes into $r = r_1$, $X = a$ to $r = r_2$, and $Y = \pm b$ to $\theta = \pm$ (Fig. 55.1$a$, $b$).

Therefore constants $A$, $B$, $C$, and $D$ are given by

$$\begin{gathered} 4\,A\,a = r_2^2 - r_1^2 \qquad 2\,B = r_1^2 + r_2^2 \qquad b\,C = \theta_0 \\ \theta_0\,D\,(r_2^2 - r_1^2) = 4\,a\,b \end{gathered} \tag{55.6}$$

For an incompressible material stress-strain relations (51.5) read

$$\begin{aligned} t^1{}_1 &= -p + 2\,\frac{A^2}{r^2}\,\frac{\partial\Sigma}{\partial \mathrm{I}} - 2\,\frac{r^2}{A^2}\,\frac{\partial\Sigma}{\partial \mathrm{II}} \\ t^2{}_2 &= -p + 2\,C^2\,r^2\,\frac{\partial\Sigma}{\partial \mathrm{I}} - \frac{2}{C^2\,r^2}\,\frac{\partial\Sigma}{\partial \mathrm{II}} \\ t^3{}_3 &= -p + 2\,D^2\,\frac{\partial\Sigma}{\partial \mathrm{I}} - \frac{2}{D^2}\,\frac{\partial\Sigma}{\partial \mathrm{II}} \end{aligned} \tag{55.7}$$

[1] This problem was treated by Rivlin [1949$a$, $b$]. For the same problem concernin orthotropic materials, see Green and Wilkes [1954].

[2] This is an example indicating the great simplicity of using the scheme of two differ ent sets of coordinates, one set for material and another for spatial representation.

all other stresses being zero. The equilibrium equations with $\mathbf{f} = 0$ reduce to

$$(55.8) \qquad \frac{\partial t^1{}_1}{\partial r} + \frac{t^1{}_1 - t^2{}_2}{r} = 0 \qquad \frac{\partial t^2{}_2}{\partial \theta} = 0 \qquad \frac{\partial t^3{}_3}{\partial z} = 0$$

From the last two of (55.7) and (55.8), and since $\Sigma = \Sigma(r)$, it follows

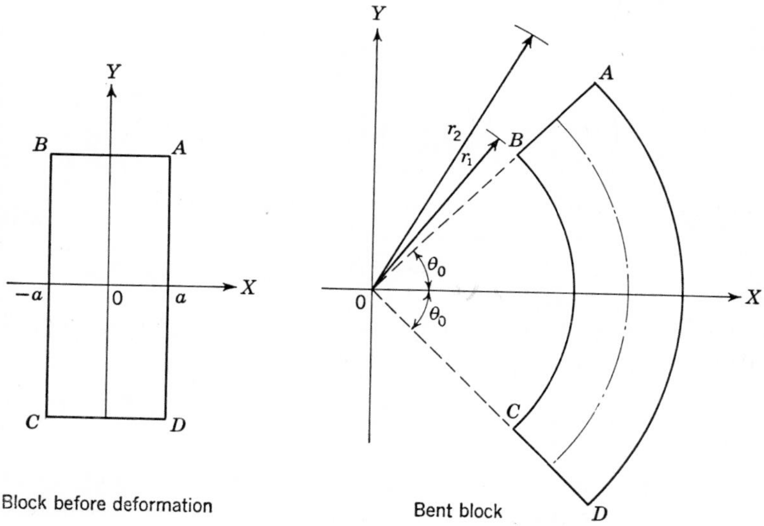


FIG. 55.1

that $p = p(r)$. From (55.7) we have

$$\frac{t^1{}_1 - t^2{}_2}{r} = 2\left(\frac{A^2}{r^3} - C^2 r\right)\frac{\partial \Sigma}{\partial \mathrm{I}} - 2\left(\frac{r}{A^2} - \frac{1}{C^2 r^3}\right)\frac{\partial \Sigma}{\partial \mathrm{II}}$$

Through (55.5) and this expression we see that

$$(55.9) \quad \frac{\partial \Sigma}{\partial r} = \frac{\partial \Sigma}{\partial \mathrm{I}}\frac{\partial \mathrm{I}}{\partial r} + \frac{\partial \Sigma}{\partial \mathrm{II}}\frac{\partial \mathrm{II}}{\partial r}$$
$$= -2\left(\frac{A^2}{r^3} - C^2 r\right)\frac{\partial \Sigma}{\partial \mathrm{I}} + 2\left(\frac{r}{A^2} - \frac{1}{C^2 r^3}\right)\frac{\partial \Sigma}{\partial \mathrm{II}}$$
$$= -\frac{t^1{}_1 - t^2{}_2}{r}$$

Consequently $(55.8)_1$ reduces to

$$\frac{d}{dr}(t^1{}_1 - \Sigma) = 0$$

which integrates into

$$t^1{}_1 - \Sigma = K$$

where $K$ is a constant. Carrying this into (55.7) and using (55.9), we ge

$$\begin{aligned} t^1{}_1 &= \Sigma + K \\ \text{(55.10)} \quad t^2{}_2 &= 2\left(C^2 r^2 - \frac{A^2}{r^2}\right)\left(\frac{\partial \Sigma}{\partial \mathrm{I}} + D^2 \frac{\partial \Sigma}{\partial \mathrm{II}}\right) + \Sigma + K \\ &= r\frac{\partial \Sigma}{\partial r} + \Sigma + K \\ t^3{}_3 &= 2\left(D^2 - \frac{A^2}{r^2}\right)\left(\frac{\partial \Sigma}{\partial \mathrm{I}} + r^2 C^2 \frac{\partial \Sigma}{\partial \mathrm{II}}\right) + \Sigma + K \end{aligned}$$

The normal force on $F$ per unit area of curved surface is

$$\text{(55.11)} \qquad F = [(\Sigma + K)]_{r_1 \text{ or } r_2}$$

If the bending is to be produced by terminal loads alone, we must have $F = 0$ at $r = r_1$ and $r = r_2$. This means

$$\text{(55.12)} \qquad \Sigma(r_1) = \Sigma(r_2) = -K$$

a condition which also makes normal tractions at the terminal surfaces $\theta = \pm\theta_0$ vanish. Since $\Sigma = \Sigma(\mathrm{I}, \mathrm{II})$, the condition (55.12) implies that $\mathrm{I}(r_1) = \mathrm{I}(r_2)$, $\mathrm{II}(r_1) = \mathrm{II}(r_2)$, or

$$\text{(55.13)} \qquad A = C r_1 r_2 \qquad \text{or} \qquad A^2 = \frac{r_1 r_2}{D}$$

Therefore we are left with only two arbitrary constants, e.g., $D$ and $r_1$.

The flexural couple $M$ per unit depth is given by

$$\text{(55.14)} \qquad M = \int_{r_1}^{r_2} r\, t^2{}_2\, dr = \tfrac{1}{2}(r_1^2 - r_2^2)K - \int_{r_1}^{r_2} r\,\Sigma\, dr$$

an equation to determine $r_1$ when $\Sigma$ is known and $M$ is prescribed. There is no indication that $r_1$ is uniquely determined.

The neutral fiber for the entire deformation is obtained by setting $c^2{}_2 = 1$, which gives $C^2 r_0^2 = 1$ or $r_0^2 = D\, r_1 r_2$. The neutral fiber for the bending is found by setting $D = 1$, i.e., $r_0^2 = r_1 r_2$, which is the same as in the linear theory.

*We again encounter the Poynting effect in the form of the stress component $t^3{}_3$ required to produce pure bending of the block.*

## 56. FINITE PLANE STRAIN[1]

For a certain class of problems which are essentially two-dimensional in nature, a great deal of simplification is achieved. A plane strain combined with a uniform extension perpendicular to this plane falls into this category. For this class of problems we have a deformation field represented by

$$x^a = x^a(X^1, X^2) \qquad x^3 = \lambda X^3 \qquad (a = 1, 2) \tag{56.1}$$

where $\lambda$ is a constant. We make the convention, in connection with plane strain, that indices $a$, $b$, $c$, $d$ have the range (1, 2). Coordinates $(x^a, x^3)$ will always be chosen to be cylindrical, with $x^3$ being the axis of the cylinder. A routine calculation shows that

$$\|g_{kl}\| = \begin{bmatrix} g_{ab} & 0 \\ 0 & 1 \end{bmatrix} \qquad \|\overset{-1}{c}{}^k{}_l\| = \begin{bmatrix} \overset{-1}{c}{}^a{}_b & 0 \\ 0 & \lambda^2 \end{bmatrix} \qquad \|c^k{}_l\| = \begin{bmatrix} c^a{}_b & 0 \\ 0 & \lambda^{-2} \end{bmatrix} \tag{56.2}$$

where $g_{ab}$, $\overset{-1}{c}{}^a{}_b$, and $c^a{}_b$ are functions of $x^1$ and $x^2$ only. In dynamical problems $x^a$ and $\lambda$ may also be taken to be functions of time. We have

$$\begin{aligned} \mathrm{I} &= \overset{-1}{c}{}^k{}_k = \lambda^2 + \overset{-1}{c}{}^a{}_a = \lambda^2 + \mathrm{I}_1 \\ \mathrm{II} &= \tfrac{1}{2}(\mathrm{I}^2 - \overset{-1}{c}{}^k{}_l\,\overset{-1}{c}{}^l{}_k) = |\overset{-1}{c}{}^a{}_b| + \lambda^2\,\mathrm{I}_1 = \mathrm{I}_2 + \lambda^2\,\mathrm{I}_1 \\ \mathrm{III} &= |\overset{-1}{c}{}^k{}_l| = \lambda^2\,|\overset{-1}{c}{}^a{}_b| = \lambda^2\,\mathrm{I}_2 \end{aligned} \tag{56.3}$$

where

$$\mathrm{I}_1 = \overset{-1}{c}{}^a{}_a \qquad \mathrm{I}_2 = |\overset{-1}{c}{}^a{}_b| \tag{56.4}$$

By use of the Cayley-Hamilton theorem we see that

$$\overset{-1}{c}{}^a{}_c\,\overset{-1}{c}{}^c{}_b = \mathrm{I}_1\,\overset{-1}{c}{}^a{}_b - \mathrm{I}_2\,\delta^a{}_b \tag{56.5}$$

Multiplying this by $c^b{}_d$, we get

$$\mathrm{I}_2\,c^a{}_b = \mathrm{I}_1\,\delta^a{}_b - \overset{-1}{c}{}^a{}_b \tag{56.6}$$

Upon substituting (56.3) and (56.6) into (51.3) and using (51.4), we find

$$t^a{}_b = \frac{2}{\lambda\sqrt{\mathrm{I}_2}}\left[\left(\frac{\partial\Sigma}{\partial\mathrm{II}} + \lambda^2\frac{\partial\Sigma}{\partial\mathrm{III}}\right)\mathrm{I}_2\,\delta^a{}_b + \left(\frac{\partial\Sigma}{\partial\mathrm{I}} + \lambda^2\frac{\partial\Sigma}{\partial\mathrm{II}}\right)\overset{-1}{c}{}^a{}_b\right]$$

$$t^3{}_3 = \frac{2\lambda}{\sqrt{\mathrm{I}_2}}\left(\frac{\partial\Sigma}{\partial\mathrm{I}} + \mathrm{I}_1\frac{\partial\Sigma}{\partial\mathrm{II}} + \mathrm{I}_2\frac{\partial\Sigma}{\partial\mathrm{III}}\right) \qquad t^a{}_3 = t^3{}_a = 0$$

[1] The present treatment differs from that of Adkins, Green, and Shield [1953], where imbedded coordinates were utilized.

Now $\Sigma$ may be looked upon as a function of $I_1$, $I_2$, and $\lambda^2$ so that

$$\frac{\partial \Sigma}{\partial I_1} = \frac{\partial \Sigma}{\partial I} + \lambda^2 \frac{\partial \Sigma}{\partial II} \qquad \frac{\partial \Sigma}{\partial I_2} = \frac{\partial \Sigma}{\partial II} + \lambda^2 \frac{\partial \Sigma}{\partial III}$$

$$\frac{\partial \Sigma}{\partial \lambda^2} = \frac{\partial \Sigma}{\partial I} + I_1 \frac{\partial \Sigma}{\partial II} + I_2 \frac{\partial \Sigma}{\partial III}$$

Consequently

$$(56.7) \qquad \begin{aligned} t^a{}_b &= \frac{2}{\lambda \sqrt{I_2}} \left( I_2 \frac{\partial \Sigma}{\partial I_2} \delta^a{}_b + \frac{\partial \Sigma}{\partial I_1} \overset{-1}{c}{}^a{}_b \right) \\ t^3{}_3 &= \frac{2\lambda}{\sqrt{I_2}} \frac{\partial \Sigma}{\partial \lambda^2} \qquad t^a{}_3 = t^3{}_a = 0 \end{aligned} \qquad \text{(compressible)}$$

For an incompressible material $III = I_2 \lambda^2 = 1$ so that $\Sigma$ is a function of $I_1$ and $\lambda^2$. For this case a similar analysis gives

$$(56.8) \qquad \begin{aligned} t^a{}_b &= -p\, \delta^a{}_b + 2 \frac{\partial \Sigma}{\partial I_1} \overset{-1}{c}{}^a{}_b \\ t^3{}_3 &= -p + 2\lambda^2 \frac{\partial \Sigma}{\partial \lambda^2} \qquad t^a{}_3 = t^3{}_a = 0 \end{aligned} \qquad \text{(incompressible)}$$

For plane strain the equations of equilibrium reduce to

$$(56.9) \qquad t^{ab}{}_{;a} + \rho f^b = \rho a^b$$

The solution of problems in plane strain thus requires the solution of (56.9) with (56.7) for compressible materials and with (56.8) for incompressible materials. The surface tractions $t^k{}_{(n)}$ are given by

$$(56.10) \qquad t^a{}_{(n)} = t^{ba} n_b \qquad t^3{}_{(3)} = t^3{}_3$$

The introduction of *Airy's stress function* provides an additional simplification for the solution of the problems concerning plane strain. The vector form of the equations of equilibrium with zero body forces, according to (32.7), is

$$(56.11) \qquad \frac{\partial}{\partial x^k} (\sqrt{g}\, \mathbf{t}^k) = 0$$

where the stress vector $\mathbf{t}^k$ is related to the stress tensor by $(31.5)_2$, i.e.,

$$(56.12) \qquad \mathbf{t}^k = t^{kl} \mathbf{g}_l$$

Through (56.2) this latter expression reduces to

$$(56.13) \qquad \mathbf{t}^a = t^{ba} \mathbf{g}_b \qquad \mathbf{t}^3 = t^{33} \mathbf{g}_3$$

Since $g$ and $\mathbf{t}^a$ are functions of $x^1$ and $x^2$, (56.11) simplifies to

(56.14) $$\frac{\partial}{\partial x^a}(\sqrt{g}\,\mathbf{t}^a) = 0$$

This equation can be satisfied by

(56.15) $$\mathbf{t}^a = \epsilon^{ca}\,\boldsymbol{\chi}_{,c}$$

where $\epsilon^{11} = \epsilon^{22} = 0$, $\epsilon^{12} = -\epsilon^{21} = 1/\sqrt{g}$ and $\boldsymbol{\chi}$ is a vector in the plane $x^3 = 0$, i.e.,

(56.16) $$\boldsymbol{\chi} = \chi^b\,\mathbf{g}_b \qquad \boldsymbol{\chi}_{,c} = \chi^b{}_{;c}\,\mathbf{g}_b$$

Hence

(56.17) $$\mathbf{t}^a = \epsilon^{ca}\,\chi^b{}_{;c}\,\mathbf{g}_b$$

Here the covariant differentiation is taken in the plane $x^3 = 0$, i.e., we use

(56.18) $$\begin{Bmatrix} a \\ bc \end{Bmatrix} = \tfrac{1}{2}\,g^{ad}\,(g_{bd,c} + g_{cd,b} - g_{bc,d})$$

Through (56.13) we get

(56.19) $$t^{ab} = \epsilon^{cb}\,\chi^a{}_{;c}$$

Now $t^{ba}$ is symmetrical, so that we may write

(56.20) $$\chi^a = \epsilon^{da}\,\phi_{,d}$$

or

(56.21) $$t^{ab} = \epsilon^{cb}\,\epsilon^{da}\,\phi_{;dc} = \epsilon^{bc}\,\epsilon^{ad}\,\phi_{;cd}$$

where $\phi = \phi(x^1, x^2)$ is *Airy's stress function.* Equation (56.21) may be solved for $\phi_;{}^a{}_b$ to give

(56.22) $$\phi_;{}^a{}_b = \epsilon^{ac}\,\epsilon_{bd}\,t^d{}_c = t^c{}_c\,\delta^a{}_b - t^a{}_b$$

If we use $(56.7)_1$ in this, we obtain

(56.23) $$\phi_;{}^a{}_b = \frac{2}{\lambda\sqrt{\mathrm{I}_2}}\left[\left(\mathrm{I}_1\frac{\partial\Sigma}{\partial\mathrm{I}_1} + \mathrm{I}_2\frac{\partial\Sigma}{\partial\mathrm{I}_2}\right)\delta^a{}_b - \frac{\partial\Sigma}{\partial\mathrm{I}_1}\,\overset{-1}{c}{}^a{}_b\right] \quad \text{(compressible)}$$

For an incompressible material from $(56.8)_1$ we similarly obtain

(56.24) $$\phi_;{}^a{}_b = \left(-p + 2\mathrm{I}_1\frac{\partial\Sigma}{\partial\mathrm{I}_1}\right)\delta^a{}_b - 2\frac{\partial\Sigma}{\partial\mathrm{I}_1}\,\overset{-1}{c}{}^a{}_b \qquad \text{(incompressible)}$$

It is possible to eliminate either $\partial\Sigma/\partial I_2$ or $\partial\Sigma/\partial I_1$ from (56.23) by noticing that

$$\phi_{;}{}^{a}{}_{a} = \frac{2}{\lambda\sqrt{I_2}}\left(I_1\frac{\partial\Sigma}{\partial I_1} + 2\,I_2\frac{\partial\Sigma}{\partial I_2}\right) \qquad \text{(compressible)}$$

(56.25)

$$\phi_{;}{}^{a}{}_{a} = -2\,p + 2\,I_1\frac{\partial\Sigma}{\partial I_1} \qquad \text{(incompressible)}$$

Hence, using $(56.25)_1$ in (56.23), we obtain the equivalent forms

$$\phi_{;}{}^{a}{}_{b} - \tfrac{1}{2}\,\phi_{;}{}^{c}{}_{c}\,\delta^{a}{}_{b} = \frac{2}{\lambda\sqrt{I_2}}\frac{\partial\Sigma}{\partial I_1}\left(\frac{I_1}{2}\,\delta^{a}{}_{b} - \overset{-1}{c}{}^{a}{}_{b}\right) \tag{56.26}$$

$$\phi_{;}{}^{a}{}_{b} - \left(\delta^{a}{}_{b} - \frac{1}{I_1}\overset{-1}{c}{}^{a}{}_{b}\right)\phi_{;}{}^{c}{}_{c} \qquad \text{(compressible)} \tag{56.27}$$

$$= \frac{4\sqrt{I_2}}{\lambda I_1}\frac{\partial\Sigma}{\partial I_2}\left(-\frac{I_1}{2}\,\delta^{a}{}_{b} + \overset{-1}{c}{}^{a}{}_{b}\right)$$

For the incompressible solid we may eliminate either $p$ or $\partial\Sigma/\partial I_1$ from (56.24). Hence

$$\phi_{;}{}^{a}{}_{b} - \frac{1}{2}\,\phi_{;}{}^{c}{}_{c}\,\delta^{a}{}_{b} = 2\frac{\partial\Sigma}{\partial I_1}\left(\frac{I_1}{2}\,\delta^{a}{}_{b} - \overset{-1}{c}{}^{a}{}_{b}\right) \tag{56.28}$$

$$\phi_{;}{}^{a}{}_{b} - \left(\delta^{a}{}_{b} - \frac{1}{I_1}\overset{-1}{c}{}^{a}{}_{b}\right)\phi_{;}{}^{d}{}_{d} \qquad \text{(incompressible)} \tag{56.29}$$

$$= \frac{2\,p}{I_1}\left(\frac{I_1}{2}\,\delta^{a}{}_{b} - \overset{-1}{c}{}^{a}{}_{b}\right)$$

A nonlinear partial differential equation for $\phi$ may be obtained from (56.23) or (56.24) (not containing $\overset{-1}{c}{}^{a}{}_{b}$) if we recall that $\overset{-1}{\mathbf{c}}$ must satisfy the strain compatibility condition of the form

$$R^{(\overset{-1}{\mathbf{c}})}{}_{klmn} = 0 \tag{56.30}$$

where $R^{(\mathbf{a})}{}_{klmn}$ are defined by (13.2). In the present two-dimensional case this tensor has only *one* nonvanishing component, $R_{1212}$. Thus, solving for $\overset{-1}{c}{}^{a}{}_{b}$ from (56.23) or (56.24) in terms of $\phi$ and substituting into the expression of $R^{(\overset{-1}{\mathbf{c}})}{}_{1212} = 0$, we obtain a fourth-order nonlinear partial differential equation in $\phi$. This equation is the generalization of the biharmonic equation $\nabla^4\phi = 0$ of the linear theory. Since we shall not have occasion to use this equation, it is not given here.

*Force and Couple Resultants.* Resultant force $\mathbf{r}$ exerted by a region 1 on a region 2 (Fig. 56.1) across an arc $p_0\,p$ and measured per unit length of the $x^3$ axis may be expressed in terms of $\phi$ as follows.

We have

$$\mathbf{r} = -\int_{p_0}^{p} \mathbf{t}_{(\mathbf{n})}\, ds \tag{56.31}$$

but from (30.4) we have

$$\mathbf{t}_{(\mathbf{n})} = \mathbf{t}^a n_a = \mathbf{t}^a \epsilon_{ab} \frac{dx^b}{ds}$$

since $n_a = \epsilon_{ab}\, dx^b/ds$. Thus, using (56.15), we shall have

$$\mathbf{r} = -\int_{p_0}^{p} \epsilon^{ca} \boldsymbol{\chi}_{,c}\, \epsilon_{ab} \frac{dx^b}{ds}\, ds = \int_{p_0}^{p} \boldsymbol{\chi}_{,b} \frac{dx^b}{ds}\, ds = \boldsymbol{\chi}$$

or

$$\mathbf{r} = \boldsymbol{\chi} = \epsilon^{ab} \phi_{,a} \mathbf{g}_b \tag{56.32}$$

The moment $\mathbf{m}$ about the $x^3$ axis of the forces exerted by region 1 on

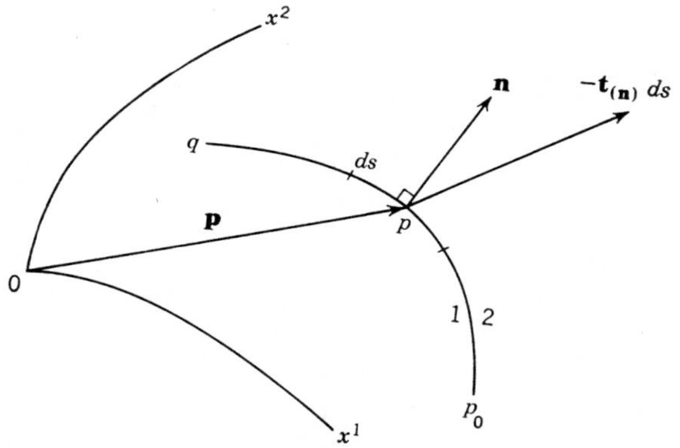


FIG. 56.1

region 2 across $p_0\, p$, measured per unit length of $x^3$ axis, is

$$\mathbf{m} = \int_{p_0}^{p} \mathbf{p} \times \boldsymbol{\chi}_{,b} \frac{dx^b}{ds}\, ds \tag{56.33}$$

Integration by parts gives

$$\mathbf{m} = [\mathbf{p} \times \boldsymbol{\chi}]_{p_0}^{p} - \int_{p_0}^{p} (\mathbf{g}_a \times \boldsymbol{\chi}) \frac{dx^a}{ds}\, ds \tag{56.34}$$

Using (56.16), we write

$$\mathbf{p} \times \boldsymbol{\chi} = p^a \chi^b \mathbf{g}_a \times \mathbf{g}_b = p^a \chi^b \epsilon_{ab} \mathbf{g}^3 = p^a \epsilon^{cb} \epsilon_{ab} \phi_{,c} \mathbf{g}^3 = p^a \phi_{,a} \mathbf{g}^3$$
$$\mathbf{g}_a \times \boldsymbol{\chi} = \chi^b \mathbf{g}_a \times \mathbf{g}_b = \epsilon^{cb} \epsilon_{ab} \phi_{,c} \mathbf{g}_3 = \phi_{,a} \mathbf{g}^3$$

Hence, apart from an arbitrary constant vector which may be absorbed into $\phi$ without affecting stresses,

$$\mathbf{m} = (p^a \phi_{,a} - \phi)\, \mathbf{g}^3 \tag{56.35}$$

The magnitude $m$ of the couple is therefore

$$m = p^a \phi_{,a} - \phi \tag{56.36}$$

If the boundary curve is free of applied loads, then

$$\mathfrak{x} = 0 \tag{56.37}$$

at all points of the boundary. Using (56.20), this gives $\phi_{,1} = \phi_{,2} = 0$ or $\phi = \text{const}$. If $\mathbf{m} = 0$, then for a simply connected region we may take $\phi = 0$ and for multiply connected regions $\phi = \text{const}$ on each boundary with different constants for each since we have absorbed a constant of integration into $\phi$.

A similar type of formulation can be made in the case of plane stress.[2] An example employing the present formulation is given in the following article.

## 57. FLEXURE OF AN INITIALLY CURVED CUBOID[1]

We select for $X^K$ and $x^k$ the same cylindrical coordinates $(R, \Theta, Z)$.

The curved surfaces $R = R_1$, $R = R_2$, $(R_2 > R_1)$; the planes $\Theta = \pm\Theta_0$ and planes $X^3 = \pm Z_0$ of a cylindrical shell are respectively deformed into curved surfaces $r = r_1$, $r = r_2$, the planes $\theta = \pm\theta_0$ and $x^3 = \pm\lambda$ of another cylindrical shell (Fig. 57.1). When $\theta_0 = \pi$, $r_1 = 0$, the deformed cylinder becomes a complete circular plate. This problem is of the type discussed by Volterra [1907] in his memoir on *dislocations;* namely, from a cylinder a pie-shaped piece between the planes $\Theta = \pm\Theta_0$ is removed. Afterward these planes are brought together, thus completing the body into a right circular cylinder. Determine the stress and deformation fields.

When $r_2 > r_1 > 0$, then the curvatures of deformed and undeformed shells have the same sign; and when $r_1 > r_2 > 0$, then they have the opposite signs. For $\Theta_0 = \pi$ and $\theta_0 = \pi$ we would have a cylinder turned inside out. Many other possibilities exist.

[2] Cf. Adkins, Green, and Nicholas [1954]. For the development of the complex function technique concerning plane problems in the theory of finite elasticity, see this and Adkins, Green, and Shield [1953]. These papers also include exact and approximate solutions of a number of interesting problems.

[1] Adkins, Green, and Shield [1953]. For anisotropic materials see Ericksen and Rivlin [1954]. We give here a simplified version of these solutions.

The metric tensors are

$$\|G_{KL}\| = \begin{bmatrix} 1 & 0 & 0 \\ 0 & R^2 & 0 \\ 0 & 0 & 1 \end{bmatrix} \qquad \|g_{kl}\| = \begin{bmatrix} 1 & 0 & 0 \\ 0 & r^2 & 0 \\ 0 & 0 & 1 \end{bmatrix} \tag{57.1}$$

Consider now the deformation

$$r = f(R) \qquad \theta = g(\Theta) \qquad z = h(Z) \tag{57.2}$$

where $f$, $g$, and $h$ are continuously differentiable functions. Through

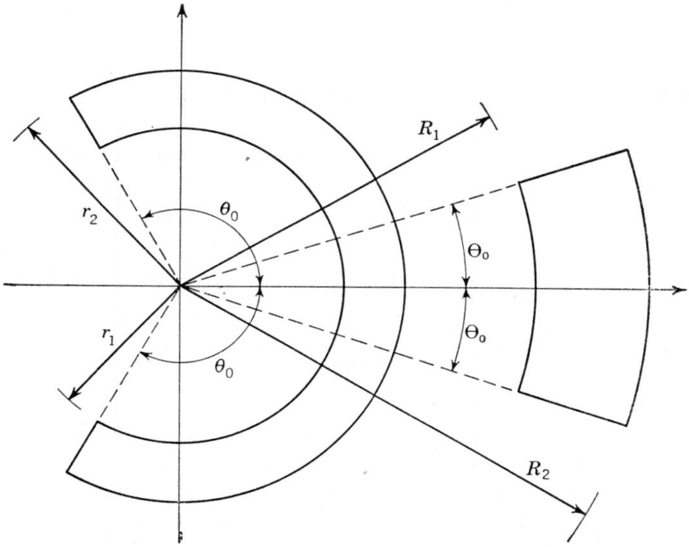


FIG. 57.1

(51.8)$_2$ we get

$$\|\overset{-1}{c}{}^k{}_l\| = \begin{bmatrix} f'^2 & 0 & 0 \\ 0 & f^2 g'^2/R^2 & 0 \\ 0 & 0 & h'^2 \end{bmatrix} \tag{57.3}$$

Consequently the condition of incompressibility gives

$$\text{III} = \left[\left(\frac{ff'}{R}\right) g' \, h'\right]^2 = 1$$

This means that $ff'/R = A$, $g' = C$, $h' = (A\,C)^{-1} = D$, where $A$, $C$, and $D$ are constants. Integration gives

$$r = (A\,R^2 + B)^{\frac{1}{2}} \qquad \theta = C\,\Theta \qquad z = D\,Z \tag{57.4}$$

where $B$ is another constant and two other integration constants, one for $\theta$ and one for $z$, are set equal to zero to center the deformed block with respect to the spatial coordinates. At the bounding surfaces of the deformed and undeformed solid, according to the description of the deformation given above, we have

$$r_1 = (A\,R_1^2 + B)^{\frac{1}{2}} \qquad r_2 = (A\,R_2^2 + B)^{\frac{1}{2}} \qquad \theta_0 = C\,\Theta_0 \qquad z_0 = D\,Z_0$$

Hence

$$A = \frac{r_2^2 - r_1^2}{R_2^2 - R_1^2} \qquad B = \frac{R_2^2\,r_1^2 - R_1^2\,r_2^2}{R_2^2 - R_1^2}$$

(57.5)

$$C = \frac{\theta_0}{\Theta_0} \qquad D = \frac{z_0}{Z_0}$$

Deformation tensors and invariants are given by

$$\|\overset{-1}{c}{}^k{}_l\| = \begin{bmatrix} \frac{A\,(r^2 - B)}{r^2} & 0 & 0 \\ 0 & \frac{A\,C^2\,r^2}{r^2 - B} & 0 \\ 0 & 0 & \frac{1}{A^2\,C^2} \end{bmatrix}$$

(57.6)

$$\|c^k{}_l\| = \begin{bmatrix} \frac{r^2}{A\,(r^2 - B)} & 0 & 0 \\ 0 & \frac{r^2 - B}{A\,C^2\,r^2} & 0 \\ 0 & 0 & A^2\,C^2 \end{bmatrix}$$

$$\mathrm{I} = \frac{A}{r^2}\,(r^2 - B) + \frac{A\,C^2\,r^2}{r^2 - B} + \frac{1}{A^2\,C^2}$$

$$\mathrm{II} = A^2\,C^2 + \frac{1}{A}\,\frac{r^2}{r^2 - B} + \frac{r^2 - B}{A\,C^2\,r^2}$$

Through $(57.1)_2$ and (57.6) it is clear that the problem is one of plane strain and that

(57.7)

$$\|g_{ab}\| = \begin{bmatrix} 1 & 0 \\ 0 & r^2 \end{bmatrix} \qquad \|\overset{-1}{c}{}^a{}_b\| = \begin{bmatrix} \frac{A\,(r^2 - B)}{r^2} & 0 \\ 0 & \frac{A\,C^2\,r^2}{r^2 - B} \end{bmatrix}$$

$$\lambda^2 = \frac{1}{A^2\,C^2} \qquad \mathrm{I}_1 = \frac{A}{r^2}\,(r^2 - B) + \frac{A\,C^2\,r^2}{r^2 - B} \qquad \mathrm{I}_2 = A^2\,C^2$$

Using (56.28), we find that $\phi = \phi\,(r)$ and

(57.8)

$$\frac{d}{dr}\left(\frac{1}{r}\,\frac{d\phi}{dr}\right) = 2\,\frac{\partial\Sigma}{\partial \mathrm{I}_1}\left[-\frac{A}{r^3}\,(r^2 - B) + \frac{A\,C^2\,r}{r^2 - B}\right]$$

But from $(57.7)_4$ by differentiation we find that

$$\frac{dI_1}{dr} = \frac{2B}{r^2 - B}\left[\frac{A}{r^3}(r^2 - B) - \frac{A C^2 r}{r^2 - B}\right]$$

Consequently

$$\frac{d}{dr}\left(\frac{1}{r}\frac{d\phi}{dr}\right) = \frac{B - r^2}{B}\frac{d\Sigma}{dr} \tag{57.9}$$

whence

$$\frac{1}{r}\frac{d\phi}{dr} = \Sigma - \frac{1}{B}\int_{r_1}^{r} x^2 \frac{d\Sigma}{dx}\,dx + E \tag{57.10}$$

where $E$ is a constant. The tractions on surfaces $r = r_1$ and $r = r_2$ vanish if $d\phi/dr = 0$ on these surfaces. Consequently

$$E = -\Sigma(r_1) \qquad \Sigma(r_2) - \frac{1}{B}\int_{r_1}^{r_2} x^2 \frac{d\Sigma}{dx}\,dx + E = 0 \tag{57.11}$$

Therefore $r_1$ and $r_2$ are connected by the relation

$$\Sigma(r_2) - \Sigma(r_1) = \frac{1}{B}\int_{r_1}^{r_2} x^2 \frac{d\Sigma}{dx}\,dx \tag{57.12}$$

If (57.11) is satisfied, then the couple $m$ per unit length of the deformed cylinder acting at each end $\theta = \pm\theta_0$ of the cylinder, according to (56.35), is

$$m = \phi(r_1) - \phi(r_2) = \tfrac{1}{2}(r_2^2 - r_1^2)\,\Sigma(r_1) - \int_{r_1}^{r_2} \Sigma(r)\, r\,dr + \frac{1}{B}\int_{r_1}^{r_2} r\,dr \int_{r_1}^{r} x^2 \frac{d\Sigma}{dx}\,dx$$

Integrating by parts, we may write this also as

$$m = \tfrac{1}{2}(r_2^2 - r_1^2)\left(1 - \frac{r_1^2}{B}\right)\Sigma(r_1) - \int_{r_1}^{r_2}\left[1 - \frac{1}{B}(2r^2 - r_2^2)\right] r\,\Sigma(r)\,dr \tag{57.13}$$

The stresses $t^{ab}$ follow from (56.21), and $t^3{}_3$ from $(56.7)_2$

$$\begin{aligned} t^1{}_1 &= t^{(1)}{}_{(1)} = \frac{1}{r}\frac{d\phi}{dr} = \Sigma(r) - \Sigma(r_1) - \frac{1}{B}\int_{r_1}^{r} x^2\frac{d\Sigma}{dx}\,dx \\ t^2{}_2 &= t^{(2)}{}_{(2)} = \frac{d^2\phi}{dr^2} = t^1{}_1 + \frac{r}{B}(B - r^2)\frac{d\Sigma}{dr} \\ t^3{}_3 &= t^{(3)}{}_{(3)} = \frac{2\lambda}{\sqrt{I_2}}\frac{\partial\Sigma}{\partial\lambda^2} \qquad t^a{}_3 = t^3{}_a = 0 \end{aligned} \tag{57.14}$$

*Special Case* 1. *Bending of a Block.* The stresses for this case may be obtained from the foregoing result by setting $1/B = 0$. The resulting formulas are easily brought to the forms obtained in Art. 55. This limit procedure is not immediately obvious, and care must be exercised in applying it to earlier results in this section.

*Special Case* 2. *Dislocation Solution for a Solid Cylinder.* In this case we set $\Theta_0 = \pi$, $R_1 = r_1 = 0$. This, through (57.5), gives

$$A = \frac{r_2^2}{R_2^2} \qquad B = 0 \qquad C = \frac{\theta_0}{\pi}$$

This makes $\mathrm{I}_1 = A\,(1 + C^2) = \text{const.}$ Hence no longer can $\mathrm{I}_1$ be differentiated with respect to $r$. We must therefore work with (57.8). Integrating this equation, we get

$$\frac{1}{r}\frac{d\phi}{dr} = 2\,A\,(1 - C^2) \int_r^{r_2} \frac{1}{x}\frac{\partial \Sigma}{\partial \mathrm{I}_1}\,dx + E \tag{57.15}$$

Since at $r = r_2$ the traction is zero, we have $E = 0$. Stresses for this case are

$$\begin{aligned} t^1{}_1 &= t^{(1)}{}_{(1)} = 2\,A\,(1 - C^2) \int_r^{r_2} \frac{1}{x}\frac{\partial \Sigma}{\partial \mathrm{I}_1}\,dx \\ t^2{}_2 &= t^{(2)}{}_{(2)} = t^1{}_1 - 2\,A\,(1 - C^2)\,\frac{\partial \Sigma}{\partial \mathrm{I}_1} \\ t^3{}_3 &= \frac{2\,\lambda}{\sqrt{\mathrm{I}_2}}\,\frac{\partial \Sigma}{\partial \lambda^2} \qquad t^a{}_3 = t^3{}_a = 0 \end{aligned} \tag{57.16}$$

Other special cases, such as the eversion of a cylindrical shell, the expansion of a cylindrical shell, etc., can be obtained in an obvious way from the foregoing general solution.

## 58. FINITE ELASTIC WAVES

The dynamical theory of finite elasticity has not been developed to the same extent as the statical theory. Excluding a few approximate solutions of approximate field equations, the only problem tackled exactly is that of propagation of a discontinuity surface (a wave) in an infinite solid. For compressible materials we cite the work of Duhem [1903] Hadamard [1903, chaps. II and IV], and Tolotti [1943] and for incompressible media that of Ericksen [1953], which we reproduce below.[1]

The basic equations governing the finite elastodynamic problem for a homogeneous isotropic incompressible elastic medium (excluding thermo-

[1] Note added at proof: For further discussion in this area we cite the recent work of Truesdell [1961].

ynamic considerations) are

$$t^{lk}{}_{;l} + \rho\,(f^k - \ddot{x}^k) = 0 \qquad \text{58.1)}$$

$$t^k{}_l = -\bar{p}\,\delta^k{}_l + 2\left(\frac{\partial\Sigma}{\partial \mathrm{I}} + \mathrm{I}\,\frac{\partial\Sigma}{\partial \mathrm{II}}\right)\overset{-1}{c}{}^k{}_l - 2\,\frac{\partial\Sigma}{\partial \mathrm{II}}\,\overset{-1}{c}{}^k{}_r\,\overset{-1}{c}{}^r{}_l \qquad \text{58.2)}$$

$$|\overset{-1}{c}{}^k{}_l| = 1 \qquad \text{58.3)}$$

here $\bar{p} \equiv p + 2\,\mathrm{II}\,(\partial\Sigma/\partial\mathrm{II})$ is an arbitrary hydrostatic pressure. Equa-ion (58.2) may be extracted from (51.5) by replacing $c^k{}_l$ obtained from 47.31) with III = 1 (valid for incompressible media). For convenience, the present problem, (58.2) replaces the usual constitutive equation 51.5). We assume that there is no body force, i.e., $f^k = 0$. Upon using 58.2) to eliminate $t^k{}_l$ from (58.1), we obtain

$$-\bar{p}_{,}{}^{k} + T^{kl}{}_{rs}\,\overset{-1}{c}{}^{rs}{}_{;l} = \rho\,\ddot{x}^k \qquad \text{58.4)}$$

here

$$\begin{aligned} T^{kl}{}_{rs} \equiv{} & \frac{\partial\Sigma}{\partial\mathrm{I}}\,(\delta^k{}_r\,\delta^l{}_s + \delta^l{}_r\,\delta^k{}_s) + 2\,\frac{\partial^2\Sigma}{\partial\mathrm{I}^2}\,g_{rs}\,\overset{-1}{c}{}^{kl} \\ & + \frac{\partial\Sigma}{\partial\mathrm{II}}\,[2\,g_{rs}\,\overset{-1}{c}{}^{kl} + \mathrm{I}\,(\delta^k{}_r\,\delta^l{}_s + \delta^l{}_r\,\delta^k{}_s) - \delta^k{}_r\,\overset{-1}{c}{}^l{}_s \\ & \quad - \delta^k{}_s\,\overset{-1}{c}{}^l{}_r - \delta^l{}_r\,\overset{-1}{c}{}^k{}_s - \delta^l{}_s\,\overset{-1}{c}{}^k{}_r] \\ & + 2\,\frac{\partial^2\Sigma}{\partial\mathrm{I}\,\partial\mathrm{II}}\,[2\,\mathrm{I}\,g_{rs}\,\overset{-1}{c}{}^{kl} - \overset{-1}{c}{}_{rs}\,\overset{-1}{c}{}^{kl} - g_{rs}\,\overset{-1}{c}{}^k{}_n\,\overset{-1}{c}{}^{nl}] \\ & + 2\,\frac{\partial^2\Sigma}{\partial\mathrm{II}^2}\,(\mathrm{I}\,g_{rs} - \overset{-1}{c}{}_{rs})\,(\mathrm{I}\,\overset{-1}{c}{}^{kl} - \overset{-1}{c}{}^{kn}\,\overset{-1}{c}{}_n{}^l) \end{aligned} \qquad \text{58.5)}$$

inite elastic wave propagation in incompressible materials is governed y (58.4) and (58.3).

Below we give kinematical and dy-amical compatibility conditions for he existence of second-order waves nd determine the wave velocity.

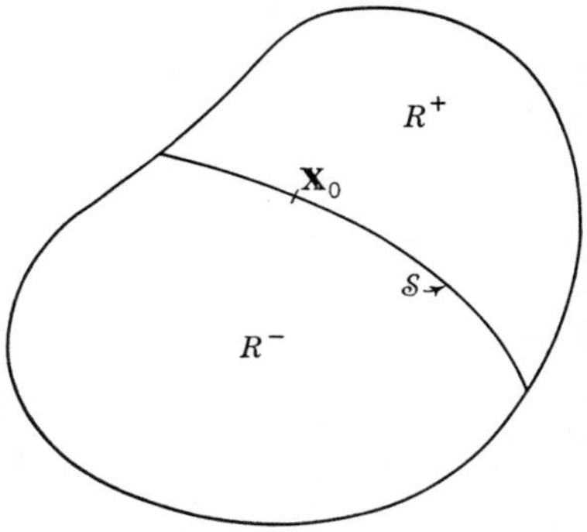

FIG. 58.1

*Kinematical Conditions of Compati-ility.* We should like to find what appens to gradients and time rates of arious field quantities upon crossing surface of discontinuity. Suppose surface $\mathcal{S}$ divides the region $R$ of pace occupied by the material points t time $t$ into two regions $R^+$ and $R^-$ Fig. 58.1). We may represent this surface either in gaussian coordinates $V^\Gamma$, $(\Gamma = 1, 2)$ by

$$X^K = X^K(V^\Gamma, t) \tag{58.6}$$

or by eliminating $V^\Gamma$ among the three equations (58.6) in the usual form

$$F(X^K, t) = 0 \tag{58.7}$$

The *jump* across $\mathcal{S}$ at point $\mathbf{X}_0$ of any quantity $\Phi(\mathbf{X}, t)$ is defined by

$$[\![\Phi]\!] \equiv \Phi^+ - \Phi^- \tag{58.8}$$

where $\Phi^+$ and $\Phi^-$ are respectively the values of $\Phi$ at $\mathbf{X}_0$ approached from $R^+$ and $R^-$. When $\Phi$ is continuous across $\mathcal{S}$, then $[\![\Phi]\!] = 0$.

The entire theory of singular surfaces rests upon a lemma due to Hadamard [1903, 72].[2]

According to Hadamard's lemma total differentiation holds for the limiting values as $\mathcal{S}$ is approached from *one side only*, e.g.,

$$d\Phi^\pm = \Phi^\pm{}_{,K}\, dX^K + \Phi^\pm{}_{,t}\, dt \tag{58.9}$$

If $\Phi$ is continuous across $\mathcal{S}$, then $d\Phi^+ = d\Phi^-$. Through (58.9) we obtain

$$[\![\Phi_{,K}]\!]\, dX^K + [\![\Phi_{,t}]\!]\, dt = 0 \tag{58.10}$$

From (58.7) we have

$$F_{,K}\, dX^K + F_{,t}\, dt = 0 \tag{58.11}$$

Comparing (58.10) and (58.11), we get

$$[\![\Phi_{,K}]\!] = A\, F_{,K} \qquad [\![\Phi_{,t}]\!] = A\, F_{,t} \tag{58.12}$$

If $\Phi_{,K}$ and $\Phi_{,t}$ are continuous, the jump conditions for the second-order derivatives are obtained by writing

$$\left( \left[\!\!\left[ \frac{\partial}{\partial X^K} \right]\!\!\right] dX^K + \left[\!\!\left[ \frac{\partial}{\partial t} \right]\!\!\right] dt \right)^2 \Phi = A\, (F_{,K}\, dX^K + F_{,t}\, dt)^2 \tag{58.13}$$

For the jumps of $n$th-order derivatives, given that all $(n-1)$st-order derivatives are continuous across $\mathcal{S}$ in (58.13), we use exponent $n$ instead of 2. From (58.13) we get

$$[\![\Phi_{,KL}]\!] = A\, F_{,K}\, F_{,L} \qquad [\![\dot{\Phi}_{,K}]\!] = A\, F_{,K}\, \dot{F} \qquad [\![\ddot{\Phi}]\!] = A\, (\dot{F})^2 \tag{58.14}$$

From these results it is not difficult to establish

$$\begin{aligned} [\![\bar{p}_{,K}]\!] &= A\, F_{,K} & [\![\dot{x}^k{}_{,K}]\!] &= A^k\, F_{,K}\, \dot{F} \\ [\![\ddot{x}^k]\!] &= A^k\, (\dot{F})^2 & [\![x^k{}_{:KL}]\!] &= [\![x^k{}_{,KL}]\!] = A^k\, F_{,K}\, F_{,L} \end{aligned} \tag{58.15}$$

[2] Hadamard gives two proofs. Lichtenstein [1929, chaps. 1, 9] gave a more elaborate proof of this lemma which was used earlier by other authors.

where the factors of proportionality $A$, $A^k$ are not all zero. Differentiate (58.3) with respect to $X^L$.

$$0 = |\overset{-1}{c}{}^k{}_l|_{,L} = \frac{\partial \overset{-1}{c}{}^k{}_l}{\partial X^L} \frac{c^l{}_k}{|c^r{}_s|} = \frac{\partial \overset{-1}{c}{}^k{}_l}{\partial X^L} c^l{}_k$$

Using (51.8) gives

$$x^k{}_{,KL} X^L{}_{,k} = 0$$

If we employ $(58.15)_4$ and recall that $X^L{}_{,k}$ is continuous across $\mathcal{S}$, we get $A^k F_{,K} F_{,L} X^K{}_{,k} = 0$. Since this must be valid for arbitrary $F_{,L}$, this yields

(58.16) $$A^k F_{,K} X^K{}_{,k} = 0 \qquad \text{on } \mathcal{S}$$

The spatial surface $s$ defined by

(58.17) $$F[X^K(\mathbf{x}, t), t] = f(x^k, t) = 0$$

is in general a surface different from the surface $\mathcal{S}$. On $s$ the first-order partial derivatives with respect to $x^k$ and $t$ of $\bar{p}$, $\overset{-1}{c}{}^{kl}$ and $\dot{x}^k$ may be discontinuous. First-order partial derivatives $\partial f/\partial x^k$, $\partial f/\partial t$ are assumed to exist and to be continuous on $s$ and

$$f_{,k} f_{,}{}^k = F_{,K} F_{,L} X^K{}_{,k} X^L{}_{,l} g^{kl} > 0$$

since $g^{kl} X^K{}_{,k} X^L{}_{,l}$ are the coefficients of a positive-definite quadratic form.

If we represent $s$ by its gaussian net $v^\gamma$,

(58.18) $$x^k = x^k(v^\gamma, t) \qquad (\gamma = 1, 2)$$

then the *velocity* $\mathbf{u}$ of the surface point $v^\gamma$ and the *speed of propagation* $u_n$ are defined by

(58.19) $$\mathbf{u} = \left.\frac{\partial \mathbf{x}}{\partial t}\right|_{v^\gamma = \text{const}} \qquad u_n = \mathbf{u} \cdot \mathbf{n}$$

where $\mathbf{n}$ is the unit normal to $s$ drawn from $R^-$ to $R^+$. From (58.17) we have

$$\frac{\partial f}{\partial t} + f_{,k} \dot{x}^k = 0$$

Dividing this by $|\text{grad } f| = \sqrt{f_{,k} f_{,}{}^k}$ and remembering that

(58.20) $$n_k = \frac{f_{,k}}{\sqrt{f_{,l} f_{,}{}^l}}$$

we get

(58.21) $$u_n = -\frac{\partial f/\partial t}{\sqrt{f_{,k} f_{,}{}^k}}$$

We observe that [see also (18.13)]

$$\dot{f} = \frac{\partial f}{\partial t} + f_{,k}\,\dot{x}^k = \sqrt{f_{,k} f_{,}^{\,k}}\,(v - u_n)$$
(58.22)
$$F_{,K} = f_{,k}\,x^k{}_{,K} \qquad f_{,k} = F_{,K}\,X^K{}_{,k}$$

where we put $v = \dot{x}^k n_k$. The jump condition given above holds on $s$ for the quantities expressed in $x^k$ and $t$. We now find

$$[\![\bar{p}_{,k}]\!] = [\![\bar{p}_{,K}]\!]\,X^K{}_{,k} = A\,f_{,k} = B\,n_k$$
(58.23)
$$[\![\ddot{x}^k]\!] = B^k\,(v - u_n)^2$$
$$\begin{aligned}[\![\overset{-1}{c}{}^{rs}{}_{;l}]\!] &= \left[\!\!\left[\frac{\partial \overset{-1}{c}{}^{rs}}{\partial x^l}\right]\!\!\right] = [\![\overset{-1}{c}{}^{rs}{}_{,L}]\!]\,X^L{}_{,l} \\ &= [\![x^r{}_{,MK}]\!]\,x^s{}_{,N}\,X^K{}_{,l}\,G^{MN} + [\![x^s{}_{,NK}]\!]\,x^r{}_{,M}\,G^{MN}\,X^K{}_{,l} \\ &= F_{,K}\,F_{,M}\,X^K{}_{,l}\,G^{MN}\,(A^r\,x^s{}_{,N} + A^s\,x^r{}_{,N}) \\ &= f_{,k}\,f_{,m}\,G^{MN}\,(A^r\,x^s{}_{,N}\,X^m{}_{,M} + A^s\,x^r{}_{,N}\,x^m{}_{,M}) \\ &= n_k\,n_m\,(B^r\,\overset{-1}{c}{}^{sm} + B^s\,\overset{-1}{c}{}^{rm}) \\ &= n_k\,(\mu^r\,B^s + \mu^s\,B^r)\end{aligned}$$

where for convenience we put

$$B \equiv A\,\sqrt{f_{,k} f_{,}^{\,k}} \qquad B^k \equiv A^k f_{,l}\,f_{,}^{\,l} \qquad \mu^k \equiv \overset{-1}{c}{}^{kl}\,n_l$$

The incompressibility jump (58.16) may be written as

(58.24) $$B^k\,n_k = 0$$

The *direction of discontinuity* for such a wave is the direction of $B^k$. A wave is *transverse* if $B^k$ is tangent to the surface of discontinuity; it is *longitudinal* if it is perpendicular to this surface.

The conditions (58.23) and (58.24) are the kinematical conditions for incompressible materials. The quantity $v - u_n$ is the normal component of the velocity of $s$ relative to the material particles that it contains.

*Dynamical Conditions of Compatibility.* These are the conditions imposed on $B$, $B^k$, $n^k$, and $v - u_n$ by the dynamical equations (58.4). Using (58.23) to determine the jump of (58.4) across $s$, we get

(58.25) $$-B\,n^k + 2\,T^{kl}{}_{rs}\,n_l\,\mu^s\,B^r = \rho\,B^k\,(u_n - v)^2$$

Multiplying this by $n_k$, summing over $k$, and using (58.24), we get

(58.26) $$B = 2\,T^{kl}{}_{rs}\,n_k\,n_l\,\mu^s\,B^r$$

Consequently (58.25) reduces to

(58.27) $$2\,(T^{kl}{}_{rs} - T^{ml}{}_{rs}\,n_m\,n^k)\,n_l\,\mu^s\,B^r = \rho\,B^k\,(u_n - v)^2$$

Using (58.5) to eliminate $T^{kl}{}_{,rs}$ from this, and employing (58.24), we find

$$U^k{}_l\, B^l = U\, B^k \tag{58.28}$$

where

$$\begin{aligned} U^k{}_l \equiv\ & 2\,\frac{\partial\Sigma}{\partial \mathrm{II}}\,(\mu^k\,\mu_l - \overset{-1}{c}{}^k{}_l\,\mu_r\,n^r) + 4\,\frac{\partial^2\Sigma}{\partial \mathrm{I}^2}\,(\mu^k - n^k\,\mu_r\,n^r)\,\mu_l \\ & + 4\,\frac{\partial^2\Sigma}{\partial \mathrm{II}^2}\,[\mathrm{I}\,(\mu^k - n^k\,\mu_r\,n^r) + n^k\,\mu_r\,\mu^r - \overset{-1}{c}{}^k{}_r\,\mu^r]\,(\mathrm{I}\,\mu_l - \overset{-1}{c}_{lm}\,\mu^m) \\ & + 4\,\frac{\partial^2\Sigma}{\partial \mathrm{I}\,\partial \mathrm{II}}\,[(\mu^k - n^k\,\mu_r\,n^r)\,(2\,\mathrm{I}\,\mu_l - \overset{-1}{c}_{lm}\,\mu^m) \\ & \qquad + n^k\,\mu_l\,\mu_r\,\mu^r - \overset{-1}{c}{}^k{}_r\,\mu^r\,\mu_l] \\ U \equiv\ & \rho\,(u_n - v)^2 - 2\,\frac{\partial\Sigma}{\partial \mathrm{I}}\,\mu^r\,n_r - 2\,\frac{\partial\Sigma}{\partial \mathrm{II}}\,(\mathrm{I}\,n_r - \mu_r)\,\mu^r \end{aligned} \tag{58.29}$$

We observe that $U^k{}_l\, n_k = 0$. Hence (58.24) follows from (58.28) except when $U = 0$.

In order for $s$ to be a dynamically possible second-order wave, a non-zero solution of (58.28) for $B^k$ must exist. At time $t$ we select a rectangular coordinate so that at a point $P$ on $s$, $n_k = \delta_{k3}$. In this case $U^3{}_k = B^3 = 0$ and (58.28) gives

$$\begin{aligned} (U^1{}_1 - U)\,B^1 + U^1{}_2\,B^2 &= 0 \\ U^2{}_1\,B^1 + (U^2{}_2 - U)\,B^2 &= 0 \end{aligned}$$

This gives a quadratic equation for $U$ whose solution is

$$U = \tfrac{1}{2}\,(U^1{}_1 + U^2{}_2) \pm \tfrac{1}{2}\,[(U^1{}_1 + U^2{}_2)^2 - 4\,(U^1{}_1\,U^2{}_2 - U^1{}_2\,U^2{}_1)]^{\frac{1}{2}}$$

This may be written in an invariant form if we remember that $U^3{}_k = 0$ and

$$U^1{}_1 + U^2{}_2 = U^k{}_k \qquad U^1{}_1\,U^2{}_2 - U^1{}_2\,U^2{}_1 = \tfrac{1}{2}\,[(U^k{}_k)^2 - U^k{}_l\,U^l{}_k]$$

Consequently in any euclidean coordinate system we have

$$U = \tfrac{1}{2}\,U^k{}_k \pm \tfrac{1}{2}\,\sqrt{2\,U^k{}_l\,U^l{}_k - (U^k{}_k)^2} \tag{58.30}$$

From this and $(58.29)_2$ we determine the wave speed

$$\begin{aligned} \rho\,(u_n - v)^2 =\ & 2\,\frac{\partial\Sigma}{\partial \mathrm{I}}\,\mu^r\,n_r + 2\,\frac{\partial\Sigma}{\partial \mathrm{II}}\,(\mathrm{I}\,n_r - \mu_r)\,\mu^r \\ & + \tfrac{1}{2}\,U^r{}_r \pm \tfrac{1}{2}\,\sqrt{2\,U^r{}_s\,U^s{}_r - (U^r{}_r)^2} \end{aligned} \tag{58.31}$$

For any set of $\Sigma$, $\overset{-1}{c}{}^{kl}$, and $n_l$, the existence of real waves requires that the right side of (58.31) be nonnegative. Now $B^k$ are the nontrivial solutions of the equations

$$U^k{}_l\,B^l = \tfrac{1}{2}\,B^k\left[U^r{}_r \pm \sqrt{2\,U^r{}_s\,U^s{}_r - (U^r{}_r)^2}\right]$$

satisfying the condition (58.24).

Let $\overset{-1}{c}_\alpha = (\lambda_\alpha)^2$ be the proper values of $\overset{-1}{c}{}^k{}_l$ [cf. (9.17)]. Then consider the special case in which

$$\mu^k = \overset{-1}{c}{}^{kl}\, n_l = (\lambda_1)^2\, n^k$$

so that $n^k$ is an eigenvector of $\overset{-1}{c}{}^k{}_l$. Now $(58.29)_1$ reduces to

$$U^k{}_l = 2\,\frac{\partial\Sigma}{\partial\mathrm{II}}\,(\lambda_1)^2\,[(\lambda_1)^2\, n^k\, n_l - \overset{-1}{c}{}^k{}_l]$$

Equation (58.31) now yields

$$\rho\,(u_n - v)^2 = 2\,(\lambda_1)^2 \left[\frac{\partial\Sigma}{\partial\mathrm{I}} + \frac{\partial\Sigma}{\partial\mathrm{II}}\,(\lambda_2)^2\right] \tag{58.32}$$

or

$$(u_n - v)^2 = 2\,(\lambda_1)^2 \left[\frac{\partial\Sigma}{\partial\mathrm{I}} + \frac{\partial\Sigma}{\partial\mathrm{II}}\,(\lambda_3)^2\right] \tag{58.33}$$

depending on the sign used. According to the restrictions (51.7) imposed on the constitutive equations, we have

$$\frac{\partial\Sigma}{\partial\mathrm{I}} + \frac{\partial\Sigma}{\partial\mathrm{II}}\,(\lambda_\alpha)^2 \geq 0 \qquad (\alpha = 1, 2, 3)$$

If this condition is satisfied, then $u_n - v$ as given by (58.31) is real. For $\partial\Sigma/\partial\mathrm{II} \neq 0$ the vector $B^k$ corresponding to either of the two possible values of $|u_n - v|$ is an eigenvector of $\overset{-1}{c}{}^k{}_l$. For $\partial\Sigma/\partial\mathrm{II} = 0$, $B^k$ is any vector perpendicular to $n_k$.

The foregoing development may be applied to the Mooney-Rivlin type of rubber. In this case

$$\Sigma = \tfrac{1}{2}\,\alpha\,(\mathrm{I} - 3) + \tfrac{1}{2}\,\beta\,(\mathrm{II} - 3) \tag{58.34}$$

where $\alpha$ and $\beta$ are constants, we find that

$$U_{kl} = U_{lk} = \beta\,(\mu_k\,\mu_l - \overset{-1}{c}_{kl}\,\mu_r\,\mu^r)$$

and in the special coordinates introduced above

$$\begin{aligned}
(U^r{}_r)^2 - U^r{}_s\, U^s{}_r &= 2\,(U^1{}_1\, U^2{}_2 - U^1{}_2\, U^2{}_1)\\
&= 2\,\beta^2\,\overset{-1}{c}_{33}\,[\overset{-1}{c}_{11}\,\overset{-1}{c}_{22}\,\overset{-1}{c}_{33} + 2\,\overset{-1}{c}_{12}\,\overset{-1}{c}_{23}\,\overset{-1}{c}_{31}\\
&\qquad - \overset{-1}{c}_{11}\,(\overset{-1}{c}_{23})^2 - \overset{-1}{c}_{22}\,(\overset{-1}{c}_{13})^2 - \overset{-1}{c}_{33}\,(\overset{-1}{c}_{12})^2]\\
&= 2\,\beta^2\,\overset{-1}{c}_{33}\,|\overset{-1}{c}_{kl}| = 2\,\beta^2\,\overset{-1}{c}_{33}\\
&= 2\,\beta^2\,\overset{-1}{c}{}^{kl}\, n_k\, n_l = 2\,\beta^2\,\mu^k\, n_k
\end{aligned}$$

which is a scalar invariant. From (58.30) there now follows

$$U = \tfrac{1}{2}\beta\,(\mu_k\,\mu^k - \mathrm{I}\,\mu_k\,n^k) \pm \tfrac{1}{2}\beta\,[(\mu_k\,\mu^k - \mathrm{I}\,\mu_k\,n^k)^2 - 4\,\mu_k\,n^k]^{\frac{1}{2}}$$

Since $U$ is an eigenvalue of a symmetric matrix, it must be real. Thus

$$(\mu_k\,\mu^k - \mathrm{I}\,\mu_k\,n^k)^2 \geq 4\,\mu^k\,n_k \tag{58.35}$$

From (58.34) and (58.31) we now get

$$\rho\,(u_n - v)^2 = \alpha\,\mu^k\,n_k + \tfrac{3}{2}\beta\,(\mathrm{I}\,n_k - \mu_k)\,\mu^k \pm \tfrac{1}{2}\beta\,[(\mu_k\,\mu^k - \mathrm{I}\,\mu_k\,n^k)^2 - 4\,\mu_k\,n^k]^{\frac{1}{2}} \tag{58.36}$$

By (58.35) the right side of this expression is always real. It is also always nonnegative whenever

$$\mu_k\,n^k > 0 \qquad \mathrm{I}\,\mu^k\,n_k - \mu^k\,\mu_k > 0$$

But since $\|\overset{-1}{c}{}^k{}_l\|$ is positive-definite, the first is the case. The second inequality can be shown to be valid by introducing a cartesian coordinate system at the point in question such that $\overset{-1}{c}_{kl} = 0$ whenever $k \neq l$ and using the fact that $\|\overset{-1}{c}_{kl}\|$ is positive-definite.

For $\beta > 0$ we therefore see that there exist two distinct $|u_n - v|$ unless

$$(\mu^k\,\mu_k - \mathrm{I}\,\mu^k\,n_k)^2 = 4\,\mu^k\,n_k$$

The vectors $B^k$ corresponding to two different values $|u_n - v|$ are orthogonal, since they are eigenvectors of $U^k{}_l$. When $\beta = 0$, $\alpha > 0$, we have

$$\rho\,(u_n - v)^2 = \alpha\,\overset{-1}{c}{}^{kl}\,n_k\,n_l$$

If the eigenvalues of $\overset{-1}{c}{}^k{}_l$ are ordered as $(\lambda_1)^2 > (\lambda_2)^2 > (\lambda_3)^2$, we see that $|u_n - v|$ will take maximum and minimum values respectively when

$$\overset{-1}{c}{}^{kl}\,n_l = (\lambda_1)^2\,n^k \qquad \overset{-1}{c}{}^{kl}\,n_l = (\lambda_3)^2\,n^k$$

These are the directions of maximum and minimum strain as measured by $e_{kl} = \tfrac{1}{2}\,(g_{kl} - c_{kl})$.

Higher-order waves are studied in a similar fashion. For *third-order waves* one assumes that $p, \mathbf{x} = \mathbf{x}\,(\mathbf{X}, t), x^k{}_{,K}, \dot{x}^k$, and their first-order partial derivatives with respect to $X^K$ and $t$ are continuous. The jump conditions on $s$ are found in a fashion similar to (58.23), e.g.,

$$\begin{aligned} [\![p_{,kl}]\!] &= B\,n_k\,n_l \qquad [\![\overset{-1}{c}{}^{kl}{}_{;rs}]\!] = n_r\,n_s\,(B^k\,\mu^l + B^l\,\mu^k) \\ [\![\ddot{x}^k{}_{;l}]\!] &= B^k\,n_l\,(v - u_n)^2 \qquad B^k\,n_k = 0 \end{aligned} \tag{58.37}$$

where not all $B$ and $B^k$ are zero.

The direction of discontinuity is the direction of $B^k$. Consequently $s$

is a transverse wave. Differentiating (58.4) with respect to $x^k$ and using (58.37), we obtain

$$-B\, n^k + w\, T^{kl}{}_{rs}\, n_l\, \mu^s\, B^r = \rho\, B^k\, (u_n - v)^2$$

This is identical to (58.25); consequently $u_n - v$ is given by (58.31).

## 59. OTHER SOLUTIONS

An independent treatment of simple tension and shear including the linear and second-order approximations, compression of spherical shells and a circular cylindrical tube, and torsion of a circular cylinder is given in the monograph by Murnaghan [1951, chaps. 6 and 7].

Murnaghan also treats the purely hydrostatic compression and compares the test results obtained by Bridgman [1948] on pressure versus volume ratio with his results (p. 72). This book also contains a matrix treatment of the theory of finite elasticity.

A number of other inverse solutions such as those given in the previous articles exist for the incompressible isotropic materials. Simultaneous extension, inflation, and torsion of a cylindrical tube are given in art. 3.4 of Green and Zerna [1954]. In the same book there are solutions for simultaneous extension, inflation, and shear of a cylindrical tube (art. 3.7), solutions for the rotation of a right circular cylinder about its axis (art. 3.9), and a chapter (chap. IV) on the formulation and solution of problems concerning small deformations superposed on finite deformation. Such problems find important applications in initially stressed bodies, indentation problems, and the instability of thin bodies under external loads.

Concerned with the problem of permissible deformations in isotropic incompressible perfectly elastic bodies, Ericksen [1954] considered the bending of an annular cylinder into a rectangular block followed by an extension and by shear perpendicular to the plane of bending. The inverse problem was also considered.

Adkins [1958] found a reciprocal property for plane strain superposed on uniform extension for isotropic and transversely isotropic incompressible elastic materials. When the displacements are known in terms of the initial coordinates, by use of this reciprocal property, the same can be found as functions of the final coordinates.

Ericksen and Rivlin [1954] formulated the large deformation of anisotropic materials and gave inverse solutions for bodies having transverse isotropy. A five-parameter family of equilibrium solutions treated includes simultaneous extension and torsion of a circular cylinder, simultaneous inflation and elongation of a hollow cylinder, dislocation of a circular cylinder, bending of a block, and rotating cylinders.

A number of problems of this same type were analyzed by Green and

Wilkes [1954] for orthotropic materials and by Adkins [1955] for materials having curvilinear anisotropy.

The simultaneous extension and torsion of a cylinder of compressible isotropic materials is treated by Green and Wilkes [1953]. These authors have also treated [1954] plane strain superposed on uniform extension, flexure of a cuboid, transversely isotropic bodies, and inflation and extension of a compressible hollow cylinder.

Elastic bodies with internal constraints, such as materials containing inextensible cords, find important application in the rubber industry. Rivlin [1955*b*] formulated the problem of the plane strain of a net formed by inextensible cords. Adkins and Rivlin [1955] and Adkins [1956*a*, *b*] gave some inverse solutions. They assumed that cords are ideally thin, inextensible, and perfectly flexible and that cords of any one set are sufficiently close together so that they may be regarded as a continuous layer in the undeformed body. Adkins [1956*a*] gave a theory for the finite plane deformation of a thin plane sheet of reinforced elastic materials by using the same assumption regarding the sets of cords in the reinforcing layer.

Cylindrically symmetrical deformations of incompressible elastic materials reinforced with inextensible cords were treated by the same author [1956*b*].

Dynamical problems in the theory of finite elasticity have received very little attention. On the subject of propagation of a discontinuity in a medium, in addition to the work mentioned in Art. 58, we find the work of Lichtenstein [1929] on the foundation of hydrodynamics, Thomas's [1953 and 1957*a*] work on singular surfaces, and Moreau's [1949 and 1953] works. A beautiful exposition of singular surfaces and waves is included in chap. C of Truesdell and Toupin's [1960] encyclopedia article.

Recently Hayes and Rivlin [1960] gave the solution of plane wave propagation in an isotropic elastic material subjected to pure homogeneous deformation.

The theory of finite oscillation for continuous media remains nearly untouched. The uniqueness of the solution of finite elasticity requires a physically sound and mathematically "well-set" formulation. Ericksen and Toupin [1956] and Hill [1957] gave uniqueness theorems emphasizing special features of the restrictions required. For plane strain of a special type of elastic material John [1960] gave some existence and uniqueness theorems.

A clear exposition of various crystal classes with a collection of recently solved problems in the theory of anisotropic elasticity is presented in the recent book by Green and Adkins [1960].[1]

[1] This book was published at the completion of the present manuscript. Therefore sufficient reference to specific topics covered in this book has not been made.

## 60. APPROXIMATE THEORIES OF CONSTITUTIVE EQUATIONS

Approximate theories of constitutive equations often provide certain mathematical simplifications enabling one to treat more difficult boundary-value problems that would otherwise be impossible to tackle. Besides this advantage, by reducing and simplifying the phenomenological coefficients, they make experimental work for the determination of these coefficients possible. Inherent in this process is the limitation of the range of application of the theory and the specification of materials to which it applies. From the engineering point of view such limitations are often a practical necessity rather than an exception. In the first place, the range of deformation to which materials can be subjected without a permanent set or failure is often limited. In the second place, the types of materials commonly used in the design of a given engineering system are limited. Therefore advantage may be taken of such limitations to simplify the theories, thus bringing the solution of certain stress-analysis problems within the realm of computation.

*Polynomial Approximations in Strain.* For an isotropic elastic solid we have shown that the strain-energy function $\Sigma$ may be considered to be a function of any one of the material or spatial strain measures $\mathbf{C}$, $\mathbf{c}$, $\overset{-1}{\mathbf{c}}$, $\mathbf{e}$, $\mathbf{E}$, etc. [cf. (45.21)]. By assuming $\Sigma$ as an analytic function of the strain measures and expanding into power series with respect to the natural state, we obtain power series in strain measures from the natural state. For example, if we consider $\Sigma = \Sigma(C_{KL})$ and then expand $\Sigma$ into a power series about $C_{KL} = G_{KL}$, by dropping terms of greater than some specified degree, we obtain a polynomial approximation to $\Sigma$ in terms of $E_{KL}$. Among many possible expansions, two that are commonly employed are

$$\begin{aligned}\Sigma &= \alpha_E \, \mathrm{I}_E + \tfrac{1}{2}(\lambda_E + 2\mu_E)\,\mathrm{I}_E^2 - 2\mu_E \, \mathrm{II}_E + l_E \, \mathrm{I}_E^2 \\ &\qquad + m_E \, \mathrm{I}_E \, \mathrm{II}_E + n_E \, \mathrm{III}_E + \cdots \\ \Sigma &= \alpha_e \, \mathrm{I}_e + \tfrac{1}{2}(\lambda_e + 2\mu_e)\,\mathrm{I}_e^2 - 2\mu_e \, \mathrm{II}_e + l_e \, \mathrm{I}_e^2 \\ &\qquad + m_e \, \mathrm{I}_e \, \mathrm{II}_e + n_e \, \mathrm{III}_e + \cdots \end{aligned} \tag{60.1}$$

Through (9.23), (9.28), and (9.29) we can express the invariants of $E^K{}_L$ in terms of those of $e^k{}_l$. When these are used in one of (60.1), we find the relations of coefficients $\alpha_E, \lambda_E, \mu_E, \ldots$ to $\alpha_e, \lambda_e, \mu_e, \ldots$, i.e.,

$$\begin{aligned} &\alpha_e = \alpha_E \qquad \lambda_e = \lambda_E \qquad \mu_e = \mu_E + 2\alpha_E \\ &l_e = l_E + 4\alpha_E \qquad m_e = m_E - 4\lambda_E - 12\mu_E - 12\alpha_E \\ &n_e = n_E + 12\mu_E + 12\alpha_E \qquad \cdots \end{aligned} \tag{60.2}$$

Putting $(60.1)_1$ into (45.26) and using such relations as (47.3) for $E^K{}_L$, we obtain[1]

$$(60.3)\quad T^K{}_L = [\alpha_E + \lambda_E \, \mathrm{I}_E + (3\, l_E + m_E)\, \mathrm{I}_E^2 + (m_E + n_E)\, \mathrm{II}_E + \cdots]\, \delta^K{}_L + [2\, \mu_E - (m_E + n_E)\, \mathrm{I}_E + \cdots]\, E^K{}_L + (n_E + \cdots)\, E^K{}_M\, E^M{}_L$$

Similarly if we use $(60.1)_2$ in $(45.35)_3$, we find

$$\begin{aligned}(60.4)\quad t^k{}_l &= (1 - 2\, \mathrm{I}_e + 4\, \mathrm{II}_e - 8\, \mathrm{III}_e)^{\frac{1}{2}}\, \{[\alpha_e + \lambda_e\, \mathrm{I}_e + (3\, l_e + m_e)\, \mathrm{I}_e^2 + (m_e + n_e)\, \mathrm{II}_e + \cdots]\, \delta^k{}_l \\ &\quad + [2\, (\mu_e - \alpha_e) - (m_e + n_e + \lambda_e)\, \mathrm{I}_e + \cdots]\, e^k{}_l + (-4\, \mu_e + n_e + \cdots)\, e^k{}_m\, e^m{}_l\} \\ &= [\alpha_e + (\lambda_e - \alpha_e)\, \mathrm{I}_e + (3\, l_e + m_e - \lambda_e - \tfrac{1}{2}\, \alpha_e)\, \mathrm{I}_e^2 + (m_e + n_e - 2\, \alpha_e)\, \mathrm{II}_e + \cdots]\, \delta^k{}_l + [2\, (\mu_e - \alpha_e) \\ &\quad - (m_e + n_e + 2\, \lambda_e + 2\, \mu_e - 2\, \alpha_e)\, \mathrm{I}_e + \cdots]\, e^k{}_l + (-4\, \mu_e + n_e + \cdots)\, e^k{}_m\, e^{ml}\end{aligned}$$

Both stress-strain relations (60.3) and (60.4) are carried as far as the second-order terms in the strain components.

In the natural state $\mathbf{E} = \mathbf{e} = 0$; thus $T^K{}_L = \alpha_E\, \delta^K{}_L$ and $t^k{}_l = \alpha_e\, \delta^k{}_l$, which represent a pure hydrostatic pressure with $p = -\alpha_E = -\alpha_e$. If the natural state is stress-free, then $\alpha_E = \alpha_e = 0$. For this case the first-order theory gives

$$(60.5)\quad \begin{aligned} T^K{}_L &= \lambda_E\, \mathrm{I}_E\, \delta^K{}_L + 2\, \mu_E\, E^K{}_L \\ t^k{}_l &= \lambda_e\, \mathrm{I}_e\, \delta^k{}_l + 2\, \mu_e\, e^k{}_l \end{aligned}$$

which is none other than the Hooke-Cauchy law of the classical isotropic elasticity theory. In this theory the strains are so small that the distinction between $E^K{}_L$ and $e^k{}_l$ disappears. Moreover for this approximation $e^k{}_l$ must be replaced by $\tilde{e}^k{}_l = \frac{1}{2}\, (u^k{}_{;l} + u_{l;}{}^k)$. If one substitutes $(60.5)_2$ into the equation of momentum balance (51.2), one obtains the celebrated Navier's equation

$$(60.6)\quad (\lambda_e + \mu_e)\, u^k{}_{;kl} + \mu_e\, u_{l;}{}^k{}_k + \rho\, (f_l - \ddot{u}_l) = 0$$

which is the fundamental source of our knowledge in the linear theory of elasticity of homogeneous isotropic elastic solids.

For incompressible materials the Mooney-Rivlin expansion [1940, p. 588; 1948] is generally found more convenient.

$$(60.7)\quad \Sigma = \alpha_{rs}\, (\mathrm{I} - 3)^r\, (\mathrm{II} - 3)^s$$

where $\mathrm{I} \equiv \underset{c}{\mathrm{I}_{-1}}$, $\mathrm{II} \equiv \underset{c}{\mathrm{II}_{-1}}$. A commonly used case is the one in which

[1] Murnaghan [1937].

only the terms for which $r = 1$, $s = 0$ and $r = 0$, $s = 1$ are left, i.e.,

$$\Sigma = \alpha(\mathrm{I} - 3) + \beta(\mathrm{II} - 3) \tag{60.8}$$

where $\alpha \geq 0$, $\beta \geq 0$ is the necessary and sufficient condition to make $\Sigma \geq 0$. The case $\beta = 0$, named by Rivlin as the *neo-hookean* material, is found to give qualitatively incorrect results for rubberlike materials. Treloar [1948] and Copeland and Mooney [1948] show that (60.8) provides a more reasonable approximation.[2] Similarly expansion of $\Sigma$ in powers of $\overset{-1}{C}{}^{KL}$ about $\overset{-1}{C}{}^{KL} = G^{KL}$ leads to other approximations.

*Polynomial Approximations in Displacement Gradients.* There exists a wide variety of other types of approximate stress-strain relations. It is possible to write $\Sigma$ as a polynomial in the deformation gradients $U_{K;L}$ or $u_{k;l}$.

$$\Sigma = \Sigma_1 + \Sigma_2 + \cdots + \Sigma_N \tag{60.9}$$

where $\Sigma_M$ is a homogeneous polynomial of degree $M$ in $U_{K;L}$. For compressible materials whenever the natural state is unstressed, we have $\Sigma_1 = 0$. The form of $\Sigma$ in $U_{K;L}$ cannot be completely arbitrary. By comparing the polynomial approximations in $E_{KL}$ with these, one obtains consistent results to various degrees of approximation. For a second-degree approximation, for example, one finds $\Sigma = \Sigma_2 = A^{KLMN}\tilde{E}_{KL}\tilde{E}_{MN}$, where material constants $A^{KLMN}$ are such that

$$A^{KLMN} = A^{LKMN} = A^{LKNM} = A^{MNKL} \tag{60.10}$$

which is the necessary and sufficient condition for $\Sigma_2 \geq 0$. A brief discussion of this approach may be found in Doyle and Ericksen's review article [1956, chap. IX, 2].

*Infinitesimal Deformations Superposed on Finite Deformation.* In a certain class of problems the elastic solid is led to undergo a large deformation of a simple nature which can be treated analytically. For example, inverse solutions such as those given in Arts. 52–59 may be used to determine the stress field in a body. If we superpose on this deformed body an infinitesimal deformation of an arbitrary nature, the field equations and boundary conditions in terms of the displacements from the initially deformed state turn out to be linear partial differential equations. Thus the solution of a large class of problems becomes possible. Into this class fall such important problems as instability, initially stressed bodies, etc. An exposition of this theory based on the work of Green, Rivlin, and Shield [1952] may be found in Green and Zerna [1954, Chap. IV]. Also see Hayes and Rivlin [1960].

*Other Approximate Theories.* Theories exist in which the strains are

[2] Cf. Art. 61 for further discussion.

nfinitesimal while large displacement gradients and rotations are etained. Such theories find application to elastic bodies having one or nore dimensions of the body small with respect to others. Bars, plates, nd shells fall into this category. For these problems it is permissible to inearize the stress-strain relations with respect to **E** and **e**, but it may ot be permissible[3] to linearize **E** and **e** with respect to the displacement radients $x^k{}_{,K}$ and $X^K{}_{,k}$. Thus from (60.3) and (60.4) we write

$$T^K{}_L = \lambda_E \, E^M{}_M \, \delta^K{}_L + 2 \, \mu_E \, E^K{}_L$$
$$t^k{}_l = J^{-1} (\lambda_e \, E^M{}_M \, \delta^K{}_L + 2 \, \mu_e \, E^K{}_L) \, x^k{}_{,K} \, x_{l,}{}^L \qquad \text{60.11)}$$

'he corresponding strain energy has precisely the same form as that of the nfinitesimal theory

$$\Sigma = \tfrac{1}{2} (\lambda_E + 2 \, \mu_E) \, \mathrm{I}_E^2 - 2 \, \mu_E \, \mathrm{II}_E \qquad \text{60.12)}$$

Theories based on (60.11) were initiated by St. Venant [1844, 1847, 863], Kirchhoff [1852], and others. For an extensive review of these nd various other related theories we refer the reader to Truesdell [1952, hap. IV C]. In this latter paper there is also an excellent review of pproximate theories regarding the magnitude of extensions, the exact uadratic theories of Signorini [1942, 1945, 1949*a*, *b*], etc.

## 1. EXPERIMENTAL INVESTIGATIONS

In the classical elasticity theory of homogeneous isotropic linear lastic solids we encounter two material constants (the Lamé constants), $_e$ and $\mu_e$. Hooke's law states that [cf. (47.37)]

$$t^k{}_l = \lambda_e \, \tilde{e}^m{}_m \, \delta^k{}_l + 2 \, \mu_e \, \tilde{e}^k{}_l \qquad \text{61.1)}$$

Since this equation is linear in strain components, only two experiments re required to determine the two constants $\lambda_e$ and $\mu_e$. For example, a imple tension test and a pure shear test are adequate for the calculation f the material constants $\lambda_e$ and $\mu_e$. The literature abounds with these nd other types of tests.[1]

Constitutive equations (51.3) of the nonlinear elasticity theory for omogeneous and isotropic materials

$$t^k{}_l = b_{-1} \, \overset{-1}{c}{}^k{}_l + b_0 \, \delta^k{}_l + b_1 \, c^k{}_l \qquad \text{61.2)}$$

ontain three functions $b_{-1}$, $b_0$, and $b_1$, which are functions of the strain

[3] Depending on flexibility of thin solids, it is permissible to further linearize **E** and **e** 'ith respect to some components of displacement gradients. An example of such heories is the Föppl-Kármán-Timoshenko theory of plates. For a systematic treat- ent of this theory see Novozhilov [1948] and Eringen [1954].

[1] For instance, see Hetenyi [1950].

invariants I, II, and III. Clearly special tests designed to measure these functions cannot, in general, be used for the general case (61.2) since the nonlinearity prohibits the use of the superposition principle. For the hyperelastic solids the constitutive coefficients $b_\alpha$ are derivable from a stress potential $\Sigma$ [cf. (51.4)], thus reducing the volume of experimental work. For a compressible solid, however, $\Sigma$ is a function of three independent variables I, II, and III, and the task is still beyond practical reach. Anisotropy and inhomogeneity add further complications, thus making the task of the experimentalist extremely discouraging. For this reason almost all experiments on the theory of finite elasticity are confined to homogeneous isotropic incompressible hyperelastic solids which obey the constitutive equations of the form (51.5), i.e.,

$$t^k{}_l = -p\,\delta^k{}_l + 2\frac{\partial\Sigma}{\partial \mathrm{I}}\overset{-1}{c}{}^k{}_l - 2\frac{\partial\Sigma}{\partial \mathrm{II}}c^k{}_l \tag{61.3}$$

where $\Sigma = \Sigma(\mathrm{I}, \mathrm{II})$. Vulcanized rubber, for a fairly wide range of deformation, approximates such a solid. Hence most investigators have confined their attentions to the determination of the strain-energy function of this material.[2]

For an incompressible solid we have $\mathrm{III} = 1$. In the undeformed state of the elastic solid $\mathrm{I} = \mathrm{II} = 3$. Therefore the stress potential of an incompressible isotropic hyperelastic solid may be expressed in a double infinite power series

$$\Sigma = \sum_{m,n=0}^{\infty} A_{mn}(\mathrm{I}-3)^m(\mathrm{II}-3)^n \qquad A_{00} = 0 \tag{61.4}$$

where $A_{mn}$ are constants. For small deformations one can show that $\mathrm{I} - 3$ and $\mathrm{II} - 3$ are, in general, small quantities, so that the approximation

$$\Sigma = A_{10}(\mathrm{I}-3) + A_{01}(\mathrm{II}-3) \tag{61.5}$$

is valid for sufficiently small deformations. This form is due to Mooney [1940]. A kinetic theory of rubberlike materials leads to a stress potential of the form[3]

$$\Sigma = A_{10}(\mathrm{I}-3) \tag{61.6}$$

Materials obeying (61.6) have been named *neo-hookean* by Rivlin.

[2] A comprehensive discussion of rubber elasticity from the experimental and the kinetic-theory viewpoints is given in the book by Treloar [1958]. For the detailed discussions of some experimental works we cite Mooney [1940], Rivlin [1947*b*], Rivlin and Saunders [1951, 1952], Gent and Rivlin [1952], Thomas [1955*e*], Gent and Thomas [1958], and Gent and Lindley [1959].

[3] An account of the theory with references to original papers is found in Treloar [1958].

Experiments of Rivlin and Saunders suggest that a better form, valid for a wider range of deformation, is

$$\Sigma = A_{10}(\mathrm{I} - 3) + f(\mathrm{II} - 3) \tag{61.7}$$

where $f$ is a function of II alone.

Other approximate forms of $\Sigma$ have been suggested but have not met with wide acceptance.[4]

Below we give a brief account of experimental findings largely due to Rivlin and Saunders.

The constitutive equations (61.3) contain one unknown pressure $p$ which is usually determined by a boundary condition. Therefore experiments can be devised so that the two constitutive coefficients $\partial\Sigma/\partial\mathrm{I}$ and $\partial\Sigma/\partial\mathrm{II}$ can be determined as functions of I and II. To this end some simple solutions, as given in the early part of this chapter, are available. Suitable for this purpose are the particular cases of homogeneous strain, i.e., pure homogeneous strain, simple extension, simple shear (Art. 52), simple torsion (Art. 53). Other solutions not treated here, such as torsion superposed on a simple extension and eversion of a tube, are also used for experimentation.

Rivlin and Saunders ran a series of experiments with a sheet of rubber to determine the forces necessary to produce various pure homogeneous deformations, for which either I or II has fixed values. From these experiments $\partial\Sigma/\partial\mathrm{I}$ and $\partial\Sigma/\partial\mathrm{II}$ were determined for various fixed values of I and II. While this experiment is suitable for independent variations of I and II, the experimental inaccuracies appear both for large deformations and for small deformations in which I and II have values less than about 5.0. In the latter range the results obtained become very sensitive to experimental errors. For large strains, experiments in the uniform two-dimensional extension of a thin sheet turn out to be more suitable. This experiment is conducted by inflating a thin membrane into a balloon.

The behavior of the material in the range of small strains is explored by experiments on pure shear and torsion of a cylindrical rod. Pure shear is defined as a pure homogeneous strain in which one of the principal extension ratios is unity and the volume remains unchanged.[5] Experimentally a large pure shear turns out to be simpler to produce than a simple shear as defined in Art. 52 (4).

*Pure Homogeneous Strain* (*uniform extension of incompressible sheet*). This case was studied in Art. 52 (1). Since the sheet is incompressible, extension ratios $\lambda_\alpha$ satisfy the condition $\lambda_1\lambda_2\lambda_3 = 1$. Moreover, the stress $t_{33}$ on the two major faces $z = \pm H/2$ is zero. Using (52.13) for

[4] Gent and Thomas [1958] suggest the form $\Sigma = A_{10}(\mathrm{I} - 3) + A_2 \ln(\frac{1}{3}\mathrm{II})$.

[5] Cf. Love [1944, p. 33].

$k = 3$, we eliminate $p$ from $t_{11}$ and $t_{22}$ so that

$$(61.8)\qquad \begin{aligned} t_{11} &= 2\left(\lambda_1^2 - \frac{1}{\lambda_1^2\lambda_2^2}\right)\left(\frac{\partial\Sigma}{\partial \mathrm{I}} + \lambda_2^2\frac{\partial\Sigma}{\partial \mathrm{II}}\right)\\ t_{22} &= 2\left(\lambda_2^2 - \frac{1}{\lambda_1^2\lambda_2^2}\right)\left(\frac{\partial\Sigma}{\partial \mathrm{I}} + \lambda_1^2\frac{\partial\Sigma}{\partial \mathrm{II}}\right)\\ t_{33} &= 0 \qquad t_{kl} = 0 \qquad (k \neq l)\end{aligned}$$

where

$$(61.9)\quad \mathrm{I} = \lambda_1^2 + \lambda_2^2 + \frac{1}{\lambda_1^2\lambda_2^2} \qquad \mathrm{II} = \frac{1}{\lambda_1^2} + \frac{1}{\lambda_2^2} + \lambda_1^2\lambda_2^2 \qquad (\lambda_1\lambda_2\lambda_3 = 1)$$

which follows from (52.11) by putting $\lambda_1\lambda_2\lambda_3 = 1$. The forces $t_1$ and $t_2$ per unit length of edge measured in the undeformed state are given by

$$(61.10)\qquad t_1 = t_{11}\frac{H}{\lambda_1} \qquad t_2 = t_{22}\frac{H}{\lambda_2}$$

where $H$ is the thickness of the sheet in its undeformed state. From (61.8) and (61.10) we can solve for $\partial\Sigma/\partial\mathrm{I}$ and $\partial\Sigma/\partial\mathrm{II}$

$$(61.11)\qquad \begin{aligned} \frac{\partial\Sigma}{\partial \mathrm{I}} &= \frac{1}{2(\lambda_1^2 - \lambda_2^2)}\left[\frac{\lambda_1^3(t_1/H)}{\lambda_1^2 - \lambda_1^{-2}\lambda_2^{-2}} - \frac{\lambda_2^3(t_2/H)}{\lambda_2^2 - \lambda_1^{-2}\lambda_2^{-2}}\right]\\ \frac{\partial\Sigma}{\partial \mathrm{II}} &= \frac{1}{2(\lambda_2^2 - \lambda_1^2)}\left[\frac{\lambda_1(t_1/H)}{\lambda_1^2 - \lambda_1^{-2}\lambda_2^{-2}} - \frac{\lambda_2(t_2/H)}{\lambda_2^2 - \lambda_1^{-2}\lambda_2^{-2}}\right]\end{aligned}$$

By measuring $t_1$ and $t_2$ for a given $\lambda_1$ and $\lambda_2$, we can calculate $\partial\Sigma/\partial\mathrm{I}$ and $\partial\Sigma/\partial\mathrm{II}$ as functions of $\lambda_1$ and $\lambda_2$. For a given $\lambda_1$ and $\lambda_2$, through (61.9) we also get I and II. Therefore $\partial\Sigma/\partial\mathrm{I}$ and $\partial\Sigma/\partial\mathrm{II}$ can be plotted as functions of I and II.

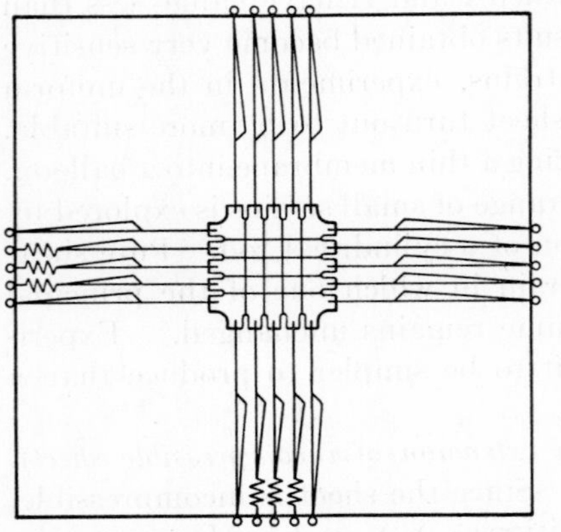

FIG. 61.1. Experimental arrangement for experiment on pure homogeneous deformation with I or II constant. (*After Rivlin and Saunders* [1951])

In order to produce a pure homogeneous deformation, a thin square rubber sheet is stretched by wires attached perpendicular to its edges (Fig. 61.1). By measuring, in the deformed state, the lengths of the squares drawn on the sheet, one knows $\lambda_1$ and $\lambda_2$; and by measuring the tensions in the springs, we get $t_1$ and $t_2$. Through (61.11) $\partial\Sigma/\partial\mathrm{I}$ and $\partial\Sigma/\partial\mathrm{II}$ can then be calculated. This experiment is carried out by adjusting various values of $\lambda_1$ and $\lambda_2$ in such a way that either I or II is constant. By selecting various values of this constant, the dependence of $\partial\Sigma/\partial \mathrm{I}$ and $\partial\Sigma/\partial \mathrm{II}$ on I and II can, in principle, be determined.

Through (61.9) we see that for a fixed value of I or II, $\lambda_1$ and $\lambda_2$ cannot be varied arbitrarily. In fact,

$$\lambda_2^2 = \tfrac{1}{2}\{(\mathrm{I} - \lambda_1^2) \pm [(\mathrm{I} - \lambda_1^2)^2 - 4\,\lambda_1^{-2}]^{\frac{1}{2}}\} \qquad \text{(for I constant)}$$

(61.12)
$$\lambda_2^2 = \frac{1}{2\,\lambda_1^2}\{(\mathrm{II} - \lambda_1^{-2}) \pm [(\mathrm{II} - \lambda_1^{-2})^2 - 4\,\lambda_1^2]^{\frac{1}{2}}\} \qquad \text{(for II constant)}$$

shows that the variation of $\lambda_2$ with $\lambda_1$ for fixed values of I or II is restricted

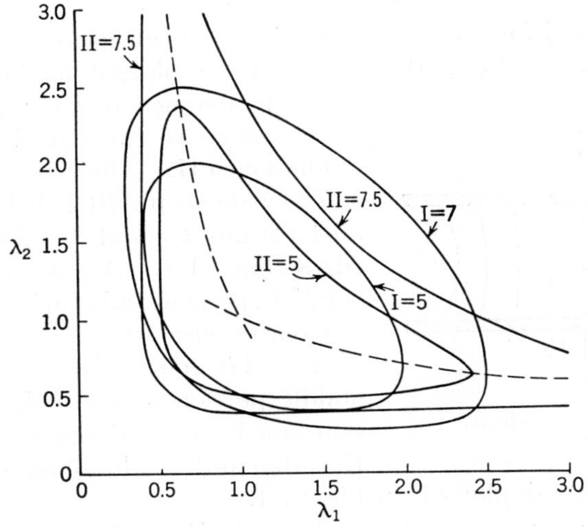


FIG. 61.2. The relation between $\lambda_1$ and $\lambda_2$ at constant I or II. (*After Rivlin and Saunders* [1951])

to some closed curves. These are shown on Fig. 61.2 for some constant values of I and II.

The broken curves represent the lines

(61.13) $\quad \lambda_2 = \lambda_1^{-2} \qquad (t_2 = 0) \qquad\qquad \lambda_1 = \lambda_2^{-2} \qquad (t_1 = 0)$

corresponding to simple extensions parallel to the edges of the sheet.

Experiments conducted by Rivlin and Saunders using a vulcanized natural rubber with the method described above showed that $\partial\Sigma/\partial \mathrm{I}$ is constant in the range of $5 \leq \mathrm{I} < 12$ and $5 \leq \mathrm{II} \leq 30$ while $\partial\Sigma/\partial \mathrm{II}$ is a function only of II. The ratio $(\partial\Sigma/\partial \mathrm{II})/(\partial\Sigma/\partial \mathrm{I})$ was found to have an approximate value of $\frac{1}{8}$ for low values of II and to decrease steadily with II. This in turn suggests that $\Sigma$ may be approximated by (61.7) to a reasonable degree. For small deformation (61.11) is very sensitive to the accuracy of calculations since it involves the small difference of large quantities. For this reason additional experiments were performed, based on the assumption $\partial\Sigma/\partial \mathrm{I} = \text{const}$, to determine whether $\partial\Sigma/\partial \mathrm{II}$ is consistent with the assumed constant value of $\partial\Sigma/\partial \mathrm{I}$.

*Pure Shear.* Pure shear is a pure homogeneous deformation of an incompressible body in which one of the extension ratios (say $\lambda_2$) is kept constant while the other two vary.

The force $t_1$ in the $X$ direction according to (61.10) and $(61.8)_1$ is given by

$$t_1 = 2H\left(\lambda_1 - \frac{1}{\lambda_1^3\lambda_2^2}\right)\left(\frac{\partial\Sigma}{\partial \mathrm{I}} + \lambda_2^2\frac{\partial\Sigma}{\partial \mathrm{II}}\right) \tag{61.14}$$

Keeping $\lambda_2$ fixed for various stretches $\lambda_1$, we can measure $t_1$ so that the factor $(\partial\Sigma/\partial \mathrm{I}) + \lambda_2^2(\partial\Sigma/\partial \mathrm{II})$ can now be plotted against II. Since $\partial\Sigma/\partial \mathrm{I}$ is assumed to have a known constant value, we can calculate $\partial\Sigma/\partial \mathrm{II}$ as a function of II. The experiment employs a thin wide strip $ABCD$ held by two parallel clamps $C_1$ and $C_2$ along its longer edges (Fig. 61.3). By stretching the rubber piece perpendicular to its edges $AB$ and $CD$, one observes that the contraction parallel to $AB$ and $CD$ is small, so that the middle portion of the strip is in a state that can be approximated by pure shear. Experimental results obtained for $\lambda_2 = 1$ and $\lambda_2 = 0.776$ are plotted[6] in Fig. 61.4.

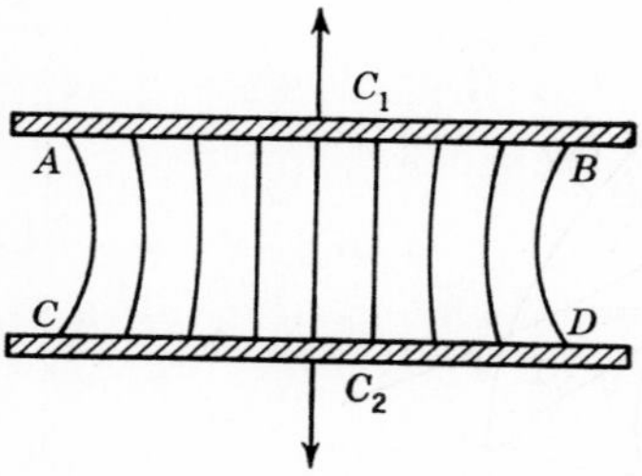

FIG. 61.3. Pure shear.

In the case for $\lambda_2 = 1$ the value $(\partial\Sigma/\partial \mathrm{II})/(\partial\Sigma/\partial \mathrm{I}) = \frac{1}{8}$ at $\mathrm{II} = 5$, obtained in the preceding experiment, is selected. From the measurement of $(\partial\Sigma/\partial \mathrm{I}) + (\partial\Sigma/\partial \mathrm{II})$ at this point from curve $A$ of Fig. 61.4 we obtain $\partial\Sigma/\partial \mathrm{I} = 1.84\ \text{kg/cm}^2$ and $\partial\Sigma/\partial \mathrm{II} = 0.23\ \text{kg/cm}^2$. Assuming that $\partial\Sigma/\partial \mathrm{I} = \text{const} = 1.84$ and that $\partial\Sigma/\partial \mathrm{II}$ depends on II alone, from curve $A$ of Fig. 61.4, we determine $\partial\Sigma/\partial \mathrm{II}$ corresponding to any value of II. With these values, $(\partial\Sigma/\partial \mathrm{I}) + (0.776)^2(\partial\Sigma/\partial \mathrm{II})$ is calculated and the results so obtained are found to agree well with the experimental values obtained from curve $B$ of Fig. 61.4.

*Simple Extension.* In a simple extension $t_{22} = t_{33} = 0$. Hence from $(61.8)_2$ we have $\lambda_1 = \lambda_2^{-2} = \lambda$. Also by using $(61.8)_1$ and (61.9), we get

$$t_{11} = 2\left(\lambda^2 - \frac{1}{\lambda}\right)\left(\frac{\partial\Sigma}{\partial \mathrm{I}} + \frac{1}{\lambda}\frac{\partial\Sigma}{\partial \mathrm{II}}\right) \tag{61.15}$$

$$\mathrm{I} = \lambda^2 + \frac{2}{\lambda} \qquad \mathrm{II} = 2\lambda + \frac{1}{\lambda^2} \tag{61.16}$$

[6] The case $\lambda_2 = 0.776$ is actually for a pure shear superposed upon a simple extension.

The force $N$ needed to extend a straight bar of uniform initial cross-sectional area $A$ is given by $N = A\,t_{11}/\lambda$. Therefore, by subjecting a bar to an axial force, we can measure $N$ for each $\lambda$. From this,

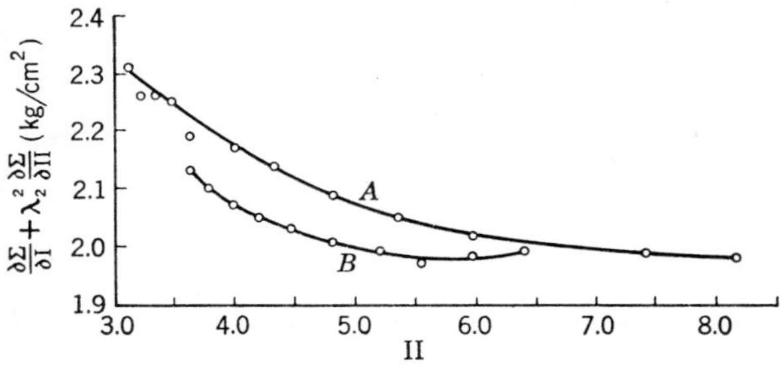


FIG. 61.4. Plot of $(\partial\Sigma/\partial\mathrm{I}) + \lambda_2^2\,(\partial\Sigma/\partial\mathrm{II})$ against II from experiments on pure shear and pure shear superposed on simple extension. Curve $A$, pure shear ($\lambda_2 = 1$); curve $B$, pure shear superposed on simple extension ($\lambda_2 = 0.776$). (*After Rivlin and Saunders* [1951])

$(\partial\Sigma/\partial\mathrm{I}) + (1/\lambda)\,(\partial\Sigma/\partial\mathrm{II})$ can be calculated. A plot of this quantity versus $1/\lambda$ is given in Fig. 61.5. By using previously obtained values of $\partial\Sigma/\partial\mathrm{I}$ and those of $\partial\Sigma/\partial\mathrm{II}$, we can also calculate $(\partial\Sigma/\partial\mathrm{I}) + (1/\lambda)\,(\partial\Sigma/\partial\mathrm{II})$. These calculations are found to agree very well with those of the tension test plotted in Fig. 61.5.

The linear portion of the curve in Fig. 61.5 at first may be interpreted as indicating that the rubber has a stored-energy function of the Mooney form (61.5) so that both $\partial\Sigma/\partial\mathrm{I}$ and $\partial\Sigma/\partial\mathrm{II}$ are constants. Based on this interpretation from the slope of the linear portion and its intercept on the axis $1/\lambda = 1$, we find $A_{01}/A_{10} \cong 0.8$. Not only does this disagree with the values obtained previously, but it also leads to the erroneous conclusion that $(\partial\Sigma/\partial\mathrm{I}) + (\partial\Sigma/\partial\mathrm{II})$ and $(\partial\Sigma/\partial\mathrm{I}) + 0.602\,(\partial\Sigma/\partial\mathrm{II})$ are constants contradicting, respectively, the results of pure shear and pure shear when superposed on a simple extension. The reason for this may be found in the fact that the higher-order coefficients in the series (61.4) are combined with $A_{01}$ and $A_{10}$ to affect $\partial\Sigma/\partial\mathrm{I}$ and $\partial\Sigma/\partial\mathrm{II}$ in (61.15).

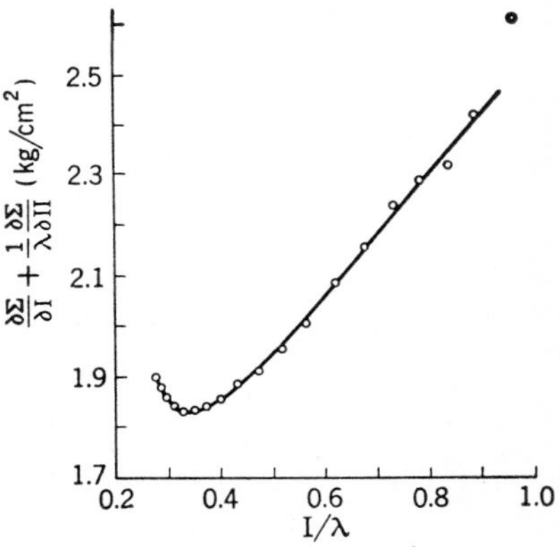


FIG. 61.5. Plot of quantity $(\partial\Sigma/\partial\mathrm{I}) + (1/\lambda)\,(\partial\Sigma/\partial\mathrm{II})$ against $1/\lambda$ from experiment on simple extension. (*After Rivlin and Saunders* [1951])

The force per unit area in the undeformed state versus the stretch $\lambda$ for a vulcanized rubber is shown in Fig. 61.6.

*Other Experiments.* In a uniform two-dimensional extension we have $\lambda_1 = \lambda_2 = \lambda$, $\lambda_3 = 1/\lambda^2$. By inflating with air pressure a thin circular

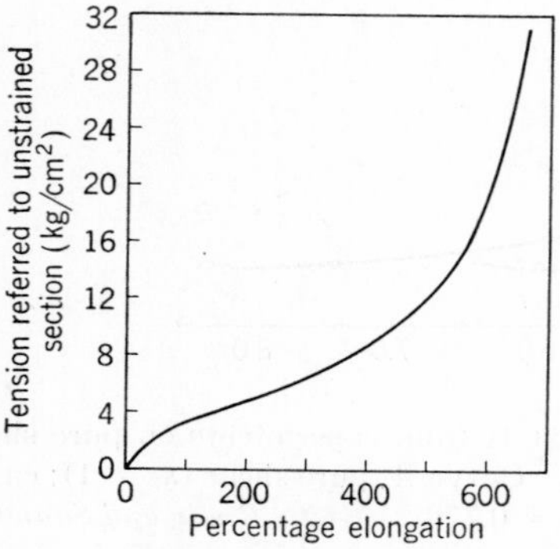


FIG. 61.6. Typical force-extension curve for vulcanized rubber. (*After Treloar* [1958])

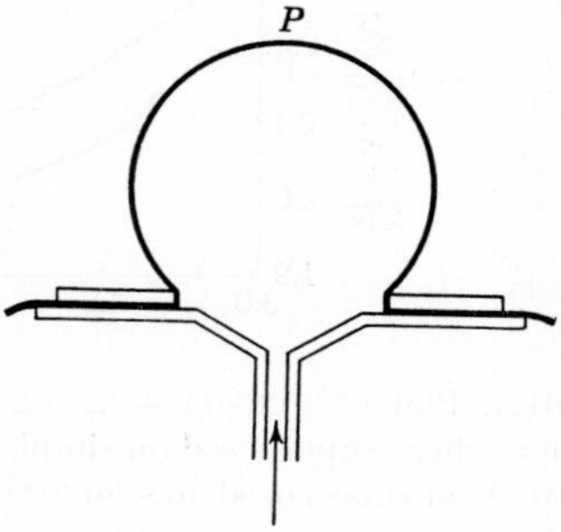


FIG. 61.7. Inflation experiment.

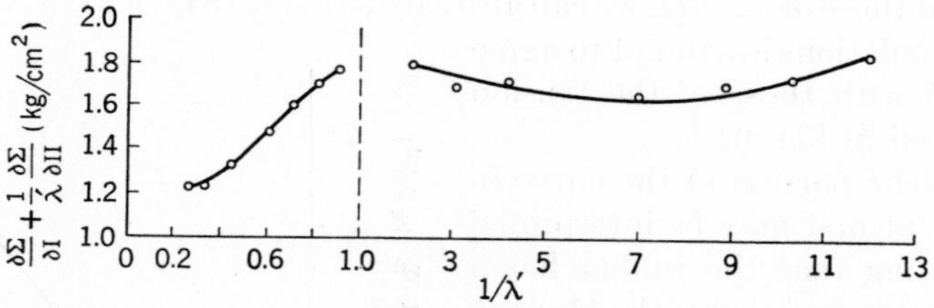


FIG. 61.8. Plot of $(\partial\Sigma/\partial I) + (1/\lambda')(\partial\Sigma/\partial II)$ against $1/\lambda'$ from experiments on simple compression and simple extension. (Note the change of scale at $1/\lambda' = 1$.) (*After Rivlin and Saunders* [1951])

sheet clamped around its edge, we can obtain such a state of deformation for the central area element (Fig. 61.7). Treloar [1943] and Rivlin and Saunders have carried out experiments for this case. The resulting curve for $(\partial\Sigma/\partial I) + (1/\lambda')(\partial\Sigma/\partial II)$ taken from the latter paper is shown in Fig. 61.8. Table 61.1 shows the dependence of $\partial\Sigma/\partial II$ on II.

Table 61.1

| $1/\lambda' \equiv \lambda^2$ | 0.5 | 0.6 | 0.7 | 0.8 | 3 | 5 | 7 | 9 | 11 |
|---|---|---|---|---|---|---|---|---|---|
| II | 4.25 | 3.69 | 3.35 | 3.14 | 9.67 | 25.4 | 49.3 | 81.2 | 121 |
| $\dfrac{(\partial\Sigma/\partial II)}{(\partial\Sigma/\partial I)}$ | 0.16 | 0.26 | 0.33 | 0.39 | 0.12 | 0.06 | 0.04 | 0.03 | 0.035 |

At the pole $P$ of the inflated sheet, the pressure $p$ and the tension $T$ per unit length of the major surface of the deformed sheet are related to each other by

$$p = \frac{2T}{r} \tag{61.17}$$

where $r$ is the radius of curvature at the pole. From (61.8) with $\lambda_1 = \lambda_2 = \lambda$, $\lambda_3 = 1/\lambda^2$, and from the fact that the deformed thickness is $H/\lambda^2$, we get

$$p = \frac{2Ht_{11}}{r\lambda^2} = \frac{4H}{r}\left(1 - \frac{1}{\lambda^6}\right)\left(\frac{\partial\Sigma}{\partial \mathrm{I}} + \lambda^2 \frac{\partial\Sigma}{\partial \mathrm{II}}\right) \tag{61.18}$$

Thus, by measuring $p$ and $r$ for each $\lambda$, we can plot $\partial\Sigma/\partial\mathrm{I} + (1/\lambda')(\partial\Sigma/\partial\mathrm{II})$ against $1/\lambda'$ where $\lambda' = 1/\lambda^2$ (Fig. 61.8). Knowing $\partial\Sigma/\partial\mathrm{I}$ = const, one constructs Table 61.1. The pressure versus $\lambda$ is shown in Fig. 61.9.

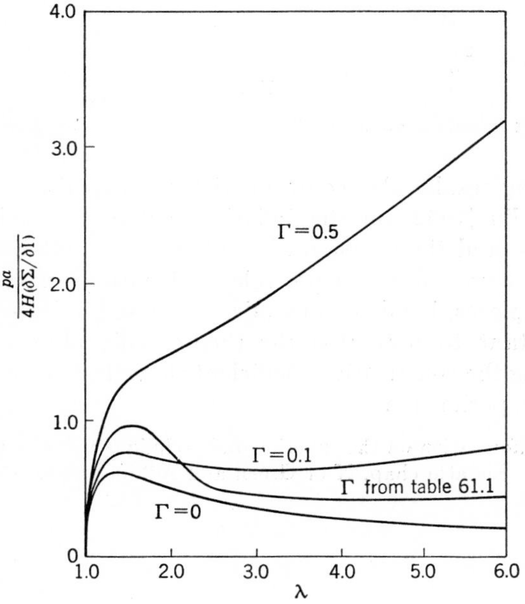


FIG. 61.9. Variation of inflating pressure with stretch for a spherical balloon for various $\Gamma \equiv (\partial\Sigma/\partial\mathrm{II})/(\partial\Sigma/\partial\mathrm{I})$. (*After Adkins and Rivlin* [1952])

These results are equally valid for an inflated spherical balloon of initial radius $a = r/\lambda$, and the plots on Fig. 61.9 are actually made for that case.

Most readers will have observed that in the inflation of a toy balloon the greatest effort is encountered at the start. The air pressure required for further inflation diminishes after the diameter of the balloon has reached a certain magnitude and then rises slowly for large stretches. This is confirmed by the curves of Fig 61.9.

Experiments were carried out also on torsion by Rivlin [1947b] and Rivlin and Saunders [1951] to determine the torque-angle of twist relationship. Again dependence of $\partial\Sigma/\partial\text{II}$ on II was recorded (Fig. 61.10)

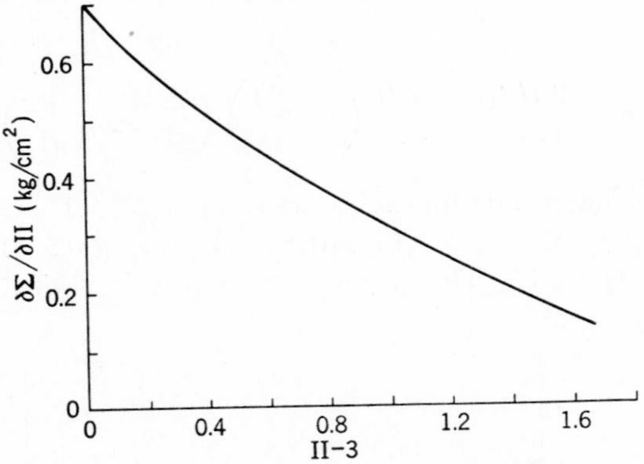


FIG. 61.10. Plot of $\partial\Sigma/\partial\text{II}$ against II − 3. (*After Rivlin and Saunders* [1951])

The foregoing results also conform with the experiments reported by Gent and Rivlin [1952] on the inflation, extension, and torsion of a cylindrical tube and the eversion of a rubber tube. Recently Gent and Lindley [1959] have suggested possible explanations of internal rupture of rubber test pieces, bonded to metals, under small deformations.[7]

It is important to note that the theoretically obtained inequalities (51.7) regarding the constitutive coefficients have been confirmed by all of the foregoing experiments.

[7] For further information on the experimental technique we refer the reader to the original papers. See also chap. X of Green and Adkins [1960].

# 7
# FLUID DYNAMICS

## 62. SCOPE OF THE CHAPTER

The constitutive equations of stokesian fluids, their various polynomial approximations, and the thermodynamical and physical restrictions imposed upon them have already been studied in Arts. 48 and 49. The present chapter is written to illustrate the solution of the basic equations of fluid dynamics. A summary of these equations is given in Art. 63. Among the basic problems treated are the rectilinear shear flow (Art. 64), Poiseuille flow (Art. 65), Couette flow (Art. 66), parallel-plate viscometer (Art. 67), and steady flow in a tube (Art. 68). These are important in the detection of major phenomena encountered in an exact theory versus the classical approximate theory. The Poynting effects and Kelvin effects (often called the normal stress effects), which constitute two basic phenomena not encountered in a theory based on linear constitutive equations, are again encountered in the exact solutions. The problems selected are also important from the experimental point of view.

Article 69 of this chapter is devoted to the formulation of the Navier-Stokes theory, which has played such an important role in classical fluid dynamics. Heat-conduction effects based on thermodynamics that are not compatible with the rigor of the present book are briefly discussed for the purpose of completing this theory. Finally Art. 70 on experimental investigations is presented to illustrate nonnewtonian characteristics of fluids.

## 63. FUNDAMENTAL EQUATIONS

The basic field equations of the theory of stokesian fluid flow are the following.

*Equation of Conservation of Mass.* Of the two different forms (25.8) and (25.10) of the continuity equations, the latter is found to be more convenient in problems in fluid flow.

(63.1) $$\frac{\partial \rho}{\partial t} + (\rho\, v^k)_{;k} = 0$$

*Equations of Balance of Momenta* (nonpolar case) (32.16) and (32.15)

$$t^{lk}{}_{;l} + (f^k - a^k) = 0 \qquad t^{lk} = t^{kl} \tag{63.2}$$

*Constitutive Equations* (48.12) or (48.18):

(63.3) $t^k{}_l = (-\pi + \alpha_0)\,\delta^k{}_l + \alpha_1 d^k{}_l + \alpha_2 d^k{}_m d^m{}_l$ (compressible)

(63.4) $t^k{}_l = -p\,\delta^k{}_l + \alpha_1 d^k{}_l + \alpha_2 d^k{}_m d^m{}_l$ (incompressible)

where

(63.5)
$$\alpha_\gamma = \alpha_\gamma(\mathrm{I}_d, \mathrm{II}_d, \mathrm{III}_d) \qquad (\gamma = 0, 1, 2) \qquad \text{(compressible)}$$
$$\alpha_\gamma = \alpha_\gamma(\mathrm{II}_d, \mathrm{III}_d) \qquad (\gamma = 1, 2) \qquad \text{(incompressible)}$$

with $\pi$ being thermodynamic pressure and $\alpha_0(0, 0, 0) = 0$ for the compressible fluids and $p$ undefined for the incompressible fluids.

The phenomenological coefficients $\alpha_\gamma$ are subject to the conditions required by the nonnegative dissipation function

(63.6)
$$\alpha_0 \mathrm{I}_d + \alpha_1(\mathrm{I}_d{}^2 - 2\,\mathrm{II}_d) + \alpha_2(\mathrm{I}_d{}^3 - 3\,\mathrm{I}_d\,\mathrm{II}_d + \mathrm{III}_d) \geq 0 \qquad \text{(compressible)}$$
$$-2\,\alpha_1 \mathrm{II}_d + \alpha_2 \mathrm{III}_d \geq 0 \qquad \text{(incompressible)}$$

Instead of these conditions one may employ the inequalities (48.29) and (48.30) obtained from mechanical considerations, i.e.,

(63.7)
$$\alpha_1 + \alpha_2(d_\alpha + d_\beta) \geq 0 \qquad \text{(compressible)}$$
$$\alpha_1 - \alpha_2 d_\alpha \geq 0 \qquad \text{(incompressible)}$$

where equal signs are superposed only for the cases of $d_\alpha = d_\beta$, $(\alpha \neq \beta)$ in $(63.7)_1$, and $d_\beta = d_\gamma$, $(\alpha, \beta, \gamma \neq)$ in $(63.7)_2$. In addition to the above equations we have the following kinematical relations.

*Kinematical Relations.* Deformation rates:

$$2\,d_{kl} = v_{k;l} + v_{l;k} \tag{63.8}$$

Velocity and acceleration vectors:

$$v^k = \frac{\partial x^k}{\partial t} \qquad a^k = \frac{Dv^k}{Dt} = \frac{\partial v^k}{\partial t} + v^k{}_{;l}\,v^l \tag{63.9}$$

In the foregoing equations the phenomenological coefficients $\alpha_\gamma(\mathrm{I}_d, \mathrm{II}_d, \mathrm{III}_d)$, $(\gamma = 0, 1, 2)$ are supposed to be determined from experimental considerations or from statistical mechanics. [Pressure $p$ in (63.4) remains an unknown of the problem to be determined from the solution.] The thermodynamic pressure $\pi$ for the compressible fluids is known through the equation of state

$$\pi = \pi(\rho, \theta) \tag{63.10}$$

where $\theta$ is the temperature. The foregoing formulation is valid for an isothermal fluid flow, where the heat-conduction phenomenon is excluded. Therefore $\theta$ in (63.10) may be considered as a parameter. In fact, $\alpha_\gamma$ will also depend on $\theta$ in this fashion.

*Boundary and Initial Conditions.* If the tractions $t^k{}_{(\mathrm{n})}$ are prescribed on the surface $\mathcal{S}$ of the body, we write

$$t^k{}_{(\mathrm{n})} = t^{lk}\, n_l = s^k \qquad \text{on } \mathcal{S} \tag{63.11}$$

According to Lamb, at a free surface or at the contacting surface of two dissimilar fluids, the stress vector should be continuous. Whether the continuity of the velocity across the surface or the interface follows from this is not known, although special examples exhibit the continuity.

The conditions to be satisfied at a solid boundary are more controversial. According to Stokes the fluid must adhere to the solid. For fluids of high viscosity and moderate pressure and stress this does appear to be the case, as verified by the law of the fourth power of the diameter of tube viscometers.[1]

For high-altitude aerodynamics the condition of adherence is known to be no longer true.[2]

According to the classical adherence condition

$$\Delta \mathbf{v} = 0 \qquad \text{on } \mathcal{S} \text{ of solid} \tag{63.12}$$

where $\Delta \mathbf{v}$ denotes the difference between fluid and solid boundary velocities.

Among the various slip conditions proposed, the most important one is

$$\Delta v_n = 0 \qquad \Delta \mathbf{v}_t = k\, \mathbf{t}_t \tag{63.13}$$

where subscripts $n$ and $t$ denote respectively the normal and tangential components at the boundary. Here the coefficient $k$ may depend on the thermodynamic variables. This law has found some support from the kinetic theory. The coefficient $k$ is found to be nearly zero, except for low pressures.

*Initial conditions* require that the velocity field $\mathbf{v}$ be prescribed throughout the region $\mathcal{V}$ occupied by the fluid at an initial time $t$, i.e.,

$$\mathbf{v}(\mathbf{x}, 0) = \mathbf{v}_0(\mathbf{x}) \qquad \text{in } \mathcal{V} \tag{63.14}$$

The boundary and initial conditions are the mathematical expressions of the physical state of the fluid media at the boundaries of the fluid and

[1] Cf Art. 65.

[2] Cf. Tsien [1946]. For various proposals and the controversy concerning slip conditions see Duhem [1901, part 4, chap. 5], Bateman [1932, part II, arts. 1.2, 1.7, 3.2], Reiner [1931, 1932*a*,*b*], and Mooney [1931]. For more recent contributions, see Truesdell [1952, art. 79] and Patterson [1956, chap. 5].

at a fixed time respectively. They must therefore be a reasonable mathematical representation of the physical situations. Without the existence of the solution of a problem and its experimental verifications, the accuracy of representations cannot be tested. Therefore no proper choice on these grounds is possible. The uniqueness of the physical phenomena for given initial and boundary conditions, however, demands that the mathematical boundary and initial conditions must be such that the solution of the field equations shall be unique. The existence and uniqueness theorems for general stokesian fluids have not been found to date except for the classical Navier-Stokes fluids.[3]

### 64. RECTILINEAR SHEARING FLOW

Here and in the following three articles we give some simple solutions.[1] Suppose that the velocity field is given by

$$\dot{x} = f(y) \qquad \dot{y} = 0 \qquad \dot{z} = 0 \tag{64.1}$$

According to (63.8) we then find

$$\|d_{kl}\| = \begin{bmatrix} 0 & \frac{1}{2}f' & 0 \\ \frac{1}{2}f' & 0 & 0 \\ 0 & 0 & 0 \end{bmatrix} \tag{64.2}$$

where $f' \equiv df/dy$. Thus the constitutive relations, according to (63.3), are

$$\mathbf{t} = (-\pi + \alpha_0)\,\mathbf{I} + \tfrac{1}{2}f'\,\alpha_1 \begin{bmatrix} 0 & 1 & 0 \\ 1 & 0 & 0 \\ 0 & 0 & 0 \end{bmatrix} + \tfrac{1}{4}f'^2\,\alpha_2 \begin{bmatrix} 1 & 0 & 0 \\ 0 & 1 & 0 \\ 0 & 0 & 0 \end{bmatrix} \tag{64.3}$$

where

$$\alpha_\gamma\,(\mathrm{I}_d, \mathrm{II}_d, \mathrm{III}_d) = \alpha_\gamma\,(0, -\tfrac{1}{4}f'^2, 0) = \alpha_\gamma\,(y) \qquad (\gamma = 0, 1, 2) \tag{64.4}$$

From (64.3) it follows that the shearing stress $t^1{}_2$ is necessarily an odd function of $f'$, the rate of shearing. Since the acceleration $\dot{\mathbf{v}} = 0$, the dynamical equations of motion (63.2), by also taking $\mathbf{f} = 0$, reduce to

$$-\frac{\partial \pi}{\partial x} + \frac{\partial}{\partial y}\,(\tfrac{1}{2}f'\,\alpha_1) = 0 \qquad \frac{\partial}{\partial y}\,(-\pi + \alpha_0 + \tfrac{1}{4}f'^2\,\alpha_2) = 0 \tag{64.5}$$

The general solutions of these equations are

$$\tfrac{1}{2}f'\,\alpha_1 = C\,y + D \qquad -\pi + \alpha_0 + \tfrac{1}{4}f'^2\,\alpha_2 = -C\,x + E$$

[3] Cf. Serrin [1959, art. 72] and the references therein.

[1] These solutions for the isochoric motions were obtained by Rivlin [1948*d*, 1949*c*]. Extensions to compressible fluids were made by Truesdell [1952, art. 72] with a note that they are not in general compatible with the energy equation. See also Oldroyd [1950] and Braun and Reiner [1952]. For fluids having memory these problems were treated by Coleman and Noll [1959*b*].

where $C$, $D$, and $E$ are constants. Upon substituting these into (64.3), we obtain

$$\begin{aligned} t^1{}_2 &= \tfrac{1}{2} f' \alpha_1 (0, -\tfrac{1}{4} f'^2, 0) = C\,y + D \\ t^1{}_1 &= t^2{}_2 = -\pi + \alpha_0 + \tfrac{1}{4} f'^2 \alpha_2 = -C\,x + E \end{aligned} \tag{64.6}$$

The former of these equations is an ordinary differential equation for the velocity profile $f(y)$. For $C = 0$ the stresses $t^1{}_2$, $t^1{}_1$, and $t^2{}_2$ are constants, so that the flow is characterized by uniform resistance per unit area. In this case $(64.6)_1$ is a transcendental equation in $f'$ in terms of the constant $D$. Since $f' \alpha_1$ is odd in $f'$, upon polynomial approximations we see that there is an odd number of velocity profiles, all linear but of different slopes $f'$, yielding the same resistance for $C = 0$.

To fix the ideas further, let us take $f = k\,y$, i.e., $f' = k$. In this case we must have $C = 0$ and

$$t^1{}_2 = \tfrac{1}{2} k\,\alpha_1 = D \qquad t^1{}_1 = t^2{}_2 = -\pi + \alpha_0 + \tfrac{1}{4} k^2 \alpha_2 = E \tag{64.7}$$

Thus the pressure $\pi$ is constant. It is clear from (64.6) or (64.7) that *to produce a shearing flow between two parallel infinite plates, in addition to a shearing force one needs additional normal stresses applied to the plates.* The normal stresses needed exceed the normal stress in the planes of flow by the amount $\tfrac{1}{4} f'^2 \alpha_2 (0, -\tfrac{1}{4} f'^2, 0)$. This excess stress is tension whenever $\alpha_2 > 0$, so that in its absence the plates tend to draw together when sheared. This is the *Poynting* effect whose presence depends on the existence of $\alpha_2$. We may apply inequalities $(63.6)_1$ and $(63.7)_1$. While both give $\alpha_1 > 0$, the first fails to produce a restriction on $\alpha_2$ although the last gives

$$\alpha_1 - \tfrac{1}{2} \alpha_2 f' > 0 \qquad \alpha_1 + \tfrac{1}{2} \alpha_2 f' > 0$$

These do not tell us whether $\alpha_2 > 0$ or $\alpha_2 < 0$.

When temperature gradients are present, then $\alpha_\gamma$ may also depend on $\theta$, which may not be a constant. To effect the solution, the dependence of $\alpha_\gamma$ on pressure and temperature must be specified explicitly.

## 65. POISEUILLE FLOW

In cylindrical coordinates $r$, $\theta$, $z$ we consider the motion given by

$$\dot r = \dot\theta = 0 \qquad \dot z = w(r) \qquad 0 \le r \le a \tag{65.1}$$

As the boundary condition we assume that the fluid adheres to the wall of the cylinder, i.e.,

$$w(a) = 0 \tag{65.2}$$

Through (63.8) we have

$$\mathbf{d} = \begin{bmatrix} 0 & 0 & \frac{1}{2} w' \\ 0 & 0 & 0 \\ \frac{1}{2} w' & 0 & 0 \end{bmatrix} \tag{65.3}$$

The constitutive equations follow from (63.3)

$$\mathbf{t} = (-\pi + \alpha_0)\,\mathbf{I} + \tfrac{1}{2}\alpha_1 w' \begin{bmatrix} 0 & 0 & 1 \\ 0 & 0 & 0 \\ 1 & 0 & 0 \end{bmatrix} + \tfrac{1}{4}\alpha_2 w'^2 \begin{bmatrix} 1 & 0 & 0 \\ 0 & 0 & 0 \\ 0 & 0 & 1 \end{bmatrix} \tag{65.4}$$

where

$$\alpha_\gamma = \alpha_\gamma\,(0, -\tfrac{1}{4} w'^2, 0) = \alpha_\gamma\,(r) \tag{65.5}$$

The dynamical equations (63.2), with $\mathbf{f} = 0$, reduce to

$$(65.6)\qquad \begin{aligned} &-\frac{\partial \pi}{\partial r} + \alpha_0{}' + \frac{1}{r}\,(\tfrac{1}{4} r\, w'^2\, \alpha_2)' = 0 \\ &\frac{\partial \pi}{\partial \theta} = 0 \qquad -\frac{\partial \pi}{\partial z} + \frac{1}{r}\,(\tfrac{1}{2} r\, w'\, \alpha_1)' = 0 \end{aligned}$$

Taking $\alpha_\gamma$ independent of pressure and temperature, it follows that

$$\pi = \pi\,(r, z) \qquad \frac{\partial \pi}{\partial z} = \frac{1}{r}\,(\tfrac{1}{2} r\, w'\, \alpha_1)' = -C$$

where $C$ is a constant. Hence

$$\pi\,(r, z) = -C\,z + f\,(r) \qquad \alpha_1 w' = -C\,r + \frac{2\,D}{r}$$

where $f\,(r)$ is a function of $r$ alone and $D$ is a constant which must be taken zero, since at $r = 0$, $w'$ must be bounded. Thus

$$\pi\,(r, z) = -C\,z + f\,(r) \qquad \alpha_1 w' = -C\,r \tag{65.7}$$

Substituting these into $(65.6)_1$ and integrating the result, we get

$$f\,(r) = \alpha_0 + \tfrac{1}{4}\alpha_2 w'^2 + \frac{C^2}{4}\int r\,\frac{\alpha_2}{\alpha_1{}^2}\,dr + C_1 \tag{65.8}$$

where $C_1$ is a constant. The stress tensor is now given by

$$(65.9)\qquad \begin{aligned} &t^r{}_r = t^z{}_z = C\,z - \tfrac{1}{4} C^2 \int r\,\frac{\alpha_2}{\alpha_1{}^2}\,dr - C_1 \\ &-t^\theta{}_\theta = p - \alpha_0 = -C\,z + \tfrac{1}{4} w'^2\,\alpha_2 + \tfrac{1}{4} C^2 \int r\,\frac{\alpha_2}{\alpha_1{}^2}\,dr + C_1 \end{aligned}$$

The mass flux $\mathfrak{M}$ is given by

$$\text{(65.10)} \quad \mathfrak{M} = \int \rho\, w\, da = \rho \int_0^a 2\,\pi\, r\, w\, dr = \pi\, \rho\, C \int_0^a (r^3/\alpha_1)\, dr$$

In obtaining the last equality an integration by parts is employed together with $(65.7)_2$. The differential equation of the velocity profile is given by $(65.7)_2$. When the explicit form of $\alpha_1$ is known, by solving this equation we obtain $w\,(r)$. For a given pressure gradient $C$, a number of velocity slopes are possible. The Poynting effect appears as the excess of the radial and downstream normal stresses over the classical value $C\,z$ of these quantities. *This excess for $\alpha_2 > 0$ is always a pressure and is always greatest on the periphery.*[1] We may examine this point in more detail if we consider a quadratic dependence of $\mathbf{t}$ on $\mathbf{d}$, since in this case coefficients $\alpha_1$ and $\alpha_2$ are constant. Writing $\alpha_1 = 2\,\mu_v$, the classical velocity profile follows from the integration of $(65.7)_2$:

$$\text{(65.11)} \qquad w = \left(\frac{C}{4\,\mu_v}\right)(a^2 - r^2)$$

The mass flux for this case is

$$\text{(65.12)} \qquad \mathfrak{M} = \pi\,\rho\, C\,\frac{a^4}{8\,\mu_v}$$

Note, however, that the pressure distribution across any normal cross section of the pipe is no longer uniform. To determine this effect in detail, suppose that the fluid is issued into an atmospheric pressure $p_0$. The force exerted on the output cross section is $\pi\, a^2\, p_0$. For this case we have

$$t^r{}_r = t^z{}_z = C\,z - \frac{1}{32}\,\frac{C^2\,\alpha_2}{\mu_v{}^2}\, r^2 - C_1$$

Therefore the force balance at the outlet section $z = 0$ requires

$$\pi\, a^2\, p_0 = -2\,\pi \int_0^a t^z{}_z\, r\, dr = \frac{\pi}{64}\,\frac{\alpha_2\, C^2}{\mu_v{}^2}\, a^4 + C_1\,\pi\, a^2$$

The force per unit area exerted on the wall is therefore given by

$$P = -\,t^r{}_r\big|_{r=a} = -C\,z + \frac{1}{64}\,\frac{\alpha_2\, C^2}{\mu_v{}^2}\, a^2 + p_0$$

Introducing $\Gamma = \mathfrak{M}/\pi\, a^2\, \rho$, the volume of flow per second per unit cross

[1] Again inequalities (63.6) or (63.7) fail to produce a sign for $\alpha_2$.

section, we have $C = 8\,\mu_v\,\Gamma/a^2$ from (65.12). Consequently the preceding equation may be written as

$$\frac{P - p_0}{(\Gamma/a)^2} = \frac{-8\mu_v\,z}{\Gamma} + \alpha_2 \tag{65.13}$$

This equation may be used to explain an interesting experimental phenomenon discovered by Merrington [1943b]; namely, the tendency of the fluid to swell out[2] at the exit section of a viscometer (Fig. 65.1). This is the same effect noted above for the general case when $\alpha_2\,(r) > 0$.

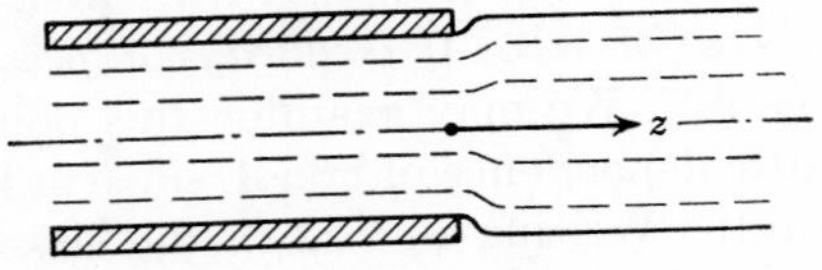


FIG. 65.1. Fluid issuing from a small-diameter viscometer. (*After Merrington* [1943b])

Thus the positive second-order viscosity coefficient is responsible for this Poynting effect, which is also found experimentally as noted above.

### 66. COUETTE FLOW

Consider a flow field in which the velocity components in a cylindrical coordinate system $(r, \theta, z)$ are given by

$$\dot r = 0 \qquad \dot\theta = \omega\,(r) \qquad \dot z = 0 \tag{66.1}$$

Such a flow field may represent the motion of a rotating fluid in a circular cylinder. Using (63.8) for the matrix of physical components of **d**, we get

$$\|d^{(k)}{}_{(l)}\| = \begin{bmatrix} 0 & \frac{1}{2}\,r\,\omega' & 0 \\ \frac{1}{2}\,r\,\omega' & 0 & 0 \\ 0 & 0 & 0 \end{bmatrix} \tag{66.2}$$

Consequently the physical components of stress are

$$\|t^{(k)}{}_{(l)}\| = (-\pi + \alpha_0)\,\mathbf{I} + \tfrac{1}{2}\,r\,\omega'\,\alpha_1 \begin{bmatrix} 0 & 1 & 0 \\ 1 & 0 & 0 \\ 0 & 0 & 0 \end{bmatrix} + \tfrac{1}{4}\,r^2\,\omega'^2\,\alpha_2 \begin{bmatrix} 1 & 0 & 0 \\ 0 & 1 & 0 \\ 0 & 0 & 0 \end{bmatrix} \tag{66.3}$$

where

$$\alpha_\gamma = \alpha_\gamma\,(0, -\tfrac{1}{4}\,r^2\,\omega'^2, 0) = \alpha_\gamma\,(r)$$

[2] See also Braun and Reiner [1952]. Merrington, however, attributes this phenomenon to the elastic recovery of the fluid stretched in the capillary tube. Merrington also gave curves of shearing stress versus rate of shear deviating from linearity

Suppose that gravity acts along the $z$ axis. We may put the equations of motion (63.2) into the form

$$\frac{\partial}{\partial r}(-\pi + \alpha_0 + \tfrac{1}{4} r^2 \omega'^2 \alpha_2) = -\rho r \omega^2$$

(66.4)
$$-\frac{1}{r}\frac{\partial \pi}{\partial \theta} + \frac{\partial}{\partial r}(\tfrac{1}{2} r \omega' \alpha_1) + \omega' \alpha_1 = 0$$

$$-\frac{\partial \pi}{\partial z} + \rho g = 0$$

A symmetrical solution is found to be

$$t^r{}_\theta = \tfrac{1}{2} r \omega' \alpha_1 (0, -\tfrac{1}{4} r^2 \omega'^2, 0) = \frac{C}{r^2} \qquad \rho = \rho(r)$$

(66.5)
$$t^z{}_z = -\pi + \alpha_0 = -\rho g z - \tfrac{1}{4} r^2 \omega'^2 \alpha_2 - \int_0^r \rho r \omega^2 \, dr + D$$

$$t^r{}_r = t^\theta{}_\theta = -\rho g z - \int_0^r \rho r \omega^2 \, dr + D$$

where $C$ and $D$ are arbitrary constants of which $2\pi C$ is the resultant couple per unit length required to produce the motion. For a given $C$ $(66.5)_1$ is a differential equation for the angular velocity profile $\omega(r)$. According to this equation there exists an odd number of angular velocities $\omega'$ for each $C$.

The Poynting effect appears in a striking form; namely, *for* $\alpha_2 > 0$ *pressures must be supplied to the planes perpendicular to the axis of rotation.* If these pressures are not present, then the fluid surface will tend to rise irrespective of the speeds and senses of rotation.

For a second-order polynomial dependence between **t** and **d**, a more explicit result can be obtained. Since $\mathrm{I}_d = \mathrm{III}_d = 0$, through (49.14) we have

$$t^k{}_l = (-\pi + \lambda_2 \mathrm{II}_d)\, \delta^k{}_l + 2 \mu_v d^k{}_l + 4 \nu_v d^k{}_r d^r{}_l$$

Hence $\alpha_0 = \lambda_2 \mathrm{II}_d = -\lambda_2 r^2 \omega'^2/4$, $\alpha_1 = 2\mu_v$, and $\alpha_2 = 4\nu_v$. Now (66.5) integrates into

$$\omega(r) = -\frac{C}{2 \mu_v r^2} + E$$

Eliminating $E$ by writing $\omega(r)$ at $r = r_1$ and $r = r_2$, we get

$$C = 2\mu_v \frac{r_1^2 r_2^2 [\omega(r_1) - \omega(r_2)]}{r_1^2 - r_2^2}$$

Neglecting the gravitational effect $\rho g z$ and the centrifugal effect $\rho r \omega^2$, the stress components read

$$(66.6)\qquad t^r{}_r = t^\theta{}_\theta = D \qquad t^r{}_\theta = 2\,\mu_v \frac{r_1{}^2\,r_2{}^2\,[\omega\,(r_1) - \omega\,(r_2)]}{r^2\,(r_1{}^2 - r_2{}^2)}$$

$$t^z{}_z = D - 4\,\nu_v \frac{r_1{}^4\,r_2{}^4\,[\omega\,(r_1) - \omega\,(r_2)]^2}{r^4\,(r_1{}^2 - r_2{}^2)^2}$$

where the constant $D$ may be adjusted to make $t^z{}_z$ on a cylindrical surface $r = r_0$ (between inner cylinder $r = r_1$ and outer cylinder $r = r_2$) be identical to the atmospheric pressure $p_0$. Hence

$$t^z{}_z + p_0 = -4\,\nu_v \frac{r_1{}^4\,r_2{}^4\,[\omega\,(r_1) - \omega\,(r_2)]^2}{(r_1{}^2 - r_2{}^2)^2}\left(\frac{1}{r^4} - \frac{1}{r_0{}^4}\right)$$

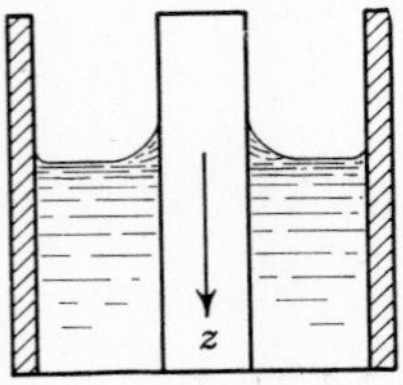

FIG. 66.1. Couette flow ($\nu_v > 0$).

Thus, if the surface $z = 0$ is left free, it may be expected to slope upward or downward toward the center according as $\nu_v > 0$ or $\nu_v < 0$. The effect is greatest near the inner cylinder irrespective of the speed and the sense of rotation. Garner and Nissan [1946] have observed that in a Couette flow with a free surface the flow climbs up the inner cylinder, a phenomenon which was demonstrated experimentally by Weissenberg [1947, 1949][1] and Reiner, Scott Blair, and Hawley [1949]. (See Fig. 66.2.) We therefore conclude that for real fluids $\nu_v$ is nonnegative.

## 67. PARALLEL-PLATE VISCOMETER

For the rotary motion of a sufficiently viscous fluid within two parallel plates, if we ignore gravity, the velocity field may be approximated by

$$(67.1)\qquad \dot r = 0 \qquad \dot\theta = \omega\,(z) \qquad \dot z = 0$$

Such a motion approximates the flow in a parallel-plate viscometer.

The matrix of physical components of $\mathbf{d}$ is now given by

$$(67.2)\qquad \mathbf{d} = \begin{bmatrix} 0 & 0 & 0 \\ 0 & 0 & \frac{1}{2}\,r\,\omega' \\ 0 & \frac{1}{2}\,r\,\omega' & 0 \end{bmatrix}$$

The matrix of the physical components of the stress tensor is

$$(67.3)\qquad \|t^{(k)}{}_{(l)}\| = (-\pi + \alpha_0)\,\mathbf{I} + \tfrac{1}{2}\,r\,\omega'\,\alpha_1 \begin{bmatrix} 0 & 0 & 0 \\ 0 & 0 & 1 \\ 0 & 1 & 0 \end{bmatrix} + \tfrac{1}{4}\,r^2\,\omega'^2\,\alpha_2 \begin{bmatrix} 0 & 0 & 0 \\ 0 & 1 & 0 \\ 0 & 0 & 1 \end{bmatrix}$$

where $\alpha_\gamma = \alpha_\gamma\,(0, -\frac{1}{4}\,r^2\,\omega'^2, 0)$.

[1] See also Wood, Nissan, and Garner [1947] and Reiner [1960]. For the history of this phenomenon see Garner, Nissan, and Wood [1950].

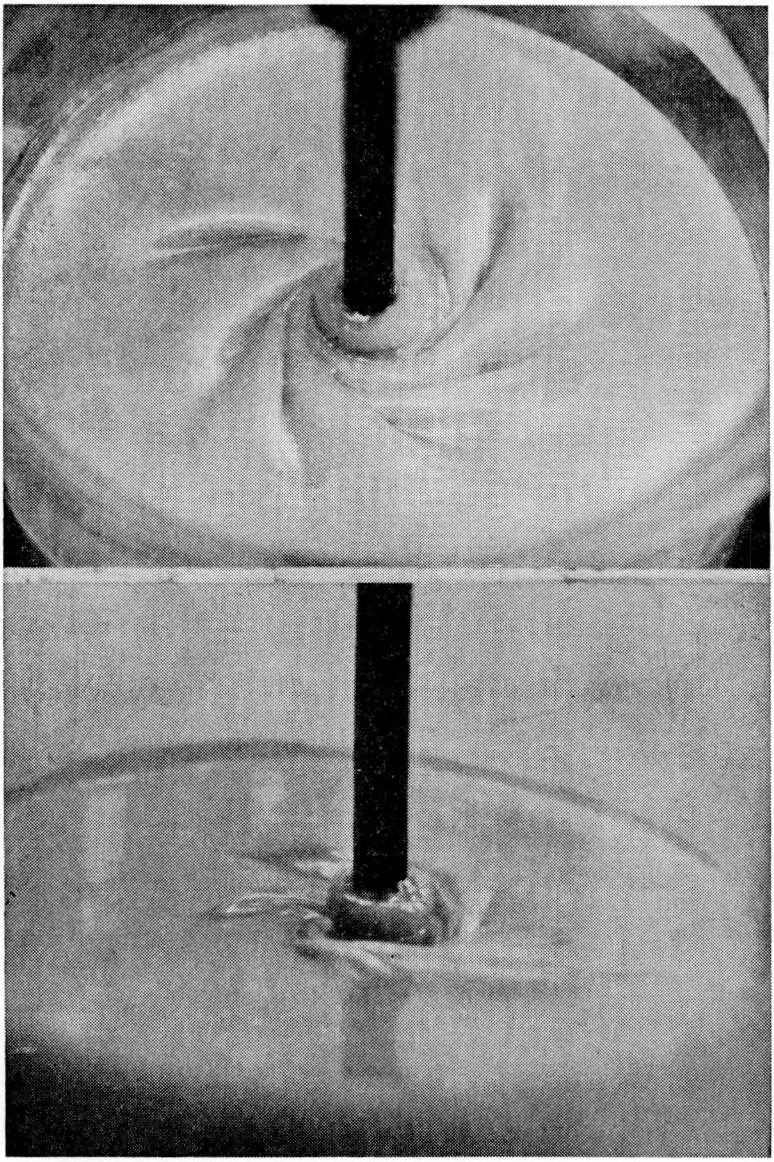

ɪɢ. 66.2. Illustration of Weissenberg effect in sweetened milk. (*After Reiner, Scott ʒlair, and Hawley* [1949])

Neglecting the inertia forces and gravity, the dynamical equations (63.2) reduce to

$$\frac{\partial}{\partial r}(-\pi + \alpha_0) - \tfrac{1}{4} r\, \omega'^2 \alpha_2 = 0$$

(67.4) $$-\frac{\partial \pi}{\partial \theta} + \tfrac{1}{2} r^2 \frac{\partial}{\partial z}(\omega' \alpha_1) = 0$$

$$\frac{\partial}{\partial z}(-\pi + \alpha_0) + \tfrac{1}{4} r^2 \frac{\partial}{\partial z}(\omega'^2 \alpha_2) = 0$$

Consider a solution in which $\partial \pi / \partial \theta = 0$. Equation $(67.4)_2$ yields

(67.5) $$\omega' \alpha_1 (0, -\tfrac{1}{4} r^2 \omega'^2, 0) = f(r)$$

and the integrability condition for $(67.4)_1$ and $(67.4)_3$ is

(67.6) $$\frac{1}{r}\frac{\partial}{\partial r}\left[-r^2 \frac{\partial}{\partial z}(\omega'^2 \alpha_2)\right] = \frac{\partial}{\partial z}(\omega'^2 \alpha_2)$$

Hence the integration gives

(67.7) $$\omega'^2 \alpha_2 (0, -\tfrac{1}{4} r^2 \omega'^2, 0) = r^{-3} g(z) + h(r)$$

where $f(r)$, $h(r)$, and $g(z)$ are arbitrary functions. If the axis $r = 0$ is within the body, the condition of boundedness of $\omega'$ requires that $g(z) = 0$. The condition of (67.7) is then satisfied if and only if $\omega' =$ const. In this case we find

(67.8) $$t^z{}_\theta = \tfrac{1}{2} \omega' r \alpha_1 \qquad t^z{}_z = \tfrac{1}{4} \omega'^2 \left(r^2 \alpha_2 + \int_a^r r \alpha_2 \, dr\right)$$

where the constant of integration is adjusted to make $t^r{}_r = 0$ on the cylindrical boundary $r = a$.

The resultant force $F$ and couple $L$ required to produce the motion are given by

$$F = \int_0^a 2\pi r\, t^z{}_z \, dr = \frac{\pi}{2} \omega'^2 \int_0^a \left(r^3 \alpha_2 + r \int_a^r r \alpha_2 \, dr\right) dr$$

$$L = \int_0^a 2\pi r^2 \, t^z{}_\theta \, dr = \pi \omega' \int_0^a r^3 \alpha_1 \, dr$$

The second term on the extreme right of the first expression may be integrated by parts, giving

(67.9) $$F = \frac{\pi}{4} \omega'^2 \int_0^a r^3 \alpha_2 \, dr \qquad L = \pi \omega' \int_0^a r^3 \alpha_1 \, dr$$

When $\alpha_2 > 0$, we see that $F > 0$. Consequently *in the absence of this force the plates of the viscometer will tend to draw together.*

For a second-order theory $\alpha_2$ = const and $(67.8)_2$ gives

$$t^z{}_z = \tfrac{1}{8}\,\omega'^2\,\alpha_2\,(3\,r^2 - a^2) \tag{67.10}$$

For this approximation $t^z{}_z$ is distributed parabolically, and it is tension for $r > a/\sqrt{3}$ and compression for $r < a/\sqrt{3}$. Braun and Reiner [1952] have observed the zero-point pressure. Greensmith and Rivlin [1951, 1953][1] have found good quantitative experimental agreement with $(67.8)_2$.

## 68. STEADY FLOW IN A TUBE

In Art. 65 we discussed the flow of a fluid through a circular cylinder and found that a rectilinear flow, in which each particle moves with a constant speed along a straight line parallel to the axis of the cylinder, adhering to the cylinder, can be maintained without the application of body forces and without making further assumptions regarding the constitutive coefficients. In the classical theory of newtonian fluids, this type of flow is possible in a cylinder of any cross section. The theoretical works of Green and Rivlin [1956], Ericksen [1956], Stone [1957], Criminale, Ericksen, and Filbey [1958], and others have shown the existence of a new phenomenon; namely, with the exception of special types of fluids for which the constitutive coefficients are related to each other, this type of flow in noncircular tubes cannot be maintained without an appropriate body-force distribution in addition to a uniform pressure gradient along the tube. Green and Rivlin have shown that without the application of body forces a steady flow will be produced consisting of a rectilinear flow along the tube plus some superposed flow distribution in planes perpendicular to the axis of the tube, independent of the position along the axis.

No satisfactory experimental work on this phenomenon has as yet been published.[1]

In rectangular coordinates employing cartesian tensors, the equations of motion, the constitutive equations, and the incompressibility condition of an incompressible fluid are respectively:

$$t_{lk,l} + \rho f_k = \rho\left(\frac{\partial v_k}{\partial t} + v_{k,l}\,v_l\right) \tag{68.1}$$

$$t_{kl} = -p\,\delta_{kl} + \alpha_1\,(\mathrm{II}_d, \mathrm{III}_d)\,d_{kl} + \alpha_2\,(\mathrm{II}_d, \mathrm{III}_d)\,d_{km}\,d_{ml} \tag{68.2}$$

$$v_{k,k} = 0 \tag{68.3}$$

[1] Roberts [1953], however, reports disagreement with the Reiner-Rivlin theory.

[1] Markovitz [1957], Markovitz and Williamson [1957], and Roberts [1953] attempted to collect experimental data and to compare these with the predictions of various theories. Some of the conclusions of Markovitz contradict some of Roberts's. For further elaboration see Art. 70.

where $p$ is an arbitrary pressure, $\rho$ the assumed constant density, $f_k$ the body force, and

$$d_{kl} = \tfrac{1}{2}(v_{k,l} + v_{l,k}) \tag{68.4}$$

$$\mathrm{II}_d = -\tfrac{1}{2} d_{kl} d_{lk} \qquad \mathrm{III}_d = \tfrac{1}{3} d_{kr} d_{rl} d_{lk} \tag{68.5}$$

The constitutive coefficients $\alpha_1$ and $\alpha_2$ are arbitrary functions of $\mathrm{II}_d$ and $\mathrm{III}_d$.

If each particle moves along a straight line parallel to the $x_3$ axis at a constant speed, then $v_1 = v_2 = 0$, and $(\partial v_3/\partial t) + v_{3,3} v_3 = 0$. Using (68.3), we get $v_{3,3} = \partial v_3/\partial t = 0$. This means that $v_3 = 2f(x_1, x_2)$, where the factor 2 is introduced for convenience. Thus the most general velocity field for this motion is

$$v_1 = v_2 = 0 \qquad v_3 = 2f(x_1, x_2) \tag{68.6}$$

The differential equation (68.3) is now satisfied identically. Using (68.6) in (68.2), we get

$$\|t_{kl}\| = -p\,\|\delta_{kl}\| + \alpha_1 \begin{bmatrix} 0 & 0 & f_{,1} \\ 0 & 0 & f_{,2} \\ f_{,1} & f_{,2} & 0 \end{bmatrix} + \alpha_2 \begin{bmatrix} f_{,1}{}^2 & f_{,1} f_{,2} & 0 \\ f_{,1} f_{,2} & f_{,2}{}^2 & 0 \\ 0 & 0 & f_{,i} f_{,i} \end{bmatrix}$$

or using $x$, $y$, $z$ for $x_1$, $x_2$, $x_3$, in components we have

$$\begin{aligned} t_{xx} &= -p + \alpha_2 f_{,x}{}^2 & t_{yy} &= -p + \alpha_2 f_{,y}{}^2 & t_{xy} &= \alpha_2 f_{,x} f_{,y} \\ t_{xz} &= \alpha_1 f_{,x} & t_{yz} &= \alpha_1 f_{,y} & t_{zz} &= -p + \alpha_2 (f_{,x}{}^2 + f_{,y}{}^2) \end{aligned} \tag{68.7}$$

Using (68.6) in (68.5), we also get

$$\mathrm{II}_d = -(f_{,x}{}^2 + f_{,y}{}^2) \qquad \mathrm{III}_d = 0 \tag{68.8}$$

Substitution of (68.7) into (68.1) gives

$$\begin{aligned} -p_{,x} + (\alpha_2 f_{,x}{}^2)_{,x} + (\alpha_2 f_{,x} f_{,y})_{,y} + \rho X &= 0 \\ -p_{,y} + (\alpha_2 f_{,x} f_{,y})_{,x} + (\alpha_2 f_{,y}{}^2)_{,y} + \rho Y &= 0 \\ -p_{,z} + (\alpha_1 f_{,x})_{,x} + (\alpha_1 f_{,y})_{,y} + \rho Z &= 0 \end{aligned} \tag{68.9}$$

where $X$, $Y$, $Z$ are used for the force components $f_1$, $f_2$, $f_3$. A solution in which $Z = 0$ satisfying $(68.9)_3$ is

$$p = p_0(x, y) + \lambda z \tag{68.10}$$

where $\lambda$ is a constant such that

$$(\alpha_1 f_{,x})_{,x} + (\alpha_1 f_{,y})_{,y} - \lambda = 0 \tag{68.11}$$

The functions $\alpha_1$ and $\alpha_2$ depend only on $\mathrm{II}_d$, which is given by (68.8). Let

$$q = -p_0 - \tfrac{1}{2} \int \alpha_2 \, d\mathrm{II}_d \tag{68.12}$$

Then

$$\begin{aligned} q_{,x} &= -p_{0,x} + \alpha_2 (f_{,x} f_{,xx} + f_{,y} f_{,xy}) \\ q_{,y} &= -p_{0,y} + \alpha_2 (f_{,x} f_{,xy} + f_{,y} f_{,yy}) \end{aligned}$$

Using these in the first two equations of (68.9), we obtain

$$\begin{aligned} q_{,x} + [(\alpha_2 f_{,x})_{,x} + (\alpha_2 f_{,y})_{,y}] f_{,x} + \rho X &= 0 \\ q_{,y} + [(\alpha_2 f_{,x})_{,x} + (\alpha_2 f_{,y})_{,y}] f_{,y} + \rho Y &= 0 \end{aligned} \tag{68.13}$$

We now consider two cases.

1. *Vanishing Body Forces.* In this case $X = Y = Z = 0$. Hence from (68.13) it follows that grad $q$ is parallel to grad $f$ or $q = q(f)$. Since $f_{,x}$ and $f_{,y}$ are assumed not to vanish, we must have

$$(\alpha_2 f_{,x})_{,x} + (\alpha_2 f_{,y})_{,y} + \frac{dq}{df} = 0 \tag{68.14}$$

In addition to this, $f$ satisfies (68.11). We therefore have two partial differential equations satisfied by a single function $f(x, y)$. Ericksen [1956] has shown that when $\alpha_1$ and $\alpha_2$ are independent functions, the rectilinear motion is not physically possible except perhaps for rigid motions or for motions in which the curves of constant speed are circles or straight lines. Stone [1957] has obtained results in agreement with this for a class of ideal materials similar in nature to those described in the theory of perfectly plastic solids.

The nontrivial solutions corresponding to the case of vanishing body forces are included in (1) $\alpha_2 = k\,\alpha_1$, $q = k\,\lambda f$, where $k$ is a constant; or (2) $f$ is a linear function of $x$ and $y$; or (3) $f$ is a function of $(x^2 + y^2)^{\frac{1}{2}}$.

2. *Nonvanishing Body Forces* $(X, Y)$. In this case a possible solution of (68.13) is

$$\begin{aligned} \rho X &= -\left[(\alpha_2 f_{,x})_{,x} + (\alpha_2 f_{,y})_{,y} + \frac{dq}{df}\right] f_{,x} \\ \rho Y &= -\left[(\alpha_2 f_{,x})_{,x} + (\alpha_2 f_{,y})_{,y} + \frac{dq}{df}\right] f_{,y} \end{aligned} \tag{68.15}$$

where $q$ is a function of $f$ only and $f$ satisfies (68.11). For a tube cross section symmetrical about the $x$ and $y$ axes from (68.11), from the fact that $f = 0$ on the boundary, and from $\alpha_1 = \alpha_1 (f_{,x}{}^2 + f_{,y}{}^2)$, we see that $f$ is an even function of $x$ and an even function of $y$. Since $dq/df$ is arbitrary, the flow may be maintained by a body force $X$ which is an odd function of $x$ and an even function of $y$; and by a body force $Y$ which is an even function of $x$ and an odd function of $y$. If these forces are not present, then there will be a circulatory motion in the $xy$ plane in which the flow in any one quadrant is the mirror image of that immediately adjacent to the quadrant.

Green and Rivlin [1956] have worked out the case of a special fluid flowing in a tube of elliptical cross section.

Using the incompressibility condition (68.3) for nonzero values of $v_1$ and $v_2$, we have

$$v_1 = -\psi_{,y} \qquad v_2 = \psi_{,x} \qquad v_3 = 2f(x, y) \tag{68.16}$$

We employ complex variables

$$\zeta = x + iy \qquad \bar{\zeta} = x - iy$$

After substitution of (68.16) into (68.2)–(68.5), we form the stress combinations and the invariants

$$\begin{aligned} t_{11} + t_{22} &= -2p + 4\alpha_2 (f_{,\zeta} f_{,\bar\zeta} + 2\psi_{,\zeta\zeta}\psi_{,\bar\zeta\bar\zeta}) \\ t_{11} - t_{22} + 2i t_{12} &= 4i\alpha_1 \psi_{,\bar\zeta\bar\zeta} + 4\alpha_2 (f_{,\bar\zeta})^2 \\ t_{13} + i t_{23} &= 2\alpha_1 f_{,\bar\zeta} + 4i\alpha_2 f_{,\zeta}\psi_{,\bar\zeta\bar\zeta} \\ t_{33} &= -p + 4\alpha_2 f_{,\zeta} f_{,\bar\zeta} \\ \mathrm{II} &= -4(f_{,\zeta} f_{,\bar\zeta} + \psi_{,\zeta\zeta}\psi_{,\bar\zeta\bar\zeta}) \\ \mathrm{III} &= 4i[(f_{,\zeta})^2 \psi_{,\bar\zeta\bar\zeta} - (f_{,\bar\zeta})^2 \psi_{,\zeta\zeta}] \end{aligned} \tag{68.17}$$

Equations of motion (68.1) for zero body forces can be expressed as

$$\begin{aligned} (t_{11} + t_{22})_{,\bar\zeta} + (t_{11} - t_{22} + 2i t_{12})_{,\zeta} &= 4\rho(\psi_{,\zeta}\psi_{,\bar\zeta\bar\zeta} - \psi_{,\bar\zeta}\psi_{,\zeta\bar\zeta}) \\ t_{33,z} + (t_{13} + i t_{23})_{,\zeta} + (t_{13} - i t_{23})_{,\bar\zeta} &= 4i\rho(f_{,\zeta}\psi_{,\bar\zeta} - f_{,\bar\zeta}\psi_{,\zeta}) \end{aligned} \tag{68.18}$$

Using (68.17) in (68.18), we have

$$\begin{aligned} &-p_{,\bar\zeta} + 2[\alpha_2 (f_{,\zeta} f_{,\bar\zeta} + 2\psi_{,\zeta\zeta}\psi_{,\bar\zeta\bar\zeta})]_{,\bar\zeta} \\ &\qquad + 2[i\alpha_1 \psi_{,\bar\zeta\bar\zeta} + \alpha_2 (f_{,\bar\zeta})^2]_{,\zeta} = 2\rho(\psi_{,\zeta}\psi_{,\bar\zeta\bar\zeta} - \psi_{,\bar\zeta}\psi_{,\zeta\bar\zeta}) \\ &-p_{,z} + 2(\alpha_1 f_{,\bar\zeta} + 2i\alpha_2 f_{,\zeta}\psi_{,\bar\zeta\bar\zeta})_{,\zeta} \\ &\qquad + 2(\alpha_1 f_{,\zeta} - 2i\alpha_2 f_{,\bar\zeta}\psi_{,\zeta\zeta})_{,\bar\zeta} = 4i\rho(f_{,\zeta}\psi_{,\bar\zeta} - f_{,\bar\zeta}\psi_{,\zeta}) \end{aligned} \tag{68.19}$$

From these equations we see that

$$p = -\lambda z + p_0(\zeta, \bar\zeta) \tag{68.20}$$

where $\lambda$ is a constant. Consequently

$$\begin{aligned} &\lambda + 2(\alpha_1 f_{,\bar\zeta} + 2i\alpha_2 f_{,\zeta}\psi_{,\bar\zeta\bar\zeta})_{,\zeta} + 2(\alpha_1 f_{,\zeta} - 2i\alpha_2 f_{,\bar\zeta}\psi_{,\zeta\zeta})_{,\bar\zeta} \\ &\qquad\qquad = 4i\rho(f_{,\zeta}\psi_{,\bar\zeta} - f_{,\bar\zeta}\psi_{,\zeta}) \\ &p_{0,\bar\zeta} + 2[\alpha_2 (f_{,\zeta} f_{,\bar\zeta} + 2\psi_{,\zeta\zeta}\psi_{,\bar\zeta\bar\zeta})]_{,\bar\zeta} + 2[i\alpha_1\psi_{,\bar\zeta\bar\zeta} + \alpha_2 (f_{,\bar\zeta})^2]_{,\zeta} \\ &\qquad\qquad = 2\rho(\psi_{,\zeta}\psi_{,\bar\zeta\bar\zeta} - \psi_{,\bar\zeta}\psi_{,\zeta\bar\zeta}) \end{aligned} \tag{68.21}$$

These are three equations (since the first equation is real, while the second ontains both real and imaginary parts) for the three unknown functions $p_0$, $f$, and $\psi$. The boundary condition required is the vanishing of the elocity on some closed curve $\mathcal{C}(\zeta, \bar{\zeta}) = 0$ in the $xy$ plane, i.e.,

$$f = 0 \qquad \psi_{,\zeta} = 0 \qquad \text{on } \mathcal{C}(\zeta, \bar{\zeta}) = 0 \tag{68.22}$$

The solution of (68.21) subject to (68.22) will be sought in the neighbor-ood of $\psi = 0$; i.e., we set

$$\psi = \epsilon\varphi + \cdots \qquad f = h + \epsilon g + \cdots \qquad \lambda = \lambda_0 + \epsilon\lambda_1 + \cdots \tag{68.23}$$

Green and Rivlin also choose a particular class of fluids in which

$$\alpha_1 = 2\mu \qquad \alpha_2 = \epsilon(c + \mathrm{II}) \tag{68.24}$$

here $\mu$ and $c$ are constants. From $(68.21)_2$ it follows that

$$p_0 = \epsilon p_1 + \cdots$$

ow the coefficients of 1 and of $\epsilon$ in $(68.21)_1$ and the coefficient of $\epsilon$ in 8.21)$_2$ are

$$\begin{aligned} &8\mu h_{,\zeta\bar{\zeta}} + \lambda_0 = 0 \\ &p_{1,\bar{\zeta}} + 4i\mu\varphi_{,\zeta\bar{\zeta}\bar{\zeta}} + 8(h_{,\zeta}{}^2 h_{,\bar{\zeta}}{}^2)_{,\bar{\zeta}} + 8(h_{,\zeta} h_{,\bar{\zeta}}{}^3)_{,\zeta} \\ &\qquad + 2c[(h_{,\zeta} h_{,\bar{\zeta}})_{,\bar{\zeta}} + (h_{,\bar{\zeta}}{}^2)_{,\zeta}] = 0 \\ &8\mu g_{,\zeta\bar{\zeta}} + \lambda_1 = 4i\rho(h_{,\zeta}\varphi_{,\bar{\zeta}} - h_{,\bar{\zeta}}\varphi_{,\zeta}) \end{aligned} \tag{68.25}$$

pon differentiating $(68.25)_2$ with respect to $\zeta$, subtracting it from its mplex conjugate, and using $(68.25)_1$, we get an equation for $\varphi$.

$$i\mu\varphi_{,\zeta\zeta\bar{\zeta}\bar{\zeta}} + (h_{,\zeta} h_{,\bar{\zeta}}{}^3)_{,\zeta\zeta} - (h_{,\bar{\zeta}} h_{,\zeta}{}^3)_{,\bar{\zeta}\bar{\zeta}} = 0 \tag{68.26}$$

We now give a solution of this equation for an elliptic tube with undary $\mathcal{C}$ given by

$$\frac{x^2}{a^2} + \frac{y^2}{b^2} = 1$$

complex coordinates this reads

$$(a^2 + b^2)\zeta\bar{\zeta} - \tfrac{1}{2}(a^2 - b^2)(\zeta^2 + \bar{\zeta}^2) - 2a^2b^2 = 0 \tag{68.27}$$

t this boundary we must have $h = \varphi_{,\zeta} = g = 0$.

Since $h = 0$ on the boundary, we try a solution of the form

$$h = A[(a^2 + b^2)\zeta\bar{\zeta} - \tfrac{1}{2}(a^2 - b^2)(\zeta^2 + \bar{\zeta}^2) - 2a^2b^2] \tag{68.28}$$

hich is found to satisfy (68.25), if

$$8\mu(a^2 + b^2)A = -\lambda_0 \tag{68.29}$$

bstitution of (68.28) into (68.26) gives

$$i\mu\varphi_{,\zeta\zeta\bar{\zeta}\bar{\zeta}} - 24A^4a^2b^2(a^4 - b^4)(\zeta^2 - \bar{\zeta}^2) = 0$$

A solution of this with $\varphi_{,\zeta}$ (hence $\varphi_{,\bar{\zeta}}$) vanishing on the boundary (68.27) i

$$(68.30) \quad i\,\mu\,\varphi = B\,[(a^2 + b^2)\,\zeta\,\bar{\zeta} - \tfrac{1}{2}\,(a^2 - b^2)\,(\zeta^2 + \bar{\zeta}^2) - 2\,a^2\,b^2]^2\,(\zeta^2 - \bar{\zeta}^2$$

provided

$$(68.31) \quad B[4\,(a^2 + b^2)^2 + (a^2 - b^2)^2] - 4\,A^4\,a^2\,b^2\,(a^4 - b^4) = 0$$

Using this, $\varphi$ may be expressed in real coordinates $x$, $y$ as:

$$(68.32) \quad \varphi = \frac{64\,A^4\,a^2\,b^2\,(a^4 - b^4)\,(b^2\,x^2 + a^2\,y^2 - a^2\,b^2)^2\,x\,y}{\mu\,[4\,(a^2 + b^2)^2 + (a^2 - b^2)^2]}$$

This represents a flow in the $xy$ plane whose streamlines $\varphi$ = const ar as shown in Fig. 68.1.

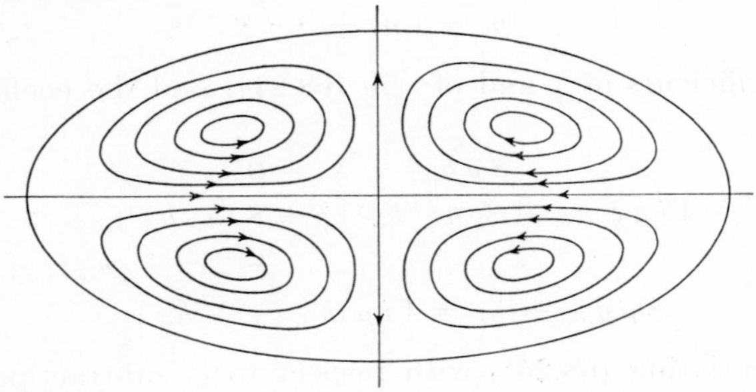

FIG. 68.1. Secondary flow in a tube with elliptical cross section ($\epsilon > 0$). (*After Gree and Rivlin* [1956])

This perturbation solution indicates the validity of the conjecture mad earlier. To complete the solution as far as terms of order $\epsilon$ are concerne one must further use (68.28) and (68.30) in $(68.25)_3$ and determine $g$ sub ject to the boundary condition $g = 0$ on $\mathfrak{C}$.

Using a more general theory of fluids proposed by Rivlin and Erickse Langlois [1957] has obtained solutions involving secondary flows in tub with boundaries of other shapes.

## 69. NAVIER-STOKES APPROXIMATION

Various polynomial approximations to the constitutive equations we given in Art. 49. Of these the most celebrated ones are the zeroth an first approximations. The zeroth approximation gives the ideal flo theory which is a subclass of the first-order approximation. The firs order approximation to the constitutive equations is

$$(69.1) \quad \begin{aligned} t^k{}_l &= (-\pi + \lambda_v\,\mathrm{I}_d)\,\delta^k{}_l + 2\,\mu_v\,d^k{}_l && \text{(compressible)} \\ t^k{}_l &= -p\,\delta^k{}_l + 2\,\mu_v\,d^k{}_l && \text{(incompressible)} \end{aligned}$$

Upon using $I_d = v^k{}_{;k}$, $2\,d^k{}_l = v^k{}_{;l} + v_l{}_;{}^k$ together with (69.1) in the equations of momentum balance (63.2), we obtain

$$\rho\left(\frac{\partial v_k}{\partial t} + v_{k;l}\,v^l\right) = \rho f_k - \pi_{,k} + (\lambda_v\, v^l{}_{;l})_{;k} + [\mu_v\,(v_{k;}{}^l + v^l{}_{;k})]_{;l} \quad \text{(compressible)}$$

(69.2)

$$\rho\left(\frac{\partial v_k}{\partial t} + v_{k;l}\,v^l\right) = \rho f_k - p_{,k} + [\mu_v\,(v_{k;}{}^l + v^l{}_{;k})]_{;l} \quad \text{(incompressible)}$$

These are the celebrated Navier-Stokes equations of the classical theory of viscous fluids. To determine the unknowns $v_k$, $\rho$, and $\pi$ for compressible fluids, we need to supply to $(69.2)_1$ the equation of mass conservation (63.1) and the equation of state (63.10). For the incompressible fluids $p$ is a primitive unknown of the theory, and to $(69.2)_2$ we need only add the incompressibility condition $I_d = 0$. We collect these equations below for constant $\lambda_v$ and $\mu_v$. For compressible fluids we have

(69.3) $$\rho\left(\frac{\partial v_k}{\partial t} + v_{k;l}\,v^l\right) = \rho f_k - \pi_{,k} + (\lambda_v + \mu_v)\, v^l{}_{;lk} + \mu_v\, v_{k;}{}^l{}_l$$

(69.4) $$\frac{\partial \rho}{\partial t} + (\rho\, v^k)_{;k} = 0$$

(69.5) $$\pi = \pi\,(\rho, \theta)$$

where $\theta$ is to be treated as a parameter. For incompressible fluids we have

(69.6) $$\rho\left(\frac{\partial v_k}{\partial t} + v_{k;l}\,v^l\right) = \rho f_k - p_{,k} + \mu_v\, v_{k;}{}^l{}_l$$

(69.7) $$v^k{}_{;k} = 0$$

In Art. 49 we also found that a necessary and sufficient condition for nonnegative dissipation is

(69.8)
$$3\,\lambda_v + 2\,\mu_v \geq 0 \qquad \mu_v \geq 0 \qquad \text{(compressible)}$$
$$\mu_v \geq 0 \qquad \text{(incompressible)}$$

Sometimes it is more convenient to employ the vector notation. By multiplying both sides of (69.3) and (69.1) by $\mathbf{g}^k$ and recalling the vector identity

$$v_{k;}{}^l{}_l\,\mathbf{g}^k = \text{grad}\, I_d - \text{curl}\,\mathbf{w}$$

where $\mathbf{w}$ is the vorticity vector, we may also write

$$\rho \frac{d\mathbf{v}}{dt} = \rho \mathbf{f} - \operatorname{grad} \pi + (\lambda_v + 2\,\mu_v) \operatorname{grad} \operatorname{div} \mathbf{v} - \mu_v \operatorname{curl} \operatorname{curl} \mathbf{v}$$

$$\frac{D\rho}{Dt} + \rho \operatorname{div} \mathbf{v} = 0 \tag{69.9}$$

$$\pi = \pi\,(\rho, \theta)$$

for compressible flow, and

$$\rho \frac{d\mathbf{v}}{dt} = \rho \mathbf{f} - \operatorname{grad} p + \mu_v \operatorname{grad} \operatorname{div} \mathbf{v} - \mu_v \operatorname{curl} \operatorname{curl} \mathbf{v} \tag{69.10}$$

$$\operatorname{div} \mathbf{v} = 0$$

for incompressible flow.

*Heat Conduction.* When the thermal changes are important, th constitutive coefficients become a function of $\theta$. In this case we have on more unknown than the number of equations. The additional equatio needed is supplied by the equation of entropy production together with a equation for heat conduction. In the present work the thermal problen has been purposely left out. By use of irreversible thermodynamica considerations it can be shown that *Fourier's heat conduction law* i compatible with the present approximations.[1] For isotropic media thi law is expressed as

$$\mathbf{q} = \kappa \operatorname{grad} \theta \tag{69.11}$$

where $\kappa$ is a scalar function of $|\operatorname{grad} \theta|$ and other thermodynamical vari ables. Upon substituting (69.11) into (40.15) for the nonpolar case an vanishing $\nu_\alpha$, we get

$$\rho\,\theta\,\dot{\eta} = {}_D t^{pq}\, d_{qp} + (\kappa\,\theta_{,}{}^{p})_{;p} + \rho h \tag{69.12}$$

In this case an equation of state

$$\epsilon = \epsilon \left(\eta, \frac{1}{\rho}\right) \tag{69.13}$$

is more convenient and replaces (69.5) so that

$$\pi = - \left.\frac{\partial \epsilon}{\partial\,(1/\rho)}\right|_{\eta = \text{const}} \qquad \theta = \left.\frac{\partial \epsilon}{\partial \eta}\right|_{1/\rho = \text{const}} \tag{69.14}$$

For a van der Waals gas, the equation of state

$$\pi = \frac{R\,\theta\,\rho}{1 - b\,\rho} - a\,\rho^2 \tag{69.15}$$

[1] For an irreversible thermodynamical approach see Eringen [1960, 1964].

vhere $R$, $a$, and $b$ are constants, has found both experimental and sta-
istical mechanical foundations. (For an *ideal gas* $a = b = 0$.) Through
Gibbs' equation $d\epsilon = -\pi\, d\,(1/\rho) + \theta\, d\eta$ and (69.15), one obtains

$$
\begin{aligned}
\epsilon &= \int c_v\, d\theta - a\,\rho + \text{const} \\
\eta &= R \ln\left(\frac{1}{\rho} - b\right) + \int c_v \frac{d\theta}{\theta} + \text{const}
\end{aligned}
\tag{69.16}
$$

vhere $c_v$ is the *specific heat at constant volume*, i.e.,

$$
c_v \equiv \left.\frac{\partial \epsilon}{\partial \theta}\right|_{1/\rho = \text{const}} = \theta \left.\frac{\partial \eta}{\partial \theta}\right|_{1/\rho = \text{const}}
\tag{69.17}
$$

vhich is found to be a constant for an ideal gas.

Using (69.16), (69.17), and the continuity equation (69.4) in (69.12), ve find

$$
\begin{aligned}
c_v\,\rho\,\dot{\theta} + R\,\rho\,\theta\,(1 - b\,\rho)^{-1} v^k{}_{;k} - (\kappa\,\theta_{,}{}^{k})_{;k} \\
= \lambda_v\,(d^k{}_k)^2 + 2\,\mu_v\,d^k{}_l\,d^l{}_k + \rho\,h
\end{aligned}
\tag{69.18}
$$

This is the additional equation required to supplement (69.3)–(69.5) or the determination of the unknowns. In the literature one often inds treatment of the ideal gas. This is obtained from (69.18) by further implifications $a = b = 0$, $\pi = \rho\,R\,\theta$, and $R = c_p - c_v$, where $c_p$ is the *pecific heat at constant pressure.* In this case (69.18) may be reduced to

$$
c_p\,\rho\,\dot{\theta} - \dot{\pi} - (\kappa\,\theta_{,}{}^{k})_{;k} = (\lambda_v + 2\,\mu_v)\,\mathrm{I}_d{}^2 - 4\,\mu_v\,\mathrm{II}_d + \rho\,h
\tag{69.19}
$$

Kinetic theory (cf. Chapman and Cowling [1952, chap. 13]) and xperimental evidence are in favor of the relation

$$
\frac{\mu_v\,c_p}{\kappa} = \text{const}
\tag{69.20}
$$

Known as the Prandtl number for an ideal gas with constant specific eats, this ratio usually takes values

$$
\frac{\mu_v\,c_p}{\kappa} = \tfrac{2}{3}, \tfrac{3}{4}, 0.72
\tag{69.21}
$$

espectively for monatomic gases, diatomic gases, and air.

In summary, (69.3), (69.4), (69.19), and (69.20) and the ideal-gas law $= \rho\,R\,\theta$ constitute the field equations of classical hydrodynamics of iscous-flow theory. Here the body force $\mathbf{f}$ and heat source $h$ are prescribed. The coefficients $\lambda_v$, $\mu_v$, $\kappa$, and $R$ are known from experimenta work or kinetic theory. The field equations supplemented with bound ary and initial conditions encompass nearly all work in hydrodynamics These equations are too complicated for exact solutions; therefore th literature is full of the treatment of special cases and approximat methods of analysis. It is because of the practical and classical impor tance of the Navier-Stokes theory that we have included this shor account.

## 70. EXPERIMENTAL INVESTIGATIONS

During the past two decades a number of significant experiments hav been carried out revealing nonnewtonian characteristics of fluids. Th main contributions of these experiments to our understanding are (1) to note some anomalous behavior of fluids beyond their newtonia character; (2) to construct rational theories explaining this unusua behavior; (3) to provide experimental evidence favoring certain theories (4) to measure the constitutive coefficients. Note that steps 1–4 con stitute the usual process of evolution of science rather than a superficia man-made method of research aimed at quick and efficient discovery. I fact, this order, while thorough, is highly inefficient. As in most case of new discoveries, the initial discoverer often fails to receive the appro priate credit on account of the difficulty in recognizing him in this connec tion. Among the various contributions to step 1 we find Merrington' [1943*b*] experiment on the determination of the stress–deformation-rat relation in a fluid flowing through a capillary tube (Fig. 65.1) into th atmosphere. As remarked in Art. 65, the swelling of fluid at the exit c the tube is certainly capable of pointing out the existence of a positiv second-order viscosity coefficient that is omitted in the newtonia theory. Merrington [1943*a*, *b*] has also measured shear stress versus rat of shear and noted the deviation of this relation from linearity. In thei experiments Garner and Nissan [1946], Wood et al. [1947], and Garner e al. [1950] have also noted deviations from the newtonian characteristics They have introduced a theory of two-component systems as a way c explaining the normal stress effects. According to this theory the liqui in a Couette viscometer should rise at the outer cylinder. This is in con flict, however, with experimental observations.

Among early significant observations of the Poynting effect (norm stress effect), the experiments carried out by Weissenberg [1946] an Reiner, Scott Blair, and Hawley [1959] appear to be most striking. I Weissenberg's experiments various types of liquids were sheared in a ga between an outer vessel rotated at various constant angular velociti and an inner cylinder that could be either fixed rigidly or moved up an down (Fig. 70.1).

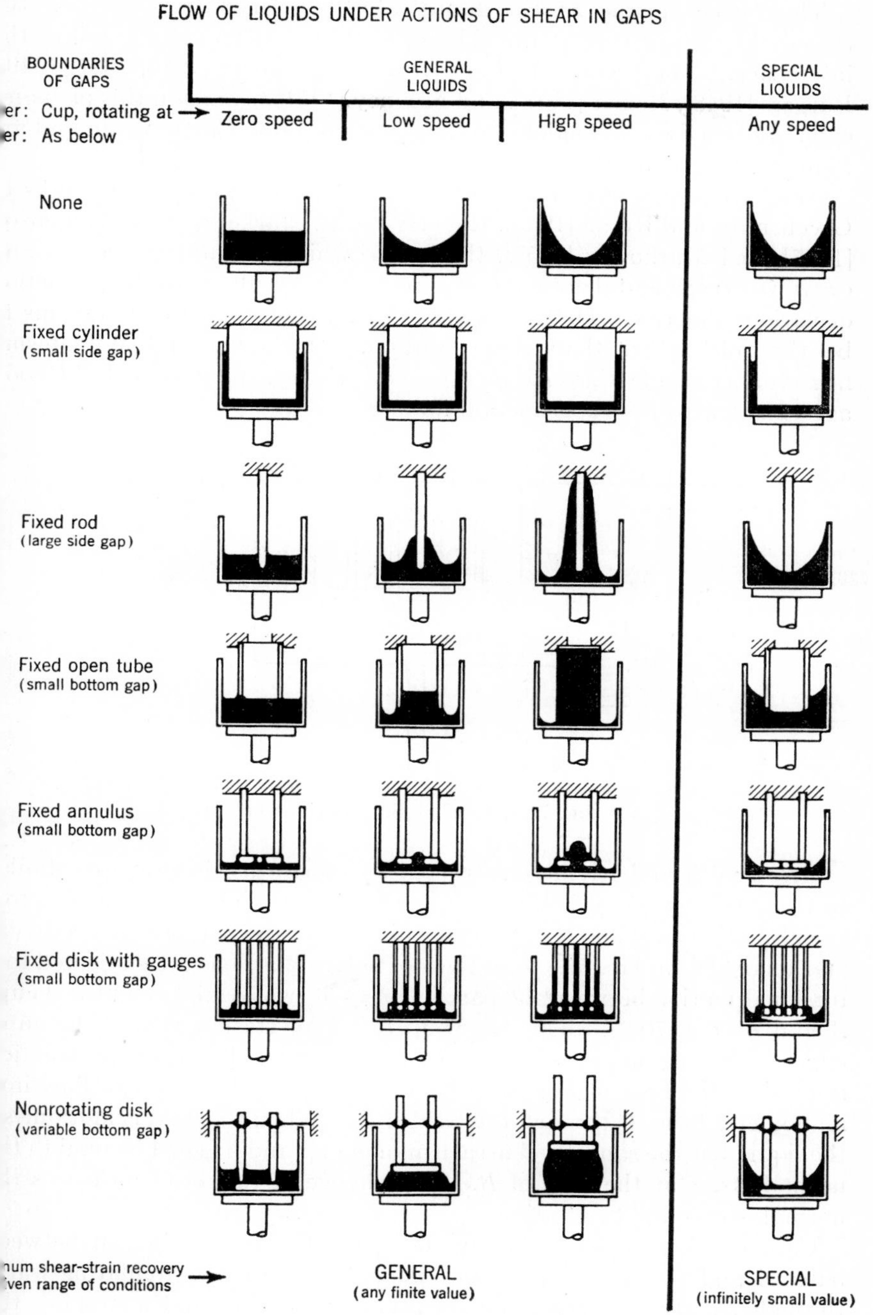


FIG. 70.1. (*After Weissenberg* [1949])

These experiments clearly demonstrate the normal stress effect by th rise of the free surface at the sides of both cylinders and the fall of th interspace. The theories introduced by Weissenberg [1946, 1947, 1949 Burgers [1948], Reiner [1948], and Mooney [1951] to explain this phenom enon are based on an analogy to the theory of finite elastic strain and ar found to be generally unsatisfactory.

Among quantitative experiments of significance we cite the works c Greensmith and Rivlin [1953], Roberts [1953], Markovitz and Williamso [1957], and Markovitz [1957], the last of which attempts to collect an organize experimental data and to compare the results with the predictio of various theories. Disagreement among various experiments seems t be the rule rather than the exception. Markovitz and Williamsor however, conclude that Rivlin's general viscoelastic theory is in goo agreement with the experimental findings.

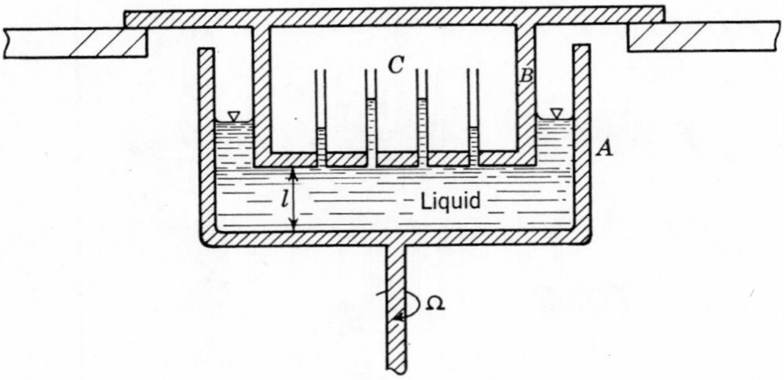


FIG. 70.2. Parallel-plate viscometer.

Greensmith and Rivlin constructed an apparatus, in principle simil to those employed by Weissenberg and Garner et al., to produce a to sional motion in a liquid approximating that of the parallel-plate viscom eter analyzed in Art. 67. Solutions of polyisobutylene are subjected to torsional motion between the parallel bases of two coaxial cylindrical cu $A$ and $B$ (Fig. 70.2). The inner cup $B$ is kept stationary and the out cup $A$ rotates at constant angular velocity. The surface tractio normal to the base of $B$ is measured by allowing the liquid to flow int manometer tubes $C$ through the base of $B$. When the fluid is motionles the liquid has the same level in each manometer and its head is equal to th normal stress at the base of $B$. The change of this head measures th normal stress due to rotation.

Care is taken to level the cup $B$, thus ensuring parallelism betwee bases $A$ and $B$. The temperature is kept constant by circulating wat through $B$. By changing the direction of rotation and averaging th eadings, the effect of any possible nonparallelism of the cup bases is liminated. In addition, corrections for centrifugal force and edge effect re made. The measurement is based on the expression of the normal tress $t^z{}_z$ given by $(67.8)_2$, i.e.,

$$t^z{}_z = \tfrac{1}{4}\,\omega'^2 \left(r^2\,\alpha_2 + \int_a^r r\,\alpha_2\,dr\right) \tag{70.1}$$

Since $t^z{}_z$ is not zero at any radius $r = a$, there exists a uniform normal ressure ${}_0t^z{}_z$ exerted by the fluid outside the radius $r = a$. (The radius is aken somewhat smaller than the outer radius of the cup $B$ so that the dge effect can be minimized.) Thus one may modify (70.1) for this oundary condition to

$$t^z{}_z - {}_0t^z{}_z = \tfrac{1}{4}\,\omega'^2 \left(r^2\,\alpha_2 + \int_a^r r\,\alpha_2\,dr\right) \tag{70.2}$$

The measured mean heights of rise $\bar{h}$ of the liquid in the manometer ubes, after corrections for centrifugal effects, may be expressed as

$$\rho\,g\,(\bar{h} - \bar{h}_0) = -\tfrac{1}{4}\,\omega'^2\,r^2\,\alpha_2 - \tfrac{1}{4}\,\omega'^2 \int_0^r r\,\alpha_2\,dr \tag{70.3}$$

here $\rho$ is the density of the liquid, $g$ is the gravitational acceleration, and $_0$ is defined by

$$\rho\,g\,\bar{h}_0 = -\,{}_0t^z{}_z + \tfrac{1}{4}\,\omega'^2 \int_0^a r\,\alpha_2\,dr \tag{70.4}$$

o that $-\rho\,g\,\bar{h}_0$ is the normal surface traction at $r = 0$. Since the ngular velocity is constant, we write

$$\omega' = \frac{\pi\,\Omega}{30\,l} \tag{70.5}$$

here $\Omega$ is the angular velocity of cup $A$ measured in rpm and $l$ is the istance between the bases of the inner and outer cups. Now (70.3) reads

$$\rho\,g\,(\bar{h} - \bar{h}_0) = -\frac{\pi^2}{3600}\left(\frac{\Omega}{l}\right)^2 \left(r^2\,\alpha_2 + \int_0^r r\,\alpha_2\,dr\right) \tag{70.6}$$

here $\alpha_2 = \alpha_2\,(\mathrm{II})$ with II given by

$$\mathrm{II} = -\frac{\pi^2}{3600}\left(\frac{\Omega\,r}{l}\right)^2 \tag{70.7}$$

By measuring $\bar{h}$ at various radial distances $r$ for various values of $\Omega$ and for fixed $l = 1.85$ mm, Fig. 70.3 was obtained. In this figure, successiv curves are shifted $\frac{1}{2}$ cm. parallel to the ordinate for clear display. From these curves the values $\bar{h}_0 - \bar{h}$ were obtained and plotted against $\Omega r$ in Fig. 70.4. By changing the values of $l$ and repeating the measurements plots of $h$ versus $r$ for various values of $\Omega$ and $l$ were made. From thes $\bar{h}_0 - \bar{h}$ was obtained as a function of $\Omega r/l$ shown in Fig. 70.5.

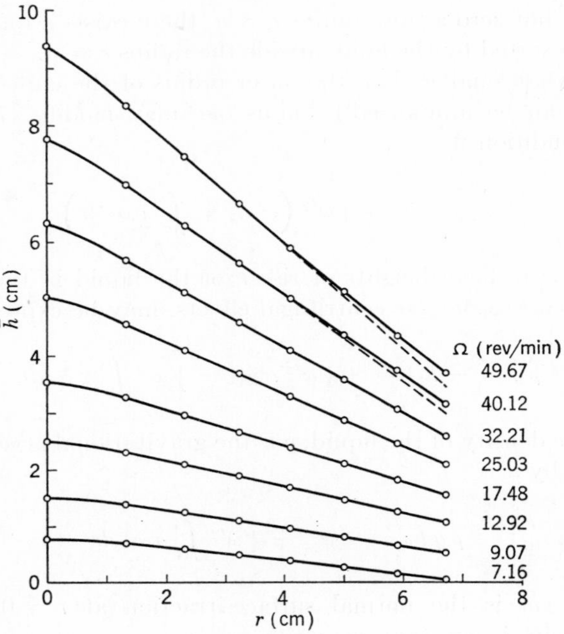


FIG. 70.3. $\bar{h}$ against $r$ relations, for various values of $\Omega$, for 6 per cent B120 polyiso butylene solution. $l = 1.85$ mm. (*After Greensmith and Rivlin* [1953])

To determine the normal stress coefficient $\alpha_2$, by using (70.6) and (70.7) we solve for $\alpha_2$

$$\text{(70.8)} \qquad \alpha_2 = \rho g \left[ -\frac{1}{\text{II}} (\bar{h}_0 - \bar{h}) + \tfrac{1}{2} (-\text{II})^{-\frac{3}{2}} \int_0^{-\text{II}} (-\text{II})^{-\frac{1}{2}} (\bar{h}_0 - \bar{h})\, d\text{II}\right.$$

From Figs. 70.4 and 70.5 one observes that $\bar{h}$ is linear over most of th range of $r$ except near the origin $r = 0$ and at higher values of $\Omega$. Thus writing

$$\text{(70.9)} \qquad \bar{h}_0 - \bar{h} = \alpha + \beta \sqrt{-\text{II}}$$

in (70.8) one finds

$$\alpha_2 = a_2 \sqrt{-\text{II}} \qquad (a_2 = \tfrac{1}{2} \rho g \beta = 15 \text{ dyne sec/cm}^2)$$

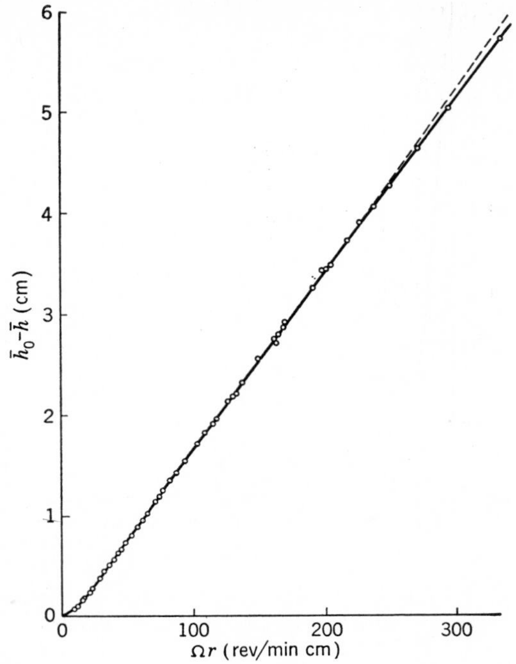


FIG. 70.4. Relation between $(\bar{h}_0 - \bar{h})$ and $\Omega r$ obtained from curves of Fig. 70.3. (*After Greensmith and Rivlin* [1953])

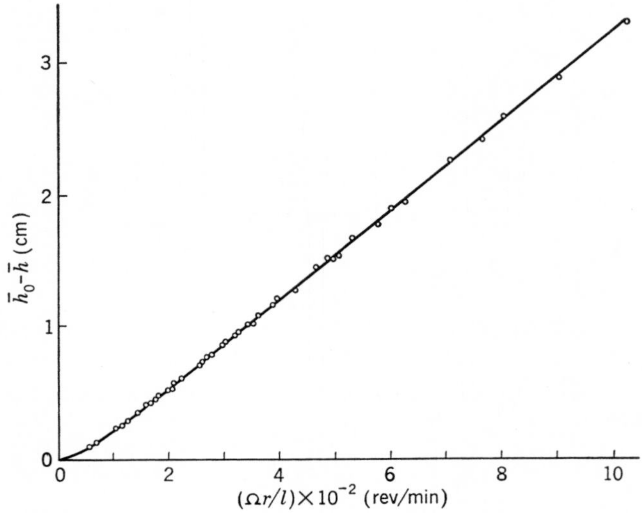


FIG. 70.5. Relation between $(\bar{h}_0 - \bar{h})$ and $\Omega r/l$. (*After Greensmith and Rivlin* [1953])

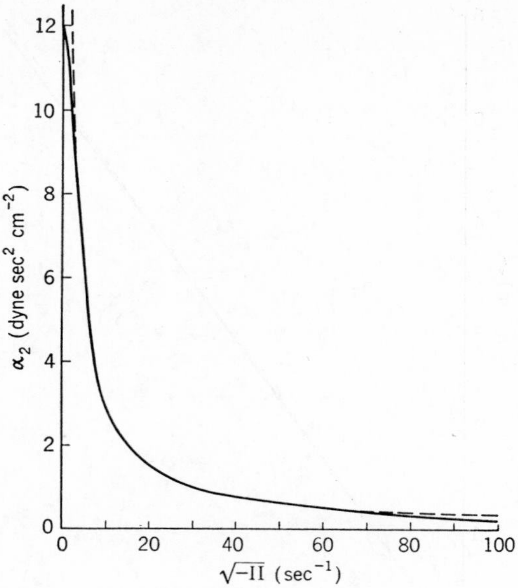


FIG. 70.6. Schematic diagram of relation between $\alpha_2$ and $\sqrt{-\text{II}}$ for 6 per cent B120 polyisobutylene solution. (*After Greensmith and Rivlin* [1953])

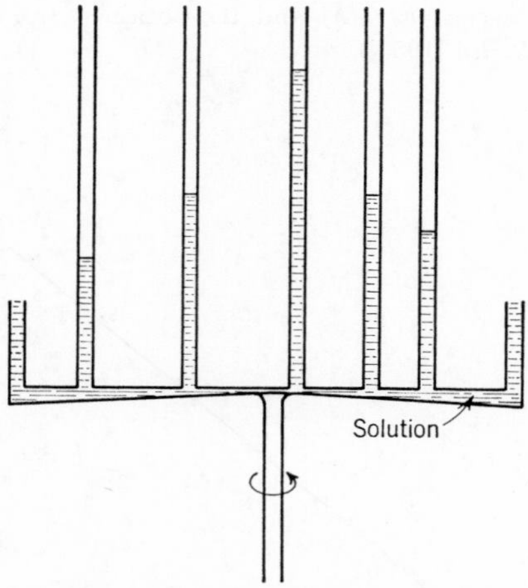


FIG. 70.7. A schematic diagram of cone and plate instrument for normal stress measurements. (*After Markovitz and Williamson* [1957])

Greensmith and Rivlin have also examined the regions in which $\bar{h}$ departs from linearity and obtained the schematic dependence shown in Fig. 70.6.

These experiments again indicate that the fluid rises in the center, gradually decreasing with $r$, as observed earlier by Weissenberg and others.

The recent experimental works of Markovitz and of Markovitz and Williamson used an apparatus similar to the above except that the polyisobutylene solutions were sheared by a conical surface rotating beneath a stationary plane (Fig. 70.7). The angle between the plane and the generator of the cone was about 4°. Different theories were examined. The experimental results were in close agreement with those of Greensmith and Rivlin. Theoretical work on more general viscoelastic fluids initiated by Rivlin [1956][1] was used for the parallel-plate viscometer. The result of this theory appears to be in close correlation with the experimental work of Markovitz and Williamson.

In spite of these serious attempts at organized experimental work, much remains to be done experimentally.

[1] See Art. 98.

# 8
# HYPOELASTICITY

## 71. SCOPE OF THE CHAPTER

Hypoelasticity is intended to explain the behavior of solid bodies with a short memory. It allows the prescription of arbitrary initial stress and permits the theoretical prediction of yield phenomena, although this latter claim is subject to some controversy. In the structure of the constitutive equations (which are now partial differential equations) the concept of stress rate plays an essential role. Article 72 is devoted to various definitions of stress rates. Constitutive equations and the definition of hypoelastic solids are given in Art. 73 and classified into various grades. After collecting the basic field equations of this novel theory in Art. 74, we bring out in Art. 75 the relation of hypoelasticity to elasticity. The remaining part of the chapter is devoted to various simple solutions.

Accelerationless motion, so trivial in lagrangian language, presents difficulties worthy of attention. Since all statical problems employ this assumption, study of it is necessary and is presented in Art. 76. Next we give an account of stress without flux in Art. 77. Static homogeneous stress and hypoelastic shear are dealt with in Arts. 78 and 79. Here for the first time we see that this rich theory can, from the solution of particular problems, predict a variety of stress-strain laws. The condensation and rarefaction of solid materials under hydrostatic pressure and the yield stress under shear arise as the result of the theory. A statical theory of simple extension is studied in Art. 80 and a dynamical theory in Art. 81. Here again we encounter the yield and failure phenomena and show how the statical theory can lead into major errors in a theory that is built on dynamical grounds.

Presently, plasticity theory is based on various yield criteria and approximate constitutive equations. The relation of this theory to hypoelasticity is postponed to the end of the next chapter, after we become acquainted with the theory of plasticity. For an example of a comparative study of hypoelastic and plastic yield in simple shear we refer the reader to Art. 90.

Hypoelasticity is now in its infancy. The lack of existence and uniqueness theorems and experimental work in this area represent the basic needs for further development.

## 72. STRESS RATE

In Arts. 45 and 46 we have seen that the constitutive equations of ideally elastic bodies may be expressed as

(72.1) stress $= f$ (strain from an unstressed state)

For a stokesian fluid, on the other hand, the constitutive equations are written as (Art. 48)

(72.2) stress $= f$ (deformation rate)

According to (72.1) an ideally elastic body has a *memory* of its initial state. According to (72.2) a stokesian fluid has no memory of its past. A mechanical medium in general will have some memory of its past, although not necessarily that of a particularly selected state. As the motion takes place, the state that the medium will remember may change. For a class of materials the state that the material has just passed is more likely remembered than the initial state occupied long ago. With this view Truesdell [1955*a*] introduced the simplest rate theory of pure elasticity by a constitutive equation of the form

stress increment $= f$ (strain increment)

which in a more precise form reads

(72.3) rate of stress $= f$ (rate of deformation)

The rate of deformation is a well-defined quantity, namely, $d_{kl} \equiv v_{(k;l)}$. What are we to use for the rate of stress? It is not difficult to show that the material derivative of the stress tensor,

$$\dot{t}^k{}_l \equiv \frac{Dt^k{}_l}{Dt} = \frac{\partial t^k{}_l}{\partial t} + t^k{}_{l;m}\, v^m \tag{72.4}$$

*cannot* be used on the left of (72.3). The reason for this is that in a rigid motion the right side of (72.3) is constant; therefore, if $\dot{t}^k{}_l$ were used on the left of (72.3), we would have the stress tensor unchanged. The fact that this is dynamically absurd can be seen from the following consideration: a bar in simple tension $t_{xx} = k \neq 0$, $t_{yy} = 0$ lying along the $x$ axis (Fig. 72.1*a*) after a rigid rotation of 90° about the $z$ axis will have $t_{xx} = 0$,

$t_{yy} = k$ (Fig. 72.1$b$). We therefore see that a rigid motion will in general change not only the stress tensor but also the stress vector.

To remedy this situation, we ask help from the principle of objectivity (Art. 27). By use of this axiom we found (Art. 35) that a tensor called the *stress flux*, defined by (35.5), satisfies the axiom of objectivity, i.e.,

$$\hat{t}^k{}_l = \dot{t}^k{}_l + t^k{}_m w^m{}_l - t^m{}_l w^k{}_m \tag{72.5}$$

The use of the stress flux so defined on the left of (72.3) is consistent with the principles of dynamics. It should be pointed out immediately that the choice is by no means unique. In fact, in that article we have already given four other possible expressions (35.6) for stress flux. Further, since

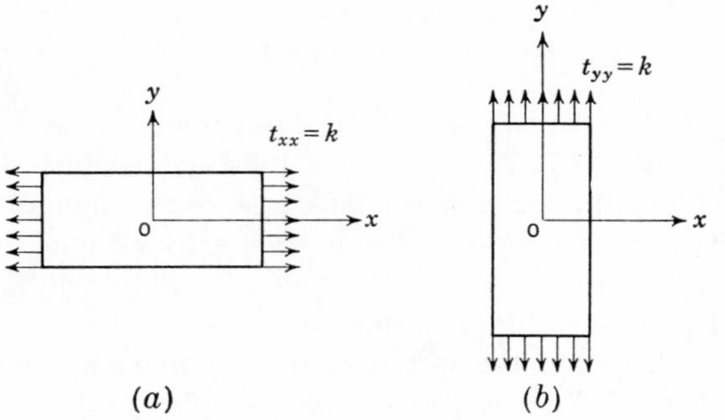


FIG. 72.1. ($a$) Bar in simple tension before rigid rotation. ($b$) Bar in simple tension after rigid rotation.

upon a rigid motion $d_{kl} = 0$ and $\hat{t}^k{}_l$ is not affected by the presence of a term containing $d_{kl}$, we may add to the right of (72.5) any function of $d_{kl}$ without violating the principle of objectivity.

The stress flux (72.5) given above is based on Noll's [1955] derivation. It was derived earlier, however, by Jaumann [1911] in a different way. There exist several other different derivations.[1] We give two other forms, one derived and used by Truesdell and the other by Oldroyd.

A vector $\mathbf{b}(\mathbf{x}, t)$ is invariant under the motion $x^k = x^k(\mathbf{X}, t)$ if $b^k$ transform as the components of a contravariant vector when the motion is regarded as a coordinate transformation, i.e.,

$$b^k = x^k{}_{,K} B^K(\mathbf{X}) \tag{72.6}$$

[1] Following the original work of Truesdell [1955$a$, $b$], several other authors gave other derivations and raised the question of priority on the definition of stress rate. Priority may be attributed to Cauchy [1829] and Zaremba [1903$b$]. Jaumann [1911] gave an independent definition. By use of convected coordinates Oldroyd [1950] obtained another definition. Cotter and Rivlin [1955] and Thomas [1955$a$, $b$] found still other approaches. The freedom of choice of the stress rate cannot be restricted without reference to constitutive equations or additional physical postulates.

We take the material derivative of this expression

$$\dot{b}^k = \frac{D}{Dt}(x^k{}_{,K})\, B^K = v^k{}_{;l}\, x^l{}_{,K}\, B^K = v^k{}_{;l}\, b^l$$

and conversely, if this holds, by integration we get (72.6).

Thus, if we define the *absolute time flux* $\mathbf{b}'$ of $\mathbf{b}$ by

(72.7) $$b'^k \equiv \dot{b}^k - v^k{}_{;l}\, b^l$$

we see that *a vector field is invariant under the motion if and only if its time flux vanishes.* We now apply this lemma.

$$(t^{kl}\, da_l)' = \frac{D}{Dt}(t^{kl}\, da_l) - v^k{}_{;m}\, t^{ml}\, da_l$$

$$= \dot{t}^{kl}\, da_l + t^{kl}\frac{D}{Dt}(da_l) - v^k{}_{;m}\, t^{ml}\, da_l$$

Using (19.9) in this expression, we may write

(72.8) $$(t^{kl}\, da_l)' = \check{t}^{kl}\, da_l$$

where

(72.9) $$\check{t}^{kl} \equiv \dot{t}^{kl} - t^{km}\, v^l{}_{;m} - t^{ml}\, v^k{}_{;m} + t^{kl}\, v^m{}_{;m}$$

It therefore appears compatible with the principles of dynamics to take the rate of stress as the quantity defined by (72.9).[2] This is the Truesdell stress rate.[3]

THEOREM. *The necessary and sufficient condition for the Piola-Kirchhoff stress tensor to be stationary in an arbitrary motion is that the Truesdell stress rate vanish.*

According to (34.7) we have

$$\frac{D}{Dt} T^{KL}(\mathbf{X}, t) = \frac{\partial T^{KL}}{\partial t} = \frac{D}{Dt}(J\, X^K{}_{,k}\, X^L{}_{,l}\, t^{kl})$$

$$= \dot{J}\, X^K{}_{,k}\, X^L{}_{,l}\, t^{kl} + J\frac{D}{Dt}(X^K{}_{,k})\, X^L{}_{,l}\, t^{kl}$$

$$+ J\, X^K{}_{,k}\frac{D}{Dt}(X^L{}_{,l})\, t^{kl} + J\, X^K{}_{,k}\, X^L{}_{,l}\, \dot{t}^{kl}$$

[2] If this method is applied to $t_{kl}$, a different form of stress rate results. The reason for this is that there is no invariant metric for the motion $x^k = x^k(\mathbf{X}, t)$, so that covariant and contravariant vectors with respect to it are different and are unrelated. The use of contravariant vectors is suggested by the fact that the stress vector is a force field rather than a field of plane elements.

[3] To avoid confusion with the infinitesimal strain $\tilde{e}^{kl}$ using "~", here we employ "ˇ" to denote Truesdell's stress rate $\check{t}^{kl}$ in place of his notation $\tilde{t}^{kl}$.

Now use expressions (19.2) and (19.7) to reduce this to

$$\frac{\partial T^{KL}}{\partial t} = \check{t}^{kl} J X^K{}_{,k} X^L{}_{,l} \tag{72.10}$$

Since $J \neq 0$ and the motion is arbitrary so that $X^K{}_{,k} \neq 0$ for the vanishing of this time rate, the only possibility is $\check{t}^{kl} = 0$. Hence the proof of the theorem.

Oldroyd [1950] introduces a stress tensor which is the same as our $T^{KL}/J$. We may arrive at Oldroyd's stress rate by applying the present theorem to $T^{KL}/J$ in place of $T^{KL}$. This gives

$$\mathring{t}^{kl} = \dot{t}^{kl} - t^{km} v^l{}_{;m} - t^{ml} v^k{}_{;m} \tag{72.11}$$

The difference between this and (72.9) is the missing last term of the latter. This term is the contribution of $\dot{J}$ in the foregoing theorem.

The use of any one of these stress rates in the constitutive equations of hypoelasticity does not produce essential differences (see the remark in Art. 73). Therefore we agree to use $\hat{\mathbf{t}}$ in the development to mean any one of $\check{\mathbf{t}}$, $\hat{\mathbf{t}}$, and $\mathring{\mathbf{t}}$.

## 73. CONSTITUTIVE EQUATIONS

The constitutive equation proposed by (72.3) is a special case of

$$\hat{\mathbf{s}} = \mathbf{f}(\mathbf{d}, \mathbf{s}) \qquad \mathbf{s} \equiv \frac{\mathbf{t}}{2\mu} \tag{73.1}$$

where $\mu$ is the elastic shear modulus. These equations must satisfy all invariance requirements. In this general tensorial form we see that material objectivity, material isomorphism, and dimensional invariance are the ones that are not satisfied. Material objectivity requires that $\hat{\mathbf{s}}$, $\mathbf{d}$, $\mathbf{s}$ in two objectively equivalent motions $\mathbf{x}$ and $\mathbf{x}'$ must have the same functional dependence as in (73.1). Let $\hat{\mathbf{s}}'$, $\mathbf{d}'$, $\mathbf{s}'$ be the stress rate, deformation rate, and the stress in a motion $\mathbf{x}'$ objectively equivalent to $\mathbf{x}$, i.e.,

$$x'^k = Q^k{}_l(t)\, x^l + b^k(t) \qquad Q^k{}_l\, Q_m{}^l = Q^l{}_m\, Q_l{}^k = \delta^k{}_m \tag{73.2}$$

Now using the matrix equivalents of (35.2) and (27.12), which are valid in general coordinates, for brevity, we have

$$\hat{\mathbf{s}}' = \mathbf{Q}\,\hat{\mathbf{s}}\,\mathbf{Q}^{-1} \qquad \mathbf{d}' = \mathbf{Q}\,\mathbf{d}\,\mathbf{Q}^{-1} \qquad \mathbf{s}' = \mathbf{Q}\,\mathbf{s}\,\mathbf{Q}^{-1} \tag{73.3}$$

The principle of objectivity demands that we have

$$\hat{\mathbf{s}}' = \mathbf{f}(\mathbf{d}', \mathbf{s}') \tag{73.4}$$

where $\mathbf{f}$ is the same function as in (73.1). Substituting from (73.3), this becomes

$$\mathbf{Q}\,\hat{\mathbf{s}}\,\mathbf{Q}^{-1} = \mathbf{f}\,(\mathbf{Q}\,\mathbf{d}\,\mathbf{Q}^{-1}, \mathbf{Q}\,\mathbf{s}\,\mathbf{Q}^{-1}) = \mathbf{Q}\,\mathbf{f}\,(\mathbf{d}, \mathbf{s})\,\mathbf{Q}^{-1} \tag{73.5}$$

or

$$\mathbf{Q}\,\mathbf{f}\,(\mathbf{d}, \mathbf{s})\,\mathbf{Q}^{-1} = \mathbf{f}\,(\mathbf{Q}\,\mathbf{d}\,\mathbf{Q}^{-1}, \mathbf{Q}\,\mathbf{s}\,\mathbf{Q}^{-1}) \tag{73.6}$$

i.e., $\mathbf{f}$ is a hemitropic function of $\mathbf{d}$ and $\mathbf{s}$. By assuming that $\mathbf{f}$ is independent of the material descriptors, we exclude anisotropic media, thus satisfying material objectivity for isotropic bodies. Now according to a result of Rivlin [1955*a*, art. 10] a hemitropic polynomial $\mathbf{f}$ of two tensor variables $\mathbf{d}$ and $\mathbf{s}$ admits a representation of the form

$$\begin{aligned}\mathbf{f}\,(\mathbf{d}, \mathbf{s}) = {} & a_{00}\,\mathbf{I} + a_{10}\,\mathbf{d} + a_{20}\,\mathbf{d}^2 + a_{01}\,\mathbf{s} + a_{02}\,\mathbf{s}^2 \\ & + a_{11}\,(\mathbf{s}\,\mathbf{d} + \mathbf{d}\,\mathbf{s}) + a_{12}\,(\mathbf{s}^2\,\mathbf{d} + \mathbf{d}\,\mathbf{s}^2) \\ & + a_{21}\,(\mathbf{s}\,\mathbf{d}^2 + \mathbf{d}^2\,\mathbf{s}) + a_{22}\,(\mathbf{s}^2\,\mathbf{d}^2 + \mathbf{d}^2\,\mathbf{s}^2)\end{aligned} \tag{73.7}$$

where $a_{\alpha\beta}$ are analytic scalar functions of $\mathbf{d}$ and $\mathbf{s}$.

A quick derivation for this result may be made as follows. Suppose that $\mathbf{f}$ is a hemitropic polynomial of two symmetric tensors $\mathbf{d}$ and $\mathbf{s}$. According to the Cayley-Hamilton theorem we have

$$\mathbf{d}^3 = \mathrm{I}_d\,\mathbf{d}^2 - \mathrm{II}_d\,\mathbf{d} + \mathrm{III}_d \qquad \mathbf{s}^3 = \mathrm{I}_s\,\mathbf{s}^2 - \mathrm{II}_s\,\mathbf{s} + \mathrm{III}_s \tag{73.8}$$

By the use of these expressions, all powers of $\mathbf{d}$ and $\mathbf{s}$ exceeding the second may be eliminated to obtain (73.7). It is clear from this brief derivation that the coefficients $a_{\alpha\beta}$ are scalar functions of the ten invariants $\mathrm{I}_d$, $\mathrm{II}_d$, $\mathrm{III}_d$, $\mathrm{I}_s$, $\mathrm{II}_s$, $\mathrm{III}_s$, $M$, $N$, $P$, and $Q$, of which the last four are the joint invariants defined as

$$\begin{aligned} M &\equiv s^k{}_l\,d^l{}_k & \qquad N &\equiv s^k{}_l\,s^l{}_m\,d^m{}_k \\ P &\equiv s^k{}_l\,d^l{}_m\,d^m{}_k & \qquad Q &\equiv s^k{}_l\,s^l{}_m\,d^m{}_n\,d^n{}_k \end{aligned} \tag{73.9}$$

Hypoelastic materials are further restricted with additional hypotheses, given below.

HYPOTHESIS 1 OF HYPOELASTICITY. *No constitutive coefficients of a hypoelastic material shall carry a dimension independent of the dimension of stress.* Here for the first time we encounter the importance of the principle of dimensional invariance. For materials having no symmetries, the constitutive moduli are tensors rather than scalars. The hypothesis of hypoelasticity dictates that the physical components of dimensional constitutive moduli shall carry the dimension of [stress]$^\alpha$ for some $\alpha$. In particular the absence of a modulus of dimension time $T$ eliminates the so-called "relaxation effect." Since $\hat{\mathbf{s}}$ and $\mathbf{d}$ are of dimensions $T^{-1}$, constitutive equation (73.1) must reduce to the form

$$\hat{s}^k{}_l = A^k{}_l{}^m{}_n\,d^n{}_m \tag{73.10}$$

where $A^k{}_l{}^m{}_n$ is a dimensionless function of $\mathbf{s}$. It now is clear that in (73.7) all terms containing second and higher powers of $\mathbf{d}$ must vanish. Thus we must have $a_{20} \equiv a_{21} \equiv 0$; $a_{10}$, $a_{11}$, and $a_{12}$ must be independent of $\mathbf{d}$ and so functions of $\mathbf{s}$ alone; and $a_{00}$, $a_{01}$, and $a_{02}$ must be of degree one in the components $d_{kl}$. Set

$$\delta \equiv \mathrm{I}_d = d^k{}_k \tag{73.11}$$

Then since $a_{\beta\gamma}$ also must be power series in $\mathbf{s}$, (73.7) may be reduced to

$$\begin{aligned}\hat{\mathbf{s}} = {} & \delta\,\alpha_0\,\mathbf{I} + \alpha_1\,\mathbf{d} + \delta\,\alpha_2\,\mathbf{s} + M\,\alpha_3\,\mathbf{I} + \tfrac{1}{2}\,\alpha_4\,(\mathbf{d}\,\mathbf{s} + \mathbf{s}\,\mathbf{d}) \\ & + \delta\,\alpha_5\,\mathbf{s}^2 + M\,\alpha_6\,\mathbf{s} + N\,\alpha_7\,\mathbf{I} + \tfrac{1}{2}\,\alpha_8\,(\mathbf{d}\,\mathbf{s}^2 + \mathbf{s}^2\,\mathbf{d}) \\ & + M\,\alpha_9\,\mathbf{s}^2 + N\,\alpha_{10}\,\mathbf{s} + N\,\alpha_{11}\,\mathbf{s}^2 \qquad \text{(compressible)}\end{aligned} \tag{73.12}$$

where $\alpha_\gamma$ are dimensionless analytic functions of the three principal invariants of $\mathbf{s}$:

$$\alpha_\gamma = \alpha_\gamma\,(\mathrm{I}_s, \mathrm{II}_s, \mathrm{III}_s) \tag{73.13}$$

For incompressible media $\delta \equiv 0$. Like other continuum models, the flux of $\mathbf{s} + (p/2\,\mu)\,\mathbf{I}$, namely, $\hat{\mathbf{s}} + \dfrac{\dot{p}}{2\mu}\,\mathbf{I} - \dfrac{p}{\mu}\,\mathbf{d}$, must now be written in place of $\hat{\mathbf{s}}$, where $p$ is an arbitrary pressure. Thus

$$\begin{aligned}\hat{\mathbf{s}} = {} & -\frac{\dot{p}}{2\,\mu}\,\mathbf{I} + \left(\alpha_1 + \frac{p}{\mu}\right)\mathbf{d} + \tfrac{1}{2}\,\alpha_4\,(\mathbf{d}\,\mathbf{s} + \mathbf{s}\,\mathbf{d}) + (\alpha_3\,M + \alpha_7\,N)\,\mathbf{I} \\ & + (\alpha_6\,M + \alpha_{10}\,N)\,\mathbf{s} + (\alpha_9\,M + \alpha_{11}\,N)\,\mathbf{s}^2 \\ & + \tfrac{1}{2}\,\alpha_8\,(\mathbf{d}\,\mathbf{s}^2 + \mathbf{s}^2\,\mathbf{d}) \qquad \text{(incompressible)}\end{aligned} \tag{73.14}$$

To include the classical theory of elasticity as a special case in the first approximation, we further agree to take

$$\alpha_1\,(0, 0, 0) = 1 \qquad \alpha_0\,(0, 0, 0) = \frac{\lambda}{2\,\mu} = \frac{\nu}{1 - \nu} \tag{73.15}$$

Here $\lambda$, $\mu$ are Lamé constants and $\nu$ is the Poisson ratio.

HYPOTHESIS 2 OF HYPOELASTICITY. The constitutive equations of hypoelasticity (73.10) are differential equations of first order. It is clear that for a unique solution of these equations we must prescribe some initial conditions which are admissible according to a *well-set* criterion. The natural initial conditions suggested by these equations are the prescription of the stress tensor at an initial time. The question arises, however, as to whether the initial stress can be prescribed without any stipulation of admissibility, as may be seen from the following consideration. Suppose that the initial stress is the one that occurs in an elastic solid. We know that in this case the stress must satisfy the compatibility conditions. A second example discovered by Bernstein

[1960*a*, *b*] is the particular case in which

$$2\,\mu\, A^{k}{}_{l}{}^{m}{}_{n} = -\tfrac{1}{3}\, t^{r}{}_{r}\, \delta^{k}{}_{l}\, \delta^{m}{}_{n}$$

For this case the constitutive differential equations written in rectangular coordinates read

$$\dot{t}_{kl} = t_{km}\, w_{lm} + t_{ml}\, w_{km} - \tfrac{1}{3}\, t_{rr}\, d_{mm}\, \delta_{kl} \tag{73.16}$$

One set of solutions of these equations is

$$t_{kl} = -a\,\rho\,\delta_{kl} \tag{73.17}$$

where $a$ is an arbitrary constant. Thus, if the stress initially is a hydrostatic pressure with an assigned value $a\,\rho$, we have obtained, by the theorem of uniqueness, the solution predicting a state of hydrostatic pressure forever. If the stress is once not a hydrostatic pressure, it can never become one during any motion. Hence (73.10) implies two essentially different materials, one for which shear must vanish and the other for which shear cannot vanish. Motivated by this consideration, Bernstein added a general hypothesis to complete the definition of hypoelastic materials as follows. Let $\mathcal{V}$ be a smooth manifold of material points over which we assign a stress field $t_{kl}$ and a displacement gradient function $x^{k}{}_{,K}\,(\mathbf{X})$ subject to compatibility conditions

$$\frac{\partial x^{k}{}_{,K}}{\partial X^{L}} = \frac{\partial x^{k}{}_{,L}}{\partial X^{K}} \tag{73.18}$$

The class of *stress-displacement pairs* in $\mathcal{V}$

$$[t_{kl},\, x^{k}{}_{,K}]$$

that can be obtained from continuous piecewise smooth functions

$$t_{kl}\,(\mathbf{X}, t) \qquad x^{k}{}_{,K}\,(\mathbf{X}, t) \qquad (\mathbf{X} \in \mathcal{V},\, t_1 \le t \le t_2)$$

by evaluating them at some values of $t$ in the interval $(t_1, t_2)$ constitutes a *stress-configuration* class for a hypoelastic material. The stress-configuration classes are said to be equivalent if they can be obtained from one class by a transformation of material coordinates $X^K$. *A hypoelastic material is defined over an equivalence class of stress-configuration classes.* This hypothesis or something equivalent to it makes it possible to define uniquely the material behavior which is left incomplete if solely prescribed by the constitutive differential equations (73.10). A hypoelastic material may now be defined as follows.

DEFINITION. *A hypoelastic material is defined by the assignment of a set of constitutive differential equations* (73.10) *and a corresponding equivalence class of stress-configuration classes. By a representation of a hypoelastic material is meant an assignment of a set of equations* (73.10) *and a corresponding stress-configuration class.*

It is of interest to note that for a Cauchy-elastic material we have $\mathbf{t} = \mathbf{f}\,(x^k{}_{,K}, \mathbf{X})$; hence the equivalence classes are the different representations of $\mathbf{f}$ since, given $\mathbf{f}$ and $x^k{}_{,K}$, we have $\mathbf{t}$ defined at $\mathbf{X}$. Therefore the foregoing definition of a material and its representation is consistent with the corresponding ones for Cauchy-elastic materials.

REMARK. It is interesting to note that the use of various definitions of stress rate in the constitutive equations does not make any fundamental difference. For instance, the term $t^{kl}\,v^m{}_{;m}$ that constitutes the only difference between the Truesdell and Oldroyd definitions (72.9) and (72.11) may as well be combined with the third term on the right of (73.12). Similarly the extra terms appearing in the Jaumann-Noll definition (72.5) over those of Truesdell may be combined with the existing terms on the right of (73.12). Differences, however, arise in various polynomial approximations. For these we use Truesdell's definition for no apparent reason other than having the convenience of the availability of the analytical work.

Below we give a few special types of simple hypoelastic bodies recognized by the highest degree of $\mathbf{s}$ appearing on the right side of constitutive equations (73.12) and (73.14). It goes without saying that each of these special types is defined over a corresponding equivalence class of stress-configuration classes.

*Hypoelastic Body of Grade Zero.* If the right side of (73.12) or (73.14) is independent of $\mathbf{s}$, we say that the body is hypoelastic of grade zero. In this case we have

$$\alpha_0 \equiv \frac{\lambda}{2\mu} \qquad \alpha_1 \equiv 1 \qquad \alpha_2 \equiv \alpha_3 \equiv \cdots \equiv \alpha_{11} \equiv 0 \qquad \text{for all } \mathbf{s} \tag{73.19}$$

Constitutive equations are

$$2\,\mu\,\check{s}^k{}_l = \lambda\,d^m{}_m\,\delta^k{}_l + 2\,\mu\,d^k{}_l \qquad \text{(compressible)} \tag{73.20}$$

$$2\,\mu\,\check{s}^k{}_l = -p\,\delta^k{}_l + 2\,\mu\,d^k{}_l \qquad \text{(incompressible)} \tag{73.21}$$

*Hypoelastic Body of Grade One.* When the constitutive coefficients are such that $\check{\mathbf{s}}$ contains only up to the first power of stress, we say that the body is hypoelastic of grade one. Thus,

$$\begin{aligned} &\alpha_0 \equiv \frac{\lambda}{2\,\mu} + \beta_0\,\mathrm{I}_s \qquad \alpha_1 \equiv 1 + \beta_1\,\mathrm{I}_s \qquad \alpha_2 \equiv \beta_2 \\ &\alpha_3 \equiv \beta_3 \qquad \alpha_4 \equiv \beta_4 \qquad \text{and} \qquad \alpha_5 \equiv \alpha_6 \equiv \cdots \equiv \alpha_{11} \equiv 0 \\ &\qquad\qquad\qquad\qquad\qquad\qquad\qquad\qquad \text{for all } \mathbf{s} \end{aligned} \tag{73.22}$$

Here $\beta_\gamma$ are dimensionless constants.

$$\check{\mathbf{s}} = \left(\frac{\lambda}{2\,\mu} + \beta_0\,\mathrm{I}_s\right)\mathrm{I}_d\,\mathbf{I} + (1 + \beta_1\,\mathrm{I}_s)\,\mathbf{d} + \beta_2\,\mathrm{I}_d\,\mathbf{s} + \beta_3\,M\,\mathbf{I} + \frac{1}{2}\beta_4(\mathbf{d}\,\mathbf{s} + \mathbf{s}\,\mathbf{d}) \qquad \text{(compressible)} \tag{73.23}$$

$$\check{\mathbf{s}} = -\frac{\dot{p}}{2\,\mu}\mathbf{I} + \left(1 + \frac{p}{\mu} + \beta_1\,\mathrm{I}_s\right)\mathbf{d} + \beta_3\,M\,\mathbf{I} + \frac{1}{2}\beta_4\,(\mathbf{d}\,\mathbf{s} + \mathbf{s}\,\mathbf{d}) \qquad \text{(incompressible)} \tag{73.24}$$

*Hypoelastic Body of Grade Two.* In this case we have

$$\begin{aligned} &\alpha_0 \equiv \frac{\lambda}{2\,\mu} + \beta_0\,\mathrm{I}_s + \gamma_0\,\mathrm{I}_s^2 + \epsilon_0\,\mathrm{II}_s \\ &\alpha_1 \equiv 1 + \beta_1\,\mathrm{I}_s + \gamma_1\,\mathrm{I}_s^2 + \epsilon_1\,\mathrm{II}_s \\ &\alpha_2 \equiv \beta_2 + \gamma_2\,\mathrm{I}_s \qquad \alpha_3 \equiv \beta_3 + \gamma_3\,\mathrm{I}_s \qquad \alpha_4 \equiv \beta_4 + \gamma_4\,\mathrm{I}_s \\ &\alpha_5 \equiv \beta_5 \qquad \alpha_6 \equiv \beta_6 \qquad \alpha_7 \equiv \beta_7 \qquad \alpha_8 \equiv \beta_8 \\ &\alpha_9 \equiv \alpha_{10} \equiv \alpha_{11} \equiv 0 \qquad \text{for all } \mathbf{s} \end{aligned} \tag{73.25}$$

here $\beta_\alpha$ and $\gamma_\alpha$ are dimensionless constants.

Each one of the foregoing cases represents a simple hypoelastic body ntaining no assumptions as to the magnitude of stress or strain, and ch one is consistent with the principles of mechanics. The material nstants $\beta_\alpha$, $\gamma_\alpha$, and $\epsilon_\alpha$ are to be determined by experimentation and by rve and model fitting.

## BASIC EQUATIONS OF HYPOELASTICITY

Basic field equations of hypoelasticity are the following.

*Conservation of Mass:*

$$\dot{\rho} + \rho\,v^k{}_{;k} = 0 \tag{74.1}$$

*Balance of Momenta:*

$$2\,\mu\,s^{lk}{}_{;l} + \rho(f^k - \dot{v}^k) = 0 \qquad s^{lk} = s^{kl} \tag{74.2}$$

*Constitutive Equations.* For compressible bodies the most general rm is given by (73.12) and for incompressible bodies by (73.14), i.e.,

$$\begin{aligned} \hat{\mathbf{s}} = {} & \delta\,\alpha_0\,\mathbf{I} + \alpha_1\,\mathbf{d} + \delta\,\alpha_2\,\mathbf{s} + M\,\alpha_3\,\mathbf{I} + \tfrac{1}{2}\,\alpha_4\,(\mathbf{d}\,\mathbf{s} + \mathbf{s}\,\mathbf{d}) \\ & + \delta\,\alpha_5\,\mathbf{s}^2 + M\,\alpha_6\,\mathbf{s} + N\,\alpha_7\,\mathbf{I} + \tfrac{1}{2}\,\alpha_8\,(\mathbf{d}\,\mathbf{s}^2 + \mathbf{s}^2\,\mathbf{d}) \\ & + M\,\alpha_9\,\mathbf{s}^2 + N\,\alpha_{10}\,\mathbf{s} + N\,\alpha_{11}\,\mathbf{s}^2 \qquad \text{(compressible)} \end{aligned} \tag{74.3}$$

$$\begin{aligned} \hat{\mathbf{s}} = {} & -\frac{\dot{p}}{2\,\mu}\mathbf{I} + \left(\alpha_1 + \frac{p}{\mu}\right)\mathbf{d} + \tfrac{1}{2}\,\alpha_4\,(\mathbf{d}\,\mathbf{s} + \mathbf{s}\,\mathbf{d}) + (\alpha_3\,M + \alpha_7\,N)\,\mathbf{I} \\ & + (\alpha_6\,M + \alpha_{10}\,N)\,\mathbf{s} + (\alpha_9\,M + \alpha_{11}\,N)\,\mathbf{s}^2 \\ & + \tfrac{1}{2}\,\alpha_8\,(\mathbf{d}\,\mathbf{s}^2 + \mathbf{s}^2\,\mathbf{d}) \qquad \text{(incompressible)} \end{aligned} \tag{74.4}$$

In addition it is assumed that for a given hypoelastic material the exists an equivalence class of stress-configuration classes.

For hypoelastic bodies of grade zero we use equations (73.20) ar (73.21); of grade one (73.23), (73.24); and of grade two (73.25) togeth with (73.12) and (73.14).

In addition to these equations we have the following relations.

*Kinematical Relations.* For the rate of stress $\hat{\mathbf{s}}$ one may use any of tl defining equations.

$$\hat{s}^k{}_l \equiv \frac{\partial s^k{}_l}{\partial t} + s^k{}_{l;m}\, v^m + s^k{}_m\, w^m{}_l - s^m{}_l\, w^k{}_m \qquad \text{(Jaumann-Noll)} \tag{74.5}$$

$$\hat{s}^k{}_l \equiv \check{s}^k{}_l = \frac{\partial s^k{}_l}{\partial t} + s^k{}_{l;m}\, v^m - s^{km}\, v_{l;m} - s^m{}_l\, v^k{}_{;m} + s^k{}_l\, v^m{}_{;m} \qquad \text{(Truesdel} \tag{74.6}$$

$$\hat{s}^k{}_l \equiv \mathring{s}^k{}_l = \frac{\partial s^k{}_l}{\partial t} + s^k{}_{l;m}\, v^m - s^{km}\, v_{l;m} - s^m{}_l\, v^k{}_{;m} \qquad \text{(Oldroyd)} \tag{74.7}$$

Deformation rate $\mathbf{d}$ and spin $\mathbf{w}$ are defined by

$$d_{kl} \equiv \tfrac{1}{2}\,(v_{k;l} + v_{l;k}) \qquad w_{kl} \equiv \tfrac{1}{2}\,(v_{k;l} - v_{l;k}) \tag{74.8}$$

Upon eliminating $\mathbf{d}$, $\mathbf{w}$, and $\mathbf{s}$ from (74.3) or (74.4) by use of (74.{ and any one of (74.5)–(74.7), we obtain six equations. Through (74.] and (74.2) we have four more equations, thus bringing the total to te equations which are necessary for the determination of ten unknowı $\rho$, $s^{kl}$, and $v^k$ in the compressible bodies and $p$, $s^{kl}$, and $v^k$ for the incon pressible bodies. For a hypoelastic body of grade zero Truesdell's for of the constitutive equations is

$$2\,\mu\left(\frac{\partial s^k{}_l}{\partial t} + s^k{}_{l;m}\, v^m - s^{km}\, v_{l;m} - s^m{}_l\, v^k{}_{;m} + s^k{}_l\, v^m{}_{;m}\right) = \lambda\, v^m{}_{;m}\, \delta^k{}_l + \mu\,(v^k{}_{;l} + v_{l;}{}^{\cdot} \tag{74.9}$$

*Boundary and Initial Conditions.* It appears that the boundary co ditions used in the theory of elasticity should carry over to hypoelasticit These conditions consist of prescribing tractions and/or displacemen on the surface of the body. A displacement condition here is mo complicated since it requires the integration of the velocity field In many cases, however, it will be equally natural to prescribe $\mathbf{v}$ insteac

The initial conditions of the theory of elasticity are again carried ov to hypoelasticity. Thus initially we may prescribe the displacement an velocity fields. The main difference beyond these conditions appea because of the term $\partial\mathbf{s}/\partial t$. *In a hypoelastic body we may expect to pr scribe an arbitrary initial stress* $\mathbf{s} = \mathbf{s}_0$ *at time* $t = 0$ *where* $\mathbf{s}_0$ *is any sol tion of* (74.2) *consistent with whatever boundary conditions are used.* Ult ately the correct boundary and initial conditions must be such as to ake the solution unique. This is secured by the prescription of admisble initial conditions for a hypoelastic material over its equivalence ass of stress-configuration classes.

## . RELATION OF HYPOELASTICITY TO ELASTICITY

In this article we seek answers to the following two questions: (1) re elastic materials hypoelastic? (2) Under what conditions is a ypoelastic material elastic? Answer to question (1) is supplied by the llowing Theorem due to Noll [1955, art. 15b]. The answer to question is provided by the subsequent theorems due to Bernstein [1960*a*]. or simplicity, in this article we employ rectangular coordinates. All roofs can be adjusted properly to carry over to any curvilinear system.

THEOREM 1. (*Noll*) *Isotropic Cauchy-elastic materials with invertible nstitutive equations constitute a special subclass of hypoelastic materials.*[1]

Cauchy's definition of an isotropic elastic material is characterized by onstitutive equations of the form[2] [cf. (46.1)]:

$$t_{kl} = f_{kl}\,(x^p{}_{,K}) \tag{75.1}$$

ubject to the invariance requirement (objectivity) as expressed by 6.5). In rectangular coordinates this reads

$$f_{rs}\,(x^p{}_{,K})\,Q_{kr}\,Q_{ls} = f_{kl}\,(Q_{pn}\,x^n{}_{,K}) \tag{75.2}$$

he material derivative of (75.1) with the use of (19.1) is given by

$$\dot{t}_{kl} = \frac{\partial f_{kl}}{\partial x^p{}_{,K}}\,v_{p,n}\,x^n{}_{,K}$$

pon writing $v_{p,n} = d_{pn} + w_{pn}$, we obtain

$$\dot{t}_{kl} = \frac{\partial f_{kl}}{\partial x^p{}_{,K}}\,d_{pn}\,x^n{}_{,K} + \frac{\partial f_{kl}}{\partial x^p{}_{,K}}\,w_{pn}\,x^n{}_{,K} \tag{75.3}$$

e evaluate the second term by differentiating (75.2) with respect to $t$ r a fixed $x^k{}_{,K}$ since (75.2) is valid for any $x^k{}_{,K}$. This gives

$$f_{rs}\,(\dot{Q}_{kr}\,Q_{ls} + Q_{kr}\,\dot{Q}_{ls}) = \frac{\partial f_{kl}}{\partial(Q_{pm}\,x^m{}_{,K})}\,\dot{Q}_{pn}\,x^n{}_{,K}$$

hich is valid for any $Q_{rs} = Q_{rs}\,(t)$. Now select

$$Q_{rs}\,(0) = \delta_{rs} \qquad \dot{Q}_{rs}\,(0) = w_{rs}$$

[1] The proof given here is somewhat different from Noll's; the procedure, however, is milar.

[2] The theorem is valid for inhomogeneous materials. The dependence on **X** is not plicitly indicated in (75.1) for simplicity in writing.

Hence

$$t_{rl}\,w_{kr} + t_{ks}\,w_{ls} = \frac{\partial f_{kl}}{\partial x^p{}_{,K}}\,w_{pn}\,x^n{}_{,K} \tag{75.4}$$

Upon substituting (75.4) for the second term on the right-hand side (75.3), we obtain

$$\dot{t}_{kl} + t_{kr}\,w_{rl} - t_{rl}\,w_{kr} = \frac{\partial f_{kl}}{\partial x^p{}_{,K}}\,d_{pn}\,x^n{}_{,K} \tag{75.5}$$

The left-hand side of this equation is the stress flux $\hat{t}_{kl}$ as defined (35.5). According to the hypothesis made, (75.1) is invertible so th

$$x^p{}_{,K} = \overset{-1}{f^p}{}_K\,(t_{kl}) \tag{75.6}$$

subject to integrability conditions

$$\overset{-1}{f^p}{}_{K,L} = \overset{-1}{f^p}{}_{L,K}$$

Using (75.6) in (75.5), we obtain

$$\hat{t}_{kl} = \frac{\partial f_{kl}\,(\overset{-1}{\mathbf{f}}\,(\mathbf{t}))}{\partial x^p{}_{,K}}\,d_{pn}\,x^n{}_{,K} \tag{75.7}$$

We therefore see that $\hat{\mathbf{t}}$ is a function of $\mathbf{d}$ and $\mathbf{t}$, being linear and homog neous in $\mathbf{d}$. By calculating $\partial f_{kl}/\partial x^p{}_{,K}$ from (75.5), we also see that t right-hand side of (75.5) is a hemitropic function of $\mathbf{d}$ and $x^n{}_{,K}$. Sin $\overset{-1}{\mathbf{f}}\,(\mathbf{t})$ is also a hemitropic function of $\mathbf{t}$, it follows that the right-hand si of (75.7) is a hemitropic function of $\mathbf{t}$ and $\mathbf{d}$. Therefore (75.7) is a speci type of hypoelastic material. Hence the proof of the theorem.

The constitutive equations (75.7) obtained by differentiating (75.1) a not exactly equivalent to (75.1). For (75.7) to be integrable to (75. we must have the initial state either stress-free or such that the stress *relievable* to the natural state. This requires the elimination of *di locations*. Hence for (75.7) to be equivalent to the constitutive equatio of an elastic solid, the initial stress must satisfy the *compatibili conditions*.

THEOREM 2. (*Bernstein*) *A necessary and sufficient condition for hypoelastic material to be Cauchy-elastic is the satisfaction of the followi integrability conditions identically in* $t_{rs}$.

$$\frac{\partial B_{klmn}}{\partial t_{rs}}\,B_{rspq} - \frac{\partial B_{klpq}}{\partial t_{rs}}\,B_{rsmn} - B_{klmq}\,\delta_{pn} + B_{klpn}\,\delta_{mq} = 0 \tag{75.8}$$

where

$$B_{klmn} \equiv \tfrac{1}{2}\,(t_{kn}\,\delta_{lm} + t_{ln}\,\delta_{km} - t_{km}\,\delta_{ln} - t_{lm}\,\delta_{kn}) + 2\,\mu\,A_{klmn} \tag{75.9}$$

ere $A_{klmn}$ (**t**) are the coefficients in the constitutive equations (73.10) of ypoelasticity; or

5.10) $$\dot{t}_{kl} = t_{km}\, w_{lm} + t_{lm}\, w_{km} + 2\, \mu\, A_{klmn}(\mathbf{t})\, d_{mn}$$

ie constitutive coefficients $A_{klmn}$ are isotropic tensor functions of the ress and possess the symmetries

$$A_{klmn} = A_{lkmn} = A_{lknm}$$

PROOF. From (19.1) we have $v^k{}_{,l} = \dot{x}^k{}_{,K}\, X^K{}_{,l}$, which upon substitution to the constitutive equations (75.10) gives

5.11) $$\dot{t}_{kl} = B_{klmn}(\mathbf{t})\, \dot{x}^m{}_{,K}\, X^K{}_{,n}$$

iere $B_{klmn}$ (**t**) is defined by (75.9). Suppose now that a hypoelastic aterial is Cauchy-elastic. If so, for **t** we must have the functional pendence given by (75.1) subject to (75.2). Hence from (75.1) and 5.11) it follows that

5.12) $$\frac{\partial t_{kl}}{\partial x^m{}_{,K}}\, \dot{x}^m{}_{,K} = B_{klmn}\, X^K{}_{,n}\, \dot{x}^m{}_{,K}$$

r arbitrary motions. Since $x^k{}_{,K}$ and $\dot{x}^k{}_{,K}$ are in general independent, for 5.1) to satisfy this equation for arbitrary $\dot{x}^m{}_{,K}$, we must have

5.13) $$\frac{\partial t_{kl}}{\partial x^m{}_{,K}} = B_{klmn}\, X^K{}_{,n}$$

onversely, if a solution (75.1) of this equation exists, then (75.12) and nce (75.11) are satisfied by this solution. By the uniqueness of the solu- n of the initial-value problem for (75.11) the stress-configuration class so termined is complete and closed. Thus the problem reduces to that of iether (75.13) admits of a solution. According to standard methods of ometry,[3] for (75.11) to admit of a solution, it must satisfy the integra- ity conditions.

5.14) $$\begin{aligned} 0 &= \frac{\partial^2 t_{kl}}{\partial x^p{}_{,K}\, \partial x^q{}_{,L}} - \frac{\partial^2 t_{kl}}{\partial x^q{}_{,L}\, \partial x^p{}_{,K}} \\ &= \frac{\partial B_{klqn}}{\partial t_{rs}} \frac{\partial t_{rs}}{\partial x^p{}_{,K}} X^L{}_{,n} + B_{klqn} \frac{\partial X^L{}_{,n}}{\partial x^p{}_{,K}} \\ &\qquad - \frac{\partial B_{klpn}}{\partial t_{rs}} \frac{\partial t_{rs}}{\partial x^q{}_{,L}} X^K{}_{,n} - B_{klpn} \frac{\partial X^K{}_{,n}}{\partial x^q{}_{,L}} \end{aligned}$$

 differentiating $(4.3)_2$ with respect to $x^m{}_{,M}$, we solve for

5.15) $$\frac{\partial X^K{}_{,k}}{\partial x^l{}_{,L}} = -X^K{}_{,l}\, X^L{}_{,k}$$

[3] Cf. Eisenhart [1947, art. 23].

Substituting this and (75.13) into (75.14) and multiplying the resultin expression by $x^a{}_{,K}\, x^b{}_{,L}$, we obtain (75.8). For $t_{kl}$ to satisfy (75.13), it necessary that it satisfy (75.8) identically. If (75.8) is not satisfie identically in $t_{kl}$, and if it does not consist of more than six independe relations, we may differentiate (75.8) with respect to $x^k{}_{,K}$ and use (75.1 to obtain the second integrability conditions for $t_{kl}$. If the total numb of integrability conditions does not exceed six, we continue this proce until either we obtain more than six relations or at some stage no ne relations are introduced and the total number of independent relations, is less than six. In the case $r > 6$ there is no solution to (75.13). In th case $r \leq 6$ there are solutions in which $6 - r$ components of $t_{kl}$ may b assigned arbitrarily for one value of $x^k{}_{,K}$ at each **X**, and for each suc assignment the solution is unique. For arbitrary assignment of $t_{kl}$ f one value of $x^k{}_{,K}$ at **X** there exists a unique solution of (75.13) if and onl if (75.8) is satisfied identically in $t_{kl}$. Hence the proof of the theorem.

As an illustration consider the hypoelastic solid defined by (73.16 In this case the totality of independent integrability conditions may b expressed as

$$t_{kl} = \frac{t_{rr}}{3}\, \delta_{kl}$$

This indicates that the hypoelastic material corresponding to (73.16) Cauchy-elastic if and only if the stress is hydrostatic.

THEOREM 3. *(Bernstein) A necessary and sufficient condition for hypoelastic material which is Cauchy-elastic to be Green-elastic is the sati faction of the following integrability conditions identically in* $t_{rs}$:

$$2\,\mu\, A_{klmn} + t_{kl}\,\delta_{mn} = 2\,\mu\, A_{mnlk} + t_{mn}\,\delta_{lk} \tag{75.16}$$

For a Green-elastic material there exists a stress potential $\Sigma\,(x^k{}_{,K}, X^K$ such that the stress is derivable from this in the form (45.29). Th equation may be rewritten as

$$\frac{\partial \Sigma}{\partial x^k{}_{,K}} = \frac{\rho_0}{\rho}\, t_{kl}\, X^K{}_{,l} \tag{75.17}$$

where $t_{kl}\,(x^r{}_{,K}, X^K)$ is supposed to be given. A necessary and sufficien condition for the existence of a solution $\Sigma$ of (75.17) is

$$0 = \frac{\partial^2 \Sigma}{\partial x^k{}_{,K}\, \partial x^l{}_{,L}} - \frac{\partial^2 \Sigma}{\partial x^l{}_{,L}\, \partial x^k{}_{,K}} = \frac{\partial}{\partial x^k{}_{,K}} \left( \frac{\rho_0}{\rho}\, t_{lm}\, X^L{}_{,m} \right) - \frac{\partial}{\partial x^l{}_{,L}} \left( \frac{\rho_0}{\rho}\, t_{km}\, X^K{}_{,m} \right. \tag{75.18}$$

'he equation of continuity in rectangular coordinates reads

$$\rho_0/\rho = \det (x^k{}_{,K}) = j$$

Jsing (19.8), we have

75.19) $$\frac{\partial}{\partial x^k{}_{,K}}\left(\frac{\rho_0}{\rho}\right) = \frac{\rho_0}{\rho} X^K{}_{,k}$$

'arrying out indicated differentiations in (75.18), using (75.19), and ıultiplying the resulting expression by $x^r{}_{,K}\, x^s{}_{,L}$, we get

75.20) $$B_{klmn} - B_{nmlk} + t_{kl}\,\delta_{mn} - t_{nm}\,\delta_{lk} - t_{km}\,\delta_{ln} + t_{mk}\,\delta_{nl} = 0$$

ubstitution for $B_{klmn}$ from (75.9) reduces to (75.16). Hence the proof f the theorem.

COROLLARY. *A necessary and sufficient condition for a hypoelastic ıaterial to be Green-elastic is the satisfaction of* (75.8) *and* (75.16) *identically ı* $t_{rs}$.

It can be seen that the special hypoelastic material (73.16) satisfies 75.16) for the Cauchy-elastic solution (73.17). Hence by the foregoing heorem the hypoelastic material it represents is Green-elastic if even the tress is hydrostatic. If, however, the stress is not hydrostatic, then the ıaterial is not elastic, even in the sense of Cauchy. We therefore see that ıe stress-configuration class is important in determining the nature of ypoelastic materials represented by a given constitutive differential quation.

In addition to Theorems 2 and 3, Bernstein gave two other theorems 'hich enlighten the nature of hypoelastic materials. Theorem 4, below, ill be stated without its lengthy proof. The last theorem is concerned 'ith the question of the isotropy of a hypoelastic material which is 'auchy-elastic. Since this brings out a class of elastic problems not ontained in hypoelasticity, we give the proof.

THEOREM 4. (*Bernstein*) *If for a given hypoelastic material the work one by the stresses is nonnegative for all (kinematically possible) motions ır which the initial and final configurations are the same, then this material is lastic in the sense of Green.*[4]

THEOREM 5. (*Bernstein*) *Given a representation of a Cauchy-elastic ıaterial which is also hypoelastic, this material is also isotropic with respect ı this representation if and only if the stress is uniform hydrostatic pressure 'hen* $x^k{}_{,K} = \delta^k{}_K$.

[4] The existence of such a result is suggested by the work of Caprioli [1955]. See also 'ricksen [1958] and Bernstein and Ericksen [1958] for the study of hypoelastic mate- als which possess a stress potential, and Thomas [1956, 1957b] for other isotropic ıaterials possessing distortion energies which are expressible by scalar invariants.

PROOF. The necessity is established by using constitutive equatio (47.30) of isotropic Cauchy-elastic materials and remembering that wh $x^k{}_{,K} = \delta^k{}_K$, then $c^k{}_l = \delta^k{}_l$. Hence

$$t^k{}_l = (g_0 + g_1 + g_2)\,\delta^k{}_l$$

which defines a state of hydrostatic pressure, since $g_\kappa\,(0, 0, 0, \mathbf{X})$ is a fun tion of $\mathbf{X}$ only.

Let $t_{kl} = f_{kl}\,(x^r{}_{,K}, X^K)$ be a solution of (75.13) which upon substitutic of $x^k{}_{,K} = \delta^k{}_K$ gives a uniform hydrostatic pressure, i.e.,

$$f_{kl}\,(\delta^r{}_{,K}, X^K) = -p\,\delta_{kl} \tag{75.21}$$

where $p$ is a constant. We must now prove that this condition is suf cient to secure the form invariance of $f_{kl}$ for the full orthogonal grou

Define

$$\begin{aligned} f'_{kl}\,(x^r{}_{,K}, X^K) &\equiv f_{kl}\,(x^r{}_{,K'}, X'^K) \\ &= f_{kl}\,(S_K{}^L\,x^r{}_{,L}, S^K{}_L\,X^L) \end{aligned} \tag{75.22}$$

By substitution into (75.13) we see that $f'_{kl}$ is a solution. Now we have representation (46.12) of the stress tensor which is objective:

$$t_{kl} = F_{KL}\,(C_{MN}, X^M)\,X^K{}_{,k}\,X^L{}_{,l} \tag{75.23}$$

in which

$$C_{MN} = \delta_{mn}\,x^m{}_{,M}\,x^n{}_{,N} \tag{75.24}$$

Upon putting $x^k{}_{,K} = \delta^k{}_K$, we obtain $C_{MN} = \delta_{MN}$. Hence through (75.2 with $X^K{}_{,k} = \delta^K{}_k$ we will have

$$-p\,\delta_{kl} = F_{KL}\,(\delta_{MN}, X^M)\,\delta^K{}_k\,\delta^L{}_l$$

Since the left side is independent of $X^M$, we must have

$$F_{KL}\,(\delta_{MN}, X^M) = F_{KL}\,(\delta_{MN}, X'^M) = -p\,\delta_{KL} \tag{75.25}$$

The stress $t'_{kl}$ at $\mathbf{X}'$ is given by

$$t'_{kl} = F_{KL}\left(\delta_{mn}\,\frac{\partial x^m}{\partial X'^M}\,\frac{\partial x^n}{\partial X'^N}, X'^M\right)\frac{\partial X'^K}{\partial x^k}\,\frac{\partial X'^L}{\partial x^l}$$

Upon writing $\partial x^k/\partial X'^K = x^k{}_{,M}\,S_K{}^M$, $\partial X'^K/\partial x^k = S^K{}_L\,X^L{}_{,k}$ and puttin $x^k{}_{,K} = \delta^k{}_K$, we reduce this as follows:

$$\begin{aligned} f'_{kl}\,(\delta^r{}_K, X^K) &= f_{kl}\,(\delta^r{}_L\,S_K{}^L, X'^K) \\ &= F_{KL}\,(\delta_{mn}\,\delta^m{}_P\,\delta^n{}_Q\,S_M{}^P\,S_N{}^Q, X'^K)\,\delta^U{}_k\,\delta^V{}_l\,S^K{}_U\,S^L{}_V \\ &= F_{KL}\,(\delta_{MN}, X'^K)\,\delta^U{}_k\,\delta^V{}_l\,S^K{}_U\,S^L{}_V \end{aligned}$$

ubstitution from (75.25) gives

$$f'_{kl}(\delta^r{}_K, X^K) = -p\,\delta_{kl} = f_{kl}(\delta^r{}_K, X^K)$$

'hus the two solutions of (75.13), $f_{kl}$ and $f'_{kl}$, coincide for one value of $^r{}_{,K}$ at each **X**. Consequently, by the uniqueness of solutions of (75.13), hese solutions must be the same for all values of $x^r{}_{,K}$ at each **X**, i.e.,

$$f_{kl}\left(\frac{\partial x^k}{\partial X'^K}, X'^K\right) = f'_{kl}\left(\frac{\partial x^k}{\partial X^K}, X^K\right) = f_{kl}(x^k{}_{,K}, X^K)$$

'hus the functions $f_{kl}$ are form-invariant under the full orthogonal roup $S^K{}_L$, and hence the theorem is established.

The following example is supplied to show that hypoelasticity does not ıclude all of elasticity.

*Example.* Consider Green-elastic material defined by

$$\Sigma \equiv [(\delta_{kl}\, x^k{}_{,K}\, x^l{}_{,L} - \delta_{KL})\, H^{KL}]^2 \tag{75.26}$$

,here $H^{11} = 1$, $H^{22} = 2$, $H^{33} = 1$, and $H^{KL} = 0$ for $K \neq L$. The stress otential (75.26) obeys the principle of objectivity. The stress tensor orresponding to this is given by

$$t^{kl} = 2\,\frac{\rho}{\rho_0}\,(\delta_{mn}\, x^m{}_{,K}\, x^n{}_{,L} - \delta_{KL})\, H^{KL}\, H^{MN}\, x^k{}_{,M}\, x^l{}_{,N} \tag{75.27}$$

'onsider the following two special cases.

$$x^1 = X^1 \qquad x^2 = 2\,X^2 \qquad x^3 = X^3 \qquad \text{(case 1)}$$
$$x^1 = X'^2 \qquad x^2 = 2\,X'^1 \qquad x^3 = X'^3 \qquad \text{(case 2)}$$

ı which $X^K$ and $X'^K$ are related to each other by the orthogonal ransformation

$$X'^1 = X^2 \qquad X'^2 = X^1 \qquad X'^3 = X^3$$

'rom (75.27), for these cases we obtain

$$t^{11} = 6 \qquad t^{22} = 8 \qquad t^{33} = 6 \qquad t^{kl} = 0 \quad \text{for } k \neq l \qquad \text{(case 1)}$$
$$t^{11} = 12 \qquad t^{22} = 6 \qquad t^{33} = 3 \qquad t^{kl} = 0 \quad \text{for } k \neq l \qquad \text{(case 2)}$$

o that this Green-elastic material is not isotropic, although from (75.27) ,e see that the stress vanishes, and hence is certainly a uniform hydrotatic pressure, when $x^k{}_{,K} = \delta^k{}_K$. Therefore we have here an example of n elastic material which according to Theorem 5 is not hypoelastic.

REMARK. *Relation of Hypoelastic Bodies to Linear Elastic Bodies.* If he displacement field **u** is sufficiently small and nearly irrotational and he initial state is stress-free, we may write

$$\dot{\mathbf{s}}\,dt \cong \mathbf{s}(t + dt) - \mathbf{s}(t) \qquad \mathbf{u} \cong \mathbf{v}\,dt \tag{75.28}$$

In this case all terms on the left of (74.9) drop out except $\partial \mathbf{s}/\partial t$. Upon use of (75.28) we get the stress-strain relations of the classical linear theory of elasticity. Thus *the equations of the theory of hypoelasticity reduce to those of the classical linear theory of elasticity under the usual assumptions of the latter theory.* Clear connection of hypoelasticity to elasticity and to other types of materials[5] requires further research work in this novel field.

## 76. ACCELERATIONLESS MOTION

In the study of equilibrium stress systems of hypoelastic bodies, it is essential to know what restriction the condition of zero acceleration imposes on the state of stress. For a motion in which

$$\ddot{\mathbf{x}} = 0 \tag{76.1}$$

we know that every particle $\mathbf{X}$ travels in a straight line with a uniform velocity $\dot{\mathbf{x}}(\mathbf{X})$. Such a simple material description of the motion in the spatial language becomes highly unmanageable.

In a common frame the material description of an accelerationless motion is

$$\mathbf{z} = \dot{\mathbf{z}}(\mathbf{Z})\, t + \mathbf{Z} \tag{76.2}$$

Since $\dot{\mathbf{z}} = \mathbf{f}(\mathbf{Z})$, we may, by writing $\mathbf{Z} = \mathbf{z} - \dot{\mathbf{z}}\, t$, obtain

$$\dot{\mathbf{z}} = \mathbf{f}(\mathbf{z} - \dot{\mathbf{z}}\, t) \tag{76.3}$$

Consequently, if (76.3) holds, by putting $\mathbf{y} = \mathbf{z} - \dot{\mathbf{z}}\, t$, we have

$$\ddot{z}^k = f^k{}_{;m}\, \dot{y}^m = f^k{}_{;m}\, (\dot{z}^m - \dot{z}^m - \ddot{z}^m\, t) \tag{76.4}$$

or

$$(\delta^k{}_m + t f^k{}_{;m})\, \ddot{z}^m = 0 \tag{76.5}$$

Since $\det(\delta^k{}_m + t f^k{}_{;m})$ may vanish only for three values of $t$, it follows that $\ddot{\mathbf{z}} = 0$. Therefore *the functional equation* (76.3) *derived by Caldonazzo* [1947] *is necessary and sufficient for the accelerationless motion.*

It is interesting to calculate the ratio of the elements of volume at time $t$ and 0. We have

$$\begin{aligned} \frac{dv}{dV} &= J = \det(z_{k,K}) = \det(\delta_{kK} + t\, \dot{z}_{k,K}) \\ &= 1 + \mathrm{I}_{\Delta}\, t + \mathrm{II}_{\Delta}\, t^2 + \mathrm{III}_{\Delta}\, t^3 \end{aligned} \tag{76.6}$$

where $\mathbf{\Delta} \equiv \|\dot{z}_{k,K}\|$. From (76.6) it follows that *an accelerationless motion*

[5] An account of the relation of hypoelasticity to plasticity is found in Art. 89 and to hygrosterics in Art. 103.

isochoric if and only if

(76.7) $$\mathrm{I}_\Delta = \mathrm{II}_\Delta = \mathrm{III}_\Delta = 0$$

Following Truesdell [1955*a*], we now obtain an integral of the accelerationless motion for homogeneous motion.

*Homogeneous Accelerationless Motion.* A motion is homogeneous if in the common frame it has the form

(76.8) $$\dot{\mathbf{z}} = \mathbf{a}\,(t) \cdot \mathbf{z} + \mathbf{b}\,(t)$$

where $\mathbf{a}\,(t)$ is a square matrix and $\mathbf{b}\,(t)$ is a vector. If we now differentiate (76.8) with respect to time and eliminate $\dot{\mathbf{z}}$ by using (76.8), we get

$$\ddot{\mathbf{z}} = (\dot{\mathbf{a}} + \mathbf{a}^2) \cdot \mathbf{z} + \dot{\mathbf{b}} + \mathbf{a} \cdot \mathbf{b}$$

Consequently a homogeneous motion is accelerationless if and only if

(76.9) $$\dot{\mathbf{a}} + \mathbf{a}^2 = 0 \qquad \dot{\mathbf{b}} + \mathbf{a} \cdot \mathbf{b} = 0$$

To solve $(76.9)_1$, let $\mathbf{A}$ be a constant matrix; then

$$\frac{d}{dt}\,[(\mathbf{I} + \mathbf{A}\,t) \cdot \mathbf{a}] = \mathbf{A} \cdot \mathbf{a} + (\mathbf{I} + \mathbf{A}\,t) \cdot \dot{\mathbf{a}} = [\mathbf{A} - (\mathbf{I} + \mathbf{A}\,t) \cdot \mathbf{a}] \cdot \mathbf{a}$$

Both sides vanish if

(76.10) $$(\mathbf{I} + \mathbf{A}\,t) \cdot \mathbf{a} = \mathbf{A}$$

Clearly $\mathbf{A} = \mathbf{a}\,(0)$. If the initial value of $\mathbf{a}\,(0) = 0$, from the uniqueness theorem of differential equations we get $\mathbf{a}\,(t) = 0$. If $\mathbf{a}\,(0) \neq 0$, then the necessary condition for solving the linear equation (76.10) is $\det (\mathbf{I} + \mathbf{A}\,t) \neq 0$. For sufficiently small $t$ this condition is always satisfied.

If $\mathbf{A}$ has positive real proper numbers, write for the largest of these $-1/t_-$; and if it has negative real proper numbers, for the smallest of these write $1/t_+$. Otherwise write $t_- = -\infty$, $t_+ = +\infty$. Then the unique solution of (76.10) for $\mathbf{a}$ exists and is a differentiable function in $t$ in the interval $t_- < t < t_+$. Moreover, when $t_0$ is the largest of the absolute values of all proper numbers of $\mathbf{A}$, then $\mathbf{a}$ is analytic for $|t| < t_0$.

To determine $\mathbf{b}$ by $(76.9)_2$ and (76.10), we have

(76.11) $$(\mathbf{I} + \mathbf{A}\,t) \cdot \dot{\mathbf{b}} + \mathbf{A} \cdot \mathbf{b} = 0$$

or

$$\frac{d}{dt}\,[(\mathbf{I} + \mathbf{A}\,t) \cdot \mathbf{b}] = 0$$

so that

(76.12) $$(\mathbf{I} + \mathbf{A}\,t) \cdot \mathbf{b} = \mathbf{B}$$

where $\mathbf{B} = \mathbf{b}(0)$ are the initial values of $\mathbf{b}(t)$. If $\mathbf{B} = 0$, then $\mathbf{b}(t) = 0$. If $\mathbf{B}(0) \neq 0$, then the conditions for solving $\mathbf{b}(t)$ from (72.11) are identical to those of $\mathbf{a}$. For descriptive purposes the following simple example suffices.

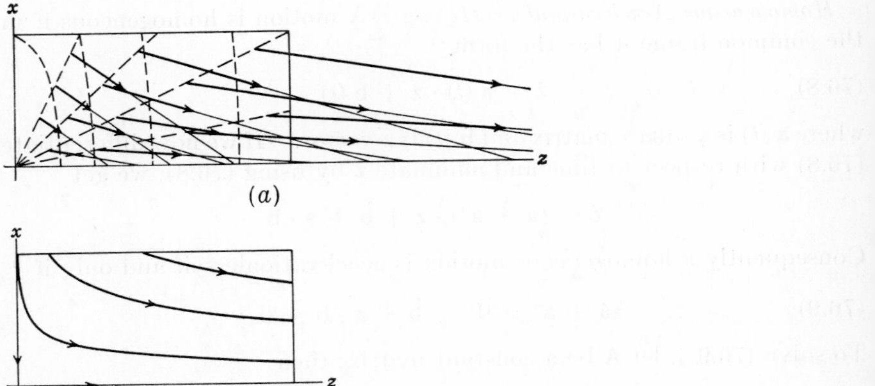

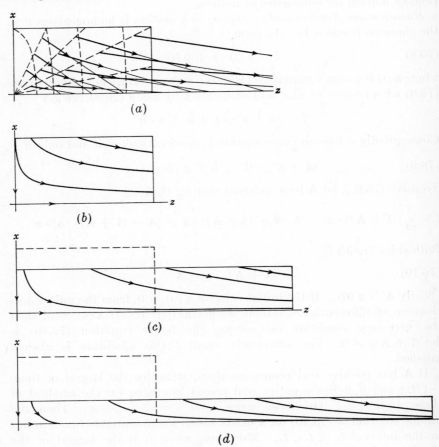

FIG. 76.1. Simple extension without acceleration, in the case $\sigma_0 = \frac{1}{3}$. (*After Truesdel* [1955*a*])

*Accelerationless Simple Extension.* Simple extension is given by

$$\mathbf{a} = k(t) \begin{bmatrix} -\sigma & 0 & 0 \\ 0 & -\sigma & 0 \\ 0 & 0 & 1 \end{bmatrix} \qquad \mathbf{b} = 0 \tag{76.13}$$

Substituting these into (76.10) gives

$$k(t) = \frac{k_0}{1 + k_0 t} \qquad \sigma(t) = \sigma_0 \frac{1 + k_0 t}{1 - k_0 \sigma_0 t} \tag{76.14}$$

n this motion a rectangular block with edges parallel to coordinate lanes is extended along the $z$ direction at the rate $k(t)$ and contracted ransversely in the ratio $\sigma(t)$. The streamlines in the $y = 0$ plane are ne curves

$$z\, x^{1/\sigma} = \text{const} \tag{76.15}$$

he ratio of the volume $v$ at time $t$ to the initial volume $V$ is

$$\frac{v}{V} = (1 + k_0 t)(1 - k_0 \sigma_0 t)^2 \tag{76.16}$$

For $k > 0$, $\sigma_0 > 0$ the block is stretched, becoming thinner with time. he volume reduces to zero when $t = 1/k_0 \sigma_0$ (Fig. 76.1).

## 7. STRESS WITHOUT FLUX

In this article we should like to find the integral of

$$\check{\mathbf{s}} = 0 \tag{77.1}$$

r a given velocity field $\mathbf{v}$. This is the state of stress with vanishing flux. mploying Truesdell's stress rate (72.9), it is not difficult to see that we eed not know the affine connection to calculate $\check{\mathbf{s}}$ in all coordinate ystems. In fact,

$$\check{s}^{kl} \equiv \frac{\partial s^{kl}}{\partial t} + s^{kl}{}_{,m}\, v^m - s^{km}\, v^l{}_{,m} - s^{ml}\, v^k{}_{,m} + \frac{s^{kl}}{\sqrt{g}} (\sqrt{g}\, v^m)_{,m} \tag{77.2}$$

et $x^k = x^k(X^1, X^2, X^3, t)$ be the three independent integrals of $dx^k = v^k\, dt$, here $X^\alpha$ are three independent functions of the initial coordinates. he deformation tensor $\overset{-1}{\mathbf{c}}$ calculated from the configuration $X^\alpha$ is

$$\overset{-1}{c}{}^{kl} = G^{\alpha\beta}\, x^k{}_{,\alpha}\, x^l{}_{,\beta} \tag{77.3}$$

here $G^{\alpha\beta}$ are the contravariant components of any second-order tensor eld depending on $X^\alpha$ only. By differentiating (77.3) and using $(19.1)_1$, e find that

$$\frac{D}{Dt}(\overset{-1}{c}{}^{kl}) = \overset{-1}{c}{}^{km}\, v^l{}_{;m} + \overset{-1}{c}{}^{ml}\, v^k{}_{;m} \tag{77.4}$$

herefore

$$\frac{D}{Dt}(\rho\, \overset{-1}{c}{}^{kl} = \rho\, (\overset{-1}{c}{}^{km}\, v^l{}_{;m} + \overset{-1}{c}{}^{ml}\, v^k{}_{;m} - \overset{-1}{c}{}^{kl}\, v^m{}_{;m}) \tag{77.5}$$

where the last term on the right is the contribution of $\dot{\rho}$. Comparison o (77.5) with (72.9) shows that $\rho \overset{-1}{c}{}^{kl}$ is a solution of (77.1). Since $X^\alpha$ ar arbitrary independent functions of the initial coordinates, the quantitie $x^k{}_{,\alpha}$ are not necessarily Kronecker deltas at $t = 0$, but may take o arbitrary values. Therefore this is a solution of the initial-value probler (77.1). Since (77.2) is linear in $\mathbf{s}$, it is the unique solution, i.e.,

$$s^{kl} = A \rho \overset{-1}{c}{}^{kl} \tag{77.6}$$

is the general solution of (77.1), where $A$ is a dimensional constant.

For hypoelastic bodies of grade zero $A^k{}_l{}^m{}_n$ in (73.10) is independent of s Therefore if $\mathbf{s}_0$ is a solution of (77.1) and $\mathbf{s}$ satisfies the constitutiv equations, then $\mathbf{s} + \mathbf{s}_0$ also satisfies these equations. Consequentl $\mathbf{s} + \mathbf{s}_0$ is a solution satisfying arbitrary initial data. This result can b used to reduce the initial- and boundary-value problem to a boundary value problem with homogeneous boundary conditions. Once $\mathbf{s}_0$ i determined as given by (77.6), we must determine $\mathbf{s}$ so that it satisfies th following:

1. The constitutive equations (73.20) or (73.21)
2. The equations of motion

$$2 \mu s^{kl}{}_{;l} = \rho (\dot{v}^k - f^k) - 2 \mu s_0{}^{kl}{}_{;l} \tag{77.7}$$

3. The boundary conditions

$$s^{kl} n_l = s^k - s_0{}^{kl} n_l \tag{77.8}$$

where $n_l$ is the unit exterior normal and $s^k$ are the prescribed surfac tractions

4. The initial conditions

$$s^{kl} = 0 \tag{77.9}$$

From (77.6) it is clear that any solution of (77.1) which satisfies th equation of motion (74.2) at $t = 0$ will in general fail to satisfy it at later time, a fact which is clear from the appearance of $s_0{}^{kl}{}_{;l}$ in (77.7 If, however, the initial conditions and motion are such that (77.6) yielc $s_0{}^{kl}{}_{;l} = 0$, then a superposition principle may be formulated. If satisfies all the differential equations of the theory, so does $\mathbf{s} + \mathbf{s}_0$.

For an incompressible body according to (73.14) the flux of $\mathbf{s}$ may b replaced by the flux of $\mathbf{s} + \frac{p}{2\mu}\mathbf{I}$. The solution (77.6) shows that in an deformation $\mathbf{x} = \mathbf{x}(\mathbf{X})$ such that $2 \mu \overset{-1}{c}{}_k{}^l{}_{;l} = p_{,k}$ for some $p$ we have solution $\overset{-1}{\mathbf{c}} - \frac{p}{2\mu}\mathbf{I}$ for the equation $\check{\mathbf{s}} + \frac{\dot{p}}{2\mu}\mathbf{I} - \frac{p}{\mu}\mathbf{d} = 0$. Among thes are all deformations that can be produced by suitable surface loads on incompressible materials.

## 78. STATIC HOMOGENEOUS STRESS

In Art. 76 we found that for an accelerationless motion we have

$$\mathbf{z} = \mathbf{a}\,(t) \cdot \mathbf{z} + \mathbf{b}\,(t) \tag{78.1}$$

where $\mathbf{a}$ is a square matrix and $\mathbf{b}$ is a vector, which are the solutions of

$$(\mathbf{I} + \mathbf{A}\,t) \cdot \mathbf{a} = \mathbf{A} \qquad (\mathbf{I} + \mathbf{A}\,t) \cdot \mathbf{b} = \mathbf{B} \tag{78.2}$$

with $\mathbf{A} = \mathbf{a}\,(0)$ and $\mathbf{B} = \mathbf{b}\,(0)$ being the initial values of $\mathbf{a}$ and $\mathbf{b}$.

For a velocity field satisfying (78.1) and (78.2), the dynamical equations (74.2) are satisfied and the constitutive equations give

$$\dot{\mathbf{s}} = \mathbf{g}\,[\mathbf{s}, \mathbf{A}/(\mathbf{I} + \mathbf{A}\,t)] \tag{78.3}$$

where we have written $\mathbf{a} = \mathbf{A}/(\mathbf{I} + \mathbf{A}\,t)$ symbolically.

Here the function $\mathbf{g}$ is analytic in its arguments for $|t| < t_0$ and continuously differentiable in the interval $t_- < t < t_+$, where $t_+$, $t_-$, and $t_0$ are defined in Art. 76. Hence we have the following theorem.

THE EXISTENCE AND UNIQUENESS THEOREM FOR HOMOGENEOUS STRESS. *In a class of linear accelerationless motions* (78.1) *and* (78.2) *of a hypoelastic body, for whatever the initial velocity of the origin* $\mathbf{B}$, *to each* $\mathbf{A}$ *and arbitrary homogeneous initial stress* $\mathbf{S}$ *there corresponds a unique homogeneous stress* $\mathbf{s}\,(t)$ *in* $t_- < t < t_+$ *for* $|t| < t_0$ *that is an analytic function of* $t$. The theorem may be carried over to the incompressible case very simply. The duration of the homogeneous stress depends therefore on $t_-$, $t_+$, and $t_0$ determined by $\mathbf{A}$, the *initial-velocity gradients,* and is not influenced by the initial stress. The occurrence of movable singularities is an essential and important feature of the theory.

We give below a special case to illustrate the basic nature of the theory. Other examples are studied in the following articles.

*Hydrostatic Stress.* Consider now the simplest possible case

$$d^k{}_l = \tfrac{1}{3}\,\delta(t)\,\delta^k{}_l \qquad s^k{}_l = -\mathfrak{p}\,(t)\,\delta^k{}_l \tag{78.4}$$

The first of these is equivalent to the accelerationless motion (78.1), in which

$$\mathbf{a} = \tfrac{1}{3}\,\delta(t)\,\mathbf{I} \qquad \mathbf{b}\,(t) = 0 \tag{78.5}$$

From (78.2) and (78.5) it follows that

$$\delta(t) = \frac{\delta_0}{1 + \frac{1}{3}\,\delta_0 t} \tag{78.6}$$

where $\delta_0 = \delta(0)$ is a constant. The equation of continuity (74.1) gives

$$\dot{\rho} + \rho\,\delta(t) = 0$$

which integrates into

$$\rho = \frac{\rho_0}{\left(1 + \frac{\delta_0}{3} t\right)^3} \tag{78.7}$$

where $\rho_0 \equiv \rho\,(0)$ is a constant.

The equation of motion (74.2) with $f^k = 0$ is satisfied identically. From (77.2) it follows that $\breve{\mathbf{s}} = -\dot{\mathfrak{p}}\mathbf{I}$. Consequently the constitutive equation (74.3) with the use of the identity $\delta = -d\,(\log \rho)/dt$ reduces to

$$\log \frac{\rho}{\rho_0} = \int_{\mathfrak{p}_0}^{\mathfrak{p}} \frac{d\zeta}{f\,(\zeta)} \tag{78.8}$$

$$f\,(\mathfrak{p}) \equiv \alpha_0 + \tfrac{1}{3}\,\alpha_1 + (\tfrac{1}{3} - \alpha_2 - \alpha_3 - \tfrac{1}{3}\,\alpha_4)\,\mathfrak{p} + (\alpha_5 + \alpha_6 + \alpha_7 + \tfrac{1}{3}\,\alpha_8)\,\mathfrak{p}^2 - (\alpha_9 + \alpha_{10})\,\mathfrak{p}^3 + \alpha_{11}\,\mathfrak{p}^4$$

where $\alpha_\gamma = \alpha_\gamma\,(-3\,\mathfrak{p}, 3\,\mathfrak{p}^2, -\mathfrak{p}^3)$. We therefore see that if the applied pressure is such that (78.7) holds, or equivalently if the ratio of volume at $t$ to that at $t = 0$ is given by

$$\frac{v}{V} = (1 + k_0\,t)^3 \tag{78.9}$$

then the pressure $p = 2\,\mu\,\mathfrak{p}$ as a function of density $\rho$ is determined to within a pair of arbitrary initial values $\mathfrak{p}_0$ and $\rho_0$.

The amount of pressure required for condensation will in general differ from the amount of tension required for rarefaction.

The physical requirement $d\rho/d\,\mathfrak{p} \geq 0$ demands that

$$f\,(\mathfrak{p}) \geq 0 \tag{78.10}$$

which is a restriction on the constitutive coefficients $\alpha_\gamma$. When $\mathfrak{p} > 0$ ($\mathfrak{p} < 0$), the body *hardens* or *softens,* depending on whether the curve $\rho = \rho\,(\mathfrak{p})$ is curved downward or upward (upward or downward). Only at $\mathfrak{p} = 0$ can the body harden both in pressure and in tension if the curvature changes sign there.

We have

$$\frac{1}{\rho}\frac{d^2\rho}{d\mathfrak{p}^2} = \frac{1 - f'}{f^2} \tag{78.11}$$

so that hardening or softening depends on the sign of $1 - f'$ except at points $\rho = 0$ or $d\rho/d\mathfrak{p} = \infty$.

For hypoelastic bodies of grades zero, one, and two we have

$$f(\mathfrak{p}) = \kappa + a\,\mathfrak{p} + b\,\mathfrak{p}^2 \tag{78.12}$$

where

$$\kappa \equiv \frac{3\lambda + 2\mu}{6\mu} > 0$$

$$a \equiv \tfrac{1}{3} \qquad b \equiv 0 \qquad \text{(grade zero)}$$

$$a \equiv \tfrac{1}{3} - 3\beta_0 - \beta_1 - \beta_2 - \beta_3 - \beta_4 \qquad b \equiv 0 \qquad \text{(grade one)} \tag{78.13}$$

$$\left.\begin{aligned} a &\equiv \tfrac{1}{3} - 3\beta_0 - \beta_1 - \beta_2 - \beta_3 - \beta_4 \\ b &\equiv 9\gamma_0 + 3\epsilon_0 + 3\gamma_1 + \epsilon_1 + 3\gamma_2 + 3\gamma_3 \\ &\quad + \gamma_4 + \gamma_5 + \gamma_6 + \gamma_7 + \tfrac{1}{3}\gamma_8 \end{aligned}\right\} \qquad \text{(grade two)}$$

In all cases the sign of $1 - a - b\,\mathfrak{p}$ determines hardening or softening except possibly at a root of (78.12) or where $\rho = 0$.

For grades zero, one, and two (78.8) now gives:

*grade zero:*

$$\frac{\rho}{\rho_0} = \left(\frac{\kappa + \frac{1}{3}\mathfrak{p}}{\kappa + \frac{1}{3}\mathfrak{p}_0}\right)^3 \tag{78.14}$$

*grade one:*

$$\frac{\rho}{\rho_0} = \begin{cases} \left(\dfrac{\kappa + a\,\mathfrak{p}}{\kappa + a\,\mathfrak{p}_0}\right)^{1/a} & (a \neq 0) \\ \exp\dfrac{\mathfrak{p} - \mathfrak{p}_0}{\kappa} & (a = 0) \end{cases} \tag{78.15}$$

*grade two:*

$$\frac{\rho}{\rho_0} = \begin{cases} \left(\dfrac{2b\,\mathfrak{p} + a - \bar{b}}{2b\,\mathfrak{p} + a + \bar{b}} \cdot \dfrac{2b\,\mathfrak{p}_0 + a + \bar{b}}{2b\,\mathfrak{p}_0 + a - \bar{b}}\right)^{1/\bar{b}} & (4\kappa b^2 < a^2) \\ \exp\left[\dfrac{4b(\mathfrak{p} - \mathfrak{p}_0)}{(2b + a\,\mathfrak{p}_0)(2b + a\,\mathfrak{p})}\right] & (4\kappa b^2 = a^2) \\ \exp\left[\dfrac{2}{\bar{b}}\left(\arctan\dfrac{2b\,\mathfrak{p} + a}{\bar{b}} - \arctan\dfrac{2b\,\mathfrak{p}_0 + a}{\bar{b}}\right)\right] & (4\kappa b^2 > a^2) \end{cases} \tag{78.16}$$

where

$$\bar{b} \equiv +\sqrt{|a^2 - 4\kappa b^2|}$$

A variety of density-pressure behaviors is included in these expressions. For example, a body of grade zero softens in compression and hardens in tension. As $\mathfrak{p} \to \infty$, $\rho \to \infty$ also, and at $\mathfrak{p} = -3\kappa$ the density vanishes. In the application the physical material will yield or fail at such a tension.

For a material having Poisson's ratio $\nu = \frac{1}{3}$, this tension is 4; i.e., $p = -8\,\mu$, which is very large.

For a body of grade one we have hardening or softening in compression if $a > 0$. For $a = 1$, (78.16) reduces to the classical linear formula. If $a < 0$, there is a pressure $\mathfrak{p} = \kappa/(-a)$ at which $\rho = \infty$. This implies that such a body will collapse under pressure but not under tension. Graphs of $\mathfrak{p} = \mathfrak{p}\,(\rho/\rho_0)$ for various $a$ are shown in Fig. 78.1 for hypoelastic bodies of grades zero and one.

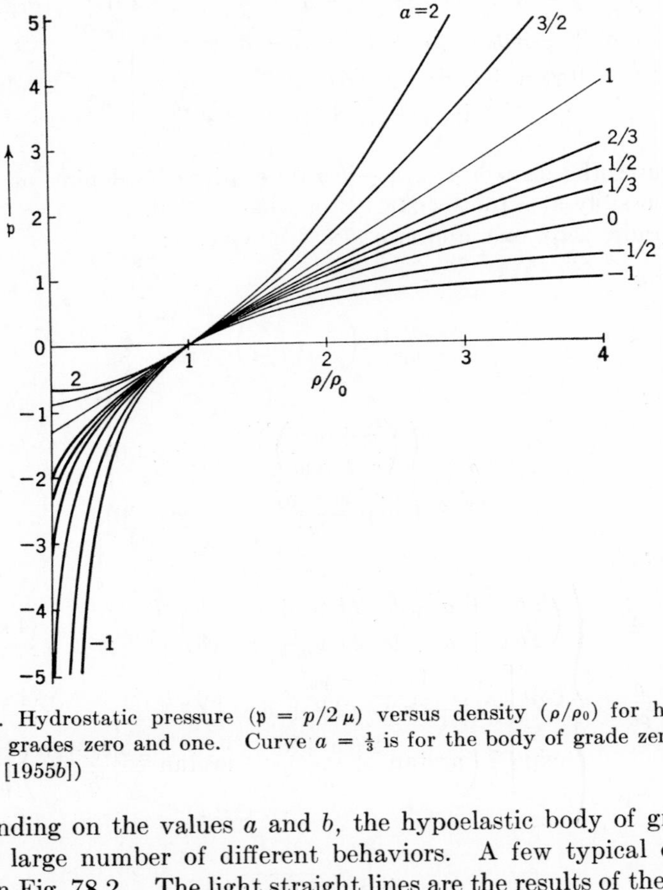


FIG. 78.1. Hydrostatic pressure ($\mathfrak{p} = p/2\,\mu$) versus density ($\rho/\rho_0$) for hypoelastic bodies of grades zero and one. Curve $a = \frac{1}{3}$ is for the body of grade zero. (*After Truesdell* [1955*b*])

Depending on the values $a$ and $b$, the hypoelastic body of grade two offers a large number of different behaviors. A few typical cases are shown in Fig. 78.2. The light straight lines are the results of the classical linear theory, dashed lines are the asymptotes, and small circles locate points of inflection. The first two figures are representative of soft bodies; the middle two are for hard bodies; the fifth figure is a hard body in tension and a soft body in compression; and the last figure represents a hard body in both tension and compression.

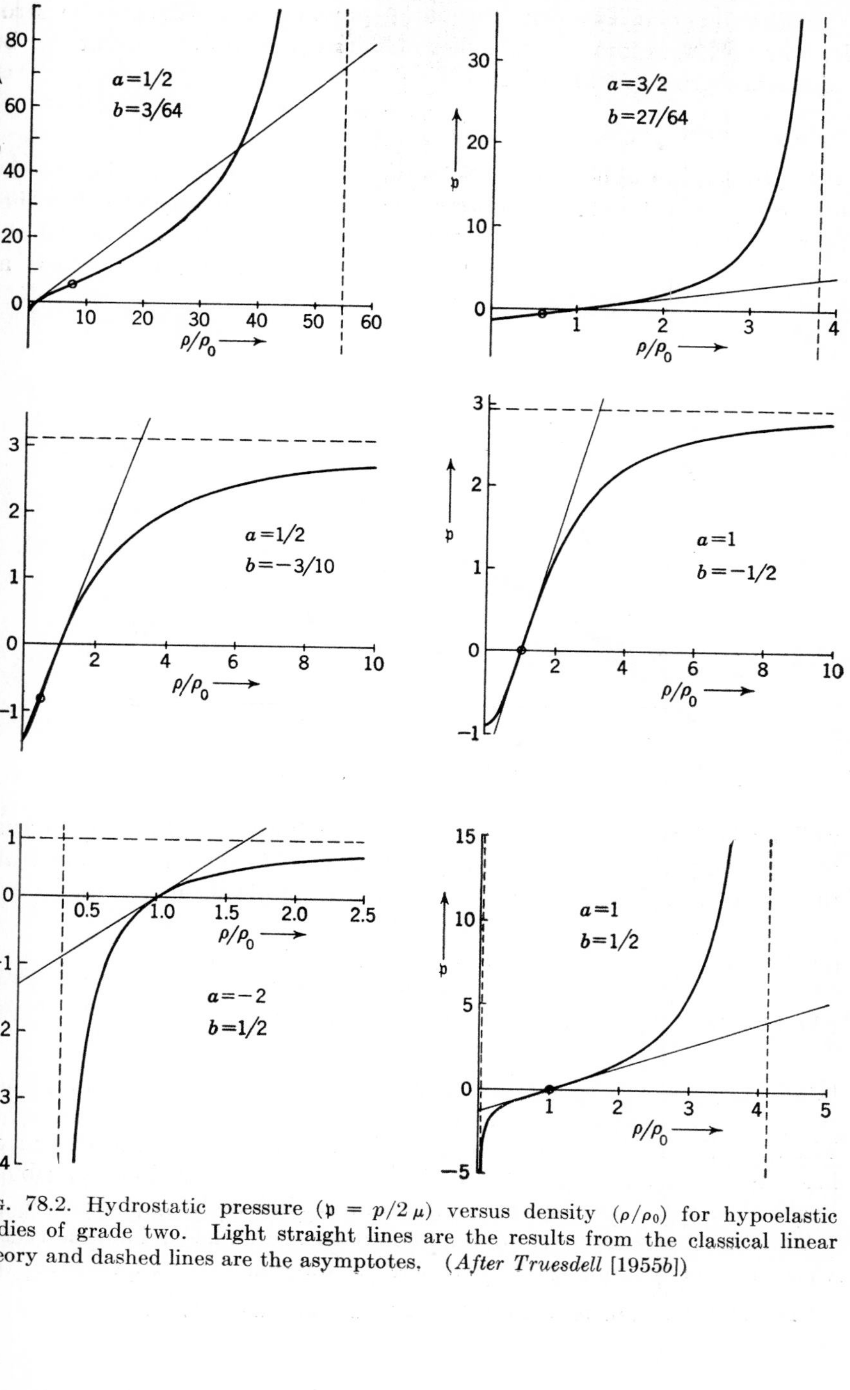


IG. 78.2. Hydrostatic pressure ($\mathfrak{p} = p/2\mu$) versus density ($\rho/\rho_0$) for hypoelastic odies of grade two. Light straight lines are the results from the classical linear heory and dashed lines are the asymptotes. (*After Truesdell* [1955*b*])

In the foregoing examples the initial pressure $\mathfrak{p}_0$ is taken to be zero. If, however, $\mathfrak{p}_0$ is known, the effect of initial pressure or tension can be determined from (78.14)–(78.16).

## 79. HYPOELASTIC SHEAR[1]

As studied in the previous article, the pressure-density relation for the case of hydrostatic stress is obtained as a solution of the theory rather than taken as a postulate. Hypoelasticity is capable of predicting the stress-strain relations. These relations depend on the initial stress as

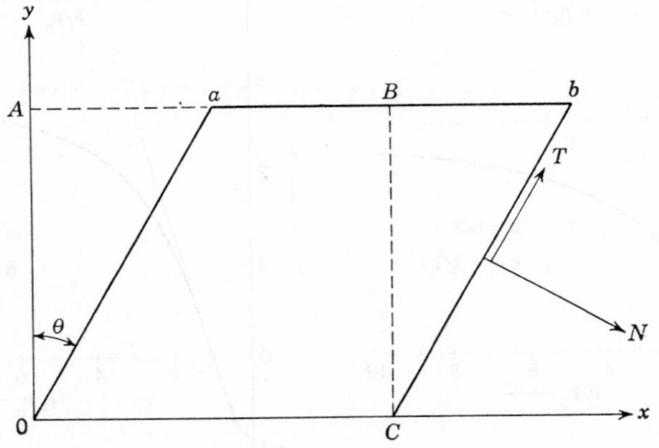


FIG. 79.1. Simple shear.

well as the type of deformation (the path followed). Moreover, by use of this theory theoretical yield points may be determined. To illustrate these points further, we consider the case of simple shear

$$v_x = 2\,k\,y \qquad v_y = v_z = 0 \qquad (k = \text{const}) \tag{79.1}$$

where rectangular coordinates are employed. Let

$$\tau \equiv 2\,k\,t \qquad \theta = \arctan \tau \tag{79.2}$$

Then $\theta$ is the angle through which a plane initially normal to the $x$ axis has been rotated at time $t$ (Fig. 79.1). Guided by the analogous problem in the theory of elasticity, we seek a solution in which $s_{xz} = s_{yz} = 0$.

The equations of continuity and motion are satisfied identically for vanishing body forces. The constitutive equations (74.3) give the

[1] Truesdell [1955*b*, p. 98; 1955*a*; 1956]. See also Green [1956*a*, *b*].

following four ordinary differential equations:

$$
(79.3)\quad \frac{d}{d\tau}\begin{bmatrix} s_{xx} & s_{xy} & 0 \\ \cdot & s_{yy} & 0 \\ \cdot & \cdot & s_{zz} \end{bmatrix} = \begin{bmatrix} 2\,s_{xy} & s_{yy} & 0 \\ \cdot & 0 & 0 \\ \cdot & \cdot & 0 \end{bmatrix} + \tfrac{1}{2}\,\alpha_1 \begin{bmatrix} 0 & 1 & 0 \\ \cdot & 0 & 0 \\ \cdot & \cdot & 0 \end{bmatrix}
$$

$$
+\, s_{xy}\,[\alpha_3 + (s_{xx} + s_{yy})\,\alpha_7] \begin{bmatrix} 1 & 0 & 0 \\ \cdot & 1 & 0 \\ \cdot & \cdot & 1 \end{bmatrix} + \tfrac{1}{2}\,\alpha_4 \begin{bmatrix} s_{xy} & \tfrac{1}{2}\,(s_{xx} + s_{yy}) & 0 \\ \cdot & s_{xy} & 0 \\ \cdot & \cdot & 0 \end{bmatrix}
$$

$$
+\, s_{xy}\,[\alpha_6 + (s_{xx} + s_{yy})\,\alpha_{10}] \begin{bmatrix} s_{xx} & s_{xy} & 0 \\ \cdot & s_{yy} & 0 \\ \cdot & \cdot & s_{zz} \end{bmatrix}
$$

$$
+\, \tfrac{1}{2}\,\alpha_8 \begin{bmatrix} s_{xy}\,(s_{xx} + s_{yy}) & \tfrac{1}{2}\,(s_{xx}^2 + s_{yy}^2) + s_{xy}^2 & 0 \\ \cdot & s_{xy}\,(s_{xx} + s_{yy}) & 0 \\ \cdot & \cdot & 0 \end{bmatrix}
$$

$$
+\, s_{xy}\,[\alpha_9 + (s_{xx} + s_{yy})\,\alpha_{11}] \begin{bmatrix} s_{xx}^2 + s_{xy}^2 & s_{xy}\,(s_{xx} + s_{yy}) & 0 \\ \cdot & s_{yy}^2 + s_{xy}^2 & 0 \\ \cdot & \cdot & s_{zz}^2 \end{bmatrix}
$$

where $\alpha_\gamma$ are functions of $s_{xx} + s_{yy} + s_{zz}$, $s_{xx}\,s_{yy} + s_{yy}\,s_{zz} + s_{zz}\,s_{xx} - s_{xy}^2$, $(s_{xx}\,s_{yy} - s_{xy}^2)\,s_{zz}$. These results follow by inspection:

1. Shearing stress alone is insufficient to maintain simple shearing. This is in accord with the theory of finite elasticity.
2. The phenomenological coefficients $\alpha_0$, $\alpha_2$, and $\alpha_5$ do not influence the response of the body.
3. $s_{zz} = 0$ is a possible solution if and only if $\alpha_3 \equiv \alpha_7 \equiv 0$.
4. $s_{yy} = 0$ is a possible solution if and only if $\alpha_3 \equiv \alpha_4 \equiv \alpha_7 \equiv \alpha_8 \equiv \alpha_9 \equiv \alpha_{11} \equiv 0$.

We now consider in detail the response of a body of grade zero and a body of grade one.

*Hypoelastic Body of Grade Zero.* The body satisfies conditions 3 and 4. Integration of (79.3) now gives the interesting results

$$
(79.4)\qquad s_{yy} - S_{yy} = 0 \qquad s_{xy} - S_{xy} = (\tfrac{1}{2} + S_{yy})\,\tau
$$
$$
s_{xx} - S_{xx} = (\tfrac{1}{2} + S_{yy})\,\tau^2 + 2\,S_{xy}\,\tau
$$

where $S_{xx}$, $S_{yy}$, and $S_{xy}$ denote initial stresses. For zero initial stress we get

$$
(79.5)\qquad s_{xx} = \tfrac{1}{2}\tau^2 \qquad s_{yy} = 0 \qquad s_{xy} = \tfrac{1}{2}\tau
$$

*For a hypoelastic body of grade zero the classical proportionality between the shear stress and shear strain continues to hold. In addition, a normal tension proportional to the square of the shear stress must be supplied on the*

$x =$ *const planes.* On the plane $Cb$ inclined to the shearing plane at angle $\frac{\pi}{2} - \theta$, the normal and tangential tractions $N$ and $T$ are calculated by

$$N = s^{kl} n_k n_l \qquad T = s^{kl} n_k t_l$$

where $n_k$ and $t_l$ are the unit exterior normal and the unit tangent to this edge. We have

$$\begin{aligned} n_1 &= +t_2 = \cos\theta = (1+\tau^2)^{-\frac{1}{2}} \\ n_2 &= -t_1 = -\sin\theta = -\tau\,(1+\tau^2)^{-\frac{1}{2}} \end{aligned}$$

Hence for zero initial stress

$$\text{(79.6)} \qquad \begin{aligned} N &= \frac{s_{xx} - 2\tau\, s_{xy} + \tau^2\, s_{yy}}{1+\tau^2} = -\frac{\tau^2}{2\,(1+\tau^2)} = -\tfrac{1}{2}\sin^2\theta \\ T &= \frac{(s_{xx} - s_{yy})\,\tau + s_{xy}\,(1-\tau^2)}{1+\tau^2} = \frac{\tau^2}{2\,(1+\tau^2)} = \tfrac{1}{4}\sin 2\,\theta \end{aligned}$$

Thus the shearing builds up to a maximum value of $\frac{1}{4}$ at $\theta = \pi/4$ and falls thereafter while the normal traction (which is a pressure) increases steadily to a value $\frac{1}{2}$ at $\theta = \pi/2$. A phenomenon similar to this was found in Art. 52 (4) where it was referred to as "the Poynting effect."

*Hypoelastic Body of Grade One.* For this case $\alpha_\gamma$ are given by (73.22). Differential equations (79.3) in this case integrate to give

$$s_{xy} = \frac{A}{\sqrt{|a_s|}} \begin{matrix}\sinh \\ \sin\end{matrix} \sqrt{|a_s|}\,\tau + S_{xy} \begin{matrix}\cosh \\ \cos\end{matrix} \sqrt{|a_s|}\,\tau$$

$$\text{(79.7)} \qquad \begin{aligned} \frac{s_{zz} - S_{zz}}{\beta_3} &= \frac{s_{yy} - S_{yy}}{\beta_3 + \frac{1}{2}\beta_4} = \frac{s_{xx} - S_{xx}}{2 + \beta_3 + \frac{1}{2}\beta_4} = \tfrac{1}{2}\,(s_{xx} - s_{yy} - S_{xx} + S_{yy}) \\ &= \int_0^\tau s_{xy}\,(\xi)\,d\xi = \frac{2\,A}{|a_s|} \begin{matrix}\sinh^2 \\ \sin^2\end{matrix} \tfrac{1}{2}\sqrt{|a_s|}\,\tau + \frac{S_{xy}}{\sqrt{|a_s|}} \begin{matrix}\sinh \\ \sin\end{matrix} \sqrt{|a_s|}\,\tau \\ a_s &\equiv \beta_1 + \beta_3 + \beta_4 + \tfrac{3}{2}\beta_1\beta_3 + \tfrac{1}{2}\beta_1\beta_4 + \tfrac{1}{2}\beta_3\beta_4 + \tfrac{1}{4}\beta_4{}^2 \\ A &\equiv \tfrac{1}{2} + \tfrac{1}{2}\,(\beta_1 + \tfrac{1}{2}\beta_4)\,S_{xx} + (1 + \tfrac{1}{2}\beta_1 + \tfrac{1}{4}\beta_4)\,S_{yy} + \tfrac{1}{2}\beta_1\,S_{zz} \end{aligned}$$

where the upper alternatives refer to the case $a_s > 0$ and the lower to $a_s < 0$. For the case $a_s = 0$ the same results hold with the exception of $(79.7)_1$ and the integral appearing in (79.7). These are replaced by

$$\text{(79.8)} \qquad s_{xy} - S_{xy} = A\,\tau \qquad \int_0^\tau s_{xy}\,(\xi)\,d\xi = \tfrac{1}{2}A\,\tau^2 + S_{xy}\,\tau$$

respectively. We now study the case of an initially unstressed block. For this case $A = \frac{1}{2}$ and we have

$$s_{xy} = \begin{cases} \dfrac{1}{2\sqrt{a_s}} \sinh \sqrt{a_s}\,\tau & \text{for } a_s > 0 \\ \dfrac{\tau}{2} & \text{for } a_s = 0 \\ \dfrac{1}{2\sqrt{-a_s}} \sin \sqrt{-a_s}\,\tau & \text{for } a_s < 0 \end{cases} \tag{79.9}$$

$$a_s \equiv \beta_1 + \beta_3 + \beta_4 + \tfrac{3}{2}\beta_1\beta_3 + \tfrac{1}{2}\beta_1\beta_4 + \tfrac{1}{2}\beta_3\beta_4 + \tfrac{1}{4}\beta_4{}^2$$

As is expected, for small shears we get the same result as in the classical linear theory, namely, $s_{xy} = \tau/2$. For large shears the situation is entirely different.

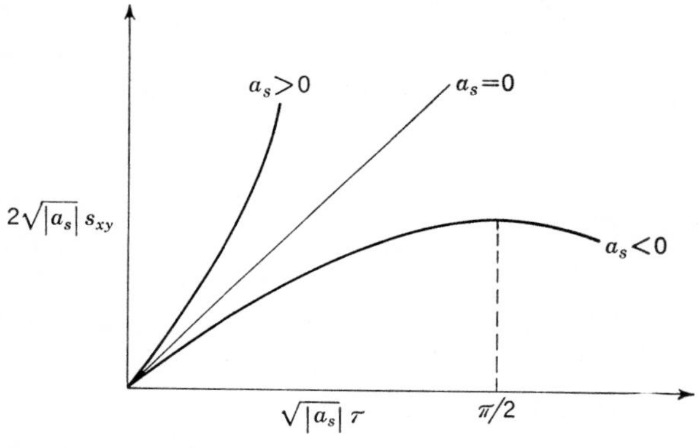


FIG. 79.2. Simple shear of hypoelastic body of grade one.

The three cases of *hard body* $a_s > 0$, *neutral body* $a_s = 0$, and *soft body* $a_s < 0$ are shown in Fig. 79.2.

The neutral body corresponds to the classical linear theory. For the soft body we have a sine curve which acquires its first maximum for $s_{xy}$ at

$$\tau = \frac{\pi}{2\sqrt{-a_s}} \tag{79.10}$$

After this point is reached, stress decreases with increasing strain. This point may be taken as the *upper bound for the yield stress.* If we decide to use $\theta = \arctan \tau$ as a measure of shear, the stress-strain curve for $s_{xy} = f(\theta)$ is no longer a sine curve. In fact, this curve is similar to measured curves in that it is strikingly like a straight line for most of its length. Maximum shear $s_s$, called *shear strength,* and the corresponding angle $\theta_s$, called *ultimate shear angle,* are therefore obtained as a result of the theory rather than being an assumption as in the plasticity theory.

For the soft hypoelastic bodies of grade one they are given by

$$(79.11) \qquad s_s = \frac{1}{2\sqrt{-a_s}} \qquad \theta_s = \arctan \frac{\pi}{2\sqrt{-a_s}}$$

As evident from (79.7), the simple accelerationless shear cannot be produced by shearing forces alone. The normal stresses that must be supplied on the shear planes for zero initial stress are given by

$$(79.12) \qquad \frac{s_{yy}}{\beta_3 + \frac{1}{2}\beta_4} = \frac{s_{zz}}{\beta_3} = \begin{cases} \dfrac{1}{a_s} \sinh^2 \left(\frac{1}{2}\sqrt{a_s}\,\tau\right) & \text{for } a_s \geq 0 \\ \dfrac{1}{-a_s} \sin^2 \left(\frac{1}{2}\sqrt{-a_s}\,\tau\right) & \text{for } a_s \leq 0 \end{cases}$$

Thus, if we fail to supply the necessary tension $s_{zz}$, we may expect the body to draw together or spread out in a direction perpendicular to the shear planes according as $a_s > 0$ or $a_s < 0$. The same situation applies to the shear planes depending on the sign of $\beta_3 + \frac{1}{2}\beta_4 > 0$ or $\beta_3 + \frac{1}{2}\beta_4 < 0$ when $s_{yy}$ is not supplied. Truesdell calls $\beta_3$ *shear elusiveness* and $\beta_3 + \frac{1}{2}\beta_4$ *shear tenseness*. A similar situation is found in the finite elastic shear, although with less freedom. In finite elasticity it is, in general, not possible to specify $s_{yy}$ and $s_{zz}$ in an arbitrary nonzero-constant ratio. For further details and variety of stress-strain curves predicted by the present theory, we refer the reader to the references cited in the footnote of this article and in Art. 90.

## 80. SIMPLE EXTENSION: A STATICAL THEORY[1]

In this article we treat the accelerationless motion of a hypoelastic body of grade zero subjected to a homogeneous stress field which can produce an extensile motion. We assume a stress field of the form

$$(80.1) \qquad \mathbf{s} = \begin{bmatrix} -Q & 0 & 0 \\ 0 & -Q & 0 \\ 0 & 0 & T \end{bmatrix}$$

where $Q$ and $T$ are functions of time alone. The simple extension is described by

$$(80.2) \qquad \mathbf{d} = k \begin{bmatrix} -\sigma & 0 & 0 \\ 0 & -\sigma & 0 \\ 0 & 0 & 1 \end{bmatrix}$$

where $k$ and $\sigma$ are functions of time. For this motion to be acceleration-

[1] For a hypoelastic body of grade zero see Truesdell [1955*b*, art. 4]. For grade one see Truesdell [1955*b*, art. 10]. For the incompressible body see Green [1956*a*, art. 5]. For a dynamical theory see Art. 81.

less, we found in (76.14) that

(80.3) $$k(t) = \frac{k_0}{1 + k_0 t} \qquad \sigma(t) = \sigma_0 \frac{1 + k_0 t}{1 - k_0 \sigma_0 t}$$

When $k(t)$ and $\sigma(t)$ are so chosen, the equations of continuity and motion (without body forces) are satisfied. Substitution of (80.1) and (80.2) into the constitutive equations (73.20) yields

(80.4) $$\begin{aligned} \frac{1}{k}\frac{dT}{dt} &= (1 + 2\sigma) T + \frac{1 - \nu - 2\sigma\nu}{1 - 2\nu} \\ \frac{1}{k}\frac{dQ}{dt} &= -Q + \frac{\sigma - \nu}{1 - 2\nu} \end{aligned}$$

In order to find the correct time behavior of $Q$ and $T$, we must solve (80.4) with $k$ and $\sigma$ given by (80.3). In the linear theory of elasticity a simple tension $T$ produces a simple extension in the direction of $T$, i.e., $Q = 0$. The dynamically correct solution with $Q = 0$ employing (80.3) is not included in (80.4). This of course is also suggested in the theory of finite elasticity; i.e., tensile stress alone is insufficient to produce simple extension. Suppose that we overlook (80.3), i.e., neglect the inertia of the material and put $Q = 0$ for all $t$, leaving $\sigma$ and $k$ arbitrary; then $(80.4)_2$ gives

(80.5) $$\sigma = \nu$$

Thus the contraction ratio at all times is equal to Poisson's ratio, just as in the classical theory. Now since $k = \frac{d}{dt}\log z$, from $(80.4)_1$ it follows that

(80.6) $$\log\frac{z}{Z} = \int_{T_0}^{T} \frac{d\xi}{(1 + 2\nu)\xi + 1 + \nu}$$

or

(80.7) $$T = T_0 + \frac{1 + \nu + (1 + 2\nu)T_0}{1 + 2\nu}[(1 + \tau)^{1+2\nu} - 1]$$

$$\tau \equiv \frac{z}{Z} - 1 = k_0 t$$

While for small strain $\tau$, as we shall see, there is some agreement between (80.6) and the exact solutions of (80.4), for large $\tau$ we shall find a large discrepancy between the two. In the linear elasticity theory we have $Q = 0$ for $\tau = 0$. Hence from $(80.4)_2$ we get

(80.8) $$\left.\frac{dQ}{d\tau}\right|_{\tau=0} = \frac{\sigma_0 - \nu}{1 - 2\nu}$$

Thus, if we choose the initial contraction ratio $\sigma_0 = \nu$, Poisson's ratio, the cross stress $Q$ at first will rise more slowly than for any other initial ratio $\sigma_0$. Hence $Q$ initially will be very nearly zero, as in the linear theory of elasticity.

Now choose $\sigma_0 = \nu$ in (80.3) and substitute it into (80.4). Hence

$$(80.9)\quad \begin{aligned} (1+\tau)(1-\nu\tau)\frac{dT}{d\tau} &= (1+2\nu+\nu\tau)\,T \\ &\quad + \frac{1+\nu}{1-2\nu}(1-2\nu-\nu\tau) \\ (1+\tau)(1-\nu\tau)\frac{dQ}{d\tau} &= -(1-\nu\tau)\,Q + \frac{\nu(1+\nu)}{1-2\nu}\tau \end{aligned}$$

The general solution of this system satisfying the initial conditions $T = T_0$, $Q = Q_0$ when $\tau = 0$ is[2]

$$(80.10)\quad \begin{aligned} T &= \frac{1+\tau}{(1-\nu\tau)^2}\left\{T_0 + \frac{1+\nu}{1-2\nu}\left[\frac{\tau(1+\nu^2\tau)}{1+\tau} - 2\nu\log(1+\tau)\right]\right\} \\ Q &= \frac{1}{1+\tau}\left[Q_0 + \frac{1+\nu}{1-2\nu}\left(\frac{1}{\nu}\log\frac{1}{1-\nu\tau} - \tau\right)\right] \end{aligned}$$

If we set $Q_0 = T_0 = 0$, we find that (80.7) and (80.10) agree with each other as far as linear terms in $\tau$. For large $\tau$ the differences are large. For $\tau = 1/\nu$ we get $T = +\infty$; i.e., to annul the volume, infinite tension is required. Reduction of length to zero, on the other hand, requires the nondimensional critical pressure $P_{cr} = (1-\nu)/(1-2\nu)$. For $\nu = \frac{1}{3}$, $P_{cr} = 2$, a very large value (the physical pressure $p = 2\mu P$).

For $\tau = \frac{1}{2}$ we have $Q = +\infty$, and for $\tau = -1$, $Q = -\infty$. Thus pulling and pushing are quite different: in pulling, $Q/T \to \infty$ as $\tau \to 1/\nu$; and in pushing, $Q/T \to \infty$ as $\tau \to -1$. Therefore in pushing, the cross stress becomes dominant sooner.

If we examine (80.7), the quasi-static solution of (80.9), we find $P \to \infty$ as $\tau \to \infty$. To produce zero length, we need $P_{cr} = (1+\nu)/(1+2\nu)$, which gives $P_{cr} = \frac{4}{5}$ for $\nu = \frac{1}{3}$, a considerably smaller value than the correct value $P_{cr} = 2$. The quasi-static solution makes the body appear much softer than it is.

Thus the theory is dynamical in nature, and the terminology is such that the small rate of loading or long-time experiment is meaningless. Since in the theory there is no time constant, in the end the rate and the time must cancel each other. Except for small extensions the quasi-static solution does not agree with the exact solution. For other details see Figs. 80.1 and 80.2.

[2] Truesdell's [1955a] results corresponding to (80.10) and some of his conclusions are erroneous. The present integrals give a much better correlation between the approximate solution and the exact one. See Figs. 80.1 and 80.2.

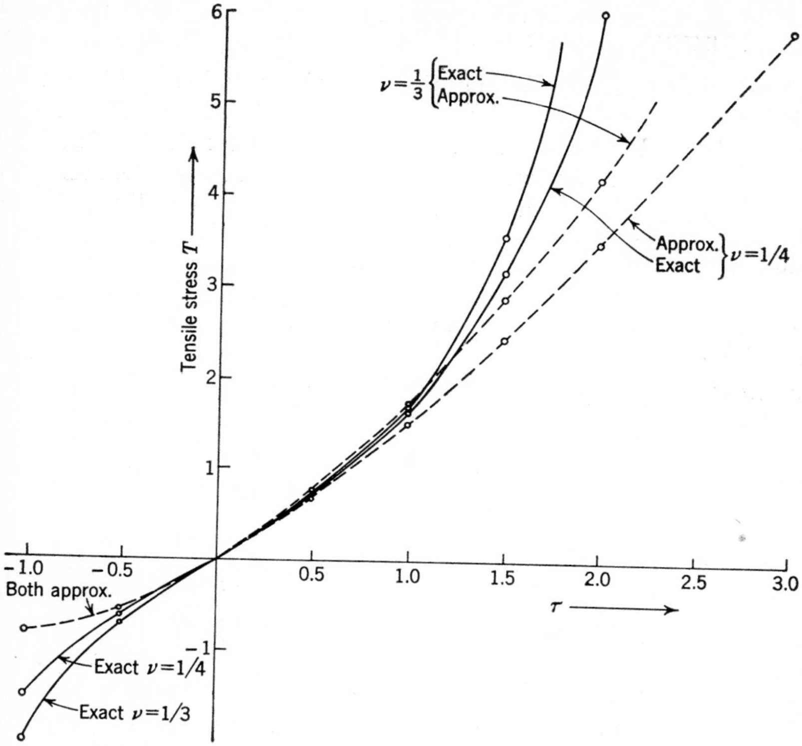


FIG. 80.1. Tensile stress $T$.

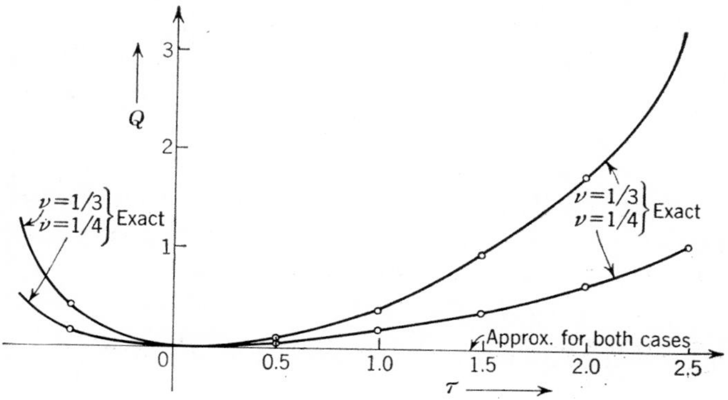


FIG. 80.2. Cross stress $Q$.

## 81. SIMPLE EXTENSION: A DYNAMICAL THEORY

Green [1956c] gave a solution for the simple extension of a hypoelasti body of grade zero. The character of this solution is different fror Truesdell's accelerationless motion studied in the previous article. Th inertia terms in the solution can be made as small as possible, in a precis way, leading to the result of accelerationless motion. Given the wa the motion takes place, however, the solution is restricted. It should b this time be clear that in the absence of a uniqueness theorem no decisio can be advanced in favor of one theory or the other. What is mor serious, perhaps, is the complete lack of experimental results.

The basic field equations and constitutive equations for a hypoelasti body of grade zero are

(81.1)
$$\frac{\partial \rho}{\partial t} + (\rho\, v^k)_{;k} = 0$$

(81.2)
$$2\,\mu\, s^{kl}{}_{;l} = \rho\left(\frac{\partial v^k}{\partial t} + v^k{}_{;l}\, v^l\right)$$

(81.3)
$$\breve{s}^{km}\, g_{ml} = \frac{\nu}{1-2\,\nu}\, d^m{}_m\, \delta^k{}_l + d^k{}_l$$

(81.4)
$$\breve{s}^{kl} \equiv \frac{\partial s^{kl}}{\partial t} + v^m\, s^{kl}{}_{;m} - s^{km}\, v^l{}_{;m} - s^{ml}\, v^k{}_{;m} + s^{kl}\, d^m{}_m$$

(81.5)
$$2\, d_{kl} = v_{k;l} + v_{l;k}$$

We take fixed rectangular coordinates $x$, $y$, $z$ and denote velocity com ponents by $v_x$, $v_y$, $v_z$ and stress components by $2\,\mu\, s_{xx}$, $2\,\mu\, s_{xy}$, . . . For simple extension the velocity field will be taken as

(81.6)
$$v_x = \dot{\eta}\, x \qquad v_y = \dot{\eta}\, y \qquad v_z = \dot{\epsilon}\, z$$

where $\eta$ and $\epsilon$ are functions of $t$ alone.

Since $\rho$ is a function of $t$ alone, the equation of continuity (81.1) now give

(81.7)
$$\frac{\partial \rho}{\partial t} + \rho\,(\dot{\epsilon} + 2\,\dot{\eta}) = 0$$

Under the condition that for $t = 0$, $\rho = \rho_0 =$ const, the solution of thi equation is

(81.8)
$$\rho = \rho_0 \exp\,(-\epsilon - 2\,\eta)$$

provided $\eta$ and $\epsilon$ vanish at $t = 0$.

We now seek a solution for the stress field of the form

(81.9)
$$\mathbf{s} = \begin{bmatrix} P & 0 & 0 \\ 0 & Q & 0 \\ 0 & 0 & T \end{bmatrix}$$

Note that the deformation-rate tensor **d**, as follows from (81.5) and (81.6), is

$$\mathbf{d} = \begin{bmatrix} \dot{\eta} & 0 & 0 \\ 0 & \dot{\eta} & 0 \\ 0 & 0 & \dot{\epsilon} \end{bmatrix} \tag{81.10}$$

Equations (81.2) now give

$$\begin{aligned} \frac{\partial P}{\partial x} &= \frac{\rho}{2\,\mu}\,(\ddot{\eta} + \dot{\eta}^2)\,x = \frac{\rho_0}{2\,\mu}\,(\ddot{\eta} + \dot{\eta}^2)\,x \exp\left(-\epsilon - 2\,\eta\right) \\ \frac{\partial Q}{\partial y} &= \frac{\rho}{2\,\mu}\,(\ddot{\eta} + \dot{\eta}^2)\,y = \frac{\rho_0}{2\,\mu}\,(\ddot{\eta} + \dot{\eta}^2)\,y \exp\left(-\epsilon - 2\,\eta\right) \\ \frac{\partial T}{\partial z} &= \frac{\rho}{2\,\mu}\,(\ddot{\epsilon} + \dot{\epsilon}^2)\,z = \frac{\rho_0}{2\,\mu}\,(\ddot{\epsilon} + \dot{\epsilon}^2)\,z \exp\left(-\epsilon - 2\,\eta\right) \end{aligned} \tag{81.11}$$

Constitutive equations (81.3) and (81.4) yield

$$\begin{aligned} &\frac{\partial P}{\partial t} + \dot{\eta}\left(x\,\frac{\partial P}{\partial x} + y\,\frac{\partial P}{\partial y}\right) + \dot{\epsilon}\,z\,\frac{\partial P}{\partial z} + P\,\dot{\epsilon} = \frac{\nu}{1 - 2\,\nu}\,(\dot{\epsilon} + 2\,\dot{\eta}) + \dot{\eta} \\ &\frac{\partial Q}{\partial t} + \dot{\eta}\left(x\,\frac{\partial Q}{\partial x} + y\,\frac{\partial Q}{\partial y}\right) + \dot{\epsilon}\,z\,\frac{\partial Q}{\partial z} + Q\,\dot{\epsilon} = \frac{\nu}{1 - 2\,\nu}\,(\dot{\epsilon} + 2\,\dot{\eta}) + \dot{\eta} \\ &\frac{\partial T}{\partial t} + \dot{\eta}\left(x\,\frac{\partial T}{\partial x} + y\,\frac{\partial T}{\partial y}\right) + \dot{\epsilon}\,z\,\frac{\partial T}{\partial z} - T\,(\dot{\epsilon} - 2\,\dot{\eta}) \\ &\qquad = \frac{\nu}{1 - 2\,\nu}\,(\dot{\epsilon} + 2\,\dot{\eta}) + \dot{\epsilon} \end{aligned} \tag{81.12}$$

For the present case a suitable solution of (81.12) is

$$\begin{aligned} P &= Q_0\,(t) + e^{-\epsilon} f\,(x\,e^{-\eta}, y\,e^{-\eta}, z\,e^{-\epsilon}) \\ Q &= Q_0\,(t) + e^{-\epsilon} g\,(x\,e^{-\eta}, y\,e^{-\eta}, z\,e^{-\epsilon}) \\ T &= T_0\,(t) + e^{\epsilon - 2\eta}\,h\,(x\,e^{-\eta}, y\,e^{-\eta}, z\,e^{-\epsilon}) \end{aligned} \tag{81.13}$$

where $f$, $g$, and $h$ are arbitrary functions of their arguments and $Q_0$ and $T_0$ are integrals of

$$\begin{aligned} \frac{dQ_0}{dt} + Q_0\,\dot{\epsilon} &= \frac{\nu}{1 - 2\,\nu}\,(\dot{\epsilon} + 2\,\dot{\eta}) + \dot{\eta} \\ \frac{dT_0}{dt} - T_0\,(\dot{\epsilon} - 2\,\dot{\eta}) &= \frac{\nu}{1 - 2\,\nu}\,(\dot{\epsilon} + 2\,\dot{\eta}) + \dot{\epsilon} \end{aligned} \tag{81.14}$$

We now select a simple special form of (81.13) that will be sufficient to satisfy (81.11)

$$\begin{aligned} P &= Q_0\,(t) + \tfrac{1}{2}\,A\,x^2 \exp\left(-\epsilon - 2\,\eta\right) \\ Q &= Q_0\,(t) + \tfrac{1}{2}\,A\,y^2 \exp\left(-\epsilon - 2\,\eta\right) \\ T &= T_0\,(t) + \tfrac{1}{2}\,B\,z^2 \exp\left(-\epsilon - 2\,\eta\right) \end{aligned} \tag{81.15}$$

where $A$ and $B$ are constants. These functions will satisfy (81.11), provided

$$\ddot{\eta} + \dot{\eta}^2 = \frac{2\,\mu\,A}{\rho_0} \qquad \ddot{\epsilon} + \dot{\epsilon}^2 = \frac{2\,\mu\,B}{\rho_0}$$

or

$$\frac{d^2\,e^\eta}{dt^2} = \frac{2\,\mu\,A}{\rho_0}\,e^\eta \qquad \frac{d^2\,e^\epsilon}{dt^2} = \frac{2\,\mu\,B}{\rho_0}\,e^\epsilon \tag{81.16}$$

These equations may be integrated completely. In the static problem we showed that for large values of the strain it was not possible to set $Q = 0$. Let us try this case again. Observe that in (81.14) we may set $Q_0 \equiv 0$, provided

$$\eta = -\nu\,\epsilon \tag{81.17}$$

This is compatible with (81.16) if

$$\epsilon = k\,t \qquad \eta = -\nu\,k\,t \tag{81.18}$$

where $k$ is a constant and

$$A = \frac{\rho_0\,\nu^2\,k^2}{2\,\mu} \qquad B = \frac{\rho_0\,k^2}{2\,\mu} \tag{81.19}$$

Now $(81.14)_2$ becomes

$$\frac{dT_0}{dt} - k\,(1 + 2\,\nu)\,T_0 = (1 + \nu)\,k \tag{81.20}$$

The integral of this for $T_0\,(0) = 0$ is

$$T_0\,(t) = \frac{1+\nu}{1+2\,\nu}\,\{\exp\,[(1 + 2\,\nu)\,\epsilon] - 1\} \tag{81.21}$$

The stress components are therefore found to be

$$\begin{aligned} P &= (\rho_0\,k^2\,\nu^2/4\,\mu)\,x^2\exp\,[-(1 - 2\,\nu)\,\epsilon] \\ Q &= (\rho_0\,k^2\,\nu^2/4\,\mu)\,y^2\exp\,[-(1 - 2\,\nu)\,\epsilon] \\ T &= \frac{1+\nu}{1+2\,\nu}\,\{\exp\,[(1 + 2\,\nu)\,\epsilon] - 1\} + \frac{\rho_0\,k^2}{4\,\mu}\,z^2\exp\,[-(1 - 2\,\nu)\,\epsilon] \end{aligned} \tag{81.22}$$

When $\nu < \frac{1}{2}$ at a fixed point, we see that the effects of inertia terms decrease rapidly as $t$ increases, so that for large $t$

$$P = Q = 0 \qquad T = \frac{1+\nu}{1+2\,\nu}\,\{\exp\,[(1 + 2\,\nu)\,\epsilon] - 1\} \tag{81.23}$$

For any case the inertia terms may be ignored whenever $\rho_0\,k^2\,L^2 \ll 4\,\mu$, where $L$ is some standard dimension.

If one goes back to the original differential equations (81.2), drops the inertia terms, and seeks a solution in which the only nonzero stress is $s_{zz} = T$, then one is led to (81.17) and (81.23). In this case, however, $\epsilon$ is an arbitrary function of time instead of having the special value $(81.18)_1$. The stress in both solutions at any instant depends on the amount of extension. Thus the solution obtained by neglecting inertia terms in the differential equations appears to be dynamically admissible.

It is to be noted that other solutions are possible in which the cross stresses $P$ and $Q$ are not necessarily small or zero. These will be included in (81.15) with $\epsilon$ and $\eta$ determined from (81.16). Truesdell's acceleration-less motion given in the previous article is included in the case $A = B = 0$. Other solutions with nonvanishing shear are also possible. Thus, for hypoelastic body of grade zero, there exist solutions corresponding to a velocity field given by (81.6).

# 9
# ELASTIC–PERFECTLY PLASTIC BODIES

## 82. SCOPE OF THE CHAPTER

Solid materials when loaded beyond a critical state of stress, called *yield*, undergo a permanent set of deformations so that upon unloading they do not return to their initial state. The theory of plasticity is intended to describe the mechanical behavior of solids in this elastic-plastic state. A description of the experimental stress-deformation relations is condensed in Art. 83. The theory of constitutive equations of solid bodies in the elastoplastic state has not as yet acquired the same type of rigor to which we are accustomed in the elasticity theory. Two of the latest axiomatic reviews are given below. The constitutive theory of Lévy–von Mises and Prandtl-Reuss, as presented in several papers by Thomas, occupies Arts. 84 to 86. The first of these does not take into account the elastic deformation in the plastic range, while the second does. Both of these currently used theories divide the analysis into two separate steps, one for the elastic region and the other for the plastic region. The two regions are then joined together with a yield condition. The determination of the boundary of the plastic region is a part of the problem. In some instances a combined theory, not dividing the problem into these two steps, is found to be simpler, although the basic equations may be more complicated. To this end we have included the material of Art. 85.

The summary of various theories is found in Art. 87. In Art. 88 we give the solution of the elastoplastic problem concerning a wedge. The solution is based on a theory that assumes infinitesimal elastic strain and small stress rate. This is the classical elastoplastic theory. The main aim in choosing this problem is to illustrate the technique and the usual problems that come up in this theory. Presently there exist no solved problems in finite elastoplastic theory.

A more recent theory due to A. E. Green, relating the theories of plasticity and hypoelasticity, is presented in Art. 89. Here we have an approach to plasticity theory that is similar to that given earlier. The magnitude of the elastic deformations, however, is no longer limited. In presenting both approaches rather than taking sides, we leave the final judgment to future investigators. While each has its own merits and limitations, it appears to the present author that the content of Art. 89 may be more appealing to mathematicians. Nevertheless, it is safe to state that the mathematical foundations of the theory have not yet been laid on unshakable grounds.

The last article of the chapter demonstrates the relation of hypoelasticity to plasticity through the solution of the problem of simple shear. Hypoelastic shear and plastic (von Mises) shear are studied in detail.

The theory of plasticity, in spite of its age, has not reached a level of maturity comparable to that of the elasticity theory. The foundation of the theory is still in a state of flux and not devoid of basic physical and mathematical questions. Knowledge of the present approaches should be considered as a minimum starting point for the beginning worker in the foundation of the theory.

## 83. EXPERIMENTAL FOUNDATIONS

The theory of plasticity has been in great flux from the viewpoint of its constitutive equations. While some serious attempts to put the theory on a strong foundation exist,[1] the theory is essentially in a state similar to that of the linear theory.

The theory is intended to describe *solid* behavior rather than *fluid* flow. The basic constitutive equations adopted are those of the linear theory in the form

$$t^k{}_l = \lambda\, d^m{}_m\, \delta^k{}_l + 2\,\mu\, d^k{}_l \tag{83.1}$$

with the exception that $\lambda$ and $\mu$ are no longer constitutive material constants representing viscosities. They are functions of $\mathbf{d}$ to be determined by additional conditions known as *plastic flow* or *yield conditions*.

The physical foundations of the theory of plasticity are explained simply as follows. Consider an elastic solid which is subjected to some small external loads for which the deformation is elastic; i.e., upon the release of these loads the body resumes its initial unstressed and undeformed shape. For simplicity, in this discussion, we consider a *linearly*

[1] Drucker [1950, 1960], Geiringer [1953], Thomas [1954, 1955*a*, *c*, *d*], and Green [1956*a*, *b*]. For extensive references on approximate theories based on small strains, see Prager [1955], Hill [1956], Freudenthal and Geiringer [1958], Hodge [1958], Koiter [1960], and Naghdi [1960]. The reader is also referred to a recent book by Thomas [1961], which appeared at the completion of the present manuscript and to which we have therefore not made adequate reference.

*elastic solid* which is homogeneous and isotropic. This means that the linear Hooke's law

$$t^k{}_l = \lambda_e \tilde{e}^m{}_m \delta^k{}_l + 2 \mu_e \tilde{e}^k{}_l \tag{83.2}$$

applies for the elastic deformation, where $\lambda_e$ and $\mu_e$ are Lamé elastic constants and $\tilde{e}^k{}_l$ is the infinitesimal strain tensor. Experiments indicate that when the external loads are increased gradually, beyond a certain value of loads the elastic character of the body is destroyed; that is, upon the release of loads the body retains some *permanent* deformations. The critical combinations of stresses for which the permanent deformation would first occur may be expressed mathematically by a *yield surface*

$$f(\mathbf{t}) = 0 \tag{83.3}$$

Upon reloading, the stress-strain relations (83.2) are found to apply again until the original departure from the unloaded condition is reached.

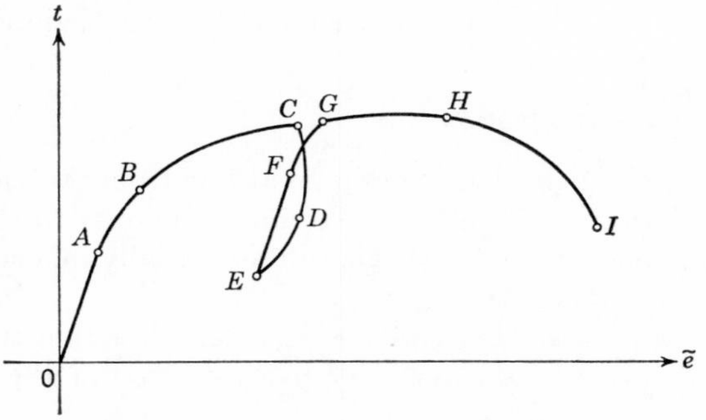


FIG. 83.1. Stress-strain curve for uniaxial tension.

From this point on, a permanent deformation continues to develop. To clarify the main ideas, a typical stress-strain diagram in simple uniaxial tension of metals is given in Fig. 83.1. In this figure the tensile stress $t$ is plotted against strain $\tilde{e}$ for the three stages of loading, unloading, and reloading. Upon the increase of loading, the strain increases monotonically until the maximum stress $t_H$ at the point $H$ is reached. Thereafter the stress decreases while the strain increases until fracture occurs at point $I$. A portion of this curve $OA$ may be approximated by a straight line. Hence the name "proportional limit" is given to the stress $t_A$ at $A$. Beyond the proportional limit there is a point $B$ called *yield*, after which the material is no longer elastic. If the stress exceeds $t_B$, then permanent deformation takes place. Suppose that we begin to unload at a point $C$. Then the strain varies along $CDE$. If we were to unload fully, we should find a permanent strain left. Reloading of the material rom point $E$ follows the curve $EFG$, after which further loading proceeds long the path $GH$.

In general, the stress-strain curve is also influenced by temperature, eformation rate, and various other effects. The theory of *elastic-plastic* aterials replaces the experimental stress-strain curve (Fig. 83.1) by the lealized curve shown in Fig. 83.2. In this idealization it is assumed that 1) the proportional limit $A$ and yield point $B$ coincide; (2) the hysteresis op $CDEFG$ is replaced by a straight line $EC$ parallel to $OA$; (3) each eloading path upon reaching the main curve $OACH$ follows this curve. hus unloading and reloading curves are straight lines parallel to $OA$ riginating on a part of $ACH$ and returning to it on the same straight line.

For compressive stresses the situation is similar. We have a compresion yield point, and loading and unloading follow a similar path. The

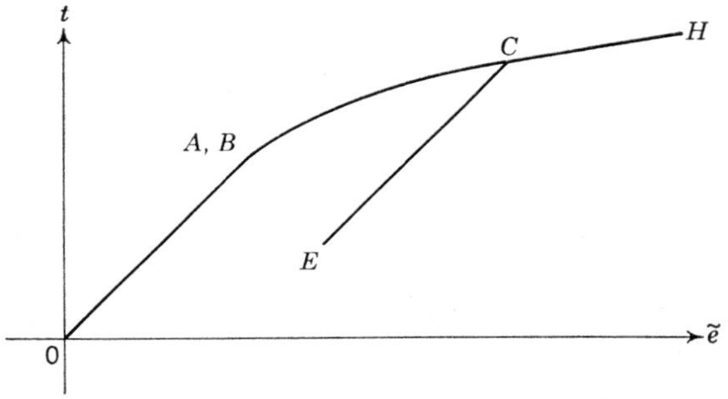


FIG. 83.2. Stress-strain curve for uniaxial loading of an elastic-plastic material.

bove assumptions, by putting $A$ and $B$ together and using $\tilde{e}$, ignore the ffects of large elastic strains and, by eliminating the hysteresis loops, disegard the hysteresis loss. By not considering the portion $HI$ of the tress-strain curve, fracture is ignored. In addition, the thermal and ate effects are completely eliminated from the constitutive equations.

The material idealized by a stress-strain curve of the type shown in ig. 83.2 includes the so-called *work-hardening* effect; i.e., in the plastic ange $ACH$ the strain increases monotonically with the stress.

The theory of *elastic–perfectly plastic materials* replaces the stress-strain urve shown in Fig. 83.2 by the one given in Fig. 83.3, thus ignoring the ork hardening. Along $OA$ ($|t| < t_A$) the solid is elastic. Beyond the oint $A$, ($t = \pm t_A$) the stress remains constant but the body continues to eform. An unloading and reloading process follows the line $CE$.

The theory of elastic–perfectly plastic solids has therefore two regions or which different constitutive equations are required: (1) the elastic egion, for which Hooke's law (83.2) is valid and (2) the *flow* region, for which a new set of constitutive equations (83.1) must be used. At the common boundary of these two regions there lies the yield surface at which a yield condition of the form (83.3) must be satisfied.

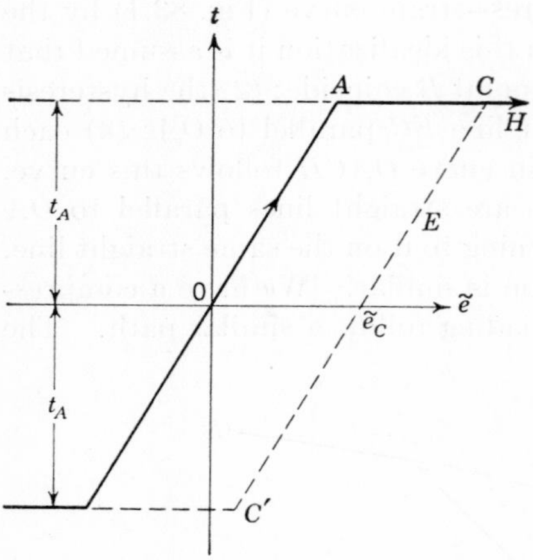


FIG. 83.3. Stress-strain curve for uniaxial loading of a perfectly plastic solid.

For a homogeneous and isotropic elastic material, until we reach the yield surface, the material is assumed to remain homogeneous and isotropic. Therefore a yield condition such as (83.3) must be expressible only in terms of stress invariants, i.e.,

$$f\,(\mathrm{I}_t, \mathrm{II}_t, \mathrm{III}_t) = 0 \tag{83.4}$$

After the development of plastic regions, the isotropy and homogeneity will, in general, be destroyed. The theory of perfectly plastic materials assumes, however, that the body remains homogeneous and isotropic at all times.

Experimentally it has also been observed that a hydrostatic pressure produces only a volume change and not a change in shape.

The foregoing ideas that originate from experimental facts are formalized mathematically as follows. First we express the stress and deformation-rate tensors in terms of their *deviatoric* parts; i.e., we decompose **t** and **d** as

$$t^k{}_l = -\bar{p}\,\delta^k{}_l + \bar{t}^k{}_l \qquad d^k{}_l = \tfrac{1}{3}\,\mathrm{I}_d\,\delta^k{}_l + \bar{d}^k{}_l \tag{83.5}$$

where

$$\begin{aligned} 3\,\bar{p} &= -\mathrm{I}_t & \bar{t}^k{}_k &= 0 \\ \mathrm{I}_d &= d^k{}_k & \bar{d}^k{}_k &= 0 \end{aligned} \tag{83.6}$$

Now equations (83.1) may be replaced by

$$-\bar{p} = (\lambda + \tfrac{2}{3}\,\mu)\,\mathrm{I}_d \qquad \bar{t}^k{}_l = 2\,\mu\,\bar{d}^k{}_l \tag{83.7}$$

Determination of $\lambda$ and $\mu$ requires two postulates, namely:

1. $\bar{p}$ is a function of $\mathrm{I}_d$ only. This assumption is the mathematical idealization of the experimental fact that the hydrostatic pressure produces only a volume change.

2. Some scalar invariant of $\bar{\mathbf{t}}$ vanishes. This assumption is the *plastic flow* or *yield condition*.

Mathematical expressions of these postulates are

$$f(\bar{p}, \mathrm{I}_d) = 0 \tag{83.8}$$

$$Y\left(\frac{\overline{\mathrm{II}}_{\bar{t}}}{\tau^2}, \frac{\overline{\mathrm{III}}_{\bar{t}}}{\tau^3}\right) = 0 \tag{83.9}$$

where

$$\overline{\mathrm{II}}_a \equiv \mathrm{I}_a^2 - 2\,\mathrm{II}_a = a^k{}_l\, a^l{}_k \qquad \overline{\mathrm{III}}_a \equiv \mathrm{I}_a^3 - 3\,\mathrm{I}_a\,\mathrm{II}_a + 3\,\mathrm{III}_a = a^k{}_l\, a^l{}_m\, a^m{}_k \tag{83.10}$$

Note that (83.8) is an expression of compressibility which replaces $(83.7)_1$, and (83.9) is an expression of the yield condition. In the latter expression a modulus $\tau$ having the dimension of stress appears. It is called the yield stress. Often the condition of compressibility (83.8) is replaced by that of incompressibility, namely,

$$\mathrm{I}_d = 0 \tag{83.11}$$

This is done since for most materials in the plastic-flow range no appreciable volume change is observed.

The most commonly used yield condition is that of von Mises [1913],

$$\overline{\mathrm{II}}_{\bar{t}} = K\,\tau^2 \tag{83.12}$$

where $K$ is a constant.

The theory of perfectly plastic solids as defined by $(83.7)_2$, (83.8), and (83.9) is that due to St. Venant [1870, 1872*a*, *b*], Lévy [1870], and von Mises [1913]. According to this theory we have

$$\begin{aligned} \overline{\mathrm{II}}_{\bar{t}} &< K\,\tau^2 \qquad \text{(elastic state)} \\ \overline{\mathrm{II}}_{\bar{t}} &= K\,\tau^2 \qquad \text{(state of yield and flow)} \end{aligned} \tag{83.13}$$

In the following articles we give a more systematic foundation of the St. Venant–Lévy–von Mises theory discussed above and its relation to another theory, namely, the Prandtl-Reuss theory. These two theories are often considered to be basic in the plasticity theory and are used in the solution of many practical problems (cf. Sokolovsky [1946], Hill [1950], Prager and Hodge [1951], Prager [1959], Freudenthal and Geiringer [1958], etc).

## 84. CONSTITUTIVE EQUATIONS: LÉVY–VON MISES THEORY

Thomas [1954] gave a theory of plasticity which appears to have far-reaching implications in respect to a systematic elastic-plastic theory. While this theory is by no means complete, it contains a nucleus of axiomatization and the beginning of a finite elastic-plastic theory. We therefore reproduce this work here. An extension of this theory is mad in Art. 89.

AXIOM 1. *The deviatoric stress* $\bar{\mathbf{t}}$ *is an isotropic function of the deviatori deformation-rate tensor* $\bar{\mathbf{d}}$, i.e.,

$$\bar{t}^k{}_l = f^k{}_l(\bar{d}^m{}_n) \qquad \bar{t}^k{}_k = 0 \tag{84.1}$$

AXIOM 2. *The relations* (84.1) *do not establish a one-to-one correspond ence between* $\bar{\mathbf{t}}$ *and* $\bar{\mathbf{d}}$.

AXIOM 3. *The plastic flow is incompressible*, i.e.,

$$d^k{}_k = 0 \tag{84.2}$$

Note that Axiom 3 is an approximation which appears to be in agree ment with the experimental evidence. In a more general theory one may replace this by a *compressibility condition*, such as $t^k{}_k$ is a function of $d^k{}_k$ This will be done in Art. 89 below. Axiom 3 implies that

$$\bar{d}^k{}_l = d^k{}_l \tag{84.3}$$

We have seen that an isotropic functional relation such as (84.1) can be expressed as

$$\bar{t}^k{}_l = \alpha_0\,\delta^k{}_l + \alpha_1\,d^k{}_l + \alpha_2\,d^k{}_m\,d^m{}_l \tag{84.4}$$

where $\alpha_0$, $\alpha_1$, and $\alpha_2$ are functions of deformation-rate invariants $\mathrm{I}_d = 0$ $\mathrm{II}_d$, and $\mathrm{III}_d$. Hence

$$\alpha_\gamma = \alpha_\gamma(\overline{\mathrm{II}}_d, \overline{\mathrm{III}}_d) \qquad (\gamma = 0, 1, 2) \tag{84.5}$$

where the invariants $\overline{\mathrm{II}}_d$ and $\overline{\mathrm{III}}_d$ are defined by

$$\begin{aligned} \overline{\mathrm{II}}_a &\equiv a^k{}_l\,a^l{}_k = \mathrm{I}_a^2 - 2\,\mathrm{II}_a \\ \overline{\mathrm{III}}_a &\equiv a^k{}_l\,a^l{}_m\,a^m{}_k = \mathrm{I}_a^3 - 3\,\mathrm{I}_a\,\mathrm{II}_a + 3\,\mathrm{III}_a \end{aligned} \tag{84.6}$$

According to Axiom 1 we have $\bar{t}^k{}_k = 0$. Hence

$$\alpha_0 = -\tfrac{1}{3}\,\alpha_2\,\overline{\mathrm{II}}_d \tag{84.7}$$

Substituting this into (84.4) gives

$$\bar{t}^k{}_l = \alpha_1\,d^k{}_l + \alpha_2\,(d^k{}_m\,d^m{}_l - \tfrac{1}{3}\,\overline{\mathrm{II}}_d\,\delta^k{}_l) \tag{84.8}$$

Here $\alpha_1$ and $\alpha_2$ are functions of $\overline{\mathrm{II}}_d$ and $\overline{\mathrm{III}}_d$. We have not as yet used Axiom 2, according to which (84.8) must not be explicitly soluble with respect to $\mathbf{d}$.

By multiplying (84.8) once by $\bar{t}^l{}_k$ and once by $\bar{t}^l{}_m\,\bar{t}^m{}_k$, we obtain the ollowing two equations:

$$\overline{\text{II}}_{\bar{t}} = \alpha_1^2\, \overline{\text{II}}_d + 2\,\alpha_1\,\alpha_2\,\overline{\text{III}}_d + \tfrac{1}{6}\,\alpha_2^2\,\overline{\text{II}}_d^2$$

$$\overline{\text{III}}_{\bar{t}} = \alpha_1^3\,\overline{\text{III}}_d + \tfrac{1}{2}\,\alpha_1^2\,\alpha_2\,\overline{\text{II}}_d^2 + \tfrac{1}{2}\,\alpha_1\,\alpha_2^2\,\overline{\text{II}}_d\,\overline{\text{III}}_d + \tfrac{1}{3}\,\alpha_2^3\,(\overline{\text{III}}_d^2 - \tfrac{1}{12}\,\overline{\text{II}}_d^3) \tag{84.9}$$

According to the implicit function theorem the unique inverse of 84.9) exists in the form of

$$\overline{\text{II}}_d = \phi\,(\overline{\text{II}}_{\bar{t}}, \overline{\text{III}}_{\bar{t}}) \qquad \overline{\text{III}}_d = \psi\,(\overline{\text{II}}_{\bar{t}}, \overline{\text{III}}_{\bar{t}}) \tag{84.10}$$

a some neighborhood $N_t$ of $\overline{\text{II}}_{\bar{t}}$ and $\overline{\text{III}}_{\bar{t}}$ if (1) $\alpha_1$ and $\alpha_2$ have continuous artial derivatives with respect to $\overline{\text{II}}_d$ and $\overline{\text{III}}_d$ in some neighborhood $N_d$ of $\overline{\text{II}}_d$ and $\overline{\text{III}}_d$ and if (2) the jacobian

$$\Delta = \begin{vmatrix} \dfrac{\partial \overline{\text{II}}_{\bar{t}}}{\partial \overline{\text{II}}_d} & \dfrac{\partial \overline{\text{II}}_{\bar{t}}}{\partial \overline{\text{III}}_d} \\[2ex] \dfrac{\partial \overline{\text{III}}_{\bar{t}}}{\partial \overline{\text{II}}_d} & \dfrac{\partial \overline{\text{III}}_{\bar{t}}}{\partial \overline{\text{III}}_d} \end{vmatrix} \tag{84.11}$$

oes *not* vanish in $N_d$. We assume that condition 1 is valid. Axiom , however, rejects nonvanishing $\Delta$. Therefore we set

$$\Delta = 0 \tag{84.12}$$

hich gives us a partial differential equation for the determination of one f the constitutive coefficients $\alpha_1$ and $\alpha_2$. The other may be determined y use of any one of (84.9). Of course, other types of degeneracies exist nd need further studies. For example, any one row or column of 84.11) may be taken zero, thus determining both $\alpha_1$ and $\alpha_2$, etc.

In order to produce explicit results, let us consider here the simpler roblem of *quasi-linear constitutive equations.* In this case we take $\alpha_2 \equiv 0$. Then (84.9) reduce to

$$\overline{\text{II}}_{\bar{t}} = \alpha_1^2\,\overline{\text{II}}_d \qquad \overline{\text{III}}_{\bar{t}} = \alpha_1^3\,\overline{\text{III}}_d \tag{84.13}$$

ince $\alpha_1 \neq 0$, the condition (84.12) now gives

$$2\,\overline{\text{II}}_d\,\frac{\partial \alpha_1}{\partial \overline{\text{II}}_d} + 3\,\overline{\text{III}}_d\,\frac{\partial \alpha_1}{\partial \overline{\text{III}}_d} + \alpha_1 = 0 \tag{84.14}$$

he general solution of this equation is

$$\alpha_1 = \frac{1}{\sqrt{\overline{\text{II}}_d}}\,\beta\left(\frac{\sqrt[3]{\overline{\text{III}}_d}}{\sqrt{\overline{\text{II}}_d}}\right) \tag{84.15}$$

where $\beta$ is an arbitrary function of its argument. The constitutive equations (84.8) with $\alpha_2 = 0$ now read

$$\bar{t}^k{}_l = 2\,\mu\, d^k{}_l \tag{84.16}$$

where

$$\mu \equiv \frac{\alpha_1}{2} \equiv \frac{1}{2\sqrt{\overline{\mathrm{II}}_d}}\,\beta\left(\frac{\sqrt[3]{\overline{\mathrm{III}}_d}}{\sqrt{\overline{\mathrm{II}}_d}}\right) \tag{84.17}$$

From (84.13) we have

$$\frac{\sqrt[3]{\overline{\mathrm{III}}_{\bar{t}}}}{\sqrt{\overline{\mathrm{II}}_{\bar{t}}}} = \frac{\sqrt[3]{\overline{\mathrm{III}}_d}}{\sqrt{\overline{\mathrm{II}}_d}} \tag{84.18}$$

Therefore (84.16) can also be expressed as

$$\bar{t}^k{}_l = \frac{1}{\sqrt{\overline{\mathrm{II}}_d}}\,\beta\left(\frac{\sqrt[3]{\overline{\mathrm{III}}_{\bar{t}}}}{\sqrt{\overline{\mathrm{II}}_{\bar{t}}}}\right) d^k{}_l \tag{84.19}$$

Either (84.16) or (84.19) may be taken as the final form of the constitutive equation of plasticity theory.

The yield condition may be derived from (84.19) by multiplying it by $\bar{t}^l{}_k$. Hence

$$\overline{\mathrm{II}}_{\bar{t}} = \left[\beta\left(\frac{\sqrt[3]{\overline{\mathrm{III}}_{\bar{t}}}}{\sqrt{\overline{\mathrm{II}}_{\bar{t}}}}\right)\right]^2 \tag{84.20}$$

which is an equation of the form (83.9). It is, however, more explicit in its content. If in (84.19) and (84.20) we select $\beta = \sqrt{K}\,\tau$ where $K$ is a numerical constant (= 2 for von Mises yield condition) and $\tau$ is a positive material constant, we obtain the stress–deformation-rate relations of the St. Venant–Lévy and von Mises yield conditions respectively.

$$\bar{t}^k{}_l = \frac{\sqrt{K}\,\tau}{\sqrt{\overline{\mathrm{II}}_d}}\, d^k{}_l \qquad \overline{\mathrm{II}}_{\bar{t}} = K\,\tau^2 \tag{84.21}$$

Expression (84.17) may be stated in terms of principal stretchings $d_1$, $d_2$, and $d_3$. If we recall that the condition of incompressibility means

$$\mathrm{I}_d = d_1 + d_2 + d_3 = 0$$

we may write $d_2 = -(d_1 + d_3)$. Now assume that the stretchings are ordered as $d_1 \geq d_2 \geq d_3$, and express $\overline{\mathrm{II}}_d$ and $\overline{\mathrm{III}}_d$ in terms of $d_1$ and $d_3$ as

$$\begin{aligned} \overline{\mathrm{II}}_d &= d_1^2 + d_2^2 + d_3^2 = d_1^2 + d_3^2 + (d_1 + d_3)^2 \\ \overline{\mathrm{III}}_d &= d_1^3 + d_2^3 + d_3^3 = d_1^3 + d_3^3 - (d_1 + d_3)^3 \end{aligned} \tag{84.22}$$

then follows that

$$\mu = \frac{1}{2\sqrt{\mathrm{II}_d}}\,\beta\left(\frac{\sqrt[3]{\mathrm{III}_d}}{\sqrt{\mathrm{II}_d}}\right) = \frac{B\,(d_3/d_1)}{2\,(d_1 - d_3)} \tag{84.23}$$

ere $B$ is an arbitrary function of $d_3/d_1$. We may now express (84.16) as

$$\bar{t}^k{}_l = \frac{B\,(d_3/d_1)}{d_1 - d_3}\,d^k{}_l \tag{84.24}$$

$$\bar{t}_\alpha = 2\,\mu\,d_\alpha \qquad (\alpha = 1, 2, 3) \tag{84.25}$$

nsequently we have

$$\frac{\bar{t}_3}{\bar{t}_1} = \frac{d_3}{d_1} \qquad \mathrm{II}_{\bar{t}} = 4\,\mu^2\,\mathrm{II}_d \qquad \mathrm{III}_{\bar{t}} = 8\,\mu^3\,\mathrm{III}_d \tag{84.26}$$

om (84.23) and (84.25) we get for the yield condition

$$\bar{t}_1 - \bar{t}_3 = \pm B\left(\frac{\bar{t}_3}{\bar{t}_1}\right) \tag{84.27}$$

*nce, after selecting* $B\,(\bar{t}_3/\bar{t}_1)$ *as an arbitrary differentiable function of* $\bar{t}_3/\bar{t}_1$ *the yield condition* (84.27), *we have the associated stress-deformation ations.* If in particular we put $B = K\,\tau$ where $K$ is a nondimensional nstant ($= 2$ when $\tau$ is selected as the yield stress in simple shear) and $\tau$ a stress called the yield stress, we get

$$\bar{t}^k{}_l = \frac{K\,\tau}{d_1 - d_3}\,d^k{}_l \tag{84.28}$$

$$\bar{t}_1 - \bar{t}_3 = \pm K\,\tau \tag{84.29}$$

which (84.28) constitutes the stress-strain relations and (84.29) the esca yield conditions.

It may be of interest to note that the method described above can be plied to (84.11) to lead to a more complicated plasticity theory in which e exact stress-deformation relations (84.8) may be used. To a rea-nable degree of engineering approximation it has been shown by idgman [1923] and verified by Crossland [1954] that the hydrostatic essure affects neither the initial yield nor the plastic deformation itself. is effect, however, is present, though small in magnitude.

By use of the assumptions of isotropy, absence of the Bauschinger effect e., the yield stress in compression is equal to that in tension), and dependence of the plastic deformation from mean normal stress, one n predict certain fundamental characteristics of the yield surface. By e assumption of isotropy we have for any yield surface

$$f\,(\mathrm{II}_{\bar{t}}, \mathrm{III}_{\bar{t}}) = 0$$

Since $f$ is independent of $I_t$, it is an infinite cylinder in the princip stress space $t_1$, $t_2$, $t_3$ (Fig. 84.1). The elements of this cylinder a parallel to the straight line through the origin with direction cosin $(1/\sqrt{3}, 1/\sqrt{3}, 1/\sqrt{3})$. The cylinder is therefore perpendicular to t plane

$$t_1 + t_2 + t_3 = 0$$

called the $\pi$ plane. The cylinder can therefore be completely describ by its intersection curve made with this plane. The Tresca yield conc tion gives a regular hexagon as a yield locus in this plane, while th von Mises yield condition gives a circle.

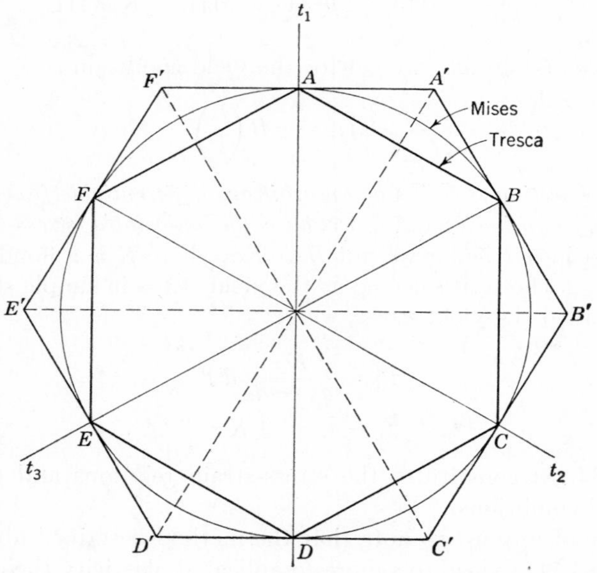


FIG. 84.1. Yield loci for isotropic materials in the $\pi$ plane.

Plasticity theory based on von Mises and Tresca yield conditions presently being used by most experts in the field.

Symmetry properties and bounds of yield loci in the $\pi$ plane can be predict by further use of isotropy, the absence of the Bauschinger effect, and convexity the yield locus (cf. Naghdi [1960]). Isotropy dictates that the labeling of a three axes $t_1$, $t_2$, $t_3$ is arbitrary; hence in the plane of Fig. 84.1 we must ha symmetry about the $t_1$, $t_2$, and $t_3$ axes. The absence of the Bauschinger effe requires symmetry with respect to the coordinate planes which in the $\pi$ pla implies symmetry with respect to lines through the origin that are perpendicul to the intersections of the coordinate planes (dotted lines). Consequently, l, we must have symmetry with respect to six lines, in the $\pi$ plane, through the rigin, and 30° apart.

Drucker [1951] has introduced a quasi-thermodynamic postulate that is based n stressing an element from an initially stressed state slowly by an external gency (*distinct* from the agency causing the initial state) and removing it slowly. he postulate in effect states: *during the application of the additional stresses and a complete cycle of application and removal of the additional stresses, the work me by an external agency is nonnegative.*

This postulate has been used to obtain the general stress–plastic-strain relaons and to prove that the yield surface is convex.[1]

Without loss in generality we may suppose that the yield surface passes through oint $A$ on the $t_1$ axis. No piecewise smooth curve symmetrical about the $t_1$ axis assing through $A$ can lie outside the straight line $F'AA'$ and yet form a convex urface. By the same token, in considering the two axes of symmetry adjacent $t_1$, no convex yield curve can fall inside the straight lines $FA$ and $AB$. Therere isotropy, convexity, absence of the Bauschinger effect, and independence of e hydrostatic stress force all conceivable yield surfaces into the region between gular hexagonal surfaces $ABCDEFA$ and $A'B'C'D'E'F'A'$. We must emphaze the fact that not all surfaces in this region are admissible as yield surfaces. hey must be convex. The inner hexagon of Fig. 84.1 is the classical yield urface of Tresca and the circle is that of von Mises. Experiments on metals ave shown that the test points generally fall closer to the von Mises yield urface. In Fig. 84.1 the maximum deviation from the von Mises circle is pproximately 15.47 per cent.

## . COMBINED ELASTIC AND VON MISES STRESS-STRAIN RELATIONS

The plasticity theory of Lévy–von Mises requires that we apply two ts of constitutive equations.

1. In the elastic range ($Y < 0$) we employ the linear Hooke's law

$$t^k{}_l = \lambda_e \, \tilde{e}^m{}_m \, \delta^k{}_l + 2\,\mu_e \, \tilde{e}^k{}_l \tag{5.1}$$

here $\lambda_e$ and $\mu_e$ are Lamé elastic constants and $Y = \overline{\text{II}}_{\bar{t}} - K\tau^2 = 0$ for e von Mises yield criteria.

2. In the plastic range ($Y = 0$)

$$d^k{}_k = 0 \qquad \bar{t}^k{}_l = 2\,\mu\, d^k{}_l \tag{5.2}$$

here $\mu$ is given by (84.17). Here the first equation is the condition of compressibility and the second the constitutive equations for deviatoric ress $\bar{\mathbf{t}}$ defined by

$$t^k{}_l = -\bar{p}\,\delta^k{}_l + \bar{t}^k{}_l \qquad \bar{t}^k{}_k = 0 \tag{5.3}$$

ith pressure $\bar{p}$ an unknown of the theory. We must note that (85.2) not contain the effects of the elastic strain in the plastic range. A

[1] Drucker [1951], Koiter [1960], and Naghdi [1960].

theory including this effect, known as the Prandtl-Reuss theory, will b
discussed in the following article.

Since during a cycle of loading and unloading we encounter bo
elastic and plastic deformations, the theory as given above can be use
only through piecewise integrations during each cycle. The bounda
between the elastic and plastic regions is not known in advance and mu
be determined as part of the problem. Attempts to overcome th
difficulty were made by Prager [1938], Thomas [1955*c*, *d*], and others,
that continuous transition from elastic to plastic states can be obtaine
Below we reproduce the work of Thomas for the Lévy–von Mises theor
In the following article we shall supply the same for the Prandtl-Reu
theory. In Art. 89 we present a more general theory that will combi
both.

The constitutive equations of hypoelasticity for the quasi-linear ca
may be expressed in terms of the deviatoric stresses as

$$a\,\hat{t}^k{}_k = d^k{}_k + b\,t^k{}_k \qquad A\,\hat{\bar{t}}^k{}_l = \bar{d}^k{}_l + B\,\bar{t}^k{}_l \tag{85.4}$$

where $a$, $b$, $A$, and $B$ are scalar invariants of $\mathbf{t}$ and $\mathbf{d}$, and the stress ra
$\hat{\mathbf{t}}$ may be defined in any one of the ways given in Art. 72. For definitene
we use the form

$$\hat{t}^k{}_l \equiv \frac{\partial t^k{}_l}{\partial t} + t^k{}_{l;m}\,v^m + t^k{}_m\,w^m{}_l - t^m{}_l\,w^k{}_m \tag{85.5}$$

At the yield point according to the theory developed in Art. 84, th
constitutive equations (85.4) must reduce to the form (85.2); i.e., $a$,
and $A$ must vanish, and the yield value $\bar{B}$ of $B$ is given by

$$-1/\bar{B} = 2\,\mu = \frac{2}{\sqrt{\mathrm{II}_d}}\,\beta\left(\frac{\sqrt[3]{\mathrm{III}_{\bar{t}}}}{\sqrt{\mathrm{II}_{\bar{t}}}}\right) \tag{85.6}$$

Consequently the constitutive equations of plastic flow are as in (84.19
i.e.,

$$d^k{}_k = 0 \qquad \bar{t}^k{}_l = \frac{1}{\sqrt{\mathrm{II}_d}}\,\beta\left(\frac{\sqrt[3]{\mathrm{III}_{\bar{t}}}}{\sqrt{\mathrm{II}_{\bar{t}}}}\right) d^k{}_l \tag{85.7}$$

and the yield condition is

$$\mathrm{II}_{\bar{t}} = \left[\beta\left(\frac{\sqrt[3]{\mathrm{III}_{\bar{t}}}}{\sqrt{\mathrm{II}_{\bar{t}}}}\right)\right]^2 \tag{85.8}$$

For the von Mises yield condition we take $\beta = \sqrt{K}\,\tau$.

The yield condition (85.8) may be expressed as

$$Y(\bar{\mathfrak{t}}) \equiv 1 - \frac{\overline{\mathrm{II}}_{\bar{t}}}{[\beta\,(\sqrt[3]{\overline{\mathrm{III}}_{\bar{t}}}/\sqrt{\overline{\mathrm{II}}_{\bar{t}}})]^2} = 0 \qquad \text{5.9)}$$

order to obtain Hooke's law on the one extreme and flow conditions on e other extreme in the simplest way, Thomas [1955*d*] assumes that for y state of stress $a$, $b$, $A$, and $B$ are given by

$$\begin{aligned} a &= \frac{Y(\bar{\mathfrak{t}})}{3\lambda_e + 2\mu_e} & b &= \frac{\gamma\, Y(\bar{\mathfrak{t}})}{3\lambda_e + 2\mu_e} \\ A &= \frac{Y(\bar{\mathfrak{t}})}{2\mu_e} & B &= \kappa\, Y(\bar{\mathfrak{t}}) - \sqrt{1 - Y(\bar{\mathfrak{d}})} \end{aligned} \qquad \text{5.10)}$$

here $\gamma$ and $\kappa$ are material constants for plastic flow and $\lambda_e$ and $\mu_e$ are the amé elastic constants. The constitutive equations (85.4) now take the rm

$$\begin{aligned} Y(\bar{\mathfrak{t}})\, \mathring{t}^k{}_k &= (3\lambda_e + 2\mu_e)\, d^k{}_k + \gamma\, Y(\bar{\mathfrak{t}})\, t^k{}_k \\ Y(\bar{\mathfrak{t}})\, \mathring{\bar{t}}^k{}_l &= 2\mu_e\, \bar{d}^k{}_l + 2\mu_e \left[\kappa\, Y(\bar{\mathfrak{t}}) - \sqrt{1 - Y(\bar{\mathfrak{d}})}\,\right] \bar{t}^k{}_l \end{aligned} \qquad \text{5.11)}$$

is further postulated that

$$0 \le Y(\bar{\mathfrak{t}}) \le 1 \qquad \text{5.12)}$$

r all flows, which certainly is satisfied for von Mises yield conditions.

The constitutive equations (85.11) possess the following important roperties:

1. They are valid for a homogeneous and isotropic medium.
2. When the yield occurs, i.e., $Y(\bar{\mathfrak{t}}) = 0$, they revert to the flow quations (85.7) of the plasticity theory.
3. When the stresses and deformations are small in comparison to those roducing yield, they give Hooke's law of the linear theory of elasticity, s may be seen by noticing that

$$\mathring{\bar{t}}^k{}_l \to \dot{\bar{t}}^k{}_l \qquad d^k{}_l \to \dot{\bar{e}}^k{}_l$$
$$Y(\bar{\mathfrak{t}}),\ Y(\bar{\mathfrak{d}}) \to 1$$

nd since, in this case, the terms containing $\gamma$ and $\kappa$ are negligible as ompared to others, we get

$$\dot{t}^k{}_k = (3\lambda_e + 2\mu_e)\, \dot{e}^k{}_k \qquad \dot{\bar{t}}^k{}_l = 2\mu_e\, \dot{\bar{e}}^k{}_l$$

or a stress-free initial state these integrate to the classical Hooke's law. n this theory one may therefore employ the set (85.11) for both elastic nd flow regions.

## 86. CONSTITUTIVE EQUATIONS: PRANDTL-REUSS THEORY

In the previous article we have pointed out that the Lévy–von Mis theory does not take into account the effect of elastic strain in the plast range. Prandtl [1924], in connection with the two-dimensional problen and Reuss [1930], dealing with the general case, gave a theory whi accounts for this effect. Here we present Thomas's [1955c] extension this theory, which treats the case of combined constitutive equations elastic and plastic flow. Again we treat an incompressible, homogeneou and isotropic medium for a quasi-linear case. A more general case w be given in Art. 90.

The constitutive equations of hypoelasticity for the quasi-linear ca may be expressed in terms of deviatoric stress and deformation rates

$$\hat{t}^k{}_k = (3\,\lambda + 2\,\mu)\,d^k{}_k + (3\,\xi + 2\,\zeta)\,t^k{}_k \tag{86.1}$$

$$\hat{\bar{t}}^k{}_l = 2\,\mu\,\bar{d}^k{}_l + 2\,\zeta\,\bar{t}^k{}_l \tag{86.2}$$

where $\lambda$, $\mu$, $\xi$, and $\zeta$ are scalars to be determined. We assume t von Mises yield condition is valid so that

$$\bar{t}^k{}_l\,\bar{t}^l{}_k \leq K\,\tau^2 \tag{86.3}$$

According to this a point $\mathbf{x}$ is a yield point whenever the equality satisfied. A region of the material will be in a *state of yield* whenever, all points of the region, (86.3) with the equality sign is satisfied. For region of yield, by taking the material derivative of (86.3), we obtain

$$\bar{t}^k{}_l\,\frac{D\bar{t}^l{}_k}{Dt} = \bar{t}^l{}_k\,\hat{\bar{t}}^l{}_k = 2\,\mu\,\bar{t}^k{}_l\,\bar{d}^l{}_k + 2\,\zeta\,\bar{t}^k{}_l\,\bar{t}^l{}_k = 0$$

Hence

$$\frac{\zeta}{\mu} = -\,\frac{\bar{d}^k{}_l\,\bar{t}^l{}_k}{K\,\tau^2} \tag{86.4}$$

Thus in a state of yield $\zeta/\mu$ is a scalar invariant of $\bar{\mathbf{d}}\bar{\mathbf{t}}$. For the gener case Thomas assumes that

$$\frac{\zeta}{\mu} = A\,\bar{d}^k{}_l\,\bar{t}^l{}_k + B\,\bar{t}^k{}_l\,\bar{t}^l{}_k + C \tag{86.5}$$

where $A$, $B$, and $C$ are scalar functions of position and time. When yiel occurs, (86.5) must reduce to (86.4). If one takes $A = -1/K\,\tau^2$ an $B\,K\,\tau^2 + C = 0$, this condition will be satisfied. Hence

$$\frac{\zeta}{\mu} = -\,\frac{\bar{d}^k{}_l\,\bar{t}^l{}_k}{K\,\tau^2} - \gamma\left(1 - \frac{\bar{t}^k{}_l\,\bar{t}^l{}_k}{K\,\tau^2}\right) \tag{86.6}$$

here $\gamma$ is a scalar function of **x** and $t$. When yield occurs, (86.6) reduces (86.4).

If we now eliminate $\zeta$ from the right-hand member of (86.2) by use of 6.6), we get

$$\hat{t}^k{}_l = 2\,\mu\left\{\bar{d}^k{}_l - \left[\frac{\bar{d}^m{}_n\,\bar{t}^n{}_m}{K\,\tau^2} + \gamma\left(1 - \frac{\bar{t}^m{}_n\,\bar{t}^n{}_m}{K\,\tau^2}\right)\right]\bar{t}^k{}_l\right\} \tag{6.7)}$$

ext we must use the condition of incompressibility to simplify (86.1). e write (86.1) as

$$a\,\hat{t}^k{}_k = d^k{}_k + b\,t^k{}_k \tag{6.8)}$$

here

$$a \equiv \frac{1}{3\,\lambda + 2\,\mu} \qquad b \equiv \frac{3\,\xi + 2\,\zeta}{3\,\lambda + 2\,\mu}$$

a region of yield we must have $d^k{}_k = 0$. Therefore $a,\ b \to 0$ as $\bar{t}^l{}_k \to K\,\tau^2$. We may therefore write

$$a = a_1 + a_2\,\bar{t}^k{}_l\,\bar{t}^l{}_k \qquad b = b_1 + b_2\,\bar{t}^k{}_l\,\bar{t}^l{}_k$$

d select $a_1 = -a_2\,K\,\tau^2$, $b_1 = -b_2\,K\,\tau^2$, thus obtaining

$$a = -a_2\,(K\,\tau^2 - \bar{t}^k{}_l\,\bar{t}^l{}_k) \qquad b = -b_2\,(K\,\tau^2 - \bar{t}^k{}_l\,\bar{t}^l{}_k)$$

pon using these in (86.8), we get

$$\hat{t}^m{}_m = \frac{h\,d^m{}_m}{1 - (\bar{t}^k{}_l\,\bar{t}^l{}_k/K\,\tau^2)} + k\,t^m{}_m \tag{6.9)}$$

here $h$ and $k$ are scalar functions of **x** and $t$. For a region of yield (86.9) duces to the equation of incompressibility $d^m{}_m = 0$.

For *homogeneous* materials the scalars $\gamma$, $h$, and $k$ appearing in the nstitutive equations (86.7) and (86.9) must satisfy the principle of aterial objectivity. Therefore, for a homogeneous medium, they are *nstants*. The original constitutive scalars $\lambda$, $\xi$, and $\zeta$ are determined in rms of $\mu$, $\gamma$, $h$, and $k$ from the equations (86.6) and

$$3\,\lambda + 2\,\mu = \frac{h}{1 - (\bar{t}^k{}_l\,\bar{t}^l{}_k/K\,\tau^2)} \qquad 3\,\xi + 2\,\zeta = k \tag{6.10)}$$

Equations (86.7) and (86.9) together with the conservation of mass d momenta

$$\dot{\rho} + \rho\,\operatorname{div}\mathbf{v} = 0 \tag{6.11)}$$

$$t^k{}_{l;k} + \rho(f_l - \dot{v}_l) = 0 \qquad t^k{}_l = t_l{}^k \tag{6.12)}$$

nstitute the basic field equations for a homogeneous isotropic elastic-astic medium.

*Constitutive Equations for Plastic Flow.* In the case of plastic flov (86.9) and (86.7) reduce to

$$d^k{}_k = 0 \qquad \hat{\bar{t}}^k{}_l = 2\,\mu_p\left(\bar{d}^k{}_l - \frac{\bar{d}^m{}_n\,\bar{t}^n{}_m}{K\,\tau^2}\,\bar{t}^k{}_l\right) \tag{86.13}$$

where $\mu_p$ and $K$ are material constants. Since $\bar{t}^k{}_k = \bar{d}^k{}_k = 0$, we the see that when we write $k = l$ in (86.13), we get an identity. Therefor there are only five independent equations in $(86.13)_2$. So if we us (86.12) and (86.13) and the yield condition (86.3) (with the equality sign), we have $3 + 1 + 5 + 1 = 10$ equations to determine ten variable $\bar{p}$, $v^k$, and $t^{kl}$. These equations make up the basic equations of th Prandtl-Reuss theory which applies to a region of plastic flow. In a elastic region a separate set of equations (Hooke's law) must replace th constitutive equations (86.13). If the constitutive equations (86.7) an (86.9) are used in place of (86.13), then there is no need for a different se of equations for the elastic and plastic regions.

To show that indeed these equations contain the limiting case of sma elastic deformations, we must remember that for small deformations a quadratic and higher-order terms in **d**, **t**, and their products may b ignored. Since also $\hat{\bar{t}}^k{}_l \to \dot{\bar{t}}^k{}_l$ and $d^k{}_k \to \dot{\bar{e}}^k{}_k$ and the coefficients of $\gamma$ and for small stresses, as compared to the yield stress, are negligible, we se that in this limit (86.7) and (86.9) reduce to

$$\frac{dt^k{}_k}{dt} = (3\,\lambda_e + 2\,\mu_e)\,\dot{\bar{e}}^k{}_k \qquad \frac{d\bar{t}^k{}_l}{dt} = 2\,\mu_e\,\dot{\bar{e}}^k{}_k$$

which, upon integration for a stress which vanishes with strain, give th celebrated Hooke's law of the classical linear theory of elasticity of homogeneous and isotropic medium.

## 87. SUMMARY OF BASIC EQUATIONS

Below we summarize the basic equations of plasticity theory.

1. *Conservation of Mass:*

$$\dot{\rho} + \rho\,\operatorname{div}\mathbf{v} = 0 \tag{87.1}$$

2. *Balance of Momenta:*

$$-\frac{\partial \bar{p}}{\partial x^k} + \bar{t}^l{}_{k;l} + \rho\,(f_k - \dot{v}_k) = 0 \qquad \bar{t}^{kl} = \bar{t}^{lk} \tag{87.2}$$

$$t^l{}_k = -\bar{p}\,\delta^l{}_k + \bar{t}^l{}_k$$

3. *Yield Criteria:*

$$\bar{t}^k{}_l\,\bar{t}^l{}_k = K\,\tau^2 \qquad \text{(von Mises)} \tag{87.3}$$

$$\bar{t}_1 - \bar{t}_3 = \pm K\,\tau \qquad \text{(Tresca)} \tag{87.4}$$

nere $\bar{t}_1$ and $\bar{t}_3$ are, algebraically, the largest and smallest principal viatoric stresses, $K$ is a nondimensional constant $(=2)$, and $\tau$ is a itical stress (yield stress).

4. *Constitutive Equations.* In the elastic range all theories must satisfy ooke's law, i.e.,

$$t^k{}_l = \lambda_e \, \mathrm{I}_{\tilde{e}} \, \delta^k{}_l + 2\,\mu_e \, \tilde{e}^k{}_l \tag{7.5)}$$

nere $\lambda_e$ and $\mu_e$ are the Lamé elastic constants and $\tilde{e}_{kl}$ is the infinitesimal ain tensor defined by

$$2\,\tilde{e}_{kl} = u_{k;l} + u_{l;k} \tag{7.6)}$$

4a. *The Lévy–von Mises and Tresca Theories.* These theories require at in the plastic range we have

$$d^k{}_k = 0 \tag{7.7)}$$

$$\bar{t}^k{}_l = 2\,\mu\,\bar{d}^k{}_l \tag{7.8)}$$

nere

$$\mu \equiv \frac{1}{\sqrt{\mathrm{II}_d}}\sqrt{K}\,\tau \qquad \text{(Lévy–von Mises)} \tag{.9)}$$

$$\mu \equiv \frac{K\,\tau}{\bar{t}_1 - \bar{t}_3} \qquad \text{(Tresca)} \tag{.10)}$$

re $\bar{\mathbf{d}}$ is the deviatoric part of $\mathbf{d}$, i.e.,

$$d^k{}_l = \tfrac{1}{3}\,\mathrm{I}_d\,\delta^k{}_l + \bar{d}^k{}_l = \tfrac{1}{2}\,(v^k{}_{;l} + v_l{}^{;k}) \tag{.11)}$$

account of (87.7) we have $\mathbf{d} = \bar{\mathbf{d}}$.

4b. *Prandtl-Reuss Theory.* This theory replaces equations (87.7) and .8) by

$$d^k{}_k = 0 \tag{.12)}$$

$$\hat{\bar{t}}^k{}_l = 2\,\mu_p\left(\bar{d}^k{}_l - \frac{\bar{d}^m{}_n\,\bar{t}^n{}_m}{K\,\tau^2}\,\bar{t}^k{}_l\right) \tag{.13)}$$

ere $\mu_p$ and $K$ $(=2)$ are material constants. In both theories, 4a and above, the material in the plastic region is assumed to be incom-ssible. For compressible materials (87.7) and (87.12) are replaced by equation of the form

$$p = \varphi\,(\mathrm{I}_d) \tag{.14)}$$

5. *Kinematical Quantities.* The velocity $\mathbf{v}$ and acceleration $\mathbf{a}$ are en by

$$v^k = \dot{x}^k \qquad a^k = \dot{v}^k = \frac{\partial v^k}{\partial t} + v^k{}_{;l}\,v^l \tag{.15)}$$

In addition, we have the deformation-rate tensor $d^k{}_l$ and the infinitesim strain tensor $\tilde{e}^k{}_l$ which are expressed by (87.11) and (87.6) respectivel

6. *Boundary and Initial Conditions.* At an external boundary of tl solid the tractions may be prescribed by

$$t^k{}_{(\mathrm{n})} = t^k{}_l\, n^l = s^k \tag{87.16}$$

If the initial values of displacement and velocity field are known, th

$$x^k(\mathbf{X}, 0) = x^k{}_0(\mathbf{X}) \qquad \dot{x}^k(\mathbf{X}, 0) = v^k{}_0(\mathbf{X}) \qquad \text{at } t = 0 \tag{87.17}$$

In addition, the surface separating the elastic region from a plastic regi will be determined by use of the yield criteria and the continuity of tl stress and displacement fields.

7. *Combined Elastic-Plastic Constitutive Equations.* In the treatment elastic-plastic problems the determination of the extent and progress plastic region in time often represents a great difficulty. The use of single set of constitutive equations may be more convenient in such cas When such is the case, then the equations of paragraph 4 are replaced the combined elastic-plastic constitutive equations of the Lévy–v Mises or the Prandtl-Reuss theory obtained in Arts. 85 and 86 respe tively. These are given by

$$\begin{aligned} Y(\bar{\mathfrak{t}})\, \hat{t}^k{}_k &= (3\,\lambda_e + 2\,\mu_e)\, d^k{}_k + \gamma\, Y(\bar{\mathfrak{t}})\, t^k{}_k \\ Y(\bar{\mathfrak{t}})\, \hat{\bar{t}}^k{}_l &= 2\,\mu_e\, \bar{d}^k{}_l + 2\,\mu_e \left[\kappa\, Y(\bar{\mathfrak{t}}) - \sqrt{1 - Y(\bar{\mathfrak{d}})}\; \bar{t}^k{}_l\right] \end{aligned} \tag{87.18}$$

where $\lambda_e$, $\mu_e$ are the Lamé elastic constants and $\gamma$, $\mu$, and $\kappa$ are plastic ma rial constants and

$$Y(\bar{\mathfrak{t}}) \equiv 1 - \frac{\overline{\mathrm{II}}_{\bar{t}}}{K\,\tau^2} \qquad 0 \le Y(\bar{\mathfrak{t}}) \le 1 \tag{87.19}$$

and $Y(\bar{\mathfrak{t}}) = 0$ for the von Mises yield criterion.

For the Prandtl-Reuss theory in place of (87.18) we have

$$\begin{aligned} \hat{t}^m{}_m &= \frac{h d^m{}_m}{1 - (\bar{t}^k{}_l\, \bar{t}^l{}_k / K\,\tau^2)} + k\, t^m{}_m \\ \hat{\bar{t}}^k{}_l &= 2\,\mu \left\{ \bar{d}^k{}_l - \left[ \frac{\bar{d}^m{}_n\, \bar{t}^n{}_m}{K\,\tau^2} + \gamma \left(1 - \frac{\bar{t}^m{}_n\, \bar{t}^n{}_m}{K\,\tau^2}\right)\right] \bar{t}^k{}_l \right\} \end{aligned} \tag{87.20}$$

where $h$, $k$, $\mu$, and $\gamma$ are material constants. The yield criterion $Y(\bar{\mathfrak{t}}) =$ with $Y(\bar{\mathfrak{t}})$ given by (81.19) remains valid for this theory.

## 88. STRESSES AND DISPLACEMENTS IN AN ELASTIC-PLASTIC WEDGE

Below we give the solution of the title problem, by use of the classi Prandtl-Reuss theory, for illustrative purposes. The word classical used to mean that in the Prandtl-Reuss theory the stress flux $\hat{\mathfrak{t}}$ w e replaced by $\dot{\mathbf{t}}$, since for small motions this is permissible. The deformation is assumed to be incompressible and to consist of plane strain.[1] he solution obtained applies to the case of included wedge angle $0 < \leq \pi/2$ subjected to a uniform pressure $\bar{p}_0$ at one of its surfaces $\theta = 0$ 'ig. 88.1). The problem is naturally divided into two parts: (1) soluon in the elastic region and (2) solution in the plastic region. By nforcing the continuity of stresses and displacements across the yield urface, the complete solution is obtained. Determination of the yield urface, of course, is a part of the problem.

We employ a cylindrical coordinate system $(r, \theta, z)$ and assume that the ondition of plane strain prevails so that the displacement $u_z = 0$.

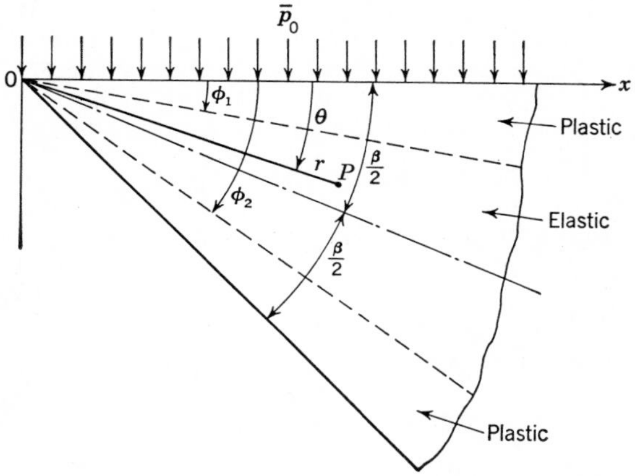


FIG. 88.1. Wedge under lateral pressure. (*After Naghdi* [1957])

sing the physical components of displacements and stresses, we give low the basic equations.

*Conservation of mass:*

$$\tilde{e}_{rr} = -\tilde{e}_{\theta\theta} \tag{8.1}$$

nce $\tilde{e}_{zz} = 0$ in a plane strain.

*Balance of momentum.* For the static case with vanishing body forces e have

$$\begin{aligned} \frac{\partial \bar{t}_{rr}}{\partial r} + \frac{1}{r}\frac{\partial \bar{t}_{r\theta}}{\partial \theta} + \frac{\bar{t}_{rr} - \bar{t}_{\theta\theta}}{r} - \frac{\partial \bar{p}}{\partial r} = 0 \\ \frac{\partial t_{r\theta}}{\partial r} + \frac{1}{r}\frac{\partial \bar{t}_{\theta\theta}}{\partial \theta} + 2\frac{t_{r\theta}}{r} - \frac{1}{r}\frac{\partial \bar{p}}{\partial \theta} = 0 \end{aligned} \tag{8.2}$$

[1] Naghdi [1957]. For compressible materials using Tresca yield condition and ociated flow rules, the same problem was treated by Bland and Naghdi [1958], and e corresponding problem for plane stress was given by Naghdi [1958]. See also irch and Naghdi [1958].

where the physical components of the stress tensor and their deviatori parts are related to each other by

$$(88.3)\qquad \begin{aligned} t_{rr} &= \bar{t}_{rr} - \bar{p} \qquad t_{\theta\theta} = \bar{t}_{\theta\theta} - \bar{p} \\ t_{zz} &= \bar{t}_{zz} - \bar{p} = -(\bar{t}_{rr} + \bar{t}_{\theta\theta}) - \bar{p} \end{aligned}$$

The infinitesimal *strain-displacement relations* for the linear theory ar

$$(88.4)\qquad \begin{aligned} \tilde{e}_{rr} &= \frac{\partial u_r}{\partial r} \qquad \tilde{e}_{\theta\theta} = \frac{u_r}{r} + \frac{1}{r}\frac{\partial u_\theta}{\partial \theta} \\ 2\,\tilde{e}_{r\theta} &= \frac{1}{r}\frac{\partial u_r}{\partial \theta} + \frac{\partial u_\theta}{\partial r} - \frac{u_\theta}{r} \end{aligned}$$

All of the foregoing expressions are valid in both elastic and plastic region

The constitutive equations in the elastic region are given by *Hooke' law:*

$$(88.5)\qquad t_{kl} = \lambda_e \, \mathrm{I}_{\tilde{e}} \, \delta_{kl} + 2\,\mu_e\, \tilde{e}_{kl} \qquad (k, l = r, \theta, z)$$

In the plastic region we use *Prandtl-Reuss* equations

$$(88.6)\qquad \begin{aligned} \dot{\bar{t}}_{kl} &= 2\,\mu_e\, \dot{\tilde{e}}_{kl} - \lambda\, \bar{t}_{kl} \\ \lambda &\equiv (2\,\mu_e/K\,\tau^2)\, \bar{t}_{mn}\, \dot{\tilde{e}}_{mn} \qquad (k, l, m, n = r, \theta, z) \end{aligned}$$

where for small deformations we also take $\mu_p = \mu_e$. The von Mise yield criterion may be expressed as

$$(88.7)\qquad \bar{t}_{rr}{}^2 + \bar{t}_{rr}\,\bar{t}_{\theta\theta} + \bar{t}_{\theta\theta}{}^2 + t_{r\theta}{}^2 = K\,\tau^2$$

where $K\,\tau^2$ is the yield limit in simple shear.

*The Fully Elastic Solution.* Equations (88.1) and (88.2) by use c (88.4) and (88.5) reduce to Navier's equations and an incompressibilit condition

$$(88.8)\qquad \begin{aligned} \mu_e \left[ \nabla^2 u_r - \frac{1}{r}\left( \frac{u_r}{r} + \frac{2}{r}\frac{\partial u_\theta}{\partial \theta} \right) \right] - \frac{\partial \bar{p}}{\partial r} &= 0 \\ \mu_e \left[ \nabla^2 u_\theta + \frac{1}{r}\left( \frac{2}{r}\frac{\partial u_r}{\partial \theta} - \frac{u_\theta}{r} \right) \right] - \frac{1}{r}\frac{\partial \bar{p}}{\partial \theta} &= 0 \end{aligned}$$

$$(88.9)\qquad \frac{\partial u_r}{\partial r} + \frac{u_r}{r} + \frac{1}{r}\frac{\partial u_\theta}{\partial \theta} = 0 \qquad \nabla^2 \equiv \frac{\partial^2}{\partial r^2} + \frac{1}{r}\frac{\partial}{\partial r} + \frac{1}{r^2}\frac{\partial^2}{\partial \theta^2}$$

A solution of (88.8) and (88.9) appropriate to the elastic wedge loade uniformly by uniform tractions is[2]

$$(88.10)\qquad \begin{aligned} \mu_e\, u_r &= -r\,(a \cos 2\,\theta + c \sin 2\,\theta) \\ \mu_e\, u_\theta &= r\,(a \sin 2\,\theta - c \cos 2\,\theta) - rd \log r \\ -\bar{p} &= 2\,(b + d\,\theta) \end{aligned}$$

[2] Cf. Timoshenko and Goodier [1951, pp. 123–125].

here $a$, $b$, $c$, and $d$ are arbitrary constants. Through Hooke's law (88.5) ɪe stresses are found to be

$$
\begin{aligned}
\bar{t}_{rr} &= -\bar{t}_{\theta\theta} = -2\,(a\cos 2\,\theta + c\sin 2\,\theta) \\
t_{r\theta} &= -d + 2\,(a\sin 2\,\theta - c\sin 2\,\theta) \qquad \text{(8.11)} \\
\bar{t}_{zz} &= 0
\end{aligned}
$$

nce in the composite solution we shall need the values of constants $b$, $c$, and $d$ for an applied uniform traction on two yield surfaces which ill turn out to be two planes $\theta = \phi_1$ and $\theta = \phi_2$ through the origin, we ve below the solution of the elastic problem subject to uniform tractions $\theta = \theta_1$ and $\theta = \theta_2$, i.e.,

$$
\begin{aligned}
t_{\theta\theta}(\theta_1) &= t_1 \qquad t_{r\theta}(\theta_1) = \tau_1 \\
t_{\theta\theta}(\theta_2) &= t_2 \qquad t_{r\theta}(\theta_2) = \tau_2
\end{aligned} \qquad \text{(8.12)}
$$

ence

$$
\begin{aligned}
a &= \frac{1}{D}\{(t_2 - t_1)(\cos 2\,\theta_2 - \cos 2\,\theta_1) + \tau_1[\sin 2\,\theta_1 - \sin 2\,\theta_2 \\
&\quad + 2\,(\theta_2 - \theta_1)\cos 2\,\theta_2] + \tau_2[\sin 2\,\theta_2 - \sin 2\,\theta_1 \\
&\quad - 2\,(\theta_2 - \theta_1)\cos 2\,\theta_1]\} \\
c &= \frac{1}{D}\{(t_2 - t_1)(\sin 2\,\theta_2 - \sin 2\,\theta_1) + \tau_1[\cos 2\,\theta_2 - \cos 2\,\theta_1 \\
&\quad + 2\,(\theta_2 - \theta_1)\sin 2\,\theta_2] + \tau_2[\cos 2\,\theta_1 - \cos 2\,\theta_2 \\
&\quad - 2\,(\theta_2 - \theta_1)\sin 2\,\theta_1]\} \\
b &= -\frac{1}{D}\{t_1[-1 + \cos 2\,(\theta_2 - \theta_1) + 2\,\theta_2\sin 2\,(\theta_2 - \theta_1)] \qquad \text{(8.13)} \\
&\quad + t_2[-1 + \cos 2\,(\theta_2 - \theta_1) - 2\,\theta_1\sin 2\,(\theta_2 - \theta_1)] \\
&\quad + \tau_1[-2\,\theta_1 - \sin 2\,(\theta_2 - \theta_1) + 2\,\theta_2\cos 2\,(\theta_2 - \theta_1)] \\
&\quad + \tau_2[-2\,\theta_2 + \sin 2\,(\theta_2 - \theta_1) + 2\,\theta_1\cos 2\,(\theta_2 - \theta_1)]\} \\
d &= \frac{1}{\mathrm{D}}\{-2\,(t_2 - t_1)\sin 2\,(\theta_2 - \theta_1) + 2\,\tau_1[-1 \\
&\quad + \cos 2\,(\theta_2 - \theta_1)] + 2\,\tau_2[-1 + \cos 2\,(\theta_2 - \theta_1)]\} \\
D &\equiv 4\sin 2\,(\theta_2 - \theta_1)[\tan(\theta_2 - \theta_1) - (\theta_2 - \theta_1)]
\end{aligned}
$$

ɔr the special case when the whole wedge is in an elastic state of stress, ɪen for $\theta_1 = 0$, $\theta_2 = \beta$ we have $t_1 = -\bar{p}_0$, $t_2 = \tau_1 = \tau_2 = 0$, and (88.13) duce to

$$
\begin{aligned}
a &= -\frac{\bar{p}_0}{4\,\kappa}\tan\beta \qquad c = \frac{\bar{p}_0}{4\,\kappa} \qquad \text{(8.14)} \\
b &= -\bar{p}_0\left(\tfrac{1}{2} - \frac{1}{4\,\kappa}\tan\beta\right) \qquad d = -\frac{\bar{p}_0}{2\,\kappa} \qquad \kappa \equiv \tan\beta - \beta
\end{aligned}
$$

his completes the elastic part of the solution.

*Initial Yield and the Elastic-Plastic Boundary.* Since $\bar{t}_{rr} = -\bar{t}_{\theta\theta}$, th von Mises yield condition (88.7) may be written as

$$\bar{t}_{\theta\theta}^2 + t_{r\theta}^2 = k^2 \qquad k^2 \equiv K\tau^2 \tag{88.15}$$

By use of (88.11) and (88.14) we may put this into the form

$$\left(\frac{\bar{p}_0}{2\kappa}\right)^2 f(\theta) = k^2 \tag{88.16}$$

where

$$f(\theta) \equiv \tan^2\beta + 2(1 - \cos 2\theta) - 2\tan\beta\sin 2\theta \tag{88.17}$$

Therefore yielding begins at the values of $\theta$ for which $f(\theta)$ attains i maximum value. An examination of $f(\theta)$ together with its first an second derivatives indicates that the angle $\theta_\beta$ for which $f(\theta)$ is maximu depends on $\beta$. In the range $0 < \beta < 2\pi$ the following table gives $\theta_\beta$.

Table 88.1. Values of $\theta = \theta_\beta$ for which $f(\theta)$ is maximum in the range $0 < \beta < 2$

| *Range of wedge angle* | | *Values of $\theta = \theta_\beta$ where yield will initiate* |
|---|---|---|
| $0 < \beta < \frac{\pi}{2}$ | | $\theta = 0, \beta$ |
| $\beta = \frac{\pi}{2}$ | all $\theta$ | $0 \le \theta \le \frac{\pi}{2}$ |
| $\frac{\pi}{2} < \beta < \frac{3\pi}{2}$ | | $\theta = \frac{\beta}{2}$ |
| $\beta = \frac{3\pi}{2}$ | all $\theta$ | $0 \le \theta < \frac{3\pi}{2}$ |
| $\frac{3\pi}{2} < \beta < 2\pi$ | | $\theta < \frac{\beta}{2} \pm \frac{\pi}{2}$ |

Thus, for example, for $0 < \beta < \pi/2$ the minimum of $f(\theta)$ is at $\theta = \beta/$ and the maxima are at $\theta = 0$ and $\theta = \beta$. For $\beta = \pi/2$, (88.17) is ind pendent of $\theta$ and the entire region becomes plastic when the load reach the value $2k$.

From here on, confining our attention to the range $0 < \beta < \pi/2$, w find that the yielding will begin simultaneously at the outside surfa $\theta = 0$ and $\theta = \beta$ when pressure $\bar{p}_0$ reaches the critical value

$$p^* = \frac{2k\kappa}{\tan\beta} \tag{88.18}$$

For a pressure $\bar{p}_0 > p^*$ a portion of the wedge near the external surfac becomes plastic. Since the yielding is independent of $r$, these yie surfaces are the planes $\theta = \phi_1$, $\theta = \phi_2$ through the origin, and the yie regions are

$$0 \leq \theta \leq \phi_1 \qquad \phi_2 \leq \theta \leq \beta \qquad \text{(yield regions)}$$

These regions are identified in Fig. 88.1.

To determine appropriate solutions of the field equations in the plastic regions, we may make some simplifications at the outset. Stresses in the elastic region $\phi_1 < \theta < \phi_2$ are independent of $r$. Hence the condition of continuity of stress components across the yield surface demands that they remain independent of $r$. This reduces (88.2) to

$$\text{(88.19)} \qquad \frac{\partial t_{r\theta}}{\partial \theta} + \bar{t}_{rr} - \bar{t}_{\theta\theta} = 0 \qquad \frac{\partial \bar{t}_{\theta\theta}}{\partial \theta} + 2\, t_{r\theta} - \frac{\partial \bar{p}}{\partial \theta} = 0$$

in the yield regions. According to (88.11) stresses at a point in the elastic domain stand in the ratios

$$\text{(88.20)} \qquad \bar{t}_{rr}:\bar{t}_{\theta\theta}:\bar{t}_{zz} = \tilde{e}_{rr}:\tilde{e}_{\theta\theta}:\tilde{e}_{zz} = 1:-1:0 \qquad \phi_1 \leq \theta \leq \phi_2$$

By (88.1) we also have

$$\text{(88.21)} \qquad \tilde{e}_{rr}:\tilde{e}_{\theta\theta}:\tilde{e}_{zz} = \dot{\tilde{e}}_{rr}:\dot{\tilde{e}}_{\theta\theta}:\dot{\tilde{e}}_{zz} = 1:-1:0 \qquad 0 < \phi_1 < \phi_2 < \beta$$

at $P$ for all states of contained plastic deformations.

Through the constitutive equations (88.6) and continuity of stresses at $\phi_1$ and $\phi_2$ it can be agreed that

$$\text{(88.22)} \qquad \dot{\bar{t}}_{rr}:\dot{\bar{t}}_{\theta\theta}:\dot{\bar{t}}_{zz} = \bar{t}_{rr}:\bar{t}_{\theta\theta}:\bar{t}_{zz} = 1:-1:0 \qquad 0 < \phi_1 < \phi_2 < \beta$$

Thus $\bar{t}_{rr}$ and $\bar{t}_{\theta\theta}$ must have the same absolute value throughout the wedge or $\bar{t}_{rr} - \bar{t}_{\theta\theta} = -2t_{r\theta}$. Using the von Mises yield condition, we now reduce $(88.19)_1$ to

$$\text{(88.23)} \qquad \frac{\partial t_{r\theta}}{\partial \theta} = \pm 2\,(k^2 - t_{r\theta}{}^2)^{\frac{1}{2}}$$

Integration of this together with (88.15) and (88.22) results in

$$\text{(88.24)} \qquad \begin{aligned} t_{r\theta} &= \pm k \sin 2\,(\theta - \gamma) \\ \bar{t}_{\theta\theta} &= -\bar{t}_{rr} = \pm k \cos 2\,(\theta - \gamma) \end{aligned}$$

If the loading is assumed to be monotonic in time, then one may interpret the time rates indicated by a dot as a differentiation with respect to a parameter $\phi$ which may be identified as $\phi_1$ or $\phi_2$. With this interpretation the factor $\gamma$ in (88.24) is a function of $\phi$, i.e., $\gamma = \gamma\,(\phi)$.

Employing (88.24) in $(88.19)_2$ gives $\partial\bar{p}/\partial\theta = 0$ or

$$\text{(88.25)} \qquad \bar{p} = \bar{p}\,(\phi)$$

Stresses in the plastic regions must satisfy the boundary conditions both along the free edges of the wedge and along the yield surfaces. Let us consider the former conditions first:

$$(88.26)\qquad \begin{array}{lll} t_{\theta\theta}(0) = -\bar{p}_0 & t_{r\theta}(0) = 0 & 0 \le \theta \le \phi_1 \\ t_{\theta\theta}(\beta) = t_{r\theta}(\beta) = 0 & & \phi_2 \le \theta < \beta \end{array}$$

The factors $\gamma$ and $\bar{p}$ are now evaluated through (88.24)–(88.26).

$$(88.27)\qquad \begin{array}{lll} \gamma = 0 & \bar{p} = \bar{p}_0 \pm k & 0 \le \theta \le \phi_1 \\ \gamma = \beta & \bar{p} = \pm k & \phi_2 \le \theta \le \beta \end{array}$$

Since $t_{r\theta}$ at $\theta = 0$ must be tensile if $\bar{t}_{\theta\theta}$ represents a pressure, we must select the lower sign in (88.24) for the region $0 \le \theta \le \phi_1$ and the upper sign for $\phi_2 \le \theta \le \beta$. Thus the stress distributions in the two plastic regions are

$$(88.28)\qquad \left.\begin{array}{ll} \bar{t}_{rr} = -\bar{t}_{\theta\theta} = k\cos 2\theta & \bar{t}_{zz} = 0 \\ t_{r\theta} = -k\sin 2\theta & \bar{p} = \bar{p}_0 - k \end{array}\right\} 0 \le \theta \le \phi_1$$

and

$$(88.29)\qquad \left.\begin{array}{ll} \bar{t}_{rr} = -\bar{t}_{\theta\theta} = -k\cos 2(\theta - \beta) & \bar{t}_{zz} = 0 \\ t_{r\theta} = k\sin 2(\theta - \beta) & \bar{p} = k \end{array}\right\} \phi_2 \le \theta \le \beta$$

We must next satisfy the conditions of continuity of elastic and plasti stresses along the yield surfaces. Continuity of stresses at the yiel surfaces together with the yield conditions

$$\bar{t}_{\theta\theta}^{\,2} + t_{r\theta}^{\,2} = k^2 \qquad \text{at } \theta = \phi_1 \text{ and } \phi_2$$

require that $\bar{p}$ be continuous across these surfaces. Hence by (88.11 (88.28), and (88.29) we get

$$(88.30)\qquad 2(b + d\,\phi_1) = -\bar{p}_0 + k \qquad 2(b + d\,\phi_2) = -k$$

Since $b$ and $d$ are given by (88.13) with $\theta_1$ and $\theta_2$ respectively replaced b $\phi_1$ and $\phi_2$, we see that the quantities $t_1$, $t_2$, $\tau_1$, and $\tau_2$, obtained from (88.1 and (88.30), are now given by

$$(88.31)\qquad \begin{array}{ll} t_1 = -\bar{p}_0 + k(1 - \cos 2\phi_1) & \tau_1 = k\sin 2\phi_1 \\ t_2 = -k[1 - \cos 2(\phi_2 - \beta)] & \tau_2 = k\sin 2(\phi_2 - \beta) \end{array}$$

This completes the stress distribution throughout the wedge. Elimina ing $\bar{p}_0$ from (88.30), after some manipulations one arrives at

$$(88.32)\qquad \phi_1 + \phi_2 = \beta$$

Therefore the two plastic regions are equal in extent and are confined equal angular regions adjacent to the two sides of the wedge.

To determine displacements, we must introduce the constitutive equ

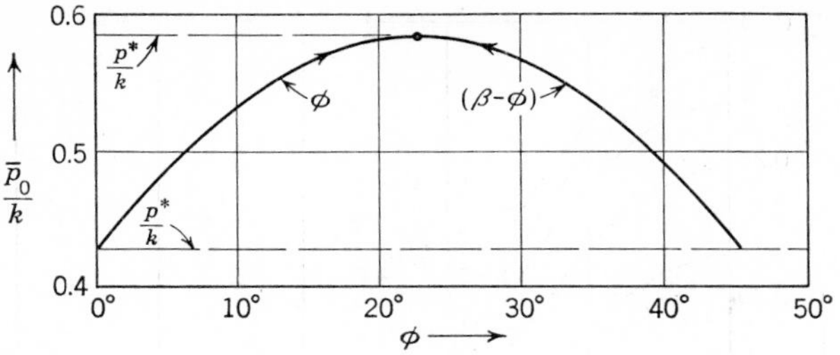


FIG. 88.2. Lateral pressure versus $\phi$ for $\beta = \pi/4$. (*After Naghdi* [1957])

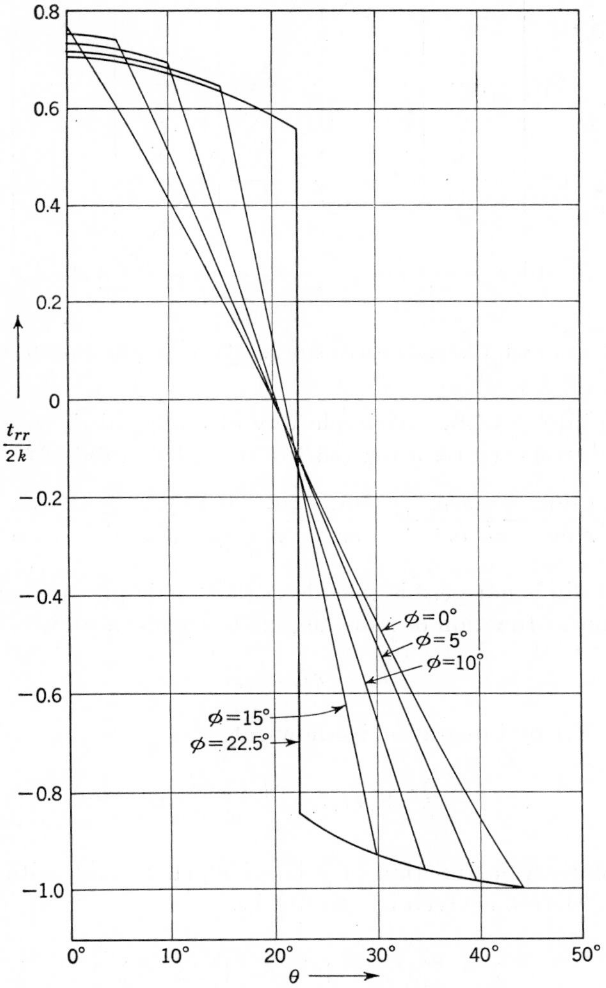


FIG. 88.3. Radial stress. (*After Naghdi* [1957])

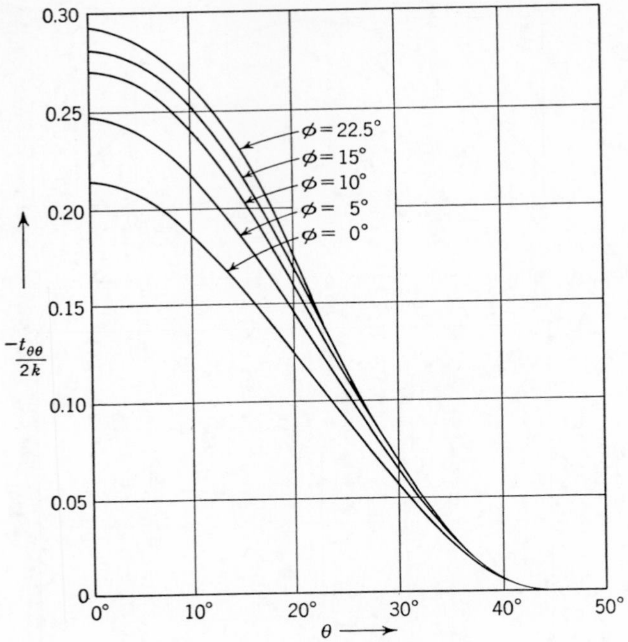


FIG. 88.4. Circumferential stress. (*After Naghdi* [1957])

tions (88.6) into (88.19). A simple way of doing this is to differentiate $(88.19)_1$ with respect to $t$, using (88.19) and (88.6) to obtain

$$\frac{1}{r}\frac{\partial^2 \dot{u}_r}{\partial \theta^2} - r\frac{\partial^2 \dot{u}_r}{\partial r^2} + 3\frac{\partial \dot{u}_r}{\partial r} + \frac{\dot{u}_r}{r} = \frac{t_{r\theta}}{\mu_e}\frac{\partial \lambda}{\partial \theta} \qquad \dot{u}_r \equiv \frac{\partial u_r}{\partial \phi} \tag{88.33}$$

Since radial slip is not permissible along the elastic-plastic boundaries, $u_r$ must be a linear function of $r$ in the plastic regions also, i.e.,

$$u_r = r\,\tilde{e}_r\,(\theta, \phi) \tag{88.34}$$

From (88.33) by integration we now get

$$\frac{\partial^2 \tilde{e}_{rr}}{\partial \theta^2} + 4\,\tilde{e}_{rr} = \int \frac{t_{r\theta}}{\mu_e}\frac{\partial \lambda}{\partial \theta}\,d\phi \tag{88.35}$$

where an integration function of $\theta$ is set equal to zero without loss in generality. Here $\lambda$ is given by $(88.6)_2$, i.e.,

$$\lambda = \frac{\mu_e}{k^2}\,(\bar{t}_{rr}\,\dot{\tilde{e}}_{rr} + \bar{t}_{\theta\theta}\,\dot{\tilde{e}}_{\theta\theta} + 2\,t_{r\theta}\,\dot{\tilde{e}}_{r\theta}) \tag{88.36}$$

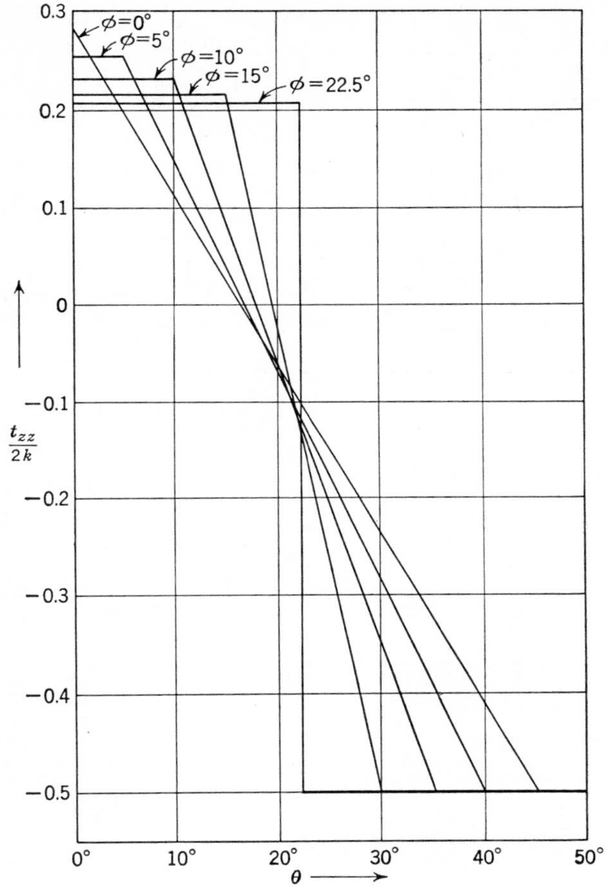


FIG. 88.5. Axial stress. (*After Naghdi* [1957])

Now $\bar{t}_{rr} = -\bar{t}_{\theta\theta}$. Moreover through (88.6) and (88.28) we have

$$\dot{\tilde{e}}_{r\theta} = -\dot{\tilde{e}}_r \tan 2\theta$$

With the aid of (88.1), (88.36), and (88.28) we find that (88.35) can be reduced to

(88.37) $$\frac{\partial^2 \tilde{e}_{rr}}{\partial\theta^2} + 2\tan\theta \frac{\partial \tilde{e}_{rr}}{\partial\theta} + 4\sec^2 2\theta\, \tilde{e}_{rr} = 0$$

An appropriate solution of this equation is given by

(88.38) $$\tilde{e}_{rr} = \cos 2\theta\,[A_1(\phi) + B_1(\phi)\log|\sec 2\theta + \tan 2\theta|]$$

This equation together with (88.34) and the incompressibility condition (88.9) gives the following displacements in the plastic region $0 \leq \theta \leq \phi_1 \equiv \phi$:

$$
\begin{aligned}
u_r &= r \cos 2\theta \, (A_1 + B_1 \log |\sec 2\theta + \tan 2\theta|) \\
u_\theta &= -r \sin 2\theta \, (A_1 + B_1 \log |\sec 2\theta + \tan 2\theta|) \\
&\quad + r\,[B_1 \log |\sec 2\theta| - 2 B_1 \log r + C_1(\phi)] \qquad (0 \leq \theta \leq \phi_1)
\end{aligned} \tag{88.39}
$$

Displacements for the region $\beta - \phi \leq \theta \leq \beta$ can be deduced from (88.39) by replacing $\theta$ by $\theta - \beta$ and $A_1$, $B_1$, $C_1$ by $A_2$, $B_2$, $C_2$ respectively.

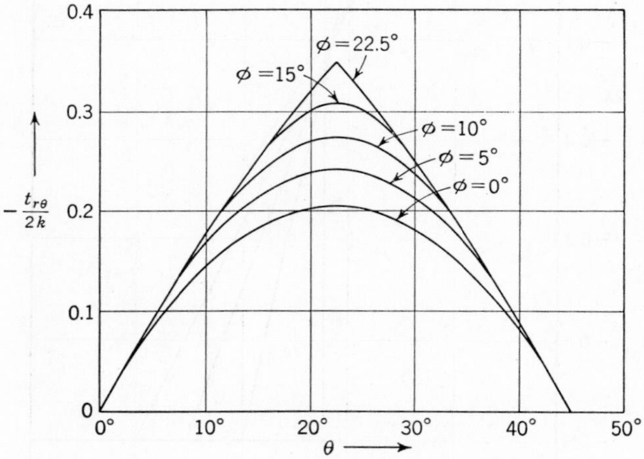


FIG. 88.6. Shear stress. (*After Naghdi* [1957])

The coefficients $A_i$, $B_i$, $C_i$ $(i = 1, 2)$ are then determined by the requirement of continuity of the displacement field at the elastic-plastic boundaries. Thus for $0 \leq \theta \leq \phi$

$$
\begin{aligned}
A_1(\phi) &= P_1(\phi) \sec 2\phi - \frac{d}{2\mu_e} \log |\sec 2\phi + \tan 2\phi| \\
B_1(\phi) &= \frac{d}{2\mu_e} \\
C_1(\phi) &= P_1(\phi) \tan 2\phi + Q_1(\phi) - \frac{d}{2\mu_e} \log |\sec 2\phi| \\
P_1(\phi) &\equiv -\frac{1}{\mu_e} (a \cos 2\phi + c \sin 2\phi) \\
Q_1(\phi) &\equiv \frac{1}{\mu_e} (a \sin 2\phi - c \cos 2\phi)
\end{aligned} \tag{88.40}
$$

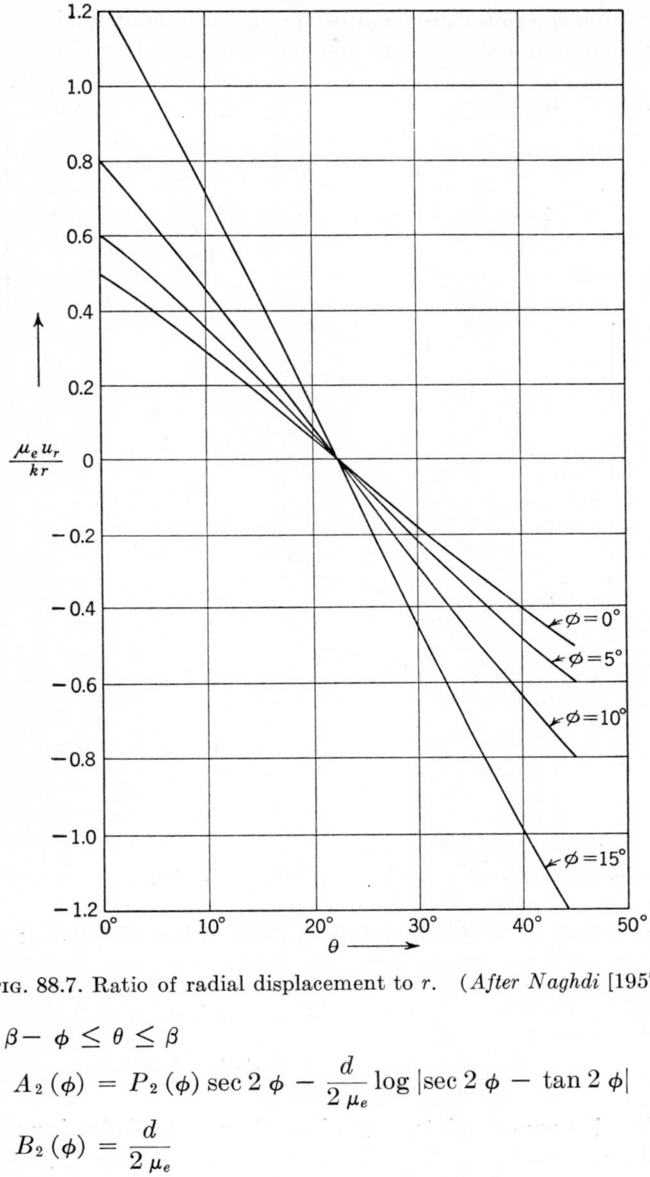


FIG. 88.7. Ratio of radial displacement to $r$. (*After Naghdi* [1957])

and for $\beta - \phi \leq \theta \leq \beta$

$$
\begin{aligned}
A_2(\phi) &= P_2(\phi)\sec 2\phi - \frac{d}{2\mu_e}\log|\sec 2\phi - \tan 2\phi| \\
B_2(\phi) &= \frac{d}{2\mu_e} \\
C_2(\phi) &= -P_2(\phi)\tan 2\phi + Q_2(\phi) - \frac{d}{2\mu_e}\log|\sec 2\phi| \qquad (88.41)\\
P_2(\phi) &\equiv -\frac{1}{\mu_e}[a\cos 2(\beta - \phi) + c\sin 2(\beta - \phi)] \\
Q_2(\phi) &\equiv \frac{1}{\mu_e}[a\sin 2(\beta - \phi) - c\cos 2(\beta - \phi)]
\end{aligned}
$$

This completes the determination of the displacement field. Finally we give the relation that determines the elastic-plastic boundary $\theta = \phi$ as a

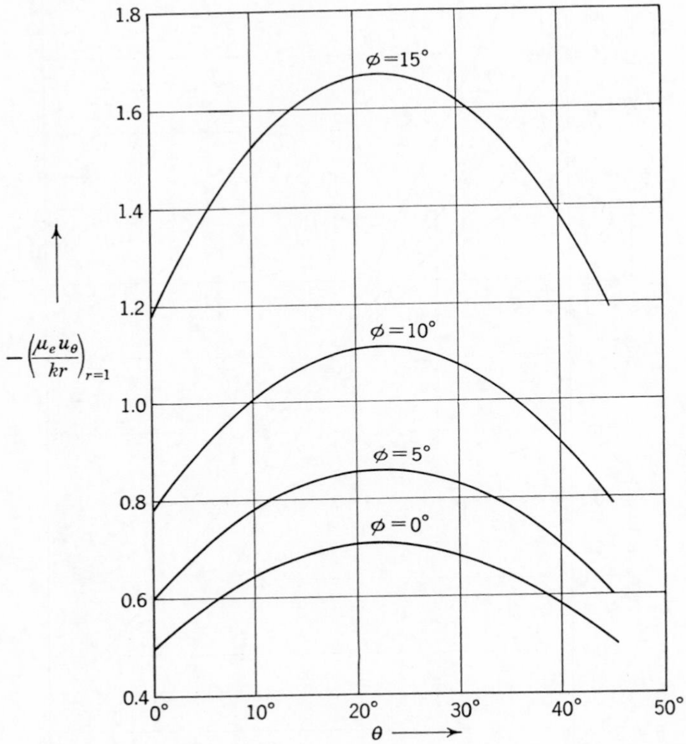


FIG. 88.8. Circumferential displacement at $r = 1$. (*After Naghdi* [1957])

function of $\beta$ and $\bar{p}_0$. This is obtained from either of (88.30):

$$\frac{\bar{p}_0}{k} = \frac{2}{\tan(\beta - 2\phi)} \{(\beta - 2\phi)\sin 2\phi\,[\tan(\beta - 2\phi) + \tan\phi] + \tan(\beta - 2\phi) - (\beta - 2\phi)\} \tag{88.42}$$

The problem is now complete. We have found the following results.

1. Displacements $u_r$, $u_\theta$ throughout the wedge $0 \le \theta \le \beta$. Equations (88.39) give plastic displacements in the plastic region $0 \le \theta \le \phi$ while the same equations with $A_1$, $B_1$, $C_1$ replaced by $A_2$, $B_2$, $C_2$ and $\theta$ by $\theta - \beta$ give the plastic displacements in the plastic regions $\beta - \phi \le \theta \le \beta$.

Elastic displacements are given by (88.10) in the elastic region $\phi \le \theta \le \beta - \phi$.

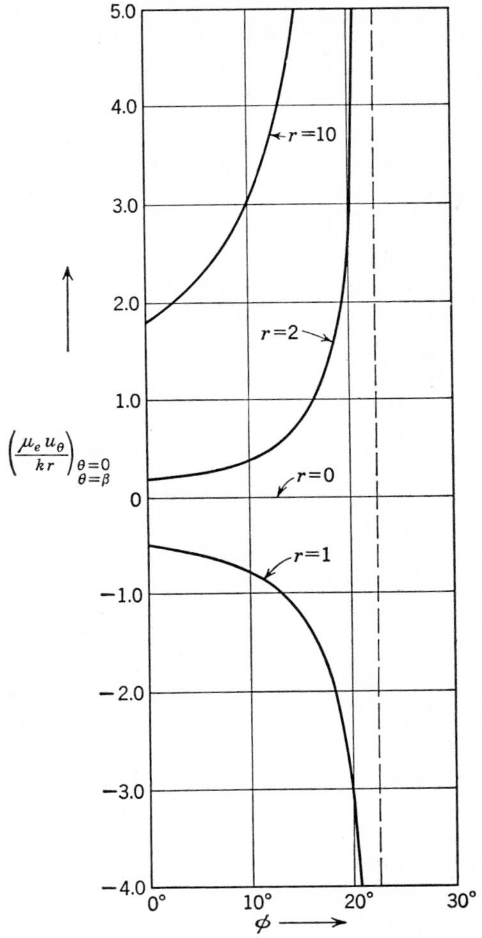


FIG. 88.9. Ratio of circumferential displacement to $r$ along outside boundaries. (*After Naghdi* [1957])

The constants $a$, $b$, $c$, and $d$ appearing in these latter equations are given by (88.13) in terms of $t_1$, $t_2$, $\tau_1$, $\tau_2$, $\theta_1$, and $\theta_2$, which are given by (88.31) and $\theta_1 \equiv \phi$, $\theta_2 \equiv \beta - \phi$.

2. The stresses in the two plastic regions are given by (88.28) and (88.29).

3. The elastic-plastic boundaries $\theta = \phi$, $\theta = \beta - \phi$ are determined from (88.42).

Numerical examples assuming $\beta = \pi/4$ were carried out by Naghdi, and the results are shown in Figs. 88.2 to 88.9.

## 89. RELATION OF HYPOELASTICITY TO PLASTICITY

In the treatment of the Prandtl-Reuss theory of plasticity in Art. 8 our starting point was similar to that used in the constitutive equation of the hypoelasticity theory. Green [1956a, b] gave a theory that exhibit the ties existing between the two theories. By use of an expositio concerning simple shear, Truesdell [1956] has illustrated some connec tions between the yield and failure criteria predicted by hypoelasticity and those postulated in the theory of plasticity. While further work i certainly needed to establish this relationship on a firmer foundation, w believe that an adequate beginning has already been made and that i warrants the closer attention of research workers.

We begin with the basic equations of the hypoelasticity theory:

$$\frac{\partial \rho}{\partial t} + (\rho\, v^k)_{;k} = 0 \tag{89.1}$$

$$2\,\mu\, s^{lk}{}_{;l} = \rho \left( \frac{\partial v^k}{\partial t} + v^k{}_{;l}\, v^l - f^k \right) \tag{89.2}$$

$$\begin{aligned} \mathring{s}^k{}_l = {} & \alpha_0\, d^m{}_m\, \delta^k{}_l + \alpha_1\, d^k{}_l + \alpha_2\, d^m{}_m\, s^k{}_l \\ & + \alpha_3\, M\, \delta^k{}_l + \tfrac{1}{2}\alpha_4\, (d^k{}_r\, s^r{}_l + s^k{}_r\, d^r{}_l) + \alpha_5\, d^m{}_m\, s^k{}_r\, s^r{}_l \\ & + \alpha_6\, M\, s^k{}_l + \alpha_7\, N\, \delta^k{}_l + \tfrac{1}{2}\alpha_8\, (d^k{}_m\, s^m{}_n\, s^n{}_l + s^k{}_m\, s^m{}_n\, d^n{}_l) \\ & + \alpha_9\, M\, s^k{}_r\, s^r{}_l + \alpha_{10}\, N\, s^k{}_l + \alpha_{11}\, N\, s^k{}_r\, s^r{}_l \end{aligned} \tag{89.3}$$

where the first and second equations are respectively the equations of conservation of mass and momenta, and the last equation is the constitutive equation of hypoelasticity equivalent to (73.12). Here $\alpha_0$, $\alpha_1, \ldots, \alpha_{11}$ are functions of stress invariants as given by (73.13), and $M$ and $N$ are defined, as in (73.9), by

$$M \equiv s^k{}_l\, d^l{}_k \qquad N \equiv s^k{}_l\, s^l{}_m\, d^m{}_k \tag{89.4}$$

We also use the Jaumann-Noll definition of stress rate for $\mathring{\mathbf{s}}$ so that[1]

$$\mathring{s}^k{}_l \equiv \frac{\partial s^k{}_l}{\partial t} + s^k{}_{l;m}\, v^m + s^k{}_m\, w^m{}_l - s^m{}_l\, w^k{}_m \tag{89.5}$$

As we know, different definitions of stress flux do not affect the constitutive relations in form, provided we understand that the constitutive coefficients $\alpha_\gamma$ for different choice of the stress flux are in general different.

In plasticity use is made of the deviatoric parts of the stress and

[1] The present approach differs from that of Green in that he uses the Oldroyd definition of stress rate and embedded coordinates.

deformation-rate tensors. Hence we introduce

$$(89.6) \qquad \bar{s}^k{}_l = s^k{}_l - \tfrac{1}{3} s^r{}_r \, \delta^k{}_l \qquad \bar{d}^k{}_l = d^k{}_l - \tfrac{1}{3} d^r{}_r \, \delta^k{}_l$$

where

$$(89.7) \qquad \bar{s}^k{}_k = 0 \qquad \bar{d}^k{}_k = 0$$

Using (89.6) and (89.7), we may express (89.3) in the form

$$(89.8) \quad \hat{\bar{s}}^k{}_l + \tfrac{1}{3} \hat{s}^m{}_m \, \delta^k{}_l = (h_0 \, \delta^k{}_l + h_2 \, \bar{s}^k{}_l + h_5 \, \bar{s}^k{}_r \, \bar{s}^r{}_l) \, d^m{}_m + h_1 \, \bar{d}^k{}_l + \tfrac{1}{2} h_4 \, (\bar{d}^k{}_m \, \bar{s}^m{}_l + \bar{s}^k{}_m \, \bar{d}^m{}_l) + (h_3 \, \bar{M} + h_7 \, \bar{N}) \, \delta^k{}_l + (h_6 \, \bar{M} + h_{10} \, \bar{N}) \, \bar{s}^k{}_l + (h_9 \, \bar{M} + h_{11} \, \bar{N}) \, \bar{s}^k{}_m \, \bar{s}^m{}_l + \tfrac{1}{2} h_8 \, (\bar{d}^k{}_m \, \bar{s}^m{}_n \, \bar{s}^n{}_l + \bar{s}^k{}_m \, \bar{s}^m{}_n \, \bar{d}^n{}_l)$$

where

$$(89.9) \qquad \bar{M} \equiv \bar{s}^k{}_m \, \bar{d}^m{}_k \qquad \bar{N} \equiv \bar{s}^k{}_m \, \bar{s}^m{}_n \, \bar{d}^n{}_k$$

and $h_0$, $h_1$, $h_2$, . . . , $h_{11}$ are dimensionless analytic functions of the invariants

$$(89.10) \quad s^k{}_k \qquad \overline{\mathrm{II}}_{\bar{s}} \equiv \bar{s}^k{}_m \, \bar{s}^m{}_k \equiv 2\,H \qquad \overline{\mathrm{III}}_{\bar{s}} \equiv \bar{s}^k{}_m \, \bar{s}^m{}_n \, \bar{s}^n{}_k \equiv 3\,K$$

For $M$ and $N$ given by (89.4), we now have

$$(89.11) \qquad M = \bar{M} + \tfrac{1}{3} s^m{}_m \, d^n{}_n \qquad N = \bar{N} + \tfrac{2}{3} \bar{M} \, s^m{}_m + \tfrac{2}{3} H \, d^m{}_m + \tfrac{1}{9} d^k{}_k \, s^m{}_m \, s^n{}_n$$

By contracting (89.8) and using (89.7) and (89.9), we obtain

$$(89.12) \quad \hat{s}^m{}_m = (3\,h_0 + 2\,h_5\,H) \, d^m{}_m + (h_4 + 3\,h_3 + 2\,h_9\,H) \, \bar{M} + (3\,h_7 + h_8 + 2\,h_{11}\,H) \, \bar{N}$$

We are now ready to introduce additional postulates for transition from hypoelasticity as formulated above to a plasticity theory which is suitable for plastic flow of metals.

AXIOM 1. *The deviatoric stress flux $\hat{\bar{s}}^k{}_l \, (k \neq l)$ is independent of the stress invariant $s^m{}_m$ and the rate of deformation invariant $d^m{}_m$.*

AXIOM 2. *The deviatoric stress flux $\hat{\bar{s}}^k{}_l$ has a constitutive equation which holds for all nonzero values of $\bar{M}$ and $\bar{N}$.*

AXIOM 3. *For a single unloading the constitutive equations have the same form as the loading. The constitutive coefficients are such as to make the constitutive equations identical whenever $\bar{M} = 0$.*

Axiom 1 can be satisfied if

$$(89.13) \qquad h_2 \equiv h_5 \equiv 0 \qquad \hat{s}^m{}_m = 3\,h_0 \, d^m{}_m$$

and $h_0, h_1, \ldots, h_{11}$ are functions of $H$ and $K$. Now (89.8) reduces to

$$\hat{\bar{s}}^k{}_l = h_1 \bar{d}^k{}_l + \tfrac{1}{2} h_4 (\bar{d}^k{}_m \bar{s}^m{}_l + \bar{s}^k{}_m \bar{d}^m{}_l) + (h_3 \bar{M} + h_7 \bar{N}) \delta^k{}_l + (h_6 \bar{M} + h_{10} \bar{N}) \bar{s}^k{}_l + (h_9 \bar{M} + h_{11} \bar{N}) \bar{s}^k{}_m \bar{s}^m{}_l + \tfrac{1}{2} h_8 (\bar{d}^k{}_m \bar{s}^m{}_n \bar{s}^n{}_l + \bar{s}^k{}_m \bar{s}^m{}_n \bar{d}^n{}_l) \tag{89.14}$$

Since $(89.13)_2$ must be identical to (89.12) for nonzero $\bar{M}$ and $\bar{N}$ in accordance with Axiom 2, we must therefore have

$$\begin{aligned} h_4 + 3 h_3 + 2 h_9 H &= 0 \\ 3 h_7 + h_8 + 2 h_{11} H &= 0 \end{aligned} \tag{89.15}$$

Constitutive equations (89.13) and (89.14) subject to (89.15) are basic in the loading process. From (89.14) we obtain two further results for the time flux $\hat{H}$ and $\hat{K}$. These are obtained by multiplying (89.14) by $\bar{s}^l{}_k$ and $\bar{s}^l{}_m \bar{s}^m{}_k$ respectively and using (89.15) and the identity

$$\bar{s}^k{}_m \bar{s}^m{}_n \bar{s}^n{}_l = K \delta^k{}_l + H \bar{s}^k{}_l \tag{89.16}$$

Hence

$$\hat{H} = [h_1 + (2 h_6 + h_8) H + 3 h_9 K] \bar{M} + (h_4 + 2 h_{10} H + 3 h_{11} K) \bar{N} \tag{89.17}$$

$$\hat{K} = [-h_3 H + (3 h_6 + h_8) K] \bar{M} + [h_1 - h_7 H + 3 h_{10} K] \bar{N} \tag{89.18}$$

which will be used in the following.

To obtain the constitutive equations applicable to a single unloading, we use Axiom 3. Thus we assume

$$\hat{\bar{s}}^m{}_m = 3 h_0' d^m{}_m \tag{89.19}$$

$$\hat{\bar{s}}^k{}_l = h_1' \bar{d}^k{}_l + \tfrac{1}{2} h_4' (\bar{d}^k{}_m \bar{s}^m{}_l + \bar{s}^k{}_m \bar{d}^m{}_l) + (h_3' \bar{M} + h_7' \bar{N}) \delta^k{}_l + (h_6' \bar{M} + h_{10}' \bar{N}) \bar{s}^k{}_l + (h_9' \bar{M} + h_{11}' \bar{N}) \bar{s}^k{}_m \bar{s}^m{}_l + \tfrac{1}{2} h_8' (\bar{d}^k{}_m \bar{s}^m{}_n \bar{s}^n{}_l + \bar{s}^k{}_m \bar{s}^m{}_n \bar{d}^n{}_l) \tag{89.20}$$

subject to

$$\begin{aligned} h_4' + 3 h_3' + 2 h_9' H &= 0 \\ 3 h_7' + h_8' + 2 h_{11}' H &= 0 \end{aligned} \tag{89.21}$$

where $h_1', h_2', \ldots, h_{11}'$ are new dimensionless analytic functions of the invariants $H$ and $K$. Equations (89.19) and (89.20) are valid for $\bar{M} < 0$. An additional postulate regarding the total dissipation of energy per unit mass, in any complete loading and unloading to the same state of stress, is needed. This quantity for plastic flow of metals must be nonnegative. This condition will naturally impose certain restrictive conditions on the constitutive coefficients. Studies on this question are presently lacking

According to Axiom 3, (89.19) and (89.20) must become identical to $(89.13)_2$ and (89.14) when $\bar{M} = 0$. A sufficient condition for this is

$$h'_0 \equiv h_0 \qquad h'_1 \equiv h_1 \qquad h'_4 \equiv h_4 \qquad h'_7 \equiv h_7$$
$$h'_8 \equiv h_8 \qquad h'_{10} \equiv h_{10} \qquad h'_{11} \equiv h_{11} \tag{89.22}$$

All of the above considerations are for a single loading followed by a complete unloading. For further loading and unloading cycles we can use the same sets of equations $(89.13)_2$ and (89.14) when $\bar{M} > 0$, and (89.19) and (89.20) when $\bar{M} < 0$, subject to the restrictions stated above. Continuity of these two sets of equations must be maintained at $\bar{M} = 0$, which requires such equations as (89.22). Together with (89.1) and (89.2) the foregoing constitutive equations provide the necessary basic field equations for the plastic flow of metals. We now give some simple theories based on the foregoing general theory.

*Special Constitutive Equations.* In order to include the classical linear theory of elasticity, we have shown in Art. 73 on hypoelasticity that we may make certain adjustments in the constitutive coefficients $h_0$ and $h_1$. Specifically, we take

$$h_0 = h'_0 = \frac{1+\nu}{3(1-2\nu)} \qquad h_1 = h'_1 = 1 \tag{89.23}$$

when $H = K = 0$, where $\nu$ is Poisson's ratio. To obtain the simplest set, we also take

$$h'_3 = h'_6 = h'_7 = h'_8 = h'_9 = h'_{10} = h'_{11} = 0 \tag{89.24}$$

for all $H$ and $K$. The conditions (89.21) now give

$$h'_4 = 0 \tag{89.25}$$

By use of (89.22)–(89.25) the equations of loading, $(89.13)_2$ and (89.14), and those of unloading, (89.19) and (89.20), now become

$$\hat{s}^m{}_m = \frac{1+\nu}{1-2\nu}\, d^m{}_m$$
$$\hat{\bar{s}}^k{}_l = \bar{d}^k{}_l + (-\tfrac{2}{3} h_9 H \delta^k{}_l + h_6 \bar{s}^k{}_l + h_9 \bar{s}^k{}_m \bar{s}^m{}_l)\, \bar{M} \tag{89.26}$$

for the loading $\bar{M} \geq 0$ and

$$\hat{s}^m{}_m = \frac{1+\nu}{1-2\nu}\, d^m{}_m$$
$$\hat{\bar{s}}^k{}_l = \bar{d}^k{}_l \tag{89.27}$$

for the unloading $\bar{M} \leq 0$.

In summary, as is shown in Art. 75, these equations integrate t Hooke's law of the classical theory of infinitesimal deformations.

The nonnegative character of the total dissipation will in general impos restrictions on the nature of functions $h_6$ and $h_9$.

A special case of (89.26) of some interest would result when

$$h_6 \equiv -\frac{2\,\alpha^2}{3} \qquad h_9 \equiv 0 \tag{89.28}$$

where $\alpha$ is a constant. In this case $(89.26)_2$ reduces to

$$\hat{\bar{s}}^k{}_l = \bar{d}^k{}_l - \tfrac{2}{3}\,\alpha^2\,\bar{M}\,\bar{s}^k{}_l \qquad (\bar{M} \geq 0) \tag{89.29}$$

Also from (89.17) we get

$$\hat{H} = \left(1 - \frac{4\,\alpha^2}{3}\,H\right)\bar{M} \tag{89.30}$$

which suggests a yield condition of the von Mises type. Truesdell [195€ has shown that yield in this sense may never occur even for infinite strai and that when it does occur, it is after a hypoelastic yield.[2] For simpl shear von Mises yield occurs for very large values of $\alpha$. Before this however, the shear stress attains a maximum value, finally sinking t the von Mises yield value asymptotically.

For *incompressible* bodies the foregoing equations are modified b writing $d^k{}_l = \bar{d}^k{}_l$, omitting the first equations of (89.26) and (89.27), an replacing $s^m{}_m$ by an arbitrary pressure $\bar{p}$. In this case the basic fiel equations are

$$\begin{gathered}
v^k{}_{;k} = 0 \\
-\frac{\partial \bar{p}}{\partial x^k} + 2\,\mu\,\bar{s}^l{}_{k;l} = \rho\left(\frac{\partial v_k}{\partial t} + v_{k;l}\,v^l - f_k\right) \\
\hat{\bar{s}}^k{}_l = d^k{}_l - \tfrac{2}{3}\,\alpha^2\,\bar{M}\,\bar{s}^k{}_l \qquad (\bar{M} \geq 0) \\
\hat{\bar{s}}^k{}_l = d^k{}_l \qquad (\bar{M} \leq 0) \\
d^k{}_l \equiv \tfrac{1}{2}\,(v^k{}_{;l} + v_{l;}{}^k)
\end{gathered} \tag{89.31}$$

A simple solution of these equations is given in the following article fo illustrative purposes.

*Plastic Flow with No Work Hardening: Prandtl-Reuss Theory.* If th work hardening is absent, we must have a functional dependence betwee $H$ and $K$ which may be expressed as

$$F\,(H, K) = c \tag{89.32}$$

where $F$ is a function of the invariants $H$ and $K$, and $c$ is a positiv

[2] Cf. Art. 90.

nstant. From (89.32) we have

9.33) $$\frac{\partial F}{\partial H} \hat{H} + \frac{\partial F}{\partial K} \hat{K} = 0$$

we substitute $\hat{H}$ and $\hat{K}$ from (89.17) and (89.18) and require that the sult hold for all nonzero $\bar{M}$ and $\bar{N}$, we get

9.34) $$\begin{gathered}[h_1 + (2\,h_6 + h_8)\,H + 3\,h_9\,K]\,\frac{\partial F}{\partial H} \\ + [-h_3\,H + (3\,h_6 + h_8)\,K]\,\frac{\partial F}{\partial K} = 0 \\ (h_4 + 2\,h_{10}\,H + 3\,h_{11}\,K)\,\frac{\partial F}{\partial H} + (h_1 - h_7\,H + 3\,h_{10}\,K)\,\frac{\partial F}{\partial K} = 0\end{gathered}$$

the nonplastic range we assume that

9.35) $$F(H, K) < c$$

d the constitutive equations are given by (89.19) and (89.20) subject to 9.21). In this range we have $\bar{M} > 0$ for loading and $\bar{M} < 0$ for loading. For the transition range the condition is

9.36) $$F(H, K) = c \qquad \bar{M} = 0$$

ne equations of plastic and nonplastic regions become identical in the ansition range leading to (89.22). Again the nonnegative character of e dissipation of energy must be secured for a complete cycle of loading d unloading.

We now specialize these equations as in the section on special con- itutive equations above:

9.37) $$\begin{gathered}\hat{\mathfrak{s}}^m{}_m = \frac{1 + \nu}{1 - 2\,\nu}\,d^m{}_m \\ \hat{\bar{\mathfrak{s}}}^k{}_l = \bar{d}^k{}_l\end{gathered}$$

the nonplastic region for which

9.38) $$F(H, K) < c$$

ere, however, $\bar{M}$ is not restricted in sign. In the plastic region we have

9.39) $$\begin{gathered}\hat{\mathfrak{s}}^m{}_m = \frac{1 + \nu}{1 - 2\,\nu}\,d^m{}_m \\ \hat{\bar{\mathfrak{s}}}^k{}_l = \bar{d}^k{}_l + (-\tfrac{2}{3}\,h_9\,H\,\delta^k{}_l + h_6\,\bar{\mathfrak{s}}^k{}_l + h_9\,\bar{\mathfrak{s}}^k{}_m\,\bar{\mathfrak{s}}^m{}_l)\,\bar{M}\end{gathered}$$

together with the yield condition

$$F(H, K) = c \tag{89.40}$$

Using the special values of $h_1, \ldots, h_{11}$, (89.34) now reduce to

$$\begin{aligned}(1 + 2h_6 H + 3h_9 K)\frac{\partial F}{\partial H} + (-h_3 H + 3h_6 K)\frac{\partial F}{\partial K} &= 0\\ \frac{\partial F}{\partial K} &= 0\end{aligned} \tag{89.41}$$

Hence $F$ is independent of $K$, and without loss in generality (89.40) ma[y] be replaced by

$$F \equiv 2H = c \tag{89.42}$$

which is the well-known von Mises yield criterion. From $(89.41)_1$ w[e] now have

$$1 + 2h_6 H + 3h_9 K = 0 \tag{89.43}$$

We now further specialize this by imposing the condition that $h_6$ and $h$[...] are independent of $K$ and by requiring the validity of 89.43 for all value[s] of $K$. Hence

$$h_9 \equiv 0 \qquad h_6 \equiv -\frac{1}{2H} \equiv -\frac{1}{c} \tag{89.44}$$

With the use of these, (89.39) now become

$$\begin{aligned}\hat{\mathfrak{s}}^m{}_m &= \frac{1+\nu}{1-2\nu}\, d^m{}_m\\ \hat{\bar{\mathfrak{s}}}^k{}_l &= \bar{d}^k{}_l - \frac{\bar{M}}{c}\,\bar{\mathfrak{s}}^k{}_l \qquad (\bar{M} \geq 0)\end{aligned} \tag{89.45}$$

subject to the yield criterion $2H = c$.

Equations (89.37) and (89.45) are the usual Prandtl-Reuss equation[s] for compressible solids in nonplastic and plastic regions respectively. Fo[r] an incompressible solid, $d^m{}_m = 0$, and they reduce to those given in Art. 8[...] if we recognize $\mu = \mu_p$ and $4c\mu^2 \equiv K\tau^2$. This is made clear if w[e] restore the factor $2\mu$ and the stress deviator $\bar{\mathfrak{t}}$ in (89.45); i.e., for plasti[c] flow we have

$$\begin{aligned}\hat{\mathfrak{t}}^m{}_m &= 2\mu\frac{1+\nu}{1-2\nu}\, d^m{}_m\\ \hat{\bar{\mathfrak{t}}}^k{}_l &= 2\mu\left(\bar{d}^k{}_l - \frac{\bar{d}^m{}_n \bar{\mathfrak{t}}^n{}_m}{K\tau^2}\,\bar{\mathfrak{t}}^k{}_l\right) \qquad (\bar{d}^m{}_n \bar{\mathfrak{t}}^n{}_m > 0)\end{aligned} \tag{89.46}$$

where constant $K$ [not to be confused with that of $(89\text{-}10)_2$] is given b[y]

$$K\tau^2 \equiv 4\mu^2 c \tag{89.47}$$

For nonplastic flow we have

$$\hat{t}^m{}_m = 2\,\mu\,\frac{1+\nu}{1-2\,\nu}\,d^m{}_m \qquad (89.48)$$

$$\hat{\bar{t}}^k{}_l = 2\,\mu\,\bar{d}^k{}_l \qquad (\bar{t}^m{}_n\bar{t}^n{}_m < K\,\tau^2)$$

We note that the left sides of $(89.46)_2$ and $(89.48)_2$ are the same as $\hat{t}^k{}_l$ given by (89.5), which was used in Art. 85.

*Rigid-plastic Deformation Theory.* If one assumes that $\mu \to \infty$ and $\nu \to 0$ in such a way that $K\,\tau^2$ and the stress tensor remain fixed, from (89.46) and (89.47) we obtain

$$(89.49) \qquad d^m{}_m = 0 \qquad \bar{d}^k{}_l = 0 \qquad \bar{t}^m{}_n\bar{t}^n{}_m < K\,\tau^2 \qquad \text{(nonplastic)}$$

$$(89.50) \qquad d^m{}_m = 0 \qquad \bar{t}^k{}_l = \frac{K\,\tau^2}{\bar{t}^m{}_n\bar{d}^n{}_m}\,\bar{d}^k{}_l \qquad \bar{t}^k{}_l\,\bar{d}^l{}_k > 0 \qquad \text{(plastic)}$$

Thus in the nonplastic state the body is rigid, and in the plastic stage it is incompressible so that $s^m{}_m$ is an arbitrary hydrostatic pressure. Also we have

$$(89.51) \qquad (\bar{t}^k{}_l\bar{d}^l{}_k)^2 = K\,\tau^2\,\bar{d}^k{}_l\,\bar{d}^l{}_k$$

Equations (89.49) and (89.50) are the usual equations of von Mises rigid-plastic flow.

## 90. HYPOELASTIC AND PLASTIC YIELDS IN SIMPLE SHEAR

In the study of hypoelastic shear (Art. 79) and simple extension (Art. 80) we found that the theory of hypoelasticity predicts maximum values for the various stress components and/or asymptotic values which may be considered as hypoelastic yield or failure. According to plasticity theory the yield is predicted by a criterion (Tresca or von Mises). Here we should like to show the relation of hypoelastic yield to von Mises yield as postulated by (86.3),

$$(90.1) \qquad \bar{s}^k{}_l\,\bar{s}^l{}_k = \frac{K\,\tau^2}{4\,\mu^2} = 2\,H$$

for $2\,H = c =$ const.

For the present purpose we assume a state of pure shear which in rectangular coordinates will have a displacement field prescribed by

$$(90.2) \qquad v_x = 2\,k\,y \qquad v_y = v_z = 0$$

where $k$ is the constant rate of shearing.

We now try a state of stress of the form

$$(90.3) \qquad \mathbf{s} = \begin{bmatrix} s_{xx} & s_{xy} & 0 \\ \cdot & s_{yy} & 0 \\ \cdot & \cdot & s_{zz} \end{bmatrix} \qquad (\mathbf{s} \equiv \mathbf{t}/2\,\mu)$$

The expression of the Prandtl-Reuss theory given by (87.12) and (87.13) and that given by (89.46) or (89.45) are identical. Equation $(89.45)_1$ is satisfied identically and $(89.45)_2$ reduce to

$$
\begin{aligned}
s'_{xy} &= \tfrac{1}{2}\left(\bar{s}_{yy} - \bar{s}_{xx} + 1 - \frac{2\, s_{xy}{}^2}{c}\right) \\
\bar{s}'_{xx} &= s_{xy}\left(1 - \frac{\bar{s}_{xx}}{c}\right) \\
\bar{s}'_{yy} &= -\, s_{xy}\left(1 + \frac{\bar{s}_{yy}}{c}\right) \\
\bar{s}'_{zz} &= -\, s_{xy}\,\frac{\bar{s}_{zz}}{c}
\end{aligned}
\tag{90.4}
$$

where a prime denotes $d/d\tau$, $\tau$ being the measure of finite strain given by

$$\tau = 2\,k\,t \tag{90.5}$$

From (90.1) we deduce that

$$H' = s_{xy}\left(1 - \frac{2\,H}{c}\right) \tag{90.6}$$

which is the special case of (89.30) and is the result used to obtain the flow equation (86.13) from (86.7). From (90.6) it follows that $H' = 0$ wherever $2\,H = c$; i.e., the von Mises yield occurs. The same applies to $d^nH/d\tau^n = 0$ whenever $2\,H = c$ for sufficiently smooth solutions.

Here we should like to investigate whether or not (90.4) possess real solutions such that $2\,H = c$.[1] Let us put

$$u \equiv \bar{s}_{xx} - \bar{s}_{yy} \qquad v \equiv \bar{s}_{xx} + \bar{s}_{yy} \tag{90.7}$$

Then from (90.4) it follows that

$$u' = s_{xy}\left(2 - \frac{u}{c}\right) \qquad v' = -\,s_{xy}\,\frac{v}{c} \tag{90.8}$$

Upon dividing $(90.8)_2$ by $(90.4)_4$, we get

$$\frac{\bar{s}'_{zz}}{\bar{s}_{zz}} = \frac{v'}{v} = -\,\frac{s_{xy}}{c}$$

[1] This problem was first studied by Truesdell [1956] who used the entire stress rather than the stress deviator used here. See also Green [1956*a*].

Integration gives

$$\bar{s}_{zz} = A_1 v \qquad v = A_2 \exp\left(-\int^{\tau} \frac{s_{xy}}{c}\, d\tau\right)$$

When $\tau = 0$, we have $\bar{s}_{zz} = 0$ and $v = 0$. It therefore follows that $A_2 = 0$. Hence

$$(90.9) \qquad \bar{s}_{zz} = 0 \qquad v = 0 \qquad \bar{s}_{yy} = -\bar{s}_{xx} \qquad u = 2\,\bar{s}_{xx} = -2\,\bar{s}_{yy}$$

Therefore

$$(90.10) \qquad H = s_{xy}{}^2 + \bar{s}_{yy}{}^2$$

Using (90.9) in $(90.4)_1$, we find

$$(90.11) \qquad s'_{xy} = \tfrac{1}{2} + \bar{s}_{yy} - \frac{s_{xy}{}^2}{c} \qquad \bar{s}'_{yy} = -s_{xy}\left(1 + \frac{\bar{s}_{yy}}{c}\right)$$

The solution of our problem is thus reduced to the solution of the system (90.11) for two unknowns $s_{xy}$ and $\bar{s}_{yy}$.

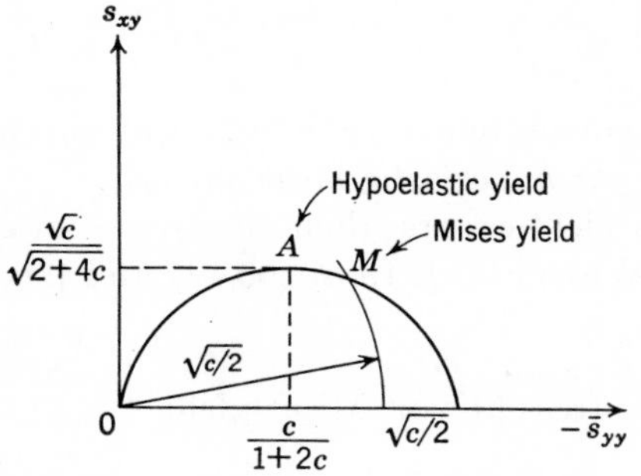


FIG. 90.1. Shear stress as a function of normal stress.

An intermediate integral of this system is

$$(90.12) \qquad s_{xy}{}^2 = -\bar{s}_{yy}\left[1 + (\tfrac{1}{2} + c)\,\frac{\bar{s}_{yy}}{c}\right]$$

Since $c > 0$, we see that $\bar{s}_{yy} < 0$ for all strains. This equation represents a semiellipse with center at $s_{xy} = 0$, $\bar{s}_{yy} = -\frac{1}{2}c/(\frac{1}{2} + c)$ and with semi-axes of lengths $\frac{1}{2}\sqrt{c}/\sqrt{\frac{1}{2} + c}$, $\frac{1}{2}c/(\frac{1}{2} + c)$ (Fig. 90.1). By (90.10) the locus of $2H = c$ is a circle with center at $s_{xy} = \bar{s}_{yy} = 0$ and a radius $\sqrt{c/2}$. Thus the von Mises yield occurs at the values of $s_{xy}$, $\bar{s}_{yy}$ corresponding to intersection $M$ of the circle and the semiellipse. Since the radius of this circle always exceeds the distance from the origin to the nearest vertex $A$ of the semiellipse, we see that the von Mises yield cannot occur until after hypoelastic yield. Moreover the intersection point may or may not exist according as $c \leq \frac{1}{2}$ or $c > \frac{1}{2}$. Thus *the necessary condition for the von Mises yield is* $c \leq \frac{1}{2}$. The sufficiency proof requires knowledge of the existence of a real strain $\tau$ corresponding to the von Mises yield point. Algebraically the condition $c \leq \frac{1}{2}$ may also be seen as follows.

Use (90.12) to put (90.10) into the form

$$H = -\bar{s}_{yy}\left(1 + \frac{\bar{s}_{yy}}{2c}\right) \tag{90.13}$$

Now at the von Mises yield point we have

$$\bar{s}_{yy} = -c \qquad s_{xy} = \sqrt{c}\sqrt{\tfrac{1}{2} - c} \leq \tfrac{1}{4} \tag{90.14}$$

The maximum yield value of $s_{xy}$ is reached for $\sqrt{c} = \frac{1}{2}$. At the hypoelastic yield point, on the other hand, we have

$$\bar{s}_{yy} = -\frac{c}{1 + 2c} > -\tfrac{1}{2} \qquad s_{xy} = s_s = \frac{\sqrt{c}}{\sqrt{2 + 4c}} < \tfrac{1}{2} \tag{90.15}$$

where the bounds correspond to $c = \infty$. *Consequently an effect of $c$ in (90.4) is to decrease the hypoelastic shear strength.*

If the von Mises yield occurs, then all stresses must be maintained at constant values. When $c < \frac{1}{2}$, from (90.14) and (90.15) we have

$$\frac{s_s}{\text{shear stress at von Mises yield}} = \frac{1}{\sqrt{1 - 4c^2}} \tag{90.16}$$

For materials obeying the von Mises yield condition, we see therefore that $c$ must be very small. As $c \to 0$ the right-hand side of (90.16) approaches 1. *Thus for small $c$ the shear stress at hypoelastic yield is substantially the same as the shear at the von Mises yield.*

We now proceed to obtain stress-strain relations by completing the integration. For a measure of finite strain, select $\phi$ as given by

$$\tan\tfrac{1}{2}\phi \equiv \begin{cases} \left(\dfrac{c + \frac{1}{2}}{c - \frac{1}{2}}\right)^{\frac{1}{2}} \tan\left(\dfrac{\sqrt{c - \frac{1}{2}}}{2\sqrt{c}}\,\tau\right) & \text{when } c > \tfrac{1}{2} \\ \tau/\sqrt{2} & \text{when } c = \tfrac{1}{2} \\ \left(\dfrac{\frac{1}{2} + c}{\frac{1}{2} - c}\right)^{\frac{1}{2}} \tanh\left(\dfrac{\sqrt{\frac{1}{2} - c}}{2\sqrt{c}}\,\tau\right) & \text{when } c < \tfrac{1}{2} \end{cases} \tag{90.17}$$

Then the solution of (90.11) corresponding to zero initial values is

$$(90.18) \qquad s_{xy} = \frac{\sqrt{c}}{\sqrt{4c+2}} \sin \phi \qquad \bar{s}_{yy} = -\frac{2c}{2c+1} \sin^2 \tfrac{1}{2} \phi$$

Hypoelastic yield occurs at $\phi = \pi/2$. Thus the ultimate shear angle $\theta_s \equiv \arctan \tau$ calculated at $\phi = \frac{\pi}{2}$, replacing $(79.11)_2$, is given by

$$(90.19) \qquad \theta_s = \begin{cases} \arctan \left[ \dfrac{2\sqrt{c}}{\sqrt{c-1}} \arctan \left( \dfrac{c-\frac{1}{2}}{c+\frac{1}{2}} \right)^{\frac{1}{2}} \right] & \text{when } c > \frac{1}{2} \\ \arctan \sqrt{2} & \text{when } c = \frac{1}{2} \\ \arctan \left[ \dfrac{\sqrt{c}}{\sqrt{\frac{1}{2}-c}} \log \dfrac{\frac{1}{2} + \sqrt{\frac{1}{4}-c^2}}{c} \right] & \text{when } c < \frac{1}{2} \end{cases}$$

*When* $c > \frac{1}{2}$, $s_{xy}$ *becomes imaginary before the von Mises yield occurs. When* $c < \frac{1}{2}$, the *von Mises yield occurs asymptotically as the strain becomes infinite.* The value $\theta_M$ at which $s_{xy}$ first reaches the von Mises yield value is given by

$$(90.20) \qquad \theta_M = \arctan \left( \frac{\sqrt{c}}{\sqrt{\frac{1}{2}-c}} \log \frac{1}{2c} \right)$$

from which it follows that

$$\frac{\theta_s}{\theta_M} \to 1 \qquad \text{as } c \to 0$$

*Therefore the shear stress at the von Mises yield point and hypoelastic yield are nearly the same when c is small.*

In the classical plasticity theory it is assumed that until the yield point is reached, the stress-strain curve is a straight line so that linear elasticity theory is valid. In the present problem the stress-strain diagram would be a straight line with slope $\frac{1}{2}$ joined to a straight horizontal line at $s_{xy} = \sqrt{c/2}$. Such a stress-strain curve is only an approximation, the horizontal part of which is approached only for $c$ small. The straight line corresponding to the elastic part with slope $\frac{1}{2}$ intersects the curve. If $\theta_l$ is the angle of shear for which the line $s_{xy} = \tau/2$ intersects the yield line $s_{xy} = \sqrt{c/2}$, by (90.20) we get

$$(90.21) \qquad \frac{\theta_M}{\theta_l} \to \infty \qquad \text{as } c \to 0$$

*Therefore the softening which occurs prior to yield cannot be neglected* even for small $c$. In Fig. 90.2 we indicate the stress-strain diagrams obtained from the hypoelastic theory by full lines. The dashed lines correspond

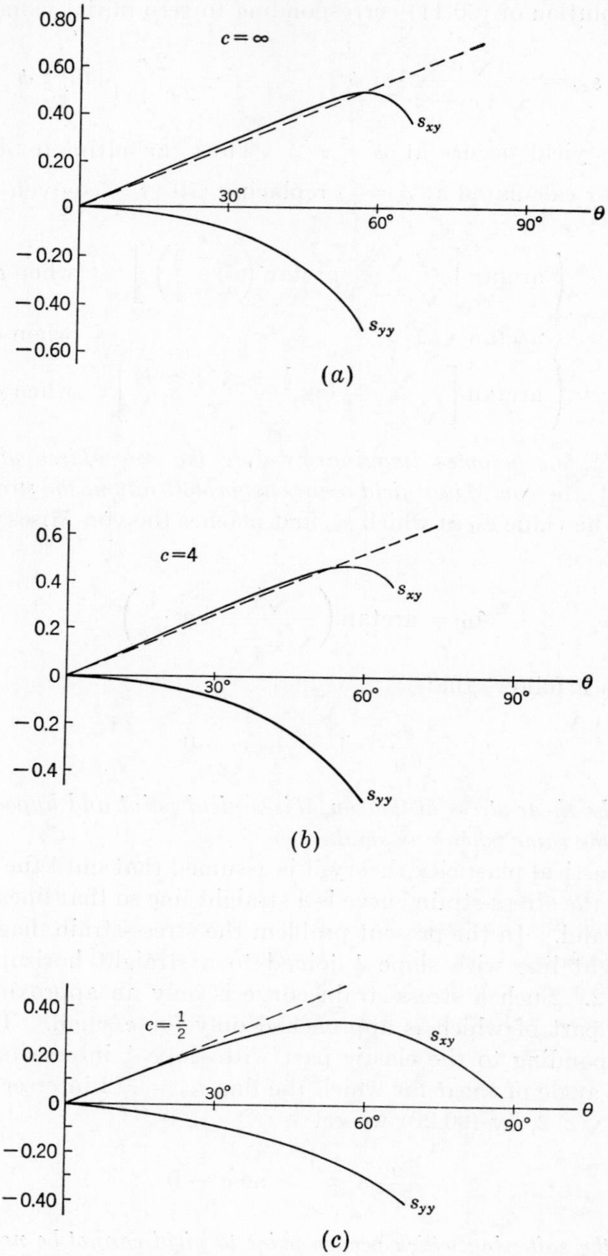


FIG. 90.2. Shear and normal stress as functions of angle of shear $\theta = \arctan \tau$. (*After Truesdell* [1956])

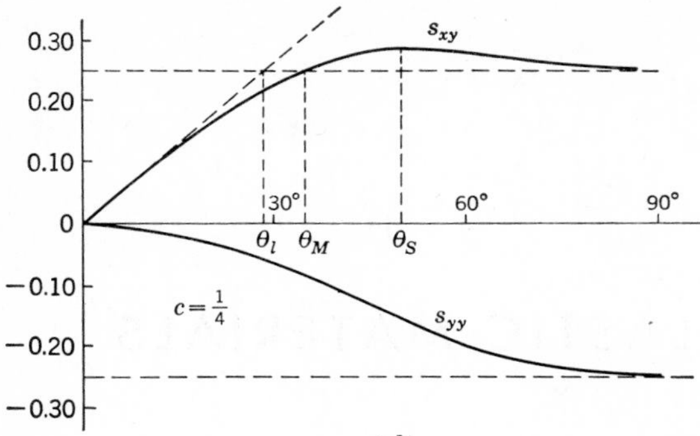


(*d*)

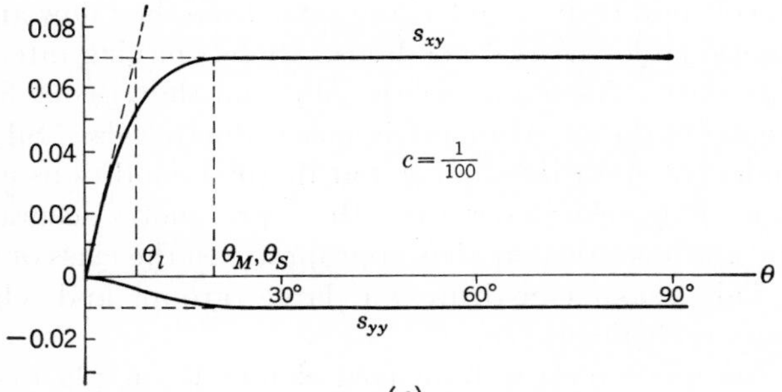


(*e*)

FIG. 90.2. (*Continued*)

to the assumptions of the linear elasticity theory joined by a von Mises yield. Note that for large values of $c$ (Fig. 90.2*a* and *b*), there is no von Mises yield, but there exists hypoelastic yield. First the von Mises yield occurs when $c = \frac{1}{2}$ (Fig. 90.2*c*). After that, as $c$ becomes smaller (Fig. 90.2*d* and *e*), the von Mises yield approaches the hypoelastic yield.

# 10

# VISCOELASTIC MATERIALS

## 91. SCOPE OF THE CHAPTER

Solid materials that possess fluid characteristics are called viscoelastic materials. These materials possess a certain amount of rigidity that is characteristic of solid bodies, and at the same time they flow and dissipate energy by frictional losses as some fluids. Solids having internal friction belong to this class. Thus the elastic solid and the viscous fluid occupy the two extremes of the spectrum of viscoelastic materials. Since the same materials under different dynamical and thermal conditions exhibit both the solid and fluid characteristics, they are more accurately represented by the mathematical models appropriate to the class of viscoelastic materials. This class constitutes a large group and characterizes materials more realistically.

With the recent extensive industrial demands on plastics and high polymers, the field of viscoelasticity has gained a new impetus both in engineering techniques and applications and in mathematical and physical foundations after nearly a century of comparatively slow progress. A brief sketch of the various theories concerning viscoelastic materials is given in Art. 92. The groundwork on the objective stress and deformation-rate tensors of any order is laid down in Art. 93. These tensors play a central role in the constitutive theory of such materials.

The general constitutive functional equations are developed and organized into various important classes in Art. 94. In the same article we discuss the materials that are constitutively independent of stress flux (the Green-Rivlin materials, simple fluids, the Rivlin-Ericksen fluids, materials having no memory of displacement gradients such as nonlinear Voigt materials) and materials constitutively dependent on stress flux (materials with no stress or strain memory, hygrosteric materials, materials that depend on strain history and stress). The restrictions of isotropy and explicit forms of the constitutive equations of certain materials are given in Art. 95. In Art. 96 we collect together the basic field equations that are valid for all materials and some constitutive equations that are restricted to a few: namely, the Rivlin-Ericksen fluids, simple fluids, and hygrosteric materials.

In Arts. 97 to 101 we give some simple solutions employing various types of constitutive theory. The steady shear flow of simple viscoelastic materials and the Rivlin-Ericksen fluids are discussed in Arts. 97 and 98 respectively, the latter of which has recently gained new importance from the experimental point of view (see Art. 70). A discussion on viscoelastic torsion and torsional flow is given in Art. 99. The helical flow of Rivlin-Ericksen fluids discussed in Art. 100 finds applications in experimental work. The theory of helical flow of simple fluids given in Art. 101 is remarkable in that it contains most of the previous cases as special cases. The early conjecture of Markovitz [1957], which classified the rheological theories by the selection of four material functions in an appropriate way, has become a reality for this class of fluid motions. In comparison with previous theories, this theory has reduced the number of constitutive variables to only a few.

In Arts. 102 and 103 we give the theory of hygrosteric materials of Noll and the classification of these materials. This theory, which possesses properly invariant constitutive equations, is a generalization of the linear Maxwell solid, encompassing the nonlinear phenomena. Hypoelastic materials, elastic materials, Reiner-Rivlin fluids, and stokesian fluids are special cases of this theory. Articles 104, 105, and 106 are devoted to some illustrative solutions of this theory: namely, pure stress relaxation, homogeneous stress, and simple shear flow.

The linear theories of viscoelasticity based on a great collection of different mechanical models and their various proliferations are beyond the scope of this book. Therefore, aside from the remarks made in Art. 92, no discussion of these theories is presented.[1]

## 92. RÉSUMÉ OF VARIOUS THEORIES

Solid materials under dynamical conditions and/or long-time stress conditions generally exhibit fluidlike behavior. For example, the amplitude of vibration of a bar in a vacuum dies out in time because of internal friction. A bar subjected to a constant axial force below the yield load will continue to elongate (creep). Thus the elastic bar in this way exhibits a viscous-flow behavior while keeping its elasticity.

The theories of viscoelasticity initiated by Maxwell [1867], Voigt [1889, 1892], and Zaremba [1903*a*, *b*, 1937] have lately undergone exhaustive developments. Linear theories are based on a superposition principle

[1] We refer the reader to Eringen [1964] for various linear theories. A comprehensive discussion on the foundations of linear viscoelasticity is given by Coleman and Noll [1961*a*]. See also Bland [1960].

which may be expressed by writing a linear stress-strain differential equation of the form

$$(92.1) \qquad \sum_{n=0}^{N} {}_nA^{k}{}_{l}{}^{r}{}_{s} \left(\frac{\partial}{\partial t}\right)^n t^s{}_r = \sum_{n=0}^{M} {}_nB^{k}{}_{l}{}^{r}{}_{s} \left(\frac{\partial}{\partial t}\right)^n \tilde{e}^s{}_r$$

where ${}_nA^{k}{}_{l}{}^{r}{}_{s}$ and ${}_nB^{k}{}_{l}{}^{r}{}_{s}$ are material constants. Such linear theories generally violate the principle of objectivity when extended to the nonlinear range of deformation gradients.

Boltzmann [1874] and Volterra [1930] proposed linear theories which assume that the stress depends on the entire previous history of strain. For this reason such materials are sometimes called *materials with hereditary characteristics* or *materials with memory*. In these theories the constitutive equations take the form

$$(92.2) \qquad t^k{}_l = B^{k}{}_{l}{}^{r}{}_{s}\, \tilde{e}^s{}_r + \int_{-\infty}^{t} K^{k}{}_{l}{}^{r}{}_{s}\,(\mathbf{x}, t-\tau)\, \tilde{e}^s{}_r\,(\mathbf{x}, \tau)\, d\tau$$

where $B^{k}{}_{l}{}^{r}{}_{s}$ are constants and $K^{k}{}_{l}{}^{r}{}_{s}\,(\mathbf{x}, t-\tau)$ are hereditary kernels appropriate to a given material. The objection raised against (92.1) is also valid for (92.2)

Ideas included in (92.1) have recently been incorporated into properly invariant forms for finite deformations and rates by Noll [1955], Rivlin and Ericksen [1955], Cotter and Rivlin [1955], Rivlin [1956, 1960*b*], Pipkin and Rivlin [1959], Ericksen [1960*a, b, c, d*], and others. In these theories it is assumed that functional relations exist among the stress **t**, deformation gradients, and their material time rates of any prescribed order.

Constitutive equations for materials possessing *continuous* memory of their past history have also been formulated recently in invariant forms by Noll [1957, 1958], Green and Rivlin [1957, 1960], Green, Rivlin, and Spencer [1959], and Coleman and Noll [1959*b*, *c*, 1960, 1961*b*]. Some of these are of such general nature as to include all previous theories within their subclasses. No attempt to incorporate thermodynamical variables into the theory has been recorded.[1]

## 93. OBJECTIVE TENSOR RATES

Constitutive equations must obey certain invariance requirements such as those studied in Art. 44. Among these requirements the axiom of material objectivity occupies a central position. According to this axiom the constitutive equations must remain form-invariant under rigid translation and rotation of the spatial frame of reference and a constant

[1] Note added at proof: See the recent work on nonlinear thermoviscoelasticity by Koh and Eringen [1962].

shift of time. This implies that first of all we must select our variables describing the mechanical state of the material objectively. Next the functional forms selected must not be altered with the rigid motion. In this article we investigate rate tensors that obey such demands.

For simplicity in representation, unless otherwise stated, we employ rectangular coordinates throughout this and the following articles.

Suppose that every material point $\mathbf{X}$ of a deformable body is at rest prior to time $\tau = 0$ relative to a fixed rectangular frame of reference $X^K$. At time $t$ the material point $\mathbf{X}$ occupies the place $\mathbf{x}$ and at time $\tau$, $0 \leq \tau \leq t$, it occupies place $\boldsymbol{\chi}$, both referred to rectangular coordinates. Thus the motion of the material point $\mathbf{X}$ may be expressed by

$$\boldsymbol{\chi}(\tau) = \mathbf{x}(\mathbf{X}, \tau) \qquad (0 \leq \tau \leq t) \tag{93.1}$$

so that

$$\mathbf{x} = \boldsymbol{\chi}(t) = \mathbf{x}(\mathbf{X}, t) \tag{93.2}$$

We assume that $\boldsymbol{\chi}(\tau)$ are single-valued functions of $\mathbf{X}$ and $\tau$ and are continuously differentiable with respect to $X^K$ and $\tau$ as many times as required except possibly at singular points, lines, and surfaces. The axiom of continuity of matter requires that

$$\det\left(\frac{\partial \chi^\kappa}{\partial X^K}\right) > 0 \tag{93.3}$$

for all $\tau$ $(0 \leq \tau \leq t)$ and all $X^K$ in the body. Consequently an inverse of (93.1) exists in some neighborhood of $\boldsymbol{\chi}$ and $\tau$, for which we write

$$\mathbf{X} = \overset{-1}{\mathbf{x}}(\boldsymbol{\chi}, \tau) = \overset{-1}{\mathbf{x}}(\mathbf{x}, t) \tag{93.4}$$

Therefore we may express (93.1) and (93.2) also as

$$\begin{aligned} \boldsymbol{\chi}(\tau) &= \mathbf{x}(\overset{-1}{\mathbf{x}}(\mathbf{x}, t), \tau) = \boldsymbol{\chi}(\mathbf{x}, \tau) \\ \mathbf{x} &= \mathbf{x}(\overset{-1}{\mathbf{x}}(\mathbf{x}, t), t) \end{aligned} \tag{93.5}$$

The motion expressed by (93.5) exhibits the dependence of $\boldsymbol{\chi}$ on time $\tau$ and the place $\mathbf{x}$ occupied by the particle at time $t$. The function $\boldsymbol{\chi}(\mathbf{x}, \tau)$ may thus be referred to as the *displacement function relative to the configuration at time t.*

The components of velocity $v_\alpha^{(1)}(\tau) \equiv v_\alpha(\tau)$ and of acceleration $v_\alpha^{(2)}(\tau) \equiv a_\alpha(\tau)$ referred to a rectangular frame of reference $\chi^\alpha$ $(\alpha = 1, 2, 3)$ at time $\tau$ are respectively given by

$$\begin{aligned} v_\alpha^{(1)}(\tau) &\equiv v_\alpha(\tau) = \frac{D\chi^\alpha(\tau)}{D\tau} \\ v_\alpha^{(2)}(\tau) &\equiv a_\alpha(\tau) = \frac{Dv_\alpha^{(1)}(\tau)}{D\tau} \end{aligned} \tag{93.6}$$

where we employ Greek indices to indicate components referred to the rectangular coordinates $\chi^\alpha$, saving the Latin minuscules, as usual, for the coordinates $x^k$ and Latin majuscules for the material coordinates $X^K$.

Extension of (93.6) to higher-order accelerations is made as follows:

$$\begin{aligned} v_\alpha^{(M+1)}(\tau) &= \frac{Dv_\alpha^{(M)}(\tau)}{D\tau} = \left[\frac{\partial}{\partial\tau} + v_\beta^{(1)}(\tau)\frac{\partial}{\partial\chi^\beta}\right] v_\alpha^{(M)}(\tau) \\ &= \left[\frac{\partial}{\partial\tau} + v_\beta^{(1)}(\tau)\frac{\partial}{\partial\chi^\beta}\right]^M v_\alpha^{(1)}(\tau) \end{aligned} \tag{93.7}$$

Clearly, if the velocity field $v_\alpha^{(1)}(\tau)$ is known, we can determine the place $\boldsymbol{\chi}(\tau)$ of the particle $\mathbf{X}$ at time $\tau$ by integrating

$$\frac{d\boldsymbol{\chi}(\tau)}{d\tau} = \mathbf{v}(\boldsymbol{\chi}(\tau), \tau) \tag{93.8}$$

subject to the end condition

$$\boldsymbol{\chi}(\tau)|_{\tau=t} = \boldsymbol{\chi}(\mathbf{x}, t) = \mathbf{x} \tag{93.9}$$

The gradient of $\boldsymbol{\chi}(\mathbf{x}, \tau)$ with respect to $\mathbf{x}$ is defined by

$$\chi^\alpha{}_{,l} \equiv \frac{\partial\chi^\alpha}{\partial x^l} \tag{93.10}$$

This is the *deformation gradient at time $\tau$ relative to the configuration at time $t$.* Clearly

$$\chi^\alpha{}_{,l}(t) = \delta^\alpha{}_l \tag{93.11}$$

According to the principle of conservation of mass we have

$$\det \chi^\alpha{}_{,l} = \frac{\rho(t)}{\rho(\tau)} \tag{93.12}$$

*Green and Piola tensors $C_{KL}(\tau)$ and $\overset{-1}{C}_{\alpha\beta}(\tau)$ relative to $\mathbf{X}$ and $\mathbf{x}$, respectively are*

$$\begin{aligned} C_{KL}(\tau) &\equiv \delta_{\alpha\beta}\,\chi^\alpha{}_{,K}\,\chi^\beta{}_{,L} \\ \overset{-1}{C}_{\alpha\beta}(\tau) &\equiv \delta_{kl}\,\chi^\alpha{}_{,k}\,\chi^\beta{}_{,l} \end{aligned} \tag{93.13}$$

so that

$$\begin{aligned} C_{KL} \equiv C_{KL}(t) &= \delta_{kl}\,x^k{}_{,K}\,x^l{}_{,L} \\ \overset{-1}{C}_{\alpha\beta}(t) &= \delta_{\alpha\beta} \end{aligned} \tag{93.14}$$

*Deformation-rate tensor* $2\,\mathbf{d}(\tau) \equiv \mathbf{A}^{(1)}(\tau)$ *at time $\tau$* is given by

$$A_{\alpha\beta}^{(1)}(\tau) \equiv 2\,d_{\alpha\beta}(\tau) = v_{\alpha,\beta}^{(1)} + v_{\beta,\alpha}^{(1)} \tag{93.15}$$

In rectangular coordinates $\chi^\alpha$ the *Rivlin-Ericksen* tensors $\mathbf{A}^{(M)}(\tau)$ defined by (19.14) take the form

$$A_{\alpha\beta}^{(M)} = v_{\alpha,\beta}^{(M)} + v_{\beta,\alpha}^{(M)} + \sum_{K=1}^{M-1} \binom{M}{K} v_{\mu,\alpha}^{(M-K)} v_{\mu,\beta}^{(K)} \qquad (M = 1, 2, \ldots) \tag{93.16}$$

These tensors satisfy

$$\frac{D^M}{D\tau^M}(ds^2) = A_{\alpha\beta}^{(M)} \, d\chi^\alpha \, d\chi^\beta \tag{93.17}$$

It is not difficult to see that tensors $\mathbf{A}^{(M)}$ are objective. To show this, consider two objectively equivalent motions at $\tau$

$$\begin{aligned} & \acute{\chi}^\alpha(\acute{\tau}) = Q^\alpha{}_\kappa(\tau)\,\chi^\kappa(\tau) + b^\alpha \\ \acute{\tau} = \tau - a \qquad & Q^\alpha{}_\mu Q_\beta{}^\mu = Q^\mu{}_\beta Q_\mu{}^\alpha = \delta^\alpha{}_\beta \qquad \det Q^\alpha{}_\beta = 1 \end{aligned} \tag{93.18}$$

Now in rectangular coordinates $\acute{\chi}^\alpha$ and $\chi^\alpha$, we have

$$ds^2 = \delta_{\alpha\beta}\, d\acute{\chi}^\alpha \, d\acute{\chi}^\beta = \delta_{\kappa\lambda}\, d\chi^\kappa \, d\chi^\lambda$$

Taking the $M$th material derivative of this and using (93.17), we get

$$\acute{A}_{\alpha\beta}^{(M)}(\acute{\tau})\, d\acute{\chi}^\alpha \, d\acute{\chi}^\beta = A_{\kappa\lambda}^{(M)}(\tau)\, d\chi^\kappa \, d\chi^\lambda$$

Now using $(93.18)_1$ to replace $d\acute{\chi}^\alpha$ for a given $\tau$, we get

$$\acute{A}_{\alpha\beta}^{(M)}(\acute{\tau}) = A_{\kappa\lambda}^{(M)}(\tau)\, Q_\alpha{}^\kappa Q_\beta{}^\lambda \tag{93.19}$$

which proves our assertion.

Next we should like to find higher-order objective stress rates. For a first-order stress flux we already have many choices [cf. (35.5), (35.6), (72.9), and (72.11)]. All of these fluxes are objective, i.e.,

$$\acute{t}_{\alpha\beta}^{(1)} = t_{\kappa\lambda}^{(1)} Q_\alpha{}^\kappa Q_\beta{}^\lambda \tag{93.20}$$

where for operational reasons we have written $\hat{t}_{\alpha\beta} \equiv t_{\alpha\beta}^{(1)}$. The result (93.20) was derived from (35.3) and the properties of $\mathbf{Q}$ inherent in (93.18). It is valid whether or not $t_{\alpha\beta}$ is the stress tensor. Thus by repeated differentiation of (93.20) we find

$$\acute{t}_{\alpha\beta}^{(M)} = t_{\kappa\lambda}^{(M)} Q_\alpha{}^\kappa Q_\beta{}^\lambda \qquad (M = 1, 2, \ldots) \tag{93.21}$$

where the tensor $\mathbf{t}^{(M)}$ may of course have different expressions depending on which of the forms (35.5), (35.6), (72.9), or (72.11) is chosen for $\mathbf{t}^{(1)}$.

For example, for the choices (35.5), $(35.6)_1$, and $(35.6)_2$ we have respectively the recurrence relations

(93.22)
$$
\begin{aligned}
t_{\alpha\beta}^{(M+1)} &= \frac{Dt_{\alpha\beta}^{(M)}}{D\tau} + t_{\alpha\mu}^{(M)}\, w_{\mu\beta} - t_{\mu\beta}^{(M)}\, w_{\alpha\mu} \\
t_{\alpha\beta}^{(M+1)} &= \frac{Dt_{\alpha\beta}^{(M)}}{D\tau} + t_{\alpha\mu}^{(M)}\, v_{\mu,\beta} + t_{\mu\beta}^{(M)}\, v_{\mu,\alpha} \\
t_{\alpha\beta}^{(M+1)} &= \frac{Dt_{\alpha\beta}^{(M)}}{D\tau} - t_{\alpha\mu}^{(M)}\, v_{\beta,\mu} - t_{\mu\beta}^{(M)}\, v_{\alpha,\mu}
\end{aligned}
$$

A comparison of $(93.22)_2$ with (19.12) reveals that the structure of this $(M+1)$st flux is identical to that of $\mathbf{A}^{(M+1)}$. For definiteness we adopt this form, with no particular reason of preference. In fact, later we shall find occasion to switch to some other definition.[1]

By following a procedure similar to the one used to arrive at (19.14), we can obtain an explicit expression for $(93.22)_2$.

By multiplying both sides of

$$\acute{t}_{\alpha\beta} = t_{\kappa\lambda}\, Q_\alpha{}^\kappa\, Q_\beta{}^\lambda$$

by $d\acute{\chi}^\alpha\, d\acute{\chi}^\beta$ and using (93.18), we see that

$$\acute{t}_{\alpha\beta}\, d\acute{\chi}^\alpha\, d\acute{\chi}^\beta = t_{\alpha\beta}\, d\chi^\alpha\, d\chi^\beta$$

Consequently

(93.23)
$$d\sigma^2 \equiv t_{\alpha\beta}\, d\chi^\alpha\, d\chi^\beta = t_{KL}\,(\tau)\, dX^K\, dX^L$$

is independent of rigid rotations superposed on the original motion. By differentiating (93.23) and using

(93.24)
$$\frac{D}{D\tau}\,(d\chi^\alpha) = dv_\alpha = v_{\alpha,\beta}\, d\chi^\beta$$

we get

(93.25)
$$\frac{D}{D\tau}\,(d\sigma^2) = t_{\alpha\beta}^{(1)}\, d\chi^\alpha\, d\chi^\beta = \frac{Dt_{KL}}{D\tau}\, dX^K\, dX^L$$

where $t_{\alpha\beta}^{(1)}$ is defined by

(93.26)
$$t_{\alpha\beta}^{(1)} \equiv \frac{Dt_{\alpha\beta}}{D\tau} + t_{\alpha\mu}\, v_{\mu,\beta} + t_{\mu\beta}\, v_{\mu,\alpha}$$

[1] This indefiniteness is certainly unfortunate at the present state of our knowledge. Although this does not affect the exact form of constitutive equations, it leads to different approximate theories. See, for instance, the concluding paragraph of Art. 72.

By repeated differentiation of (93.25) we thus get

$$\frac{D^M}{D\tau^M}(d\sigma^2) = t_{\alpha\beta}^{(M)}\, d\chi^\alpha\, d\chi^\beta = \frac{D^M t_{KL}}{D\tau^M}\, dX^K\, dX^L \tag{93.27}$$

If one uses $d\sigma^2$ given by $(93.23)_1$, one may also write

$$\frac{D^M}{D\tau^M}(d\sigma^2) = \sum_{K=0}^{M}\left[\binom{M}{K}\frac{D^{M-K}t_{\alpha\beta}}{D\tau^{M-K}}\sum_{H=0}^{K}\binom{K}{H}\frac{D^{K-H}d\chi^\alpha}{D\tau^{K-H}}\frac{D^H d\chi^\beta}{D\tau^H}\right]$$

Equating this to (93.27) and using

$$\frac{D^K}{D\tau^K}(d\chi^\alpha) = dv_\alpha^{(K)} = v_{\alpha,\beta}^{(K)}\, d\chi^\beta \qquad \frac{\partial v_\alpha^{(0)}}{\partial \chi^\beta} = \delta_{\alpha\beta}$$

we obtain the explicit expression

$$t_{\alpha\beta}^{(M)} = \frac{D^M t_{\alpha\beta}}{D\tau^M} + \sum_{K=1}^{M}\left[\binom{M}{K}\frac{D^{M-K}t_{\kappa\lambda}}{D\tau^{M-K}}\sum_{H=0}^{K}\binom{K}{H} v_{\kappa,\alpha}^{(K-H)}\, v_{\lambda,\beta}^{(H)}\right] \tag{93.28}$$

If $t_{\alpha\beta}$ has the special value $\delta_{\alpha\beta}$, we find from this expression that

$$\mathbf{t}^{(M)}\Big|_{\mathbf{t}=\mathbf{I}} = \mathbf{A}^{(M)} \tag{93.29}$$

showing the connection of $\mathbf{t}^{(M)}$ to $\mathbf{A}^{(M)}$ where for $\mathbf{t}^{(M)}$ the definition $(93.22)_2$ is selected.

We are now in the possession of objective rate tensors of various orders for the deformation and the stress. Consequently the general constitutive equations of materials with memory can now be constructed.

## 94. CONSTITUTIVE FUNCTIONAL EQUATIONS

A general class of materials with memory will now be considered. This class possesses six constitutive equations of the form

$$f_{\alpha\beta} = f_{\beta\alpha} = 0 \tag{94.1}$$

where $\mathbf{f}$ is a function of the following set of quantities calculated at $R + 1$ distinct times $\tau_1, \tau_2, \ldots, \tau_R, \tau_0\ (= t)$ in the interval $0 \le \tau \le t$:

1. Displacement, velocity, acceleration, . . . , $(N - 1)$st acceleration of a particle $\mathbf{X}$ at a prescribed time $\tau_K$;

$$\chi^\alpha(\tau_K), v_\alpha(\tau_K), v_\alpha^{(2)}(\tau_K), \ldots, v_\alpha^{(N)}(\tau_K), \tau_K \tag{94.2}$$

2. Displacement gradients with respect to $X^L$ and $x^l$, velocity gradients,

acceleration gradients, . . . , $(N-1)$st acceleration gradients;

$$(94.3) \qquad \chi^{\alpha}{}_{,L}(\tau_K),\ \chi^{\alpha}{}_{,k}(\tau_K),\ v_{\alpha,\beta}(\tau_K),\ v^{(2)}_{\alpha,\beta}(\tau_K),\ \ldots,\ v^{(N)}_{\alpha,\beta}(\tau_K)$$

3. Components of the stress tensor and their various time rates up to order $M$ at the particle $\mathbf{X}$;

$$(94.4) \qquad t_{\alpha\beta}(\tau_K),\ \frac{D}{D\tau_K}t_{\alpha\beta}(\tau_K),\ \ldots,\ \frac{D^M}{D\tau_K^M}t_{\alpha\beta}(\tau_K)$$

4. Density $\rho(\tau_K)$ and its time rates $D\rho/D\tau_K$, the coordinates $x^l$, the temperature $T(\tau_K)$ at the point $\mathbf{x}$.

By superposition of an arbitrary rigid-body translation to the velocity, acceleration, . . . , $(N-1)$st acceleration at every point of the body, at each value of time $\tau = \tau_K$ $(K = 0, 1, \ldots, M)$, we add arbitrary constant quantities without changing the quantities appearing in the lists [(94.3) and (94.4)]. If the constitutive equations (94.1) are to be objective, they must not change with such rigid-body translations. Moreover a shift of time scale should not change the form $\mathbf{f}$; therefore $\mathbf{f}$ is independent of the quantities listed in (94.2). By using the continuity equations

$$(94.5) \qquad \begin{aligned} \frac{D\rho}{D\tau} + \rho\, v_{\alpha,\beta} &= 0 \\ \frac{\rho(\tau)}{\rho_0} = \sqrt{\mathrm{III}(\tau)} &= \det(\chi^{\alpha}{}_{,l}) \end{aligned}$$

we can eliminate the time rates of $\rho$ and replace $\rho/\rho_0$ by $\sqrt{\mathrm{III}(\tau)}$, where the density $\rho_0$ at time $t$ is constant.

Therefore the constitutive equations read

$$(94.6) \qquad f_{kl}\Bigg[x^l,\ T(\tau_K),\ \frac{1}{\sqrt{\mathrm{III}(\tau_K)}},\ \frac{\partial\chi^{\lambda}(\tau_K)}{\partial X^L},\ \frac{\partial\chi^{\lambda}(\tau_K)}{\partial x^l};\ \frac{\partial v^{(1)}_{\lambda}(\tau_K)}{\partial\chi^{\mu}(\tau_K)},\ \ldots,\ \frac{\partial v^{(N)}_{\lambda}(\tau_K)}{\partial\chi^{\mu}(\tau_K)};\ t_{\lambda\mu}(\tau_K),\ \frac{Dt_{\lambda\mu}(\tau_K)}{D\tau_K},\ \ldots,\ \frac{D^M t_{\lambda\mu}(\tau_K)}{D\tau_K^M}\Bigg] = 0$$

For simplicity in writing, we may also omit $x^l$, $T(\tau_K)$ similar to other absolute scalars that have been omitted. They can be restored later whenever such dependence need be shown explicitly.

From (93.28) it is clear that $D^M t_{\alpha\beta}/D\tau^M$ is expressible as the sum of $t^{(M)}_{\alpha\beta}$ and a polynomial in $D^{M-1}t_{\alpha\beta}/D\tau^{M-1}$, . . . , $Dt_{\alpha\beta}/D\tau$, $t_{\alpha\beta}$, $v^{(M)}_{\alpha,\beta}$, . . . , $v^{(1)}_{\alpha,\beta}$ with similar results being valid for $M$ replaced by $M-1$, $M-2$, etc. Consequently (94.6) can be written as

$$(94.7)\quad f_{\alpha\beta}\left[\frac{1}{\sqrt{\mathrm{III}\,(\tau_K)}},\ \frac{\partial\chi^\lambda\,(\tau_K)}{\partial X^L},\ \frac{\partial\chi^\lambda\,(\tau_K)}{\partial x^l};\ \frac{\partial v_\lambda^{(1)}\,(\tau_K)}{\partial\chi^\mu\,(\tau_K)},\ \ldots,\ \frac{\partial v_\lambda^{(N)}\,(\tau_K)}{\partial\chi^\mu\,(\tau_K)};\ t_{\lambda\mu}\,(\tau_K),\ t_{\lambda\mu}^{(1)}\,(\tau_K),\ \ldots,\ t_{\lambda\mu}^{(M)}\,(\tau_K)\right] = 0 \qquad (N \geq M)$$

$$(94.8)\quad f_{\alpha\beta}\left[\frac{1}{\sqrt{\mathrm{III}\,(\tau_K)}},\ \frac{\partial\chi^\lambda\,(\tau_K)}{\partial X^L},\ \frac{\partial\chi^\lambda\,(\tau_K)}{\partial x^l};\ \frac{\partial v_\lambda^{(1)}\,(\tau_K)}{\partial\chi^\mu\,(\tau_K)},\ \ldots,\ \frac{\partial v_\lambda^{(M)}\,(\tau_K)}{\partial\chi^\mu\,(\tau_K)};\ t_{\lambda\mu}\,(\tau_K),\ t_{\lambda\mu}^{(1)}\,(\tau_K),\ \ldots,\ t_{\lambda\mu}^{(M)}\,(\tau_K)\right] = 0 \qquad (N \leq M)$$

When (94.6) is a polynomial in its arguments, so are (94.7) and (94.8) in their arguments. Since (94.7) contains (94.8), without loss in generality we may consider only (94.7) for which $N \geq M$.

We shall now show that we can eliminate $\partial\chi^\lambda\,(\tau_K)/\partial x^l$ and III $(\tau_K)$ from the list of independent variables contained in **f**. To this end note that

$$(94.9)\qquad \frac{\partial\chi^\lambda\,(\tau)}{\partial x^l} = \frac{\partial\chi^\lambda\,(\tau)}{\partial X^L}\,\frac{\partial X^L}{\partial x^l}$$

and

$$(94.10)\qquad \frac{\partial X^L}{\partial x^l} = \frac{1}{2\sqrt{\det C_{RS}}}\,e_{lkm}\,e_{LKM}\,\frac{\partial x^k}{\partial X^K}\,\frac{\partial x^m}{\partial X^M} = \frac{1}{2\sqrt{\det C_{RS}\,(\tau)}}\,e_{l\kappa\mu}\,e_{LKM}\,\frac{\partial\chi^\kappa\,(\tau)}{\partial X^K}\,\frac{\partial\chi^\mu\,(\tau)}{\partial X^M}\bigg|_{\tau=t}$$

where

$$(94.11)\qquad C_{RS} = C_{RS}\,(\tau)\bigg|_{\tau=t} = \delta_{\alpha\beta}\,\frac{\partial\chi^\alpha\,(\tau)}{\partial X^R}\,\frac{\partial\chi^\beta\,(\tau)}{\partial X^S}\bigg|_{\tau=t} = \delta_{rs}\,\frac{\partial x^r}{\partial X^R}\,\frac{\partial x^s}{\partial X^S}$$

Therefore the dependence of **f** on $\partial\chi^\lambda\,(\tau_K)/\partial x^l$, and by the same token on $\sqrt{\mathrm{III}\,(\tau_K)}$, can be omitted, reducing (94.7) to[1]

$$(94.12)\quad f_{\alpha\beta}\left[\frac{\partial\chi^\lambda\,(\tau_K)}{\partial X^L};\ \frac{\partial v_\lambda^{(1)}\,(\tau_K)}{\partial\chi^\mu\,(\tau_K)},\ \ldots,\ \frac{\partial v_\lambda^{(N)}\,(\tau_K)}{\partial\chi^\mu\,(\tau_K)};\ t_{\lambda\mu}\,(\tau_K),\ t_{\lambda\mu}^{(1)}\,(\tau_K),\ \ldots,\ t_{\lambda\mu}^{(M)}\,(\tau_K)\right] = 0$$

where $K = 0, 1, 2, \ldots, R$.

[1] Note, however, that if (94.7) is a polynomial in its arguments, (94.12) may not be. However, since III $(\tau_K)$ is always greater than or equal to 1, and is a continuous function of $\partial\chi^\lambda\,(\tau_K)/\partial x^l$, the quantity $1/\sqrt{\mathrm{III}\,(\tau_K)}$ may be approximated to any desired degree of accuracy by a polynomial in $\partial\chi^\lambda\,(\tau_K)/\partial x^l$ if it is uniformly bounded.

In any two objectively equivalent motions $\acute{\chi}^\alpha(\acute{\tau}_K)$ and $\chi^\alpha(\tau_K)$ related to each other by (93.18), all quantities $\partial v_\lambda^{(L)}(\tau_K)/\partial\chi^\mu(\tau_K)$ change, thus changing the form of $f_{\alpha\beta}$. If $f_{\alpha\beta}$ is to be form-invariant with respect to rigid motions at $\tau_K$, these quantities must be replaced by an equal number of independent quantities such as $A_\lambda^{(L)}(\tau_K)$ which are objective. This point can be seen further by the fact that we can solve $v_{\alpha,\beta}^{(M)}$ for each $M$ as a polynomial in terms of $A_{\alpha\beta}^{(L)}$ and $w_{\alpha\beta}^{(L)}$ $(L = 1, 2, \ldots, N)$ defined by

$$2\,w_{\alpha\beta}^{(L)} \equiv v_{\alpha,\beta}^{(L)} - v_{\beta,\alpha}^{(L)} \tag{94.13}$$

where

$$v_\alpha^{(L)} = \frac{Dv_\alpha^{(L-1)}}{Dt} \qquad v_\alpha^{(0)} = \chi^\alpha(\tau)$$

$w_{\alpha\beta}^{(L)}$ is not independent of the $L$th angular acceleration of the rigid rotation. Therefore $\mathbf{f}$ should not depend on $w_{\alpha\beta}^{(L)}$, $(L = 1, 2, \ldots, N)$. Consequently

$$f_{\alpha\beta}[x^\lambda{}_{,L}(\tau_K);\ A_{\lambda\mu}^{(1)}(\tau_K), \ldots, A_{\lambda\mu}^{(N)}(\tau_K);\ t_{\lambda\mu}(\tau_K)\\ t_{\lambda\mu}^{(1)}(\tau_K), \ldots, t_{\lambda\mu}^{(M)}(\tau_K)] = 0 \qquad (N \geq M) \tag{94.14}$$

This is the general constitutive equation of a material having memory of its past state at $R$ intervals of time $\tau_1, \tau_2, \ldots, \tau_R, \tau_0\,(= t)$ prior to its present state at time $t$.

If we now let $(R + 1) \to \infty$ so that $f_{\alpha\beta}$ becomes a *functional*,[2] we will have

$$f_{\alpha\beta}[x^\lambda{}_{,L}(\tau);\ A_{\lambda\mu}^{(1)}(\tau), \ldots, A_{\lambda\mu}^{(N)}\underset{\tau=0}{\overset{t}{(\tau)}};\ t_{\lambda\mu}(\tau),\ t_{\lambda\mu}^{(1)}(\tau), \ldots,\\ t_{\lambda\mu}^{(M)}(\tau)] = 0 \qquad (N \geq M) \tag{94.15}$$

In this form we have six functional equations which are capable of describing the rheological state of a large class of materials with memory.

Next we should like to consider some interesting special cases.

1. *Materials Constitutively Independent of Stress Flux.* For such materials $f_{\alpha\beta}$ is independent of all $\mathbf{t}^{(R)}(\tau_K)$ (i.e., $M = 0$). For convenience we write $f_{\alpha\beta} = 0$ in the form

$$t_{pq} - F_{pq}[\chi^\lambda{}_{,L}(\tau_K);\ A_{\lambda\mu}^{(1)}(\tau_K), \ldots, A_{\lambda\mu}^{(N)}(\tau_K);\ t_{\lambda\mu}(\tau_K)] = 0\\ (K = 0, 1, 2, \ldots, R) \tag{94.16}$$

where $t_{pq}$ is the stress tensor at $\tau = t$. Now if we let $(R + 1)$, the number

[2] When the range of the functional $[_{\tau=0}^{\,t}]$ appears at the middle of the bracketed arguments, it is understood to apply to all arguments. When it appears at the first argument, it applies only to that argument. [Cf. (94.29).]

of divisions of the time interval $(0, t)$, approach infinity so that $F_{pq}$ becomes a functional, we will have

$$t_{pq} = F_{pq}[\chi^{\lambda}{}_{,L}(\tau);\ A^{(1)}_{\lambda\mu}(\tau),\ \overset{t}{\underset{\tau=0}{\ldots}},\ A^{(N)}_{\lambda\mu}(\tau);\ t_{\lambda\mu}(\tau)] \tag{94.17}$$

An alternative expression may be found if we use (19.15) in the coordinates $\chi^{\alpha}$, i.e.,

$$A^{(M)}_{\kappa\lambda}(\tau) = C^{(M)}_{KL}(\tau)\, X^{K}{}_{,\kappa} X^{L}{}_{,\lambda} \qquad C^{(M)}_{KL} \equiv \frac{D^{M} C_{KL}(\tau)}{D\tau^{M}} \tag{94.18}$$

and since $X^{K}{}_{,\kappa}$ is expressible in terms of $\chi^{\lambda}{}_{,L}$ [cf. (94.10)],

$$t_{pq} = F_{pq}[\chi^{\lambda}{}_{,L}(\tau);\ C^{(1)}_{KL}(\tau),\ \overset{t}{\underset{\tau=0}{\ldots}},\ C^{(N)}_{KL}(\tau);\ t_{\lambda\mu}(\tau)] \tag{94.19}$$

Constitutive equations (94.17) and (94.19) are further simplified by integration by parts over the time intervals in the region $0 \leq \tau < t$. To accomplish this in the simplest way, we start from the expression (94.12), impose the assumption of independence from the stress flux, and assume the special form[3]

$$t_{pq} = F_{pq}[\chi^{\lambda}{}_{,L}(\tau_K);\ v^{(1)}_{\lambda,\mu}(\tau_K),\ \ldots,\ v^{(N)}_{\lambda,\mu}(\tau_K)] \qquad (K = 0, 1, \ldots, R) \tag{94.20}$$

Now let $R + 1 \to \infty$ so that $F_{pq}$ becomes a functional. Hence

$$t_{pq} = F_{pq}[\chi^{\lambda}{}_{,L}(\tau);\ v^{(1)}_{\lambda,\mu}(\tau),\ \overset{t}{\underset{\tau=0}{\ldots}},\ v^{(N)}_{\lambda,\mu}(\tau)] \tag{94.21}$$

We assume that $t_{pq}$ in (94.21) is a continuous functional of the argument functions in the range $0 \leq \tau < t$ and is particularly independent of the values of the arguments at $\tau = t$. Using the relation (94.7), we see that $\mathbf{t}$ is a continuous functional of $\chi^{\lambda}{}_{,L}(\tau), v^{(1)}_{\lambda,L}(\tau), \ldots, v^{(N)}_{\lambda,L}(\tau)$ in the range $0 \leq \tau < t$ and is an ordinary function of the values of these functions at $\tau = t$.

Assuming sufficient regularity, we may uniformly approximate $\mathbf{t}$ by a polynomial in $x^{l}{}_{,L}, v^{(1)}_{l,L}, \ldots, v^{(N)}_{l,L}$ having coefficients which are continuous functionals[4] of $\chi^{\lambda}{}_{,L}(\tau), v^{(1)}_{\lambda,L}(\tau), \ldots, v^{(N)}_{\lambda,L}(\tau)$. A typical term

[3] Note that (94.20) is more restricted than (94.16) in that here stress $t_{pq}$ does not possess a memory of stress.

[4] For power-series-expansion theorems of functionals we refer the reader to Hille and Phillips [1957].

in this expansion has the form

$$v^{(M_1)}_{k_1,K_1} v^{(M_2)}_{k_2,K_2} \cdots v^{(M_R)}_{k_R,K_R} \int_0^t \cdots \int_0^t [\varphi_{\alpha\beta k_1 K_1 \ldots k_R K_R \lambda_1 L_1 \ldots \lambda_S L_S} (t, \tau_1, \ldots, \tau_S) v^{(N_1)}_{\lambda_1,L_1}(\tau_1) v^{(N_2)}_{\lambda_2,L_2}(\tau_2) \cdots v^{(N_S)}_{\lambda_S,L_S}(\tau_S)] \, d\tau_1 \, d\tau_2 \cdots d\tau_S$$

where the kernels $\varphi_{\ldots}$ are continuous functions of their arguments $M_1, \ldots, M_R$ and $N_1, \ldots, N_S$ are chosen from the integers $(0, 1, 2, \ldots, N)$; and $\mathbf{v}^{(0)}$ denotes $\mathbf{x}$. We now use integration by parts of the form

$$\int_0^t \varphi_{\ldots} v^{(M_K)}_{\lambda_K,L_K}(\tau_K) \, d\tau_K = [\varphi_{\ldots} v^{(M_K-1)}_{\lambda_K,L_K}(\tau_K)]^t_{\tau_K=0} - \int_0^t \frac{D\varphi}{D\tau_K} \cdots v^{(M_K-1)}_{\lambda_K,L_K}(\tau_K) \, d\tau_K$$

and recall that at $\tau = 0$ the body is assumed to be at rest, so that the term in the bracket for the lower limit $\tau_K = 0$ is zero for all $M_K$ except $M_K = 1$ in which case it gives $\varphi_{\ldots} \chi^{\lambda_K}{}_{,L_K}$. Consequently, for continuously differentiable kernels $\varphi_{\ldots}$, $t_{kl}$ may be uniformly approximated by a polynomial in $x^k{}_{,K}$, $v_{k,K}$, $v^{(2)}_{k,K}$, $\ldots$, and $v^{(N)}_{k,K}$, the coefficients of which are continuous functions of $\chi^\lambda{}_{,L}(\tau)$, i.e.,

$$t_{pq} = \underset{\tau=0}{\overset{t}{F_{pq}}} [\chi^\lambda{}_{,L}(\tau); x^k{}_{,K}, v^{(1)}_{k,K}, \ldots, v^{(N)}_{k,K}] \tag{94.22}$$

In the manner of arriving at (94.17) and (94.19), by the use of the principle of objectivity we pass from this to either of

$$\begin{aligned} t_{pq} &= \underset{\tau=0}{\overset{t}{F_{pq}}} [\chi^\lambda{}_{,L}(\tau); x^k{}_{,K}, A^{(1)}_{lm}, \ldots, A^{(N)}_{lm}] \\ t_{pq} &= \underset{\tau=0}{\overset{t}{F_{pq}}} [\chi^\lambda{}_{,L}(\tau); x^k{}_{,K}, C^{(1)}_{KL}, \ldots, C^{(N)}_{KL}] \end{aligned} \tag{94.23}$$

The above constitutive equations can be simplified further by applying the principle of objectivity. To this end let us note that in two objectively equivalent motions (93.18) the stress tensor $t^{PQ}(\tau)$ defined by

$$t^{PQ} \equiv t^{pq} X^P{}_{,p} X^Q{}_{,q}$$

remains unaltered, i.e.,

$$t^{PQ} = t^{pq} \frac{\partial X^P}{\partial x^p} \frac{\partial X^Q}{\partial x^q} = \acute{t}^{rs} \frac{\partial X^P}{\partial \acute{x}^r} \frac{\partial X^Q}{\partial \acute{x}^s} \tag{94.24}$$

as can easily be verified by substituting in $(94.24)_1$

$$\frac{\partial X^P}{\partial x^p} = \frac{\partial X^P}{\partial \acute{x}^r} \frac{\partial \acute{x}^r}{\partial x^p} = \frac{\partial X^P}{\partial \acute{x}^r} Q^r{}_p \qquad \acute{t}^{rs} = t^{pq} Q^r{}_p Q^s{}_q$$

'rom (94.24), $(94.23)_2$, and (94.10) we therefore see that

$$(94.25)\qquad t^{PQ} = X^P{}_{,p} X^Q{}_{,q} F^{pq} \mathop{[}_{\tau=0}^{t} \chi^\lambda{}_{,L}(\tau), x^k{}_{,L}, C^{(1)}_{KL}, \ldots, C^{(N)}_{KL}]$$

$$= F^{PQ} \mathop{[}_{\tau=0}^{t} \chi^\lambda{}_{,L}(\tau), x^k{}_{,L}, C^{(1)}_{KL}, \ldots, C^{(N)}_{KL}]$$

Ve now replace the functional dependence of $t^{PQ}$ on $\chi^\lambda{}_{,L}(\tau)$ by a poly- omial dependence on $\chi^\lambda{}_{,L}(\tau_K)$ at $R+1$ points $\tau_K$ $(K = 0, 1, \ldots, R)$ vith $\tau_0 = t$. Thus

$$t^{PQ} = f^{PQ}[\chi^\lambda{}_{,L}(\tau_K), C^{(1)}_{KL}, \ldots, C^{(N)}_{KL}]$$

Next consider all objectively equivalent motions about each of the times $_K$ $(K = 0, 1, \ldots, R)$. For these motions $t^{PQ}$ and $\mathbf{C}^{(1)}, \ldots, \mathbf{C}^{(N)}$ do ot change, but $\chi^\lambda{}_{,L}$ becomes $\acute{\chi}^\lambda{}_{,L}$ for each $\tau_K$, e.g.,

$$^{PQ}[\chi^\lambda{}_{,L}(\tau_H), \chi^\lambda{}_{,L}(\tau_K), C^{(1)}_{KL}, \ldots, C^{(N)}_{KL}]$$
$$= f^{PQ}[\acute{\chi}^\lambda{}_{,L}(\acute{\tau}_H), \chi^\lambda{}_{,L}(\tau_K), C^{(1)}_{KL}, \ldots, C^{(N)}_{KL}] \qquad (K \neq H)$$

Clearly then $f^{PQ}$ is a scalar invariant under proper orthogonal transforma- ions of the vectors $\partial\chi^\lambda(\tau_H)/\partial X^1$, $\partial\chi^\lambda(\tau_H)/\partial X^2$, and $\partial\chi^\lambda(\tau_H)/\partial X^3$. Ience, according to a theorem stated in Art. 46, it is expressible as a unction of $C_{KL}(\tau_H)$ and $\sqrt{\det C_{KL}(\tau_H)}$ where $C_{KL}(\tau)$ is defined in $93.13)_1$. Hence

$$(94.26)\qquad t^{PQ} = f^{PQ}[C_{KL}(\tau_K), \sqrt{\det C_{KL}(\tau_K)}, C^{(1)}_{KL}, \ldots, C^{(N)}_{KL}]$$

Now we let $R + 1 \to \infty$ to obtain

$$(94.27)\qquad t^{PQ} = F^{PQ} \mathop{[}_{\tau=0}^{t} C_{KL}(\tau); C_{KL}, C^{(1)}_{KL}, \ldots, C^{(N)}_{KL}]$$

'rom (94.24) and (94.27) it now follows that

$$(94.28)\qquad t^{pq} = \frac{\partial x^p}{\partial X^P}\frac{\partial x^q}{\partial X^Q} F^{PQ} \mathop{[}_{\tau=0}^{t} C_{KL}(\tau); C_{KL}, C^{(1)}_{KL}, \ldots, C^{(N)}_{KL}]$$

f one employs (94.18), this may also be expressed as

$$(94.29)\qquad t^{pq} = \frac{\partial x^p}{\partial X^P}\frac{\partial x^q}{\partial X^Q} F^{PQ} \mathop{[}_{\tau=0}^{t} C_{KL}(\tau); C_{KL}, A^{(1)}_{kl} x^k{}_{,K} x^l{}_{,L}, \ldots, A^{(N)}_{kl} x^k{}_{,K} x^l{}_{,L}]$$

n these equations $F^{PQ}$ is a functional of $C_{KL}(\tau)$ and a function of the emaining variables.

Green-Rivlin Materials. Materials having constitutive equations f the form (94.28) which are independent of $x^k{}_{,K}$ will be called *Green- Rivlin materials.* Such constitutive equations result when one puts

$x^k{}_{,K} = \delta^k{}_K$ in (94.28). The constitutive functional equations now reduc to

(94.30) $$t_{pq} = \underset{\tau=0}{\overset{t}{F_{pq}}}\,[C_{KL}(\tau); A^{(1)}_{lm}, \ldots, A^{(N)}_{lm}]$$

These materials can be grouped as three special subclasses.

*a. Simple Fluids.* Green-Rivlin materials having constitutive equa tions that are independent of $\mathbf{A}^{(K)}$ $(K = 1, 2, \ldots, N)$ have bee studied by Noll [1958] and by Coleman and Noll [1961*a*, *b*]. Such mate rials are called *simple fluids.* For these fluids the constitutive equation take the form

(94.31) $$t_{pq} = \underset{\tau=0}{\overset{t}{F_{pq}}}\,[C_{KL}(\tau)]$$

Many special types of fluids, e.g., Reiner-Rivlin fluids and stokesia fluids, fall into this class.

*b. Rivlin-Ericksen Fluids.* Green-Rivlin materials whose dependenc on the history of $\mathbf{C}(\tau)$ is absent are known as the *Rivlin-Ericksen fluid*. The constitutive equations for these materials take the form

(94.32) $$t_{pq} = F_{pq}\,[A^{(1)}_{lm}, A^{(2)}_{lm}, \ldots, A^{(N)}_{lm}]$$

Stokesian fluids are a special case of these fluids for which $\mathbf{F}$ depends onl on $\mathbf{A}^{(1)}$.

*c. Materials with No Memory of Displacement Gradients.* Green-Rivli materials having constitutive equations that are independent of th history of displacement gradients comprise this class. The constitutiv equations take the form

(94.33) $$t_{pq} = F_{pq}\,[x^k{}_{,K}; A^{(1)}_{lm}, A^{(2)}_{lm}, \ldots, A^{(N)}_{lm}]$$

These materials generalize the linear viscoelastic solids of the *Voigt* type Hence the special case in which $\mathbf{t} = \mathbf{F}\,[x^k{}_{,K}, \mathbf{A}^{(1)}]$ may be called the genera *nonlinear Voigt materials.*

Further special forms of (94.33) exist in which two of the rates $\mathbf{A}^{(1)}$ an $\mathbf{A}^{(2)}$, or one, or none appear. The first, which has been studied by Rivli [1956] and Ericksen [1960*a*, *b*, *c*, *d*] has the constitutive equations

(94.34) $$t_{pq} = F_{pq}\,[x^k{}_{,K}, A^{(1)}_{lm}, A^{(2)}_{lm}]$$

The materials for which in (94.34) only one $\mathbf{A}$ appears are also *nonlinea Voigt materials,* and the materials for which none appear are the *nonlinea Cauchy-elastic materials.*

2. *Materials Constitutively Dependent on Stress Flux.* These compris the general class of materials having constitutive equations of the form

(94.14) or (94.15). Among these materials the following two special subclasses are worth attention.

*a. Materials with No Stress or Strain Memory.* For such materials the constitutive equations have the form

$$f_{pq}[x^k{}_{,K};\ A^{(1)}_{lm},\ \ldots,\ A^{(N)}_{lm};\ t_{lm}, t^{(1)}_{lm},\ \ldots,\ t^{(M)}_{lm}] = 0 \qquad (N \geq M) \tag{94.35}$$

In this class of materials are included the Rivlin-Ericksen fluids and a

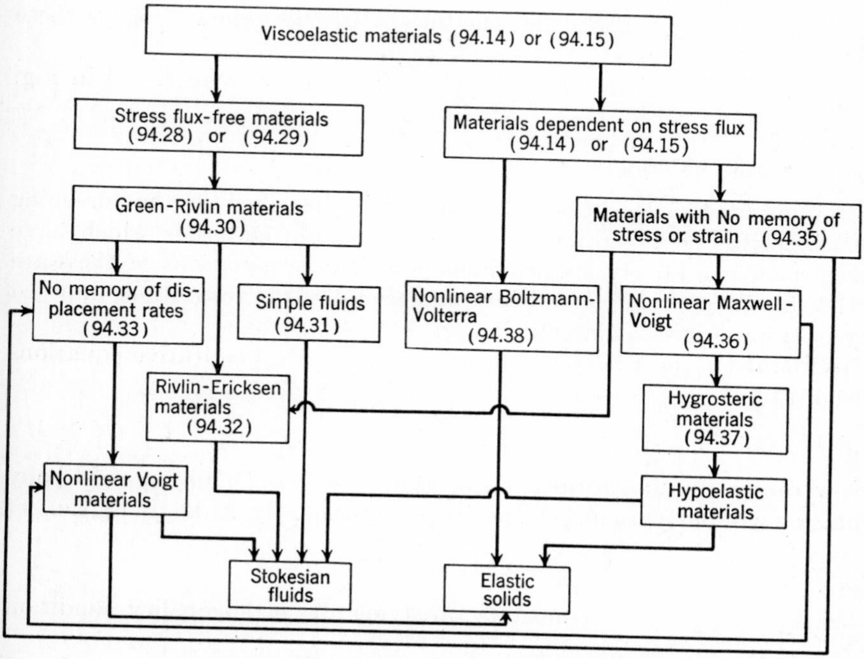


FIG. 94.1. Classification of viscoelastic materials.

large class of nonlinear Maxwell-Voigt materials with constitutive equations of the form

$$f_{pq}[x^k{}_{,K}, \mathbf{A}^{(1)}, \mathbf{t}, \mathbf{t}^{(1)}] = 0 \tag{94.36}$$

whose special form is

$$\hat{\mathbf{t}} = \mathbf{f}(\mathbf{d}, \mathbf{t}) \tag{94.37}$$

where $2\,\mathbf{d} = \mathbf{A}^{(1)}$, $\hat{\mathbf{t}} = \mathbf{t}^{(1)}$. Noll [1955] christened these materials *hygrosteric materials.*[5] A discussion of these materials is given in Arts. 102

[5] From ὑγρός, "fluid," and στερεός, "solid."

to 106. Reiner-Rivlin fluids, stokesian fluids, hypoelastic solids, and elastic solids are special cases of these materials.

*b. Materials That Depend on Strain History and Stress.* Constitutive equations for these materials may be put into the form

$$f_{\alpha\beta}\,[\chi^{\lambda}{}_{,L}\,(\tau)\,;\,t_{\lambda\mu}\,(\tau)] \underset{\tau=0}{\overset{t}{}} = 0 \tag{94.38}$$

These materials generalize the linear viscoelastic materials of the Boltzmann-Volterra type. Hence they may be called the *nonlinear Boltzmann-Volterra materials.* Except for the linear case, no serious study of these materials as yet exists.

A classification chart for materials with memory is displayed in Fig. 94.1.

## 95. ISOTROPIC MATERIALS

Among the various classes of materials described in the foregoing article, with the exception of simple fluids, the materials which have been most extensively studied have constitutive equations of the form (94.35). We therefore give below an account of the restrictions imposed by isotropy on these materials.[1]

Without loss in generality we may replace the constitutive equations (94.35) by

$$t_{pq} = F_{pq}\,[x^k{}_{,K}\,;\,A_{kl}^{(1)},\ \ldots\ ,A_{kl}^{(N)}\,;\,t_{kl},\,t_{kl}^{(1)},\ \ldots\ ,t_{kl}^{(M)}] \qquad (N \geq M) \tag{95.1}$$

Now rotate the undeformed position of the body $X^K$ by a rigid-body rotation without changing the position $x^k$ of the body at the time $t$; i.e., let

$$\acute{X}^K = S^K{}_L\,X^L \tag{95.2}$$

where $S^K{}_L$ are sets of constants satisfying the orthogonality condition

$$S^K{}_M\,S_L{}^M = S^M{}_L\,S_M{}^K = \delta^K{}_L \qquad \det S^K{}_L = \pm 1 \tag{95.3}$$

The tensors $\mathbf{A}^{(K)}$, $\mathbf{t}$, and $\mathbf{t}^{(K)}$ are unaltered. If the body is isotropic at its undeformed position $X^K$, then

$$F_{pq}\left[\frac{\partial x^k}{\partial X^K};\,\mathbf{A}^{(1)},\ \ldots\ ,\mathbf{A}^{(N)};\,\mathbf{t},\,\mathbf{t}^{(1)},\ \ldots\ ,\mathbf{t}^{(M)}\right]$$
$$= F_{pq}\left[\frac{\partial x^k}{\partial \acute{X}^K};\,\mathbf{A}^{(1)},\ \ldots\ ,\mathbf{A}^{(N)};\,\mathbf{t},\,\mathbf{t}^{(1)},\ \ldots\ ,\mathbf{t}^{(M)}\right]$$

Therefore $F_{pq}$ is form-invariant under all proper orthogonal transformations of the form (95.2). Regarding the arguments $\partial x^k/\partial X^1$, $\partial x^k/\partial X^2$,

[1] For an account of the restriction of material symmetry on more general hereditary materials the reader is referred to Rivlin [1960*b*].

and $\partial x^k/\partial X^3$ as the components of three vectors in the coordinates $x^k$, according to Theorem 1 of Art. 46 we see that if $F_{pq}$ in (95.1) is a polynomial in its arguments, $F_{pq}$ must be expressible as a polynomial in

$$\overset{-1}{c}_{kl} = \delta^{KL} \frac{\partial x^k}{\partial X^K} \frac{\partial x^l}{\partial X^L} \tag{95.4}$$

and in $\sqrt{\det \overset{-1}{c}_{kl}}$. Since the latter can be approximated by a polynomial in $\overset{-1}{c}_{kl}$, we see that

$$t_{pq} = F_{pq}[\overset{-1}{c}_{kl}, A^{(1)}_{kl}, \ldots, A^{(N)}_{kl}; t_{kl}, t^{(1)}_{kl}, \ldots, t^{(M)}_{kl}] \tag{95.5}$$

where $F_{pq}$ is a polynomial in all of its arguments.[2]

We also know that $t_{pq}$ referred to coordinates $x^k$ are objective, so that in two objectively equivalent motions $\acute{x}^k$ and $x^k$ we have the relation

$$\begin{aligned} F_{pq}[\overset{-1}{\acute{c}}_{kl}, \acute{A}^{(1)}_{kl}, \ldots, \acute{A}^{(N)}_{kl}; \acute{t}_{kl}, \acute{t}^{(1)}_{kl}, \ldots, \acute{t}^{(M)}_{kl}] \\ = Q_p{}^r Q_q{}^s F_{rs}[\overset{-1}{c}_{kl}, A^{(1)}_{kl}, \ldots, A^{(N)}_{kl}; t_{kl}, t^{(1)}_{kl}, \ldots, t^{(M)}_{kl}] \end{aligned} \tag{95.6}$$

for all arbitrary nonsingular orthogonal matrices $\mathbf{Q}(t)$. Here

$$\begin{aligned} &\overset{-1}{c}{}'_{kl} = Q_k{}^r Q_l{}^s \overset{-1}{c}_{rs} \qquad \acute{t}_{kl} = Q_k{}^r Q_l{}^s t_{rs} \\ &\acute{A}^{(R)}_{kl} = Q_k{}^r Q_l{}^s A^{(R)}_{rs} \qquad \acute{t}^{(R)}_{kl} = Q_k{}^r Q_l{}^s t^{(R)}_{rs} \qquad (R = 1, 2, \ldots) \end{aligned} \tag{95.7}$$

Thus, according to (95.6), $F_{pq}$ is a symmetric isotropic polynomial in symmetric variables $\mathbf{c}; \mathbf{A}^{(1)}, \ldots, \mathbf{A}^{(N)}; \mathbf{t}, \mathbf{t}^{(1)}, \ldots, \mathbf{t}^{(M)}$. Reduction of such symmetric polynomials to canonical form has been studied by Rivlin [1955*a*] and Spencer and Rivlin [1959*a*, *b*, 1960].

Below we give the canonical forms for a few special materials.

1. *Simple Viscoelastic Materials.* By this we mean materials having constitutive equations in which stress depends on displacement gradients and velocity gradients, i.e.,

$$t_{pq} = F_{pq}(x^k{}_{,K}, v_{k,l}) \tag{95.8}$$

As we know, there is no difficulty in introducing temperature $T$ or other scalars. Density $\rho$ introduces $1/\sqrt{\mathrm{III}}$ into this equation but does not change the form except in making it possible to have the final form of $F_{pq}$ approximated by a polynomial in $x^k{}_{,K}$ and in $v_{k,l}$. More generally, the constitutive coefficients may be regarded as functions of $\rho$, thus eliminating the need for this last approximation. This situation is indeed valid for all other cases given below; hence it will not be mentioned again unless specific reference to $\rho$ is needed.

[2] For the case of aeolotropic materials see Green and Adkins [1960, pp. 328–332].

If the body is initially isotropic, then (95.8) reduces to

$$t_{pq} = F_{pq}(\overset{-1}{c}_{kl}, d_{kl}) \qquad \text{or} \qquad \mathbf{t} = \mathbf{F}(\overset{-1}{\mathbf{c}}, \mathbf{d}) \tag{95.9}$$

By the argument advanced in Art. 45, for isotropic materials dependence of $\mathbf{t}$ on $\overset{-1}{\mathbf{c}}$ may be replaced by dependence on any of $\mathbf{c}$, $\mathbf{C}$, $\overset{-1}{\mathbf{C}}$, or $\mathbf{e}$. Thus

$$\mathbf{t} = \mathbf{F}(\mathbf{c}, \mathbf{d}) = \mathbf{F}(\mathbf{C}, \mathbf{d}) = \mathbf{F}(\overset{-1}{\mathbf{C}}, \mathbf{d}) = \mathbf{F}(\mathbf{e}, \mathbf{d}) \tag{95.10}$$

An isotropic matrix polynomial $\mathbf{F}$ of two symmetric matrices can be expressed in canonical form as shown in Art. 73 [cf. (73.7)]. Thus

$$\begin{aligned} \mathbf{t} = {} & a_{00}\mathbf{I} + a_{10}\mathbf{c} + a_{20}\mathbf{c}^2 + a_{01}\mathbf{d} + a_{02}\mathbf{d}^2 \\ & + a_{11}(\mathbf{c}\,\mathbf{d} + \mathbf{d}\,\mathbf{c}) + a_{12}(\mathbf{c}\,\mathbf{d}^2 + \mathbf{d}^2\,\mathbf{c}) \\ & + a_{21}(\mathbf{c}^2\,\mathbf{d} + \mathbf{d}\,\mathbf{c}^2) + a_{22}(\mathbf{c}^2\,\mathbf{d}^2 + \mathbf{d}^2\,\mathbf{c}^2) \end{aligned} \tag{95.11}$$

where $a_{\kappa\lambda}$ are scalar polynomials of the joint invariants of $\mathbf{c}$ and $\mathbf{d}$; i.e. they are polynomials in the ten invariants

$$\begin{array}{cccc} & \operatorname{tr}\mathbf{c} & \operatorname{tr}\mathbf{c}^2 & \operatorname{tr}\mathbf{c}^3 \\ & \operatorname{tr}\mathbf{d} & \operatorname{tr}\mathbf{d}^2 & \operatorname{tr}\mathbf{d}^3 \\ \operatorname{tr}\mathbf{c}\,\mathbf{d} & \operatorname{tr}\mathbf{c}\,\mathbf{d}^2 & \operatorname{tr}\mathbf{c}^2\,\mathbf{d} & \operatorname{tr}\mathbf{c}^2\,\mathbf{d}^2 \end{array} \tag{95.12}$$

In the special cases where dependence on $\mathbf{d}$ disappears, we obtain elastic solids studied in Arts. 45 to 47 and Chap. 6. Where the dependence on $\mathbf{c}$ disappears, we get the stokesian fluids studied in Art. 48 and Chap. 7.

2. *Rivlin-Ericksen Fluids.* The general constitutive equations for such fluids are given by (94.32). It is clear that such fluids are initially isotropic. The simplest of such fluids are stokesian fluids with constitutive equations

$$\mathbf{t} = \mathbf{f}(\mathbf{d}) \tag{95.13}$$

where $\mathbf{d} = \frac{1}{2}\mathbf{A}^{(1)}$. Such fluids were studied in Art. 48 and in Chap. 7.

The next important class of Rivlin-Ericksen fluids has constitutive equations of the form

$$\mathbf{t} = \mathbf{f}[\mathbf{A}^{(1)}, \mathbf{A}^{(2)}] \tag{95.14}$$

where $\mathbf{f}$ is a polynomial in its arguments. Eq. (95.14) can be written in the form of (95.11) and (95.12) with $\mathbf{c}$ and $\mathbf{d}$ respectively replaced by $\mathbf{A}^{(1)}$ and $\mathbf{A}^{(2)}$.

3. *Hygrosteric Materials.* Such materials take the special form (94.37)

$$\hat{\mathbf{t}} = \mathbf{f}(\mathbf{d}, \mathbf{t}) \tag{95.15}$$

where for the stress flux $\hat{\mathbf{t}}$ any one of the forms given by (35.5), (35.6), (72.9), or (72.11) may be used. These materials are necessarily isotropic in the initial state. Again, if **f** is a polynomial function of its arguments, it can be expressed in the form of (95.11) and (95.12) with **c** and **d** replaced by **d** and **t** respectively. We also recall that the constitutive coefficients $a_{\kappa\lambda}$ may be assumed to depend on other scalars such as temperature $T$ and density $\rho$.

Hypoelastic materials studied in Chap. 8 constitute a special case of hygrosteric materials. For hypoelastic materials **f** is linear in **d**. An account of hygrosteric materials is found in Arts. 102 to 106.

4. *More General Viscoelastic Materials.* Finally we mention two larger classes of viscoelastic materials containing groups 1 and 2 or groups 1 and 3, respectively having constitutive equations of the form

$$\mathbf{t} = \mathbf{f}\,[\mathbf{c}, \mathbf{A}^{(1)}, \mathbf{A}^{(2)}] \tag{95.16}$$

$$\hat{\mathbf{t}} = \mathbf{f}\,(\mathbf{c}, \mathbf{d}, \mathbf{t}) \tag{95.17}$$

Isotropic polynomials of three symmetric matrices have been studied by Spencer and Rivlin [1959*a*, *b*, 1960], who have shown that a symmetric isotropic polynomial **f** (**a**, **b**, **c**) of three symmetric matrices **a**, **b**, **c** may be expressed as the sum of the following terms and terms formed from these by permutations of **a**, **b**, **c**, with scalar coefficients:

$$\begin{gathered} \mathbf{I} \qquad \mathbf{a} \qquad \mathbf{a}^2 \qquad \mathbf{a}\,\mathbf{b} + \mathbf{b}\,\mathbf{a} \qquad \mathbf{a}^2\,\mathbf{b} + \mathbf{b}\,\mathbf{a}^2 \qquad \mathbf{a}^2\,\mathbf{b}^2 + \mathbf{b}^2\,\mathbf{a}^2 \\ \mathbf{a}\,\mathbf{b}\,\mathbf{c} + \mathbf{c}\,\mathbf{b}\,\mathbf{a} \qquad \mathbf{a}^2\,\mathbf{b}\,\mathbf{c} + \mathbf{c}\,\mathbf{b}\,\mathbf{a}^2 \qquad \mathbf{b}\,\mathbf{a}^2\,\mathbf{c} + \mathbf{c}\,\mathbf{a}^2\,\mathbf{b} \\ \mathbf{a}^2\,\mathbf{b}^2\,\mathbf{c} + \mathbf{c}\,\mathbf{b}^2\,\mathbf{a}^2 \qquad \mathbf{a}\,\mathbf{b}\,\mathbf{c}\,\mathbf{a}^2 + \mathbf{a}^2\,\mathbf{c}\,\mathbf{b}\,\mathbf{a} \end{gathered} \tag{95.18}$$

The scalar coefficients are functions of the invariants of the form (95.12) for the three sets of two matrices which can be selected from **a**, **b**, **c**, together with the invariants

$$\begin{gathered} \mathrm{tr}\,\mathbf{a}\,\mathbf{b}\,\mathbf{c} \qquad \mathrm{tr}\,\mathbf{a}\,\mathbf{b}\,\mathbf{c}^2 \qquad \mathrm{tr}\,\mathbf{b}\,\mathbf{c}\,\mathbf{a}^2 \qquad \mathrm{tr}\,\mathbf{c}\,\mathbf{a}\,\mathbf{b}^2 \qquad \mathrm{tr}\,\mathbf{a}\,\mathbf{b}^2\,\mathbf{c}^2 \\ \mathrm{tr}\,\mathbf{b}\,\mathbf{c}^2\,\mathbf{a}^2 \qquad \mathrm{tr}\,\mathbf{c}\,\mathbf{a}^2\,\mathbf{b}^2 \end{gathered} \tag{95.19}$$

By selecting for **a**, **b**, **c**, the argument matrices $\mathbf{c}, \mathbf{A}^{(1)}, \mathbf{A}^{(2)}$ appearing in (95.16) or **c**, **d**, **t** appearing in (95.17), we will have explicit forms for these constitutive equations. Since these equations are very lengthy, they are not written down.

Materials characterized by (95.16) and (95.17) are not studied to date except in their special cases (groups 1 to 3).

## 96. BASIC EQUATIONS

Any motion of viscoelastic materials must satisfy the equations of conservation of mass and momenta, and the appropriate constitutive equations. In addition, certain initial and boundary conditions must be imposed so as to provide unique solutions to a physically well-defined problem. These conditions are not fully explored for the general class of materials treated here. Generally it is accepted that the fluids adhere to the walls of the rigid bodies, and stresses and deformations are continuous across an interface. The initial conditions ordinarily assume the knowledge of the initial state of the body.

*Conservation of mass:*

$$\dot{\rho} + \rho v^k{}_{;k} = 0 \tag{96.1}$$

*Balance of momenta:*

$$t^l{}_{k;l} + \rho (f_k - \dot{v}_k) = 0 \qquad t^l{}_k = t_k{}^l \tag{96.2}$$

*Constitutive equations.* 1. *Simple Viscoelastic Materials* (95.11):

$$\begin{aligned} \mathbf{t} = a_{00}\,\mathbf{I} &+ a_{10}\,\mathbf{c} + a_{20}\,\mathbf{c}^2 + a_{01}\,\mathbf{d} + a_{02}\,\mathbf{d}^2 \\ &+ a_{11}\,(\mathbf{c}\,\mathbf{d} + \mathbf{d}\,\mathbf{c}) + a_{12}\,(\mathbf{c}\,\mathbf{d}^2 + \mathbf{d}^2\,\mathbf{c}) \\ &+ a_{21}\,(\mathbf{c}^2\,\mathbf{d} + \mathbf{d}\,\mathbf{c}^2) + a_{22}\,(\mathbf{c}^2\,\mathbf{d}^2 + \mathbf{d}^2\,\mathbf{c}^2) \end{aligned} \tag{96.3}$$

where $a_{\kappa\lambda}$ are scalar invariants of the ten joint invariants

$$\begin{array}{cccccc} \operatorname{tr}\mathbf{c} & \operatorname{tr}\mathbf{c}^2 & \operatorname{tr}\mathbf{c}^3 & \operatorname{tr}\mathbf{d} & \operatorname{tr}\mathbf{d}^2 & \operatorname{tr}\mathbf{d}^3 \\ & \operatorname{tr}\mathbf{c}\,\mathbf{d} & \operatorname{tr}\mathbf{c}\,\mathbf{d}^2 & \operatorname{tr}\mathbf{c}^2\,\mathbf{d} & \operatorname{tr}\mathbf{c}^2\,\mathbf{d}^2 & \end{array} \tag{96.4}$$

The Cauchy deformation tensor $\mathbf{c}$ and deformation-rate tensor $\mathbf{d}$ are defined by

$$c_{kl} = G_{KL}\, X^K{}_{,k}\, X^L{}_{,l} \qquad d_{kl} = \tfrac{1}{2}\,(v_{k;l} + v_{l;k}) \tag{96.5}$$

where $\mathbf{v} = \dot{\mathbf{x}}$ is the velocity vector.

2. *Rivlin-Ericksen Fluids.* The general case is given by (94.32). Here we give the simple case (95.14) which is commonly encountered:

$$\begin{aligned} \mathbf{t} = a_{00}\,\mathbf{I} &+ a_{10}\,\mathbf{A}_1 + a_{20}\,\mathbf{A}_1{}^2 + a_{01}\,\mathbf{A}_2 + a_{02}\,\mathbf{A}_2{}^2 \\ &+ a_{11}\,(\mathbf{A}_1\,\mathbf{A}_2 + \mathbf{A}_2\,\mathbf{A}_1) + a_{12}\,(\mathbf{A}_1\,\mathbf{A}_2{}^2 + \mathbf{A}_2{}^2\,\mathbf{A}_1) \\ &+ a_{21}\,(\mathbf{A}_1{}^2\,\mathbf{A}_2 + \mathbf{A}_2\,\mathbf{A}_1{}^2) + a_{22}\,(\mathbf{A}_1{}^2\,\mathbf{A}_2{}^2 + \mathbf{A}_2{}^2\,\mathbf{A}_1{}^2) \end{aligned} \tag{96.6}$$

where $a_{\kappa\lambda}$ are scalar invariants of the ten joint invariants obtained from (96.4) by replacing $\mathbf{c}$ and $\mathbf{d}$ by $\mathbf{A}_1$ and $\mathbf{A}_2$ respectively.

$$\begin{aligned} A^{(1)}_{kl} &\equiv 2\,d_{kl} = v_{k;l} + v_{l;k} \\ A^{(2)}_{kl} &\equiv \frac{D A^{(1)}_{kl}}{Dt} + A^{(1)}_{mk}\, v^m{}_{;l} + A^{(1)}_{ml}\, v^m{}_{;k} \end{aligned} \tag{96.7}$$

For more general viscoelastic materials see Art. 95 (4).

3. *Simple Fluids.* The constitutive functional equations for these materials are given by (94.31), i.e.,

$$\mathbf{t} = \mathbf{F}\,[\overset{t}{\underset{\tau=0}{\mathbf{C}}}(\tau)] \tag{96.8}$$

where $\mathbf{F}$ is an objective tensor functional of $\mathbf{C}(\tau)$ given by $(93.13)_1$, i.e.,

$$C_{KL}(\tau) = \delta_{\alpha\beta}\, \chi^{\alpha}{}_{,K}\, \chi^{\beta}{}_{,L} \tag{96.9}$$

4. *Hygrosteric Materials.* The constitutive equations are given by (95.15)

$$\hat{\mathbf{t}} = \mathbf{f}(\mathbf{d}, \mathbf{t}) \tag{96.10}$$

where $\mathbf{f}$ is an objective tensor which has the form of the right-hand side of (96.3) with $\mathbf{c}$ replaced by $\mathbf{t}$. Specific forms and special classes are discussed in Art. 103.

$$\begin{gathered} \hat{t}^k{}_l \equiv \dot{t}^k{}_l + t^k{}_r\, w^r{}_l - w^k{}_r\, t^r{}_l \\ d_{kl} \equiv \tfrac{1}{2}(v_{k;l} + v_{l;k}) \qquad w_{kl} \equiv \tfrac{1}{2}(v_{k;l} - v_{l;k}) \end{gathered} \tag{96.11}$$

In addition, the initial stress must satisfy certain compatibility conditions similar to those discussed in Art. 75.

For *incompressible materials* replace $a_{00}$ by a hydrostatic pressure $-p$ which is undetermined, drop the dependence on $\operatorname{tr}\mathbf{d}$ or $\operatorname{tr}\mathbf{A}_1$ in (96.3)–(96.6), and add $-p\,\mathbf{I}$ to the right-hand side of (96.8).

## 97. STEADY SHEAR FLOW OF SIMPLE VISCOELASTIC MATERIALS[1]

Here we consider an illustrative solution of simple viscoelastic materials whose constitutive equations are given by (95.11). If the material is incompressible, the stress is determined within an arbitrary isotropic pressure $p$ so that (95.11) is slightly modified by replacing the term $a_{00}\,\mathbf{I}$ by $-p\,\mathbf{I}$ and the remaining coefficients are independent of $\operatorname{tr}\mathbf{d}$, i.e.,

$$\begin{aligned} \mathbf{t} = {} & -p\,\mathbf{I} + a_{10}\,\mathbf{c} + a_{20}\,\mathbf{c}^2 + a_{01}\,\mathbf{d} + a_{02}\,\mathbf{d}^2 \\ & + a_{11}(\mathbf{c}\,\mathbf{d} + \mathbf{d}\,\mathbf{c}) + a_{12}(\mathbf{c}\,\mathbf{d}^2 + \mathbf{d}^2\,\mathbf{c}) \\ & + a_{21}(\mathbf{c}^2\,\mathbf{d} + \mathbf{d}\,\mathbf{c}^2) + a_{22}(\mathbf{c}^2\,\mathbf{d}^2 + \mathbf{d}^2\,\mathbf{c}^2) \end{aligned} \tag{97.1}$$

where $a_{\kappa\lambda}$ are functions of the nine invariants

$$\begin{matrix} \operatorname{tr}\mathbf{c} & \operatorname{tr}\mathbf{c}^2 & \operatorname{tr}\mathbf{c}^3 & \operatorname{tr}\mathbf{d}^2 & \operatorname{tr}\mathbf{d}^3 \\ \operatorname{tr}\mathbf{c}\,\mathbf{d} & \operatorname{tr}\mathbf{c}\,\mathbf{d}^2 & \operatorname{tr}\mathbf{c}^2\,\mathbf{d} & \operatorname{tr}\mathbf{c}^2\,\mathbf{d}^2 & \end{matrix} \tag{97.2}$$

The simple shearing motion is described by

$$x = X + \kappa(t - \tau)\,Y \qquad y = Y \qquad z = Z \tag{97.3}$$

or

$$v_x = \kappa\, y \qquad v_y = v_z = 0 \tag{97.4}$$

where $\kappa$ is a constant and $\tau$ is the time corresponding to the undeformed

[1] These results are new.

state. It follows that

$$\mathbf{c} = \begin{bmatrix} 1 & -K & 0 \\ -K & 1+K^2 & 0 \\ 0 & 0 & 1 \end{bmatrix} \qquad K \equiv \kappa\,(t-\tau) \tag{97.5}$$

$$\mathbf{d} = \tfrac{1}{2}\begin{bmatrix} 0 & \kappa & 0 \\ \kappa & 0 & 0 \\ 0 & 0 & 0 \end{bmatrix} \tag{97.6}$$

Hence, using (97.1) and (97.2), we get

$$\begin{aligned} \mathbf{t} = -p\,\mathbf{I} &+ a_{10}\begin{bmatrix} 1 & -K & 0 \\ -K & 1+K^2 & 0 \\ 0 & 0 & 1 \end{bmatrix} \\ &+ a_{20}\begin{bmatrix} 1+K^2 & -K\,(2+K^2) & 0 \\ -K\,(2+K^2) & K^2+(1+K^2)^2 & 0 \\ 0 & 0 & 1 \end{bmatrix} \\ &+ a_{01}\frac{\kappa}{2}\begin{bmatrix} 0 & 1 & 0 \\ 1 & 0 & 0 \\ 0 & 0 & 0 \end{bmatrix} + a_{02}\frac{\kappa^2}{4}\begin{bmatrix} 1 & 0 & 0 \\ 0 & 1 & 0 \\ 0 & 0 & 0 \end{bmatrix} \\ &+ a_{11}\frac{\kappa}{2}\begin{bmatrix} -2\,K & 2+K^2 & 0 \\ 2+K^2 & -2\,K & 0 \\ 0 & 0 & 0 \end{bmatrix} + a_{12}\frac{\kappa^2}{2}\begin{bmatrix} 1 & -K & 0 \\ -K & 1+K^2 & 0 \\ 0 & 0 & 0 \end{bmatrix} \\ &+ a_{21}\frac{\kappa}{2}\begin{bmatrix} -2\,K\,(2+K^2) & 1+2\,K^2+(1+K^2)^2 & 0 \\ 1+2\,K^2+(1+K^2)^2 & -2\,K\,(2+K^2) & 0 \\ 0 & 0 & 0 \end{bmatrix} \\ &\qquad + a_{22}\frac{\kappa^2}{2}\begin{bmatrix} 1+K^2 & -K\,(2+K^2) & 0 \\ -K\,(2+K^2) & K^2+(1+K^2)^2 & 0 \\ 0 & 0 & 0 \end{bmatrix} \end{aligned} \tag{97.7}$$

where $a_{\kappa\lambda}$ are functions of $\kappa$ and $K \equiv \kappa\,(t-\tau)$, i.e.,

$$\begin{gathered} \operatorname{tr}\mathbf{c} = 3+K^2 \qquad \operatorname{tr}\mathbf{c}^2 = (1+K^2)\,(3+K^2) \\ \operatorname{tr}\mathbf{c}^3 = 3+9\,K^2+6\,K^4+K^6 \qquad \operatorname{tr}\mathbf{d}^2 = \tfrac{1}{2}\,\kappa^2 \qquad \operatorname{tr}\mathbf{d}^3 = 0 \\ \operatorname{tr}\mathbf{c}\,\mathbf{d}^2 = \tfrac{1}{4}\,\kappa^2\,(2+K^2) \qquad \operatorname{tr}\mathbf{c}^2\,\mathbf{d} = -\kappa\,K\,(2+K^2) \\ \operatorname{tr}\mathbf{c}^2\,\mathbf{d}^2 = \tfrac{1}{4}\,\kappa^2\,[1+2\,K^2+(1+K^2)^2] \end{gathered} \tag{97.8}$$

The equations of motion for vanishing body forces are satisfied if $p = p(t)$. We may write (97.7) as

$$\begin{gathered} t_{xx} = -\bar{p} + \beta_3\,\kappa^2 \qquad t_{yy} = -\bar{p} + 2\,\beta_2\,\kappa^2 \\ t_{zz} = -\bar{p} \qquad t_{xy} = \beta_1\,\kappa \qquad t_{xz} = t_{yz} = 0 \end{gathered} \tag{97.9}$$

where

$$
\begin{aligned}
\beta_1(K,\kappa) &\equiv -a_{10}\frac{K}{\kappa} - a_{20}\frac{K}{\kappa}(2+K^2) + \tfrac{1}{2}a_{01} \\
&\quad + \tfrac{1}{2}a_{11}(2+K^2) - \tfrac{1}{2}a_{12}\kappa K + \tfrac{1}{2}a_{21}[1+2K^2 \\
&\qquad + (1+K^2)^2] - \tfrac{1}{2}a_{22}\kappa K(2+K^2) \\
\beta_2(K,\kappa) &\equiv \tfrac{1}{2}a_{10}\frac{K^2}{\kappa^2} + \tfrac{1}{2}a_{20}\frac{K^2}{\kappa^2}(3+K^2) + \tfrac{1}{8}a_{02} \\
&\quad - \tfrac{1}{2}a_{11}\frac{K}{\kappa} + \tfrac{1}{4}a_{12}(1+K^2) - \tfrac{1}{2}a_{21}\frac{K}{\kappa}(2+K^2) \\
&\qquad + \tfrac{1}{4}a_{22}[K^2+(1+K^2)^2] \\
\beta_3(K,\kappa) &\equiv a_{20}\frac{K^2}{\kappa^2} + \tfrac{1}{4}a_{02} - a_{11}\frac{K}{\kappa} + \tfrac{1}{2}a_{12} \\
&\qquad - a_{21}\frac{K}{\kappa}(2+K^2) + \tfrac{1}{2}a_{22}(1+K^2) \\
\bar{p} &\equiv p - a_{10} - a_{20}
\end{aligned}
\tag{97.10}
$$

## 98. STEADY SHEAR FLOW OF RIVLIN-ERICKSEN FLUIDS[1]

Rivlin-Ericksen materials are characterized by constitutive equations of the form (94.32). If the fluids are incompressible, we may add to the right-hand side of the equation an arbitrary hydrostatic pressure so that

$$\mathbf{t} = -p\,\mathbf{I} + \mathbf{f}[\mathbf{A}^{(1)}, \mathbf{A}^{(2)}, \ldots, \mathbf{A}^{(N)}] \tag{98.1}$$

Steady shear flow according to (97.4) has the velocity field

$$v_x = \kappa y \qquad v_y = v_z = 0 \tag{98.2}$$

where $\kappa$ is a constant. Using the defining equations (93.16), we see that

$$\mathbf{A}^{(1)} = \begin{bmatrix} 0 & \kappa & 0 \\ \kappa & 0 & 0 \\ 0 & 0 & 0 \end{bmatrix} \qquad \mathbf{A}^{(2)} = \begin{bmatrix} 0 & 0 & 0 \\ 0 & 2\kappa^2 & 0 \\ 0 & 0 & 0 \end{bmatrix} \qquad \mathbf{A}^{(K)} = 0 \quad (K > 2) \tag{98.3}$$

Therefore in (98.1) $\mathbf{f}$ is a symmetric isotropic tensor polynomial of the two symmetric matrices $\mathbf{A}^{(1)}$ and $\mathbf{A}^{(2)}$. According to Art. 95 (2) the constitutive equations must reduce to

$$
\begin{aligned}
\mathbf{t} = -p\,\mathbf{I} &+ a_{10}\mathbf{A}_1 + a_{20}\mathbf{A}_1^2 + a_{01}\mathbf{A}_2 + a_{02}\mathbf{A}_2^2 \\
&+ a_{11}(\mathbf{A}_1\mathbf{A}_2 + \mathbf{A}_2\mathbf{A}_1) + a_{12}(\mathbf{A}_1\mathbf{A}_2^2 + \mathbf{A}_2^2\mathbf{A}_1) \\
&\quad + a_{21}(\mathbf{A}_1^2\mathbf{A}_2 + \mathbf{A}_2\mathbf{A}_1^2) + a_{22}(\mathbf{A}_1^2\mathbf{A}_2^2 + \mathbf{A}_2^2\mathbf{A}_1^2)
\end{aligned}
\tag{98.4}
$$

where for simplicity in writing we have put $\mathbf{A}_1 \equiv \mathbf{A}^{(1)}$ and $\mathbf{A}_2 \equiv \mathbf{A}^{(2)}$.

[1] These and the solutions presented in Arts. 99 and 100 were obtained by Rivlin [1956].

The constitutive coefficients $a_{\kappa\lambda}$ are functions of the invariants

$$
\begin{aligned}
&\operatorname{tr} \mathbf{A}_1^2 = 2\kappa^2 \qquad &&\operatorname{tr} \mathbf{A}_1^3 = 0 \qquad &&\operatorname{tr} \mathbf{A}_2 = 2\kappa^2 \\
&\operatorname{tr} \mathbf{A}_2^2 = 4\kappa^4 &&\operatorname{tr} \mathbf{A}_2^3 = 8\kappa^6 &&\operatorname{tr} \mathbf{A}_1 \mathbf{A}_2 = 0 \\
&\operatorname{tr} \mathbf{A}_1^2 \mathbf{A}_2 = 2\kappa^4 &&\operatorname{tr} \mathbf{A}_1 \mathbf{A}_2^2 = 0 &&\operatorname{tr} \mathbf{A}_1^2 \mathbf{A}_2^2 = 4\kappa^6
\end{aligned} \tag{98.5}
$$

Substituting (98.3) into (98.4), we may express the latter also as[2]

$$
\mathbf{t} = -p\,\mathbf{I} + \beta_1 \mathbf{A}_1 + \beta_2 \mathbf{A}_2 + \beta_3 (\mathbf{A}_1^2 - \tfrac{1}{2}\mathbf{A}_2) \tag{98.6}
$$

where

$$
\begin{aligned}
\beta_1(\kappa^2) &= a_{10} + 2\,a_{11}\,\kappa^2 + 4\,a_{12}\,\kappa^4 \\
\beta_2(\kappa^2) &= a_{01} + \tfrac{1}{2}\,a_{20} + 2\,(a_{02} + a_{21})\,\kappa^2 + 4\,a_{22}\,\kappa^4 \\
\beta_3(\kappa^2) &= a_{20}
\end{aligned} \tag{98.7}
$$

or

$$
\begin{aligned}
&t_{xx} = -p + \beta_3\,\kappa^2 \qquad &&t_{yy} = -p + 2\,\beta_2\,\kappa^2 \\
&t_{zz} = -p \qquad t_{xy} = \beta_1\,\kappa &&t_{xz} = t_{yz} = 0
\end{aligned} \tag{98.8}
$$

If the body forces are zero, it is clear that the equations of motion are satisfied for the stress components (98.8) and that $p$ is constant throughout the fluid.

A comparison of (98.8) and (97.9) shows that the stresses have the same form. The only difference between the viscoelastic fluid and the Rivlin-Ericksen fluid lies in the fact that a dependence of the coefficients $\beta_1$, $\beta_2$, and $\beta_3$ on time $t$ exists in the former case. Thus, as far as shear flow is concerned, by assuming that the constitutive coefficients of Rivlin-Ericksen fluids are also functions of time, we get the viscoelastic shear flow. This fact remains unaltered for elastic solids also (cf. (52.29) and Rivlin [1956]). Consequently on the basis of shear experiments alone the character of the fluid cannot be fully determined.

One other fact may be worth mentioning: namely, the normal stress differences $t_{xx} - t_{yy}$ and $t_{yy} - t_{zz}$, as well as the apparent viscosity $t_{xy}/\kappa$, are even functions of the rate of shear $\kappa$, while the shear stresses $t_{xz}$ and $t_{yz}$ vanish. These results of the theory often are reached by heuristic arguments as being obvious on symmetry grounds.

We should like to emphasize further the fact that the foregoing solution makes use of the full constitutive equation (98.1) with all $\mathbf{A}^{(K)}$ present; however, on the basis of the simplicity inherent in the solution (98.2), all $\mathbf{A}^{(K)}$ drop out except $\mathbf{A}^{(1)}$ and $\mathbf{A}^{(2)}$. Thus the present solution may be considered *exact* in this sense.

The solutions clearly contain the normal stress effect that is exhibited by most nonlinear materials. In Art. 64 we found that stokesian fluids exhibit the same effect, with the exception, of course, of the fact that the

[2] Ericksen [1960*e*].

magnitude of the normal stress is further affected by the coefficients of terms containing $\mathbf{c}$ in (97.1) and $\mathbf{A}_2$ in (98.4). Before these latter theories were advanced, Oldroyd [1950] had pointed to this effect in his criticism that the stokesian fluids are not elastic. To clarify this point further, let us calculate $\mathbf{c}$ for the Rivlin-Ericksen fluids above. For the displacement field (97.3) corresponding to shear flow, $\mathbf{c}$ is given by (97.5). We may express $\mathbf{c}$ in terms of kinematical matrices $\mathbf{A}_1$ and $\mathbf{A}_2$ given by (98.3) as

$$\mathbf{c} = \mathbf{I} - (t - \tau)\,\mathbf{A}_1 + \tfrac{1}{2}\,(t - \tau)^2\,\mathbf{A}_2 \tag{98.9}$$

From (98.3) we have

$$\mathbf{A}_1\,\mathbf{A}_2 + \mathbf{A}_2\,\mathbf{A}_1 = 2\,\kappa^2\,\mathbf{A}_1 \qquad \mathbf{A}_2{}^2 = 2\,\kappa^2\,\mathbf{A}_2 \tag{98.10}$$

Therefore for an equivalent incompressible elastic solid with time-dependent constitutive coefficients

$$\mathbf{t} = -\bar{p}\,\mathbf{I} + a_1\,\mathbf{c} + a_2\,\mathbf{c}^2 \tag{98.11}$$

By use of (98.9) and (98.10) we see that (98.11) will take the same form as (98.6) provided we agree to choose $\bar{p}$, $a_1$, and $a_2$ such that

$$\begin{aligned} p &= \bar{p} - a_1 - a_2 \\ \beta_1 &= -(t - \tau)\,\{a_1 + [2 + (t - \tau)^2\,\kappa^2]\,a_2\} \\ \beta_2 &= \tfrac{1}{2}\,(t - \tau)^2\,\{a_1 + a_2\,[3 + \kappa^2\,(t - \tau)^2]\} \\ \beta_3 &= (t - \tau)^2\,a_2 \end{aligned} \tag{98.12}$$

For stokesian materials this analogy breaks down, since $t - \tau = 0$. Therefore, in agreement with Oldroyd's contention, stokesian materials cannot even in analogy represent the elastic materials. We see, however, that for steady shear flow (and as we shall see below, for some similar flows) the Rivlin-Ericksen fluids with time-dependent constitutive coefficients can represent the elastic solid.

Moreover, as pointed out by Ericksen [1960*e*], Rivlin-Ericksen fluids (98.6) are applicable to any motion for which

$$\mathbf{R}\,\mathbf{A}_1\,\mathbf{R}^{-1} = \begin{bmatrix} 0 & \kappa & 0 \\ \kappa & 0 & 0 \\ 0 & 0 & 0 \end{bmatrix} \qquad \mathbf{R}\,\mathbf{A}_2\,\mathbf{R}^{-1} = \begin{bmatrix} 0 & 0 & 0 \\ 0 & 2\,\kappa^2 & 0 \\ 0 & 0 & 0 \end{bmatrix} \tag{98.13}$$

$$\mathbf{A}_K = 0 \qquad (K > 2)$$

and

$$\mathbf{c} = \mathbf{I} - (t - \tau)\,\mathbf{A}_1 + \tfrac{1}{2}\,(t - \tau)^2\,\mathbf{A}_2 \tag{98.14}$$

where $\mathbf{R}$ is a rotation matrix and $\kappa$ is a scalar, both of which may vary with position and time. Motions satisfying (98.13) and (98.14) are called *laminar shear flows.* For sufficiently smooth motions, by expanding $ds^2(\tau)$ in a power series about time $t$, we can show that (98.14) follows from (98.13) (Dupont [1933]). These are the only relations of the Rivlin-Ericksen fluids that reduce to (98.6). Some known examples of laminar shear flows follow.

*Rectilinear motions:*

$$v_x = f(y, z) \qquad v_y = v_z = 0 \tag{98.15}$$

*Torsional flow:*

$$v_x = -\kappa\, y\, z \qquad v_y = \kappa\, x\, z \qquad v_z = 0 \qquad (\kappa = \text{const}) \tag{98.16}$$

*Helical flow (Couette-Poiseuille flow):*

$$v_x = -y\,\omega(r) \qquad v_y = x\,\omega(r) \qquad v_z = u(r) \qquad (r = \sqrt{x^2 + y^2}) \tag{98.17}$$

*The motions:*

$$\begin{aligned} v_x &= -y f(r, \theta) \qquad v_y = x f(r, \theta) \qquad v_z = 0 \\ r^2 &\equiv x^2 + y^2 + z^2 \qquad \tan^2\theta = \frac{z^2}{x^2 + y^2} \end{aligned} \tag{98.18}$$

In the following three articles we give examples for torsional and helical flows. For an example of the general motion characterized by (98.18) see the work of Ericksen [1960*e*, art. IV] on flow between coaxial cones.

## 99. VISCOELASTIC TORSION AND TORSIONAL FLOW

Consider a circular cylinder of radius $a$ and length $L$, having a force-free curved surface and subjected to a twist by means of two disks in contact with the plane ends.

According to (53.1) the displacement field may be expressed in cylindrical coordinates as

$$r = R \qquad \theta = \Theta + K\,Z \qquad z = Z \tag{99.1}$$

where $K = K(t)$. The corresponding velocity field is given by

$$\dot{r} = 0 \qquad \dot{\theta} = \dot{K}\,z \qquad \dot{z} = 0 \tag{99.2}$$

or in rectangular components

$$v_x = -\dot{K}\,y\,z \qquad v_y = \dot{K}\,x\,z \qquad v_z = 0 \tag{99.3}$$

where the $x_3$ axis coincides with the $z$ axis. Consider the case of constant angular velocity $\Omega$ so that $\dot{K}\,L = \Omega = \kappa\,L$ or

$$\kappa = \frac{\Omega}{L} = \dot{K} \qquad \text{or} \qquad K = \kappa\,(t - \tau) \tag{99.4}$$

where the initial undeformed state of the body is at $t = \tau$.

According to $(53.3)_2$ we have for the components of $\mathbf{c}$ in cylindrical coordinates

$$\|c^k{}_l\| = \begin{bmatrix} 1 & 0 & 0 \\ 0 & 1 & -K \\ 0 & -K r^2 & K r^2 + 1 \end{bmatrix} \tag{99.5}$$

The physical components of $\mathbf{c}$, $c^{(k)}{}_{(l)}$ in polar coordinates are given by

$$\|c^{(k)}{}_{(l)}\| = \begin{bmatrix} 1 & 0 & 0 \\ 0 & 1 & -K r \\ 0 & -K r & K r^2 + 1 \end{bmatrix} \tag{99.6}$$

To determine the physical components of $\mathbf{A}_1$ and $\mathbf{A}_2$, we first calculate the rectangular components from (93.16)

$$\mathbf{A}_1 = \begin{bmatrix} 0 & 0 & -\kappa y \\ 0 & 0 & \kappa x \\ -\kappa y & \kappa x & 0 \end{bmatrix} \qquad \mathbf{A}_2 = \begin{bmatrix} 0 & 0 & 0 \\ 0 & 0 & 0 \\ 0 & 0 & 2\kappa^2 r^2 \end{bmatrix} \qquad \mathbf{A}_M = 0 \qquad (M > 2)$$

If the direction of the $x$ axis is chosen so that $y = 0$ for the point of the fluid considered, we then put $x = r$, thus obtaining the physical components of $\mathbf{A}_1$ and $\mathbf{A}_2$ in cylindrical coordinates, i.e.,

$$\|A_1{}^{(k)}{}_{(l)}\| = \begin{bmatrix} 0 & 0 & 0 \\ 0 & 0 & \kappa r \\ 0 & \kappa r & 0 \end{bmatrix} \qquad \|A_2{}^{(k)}{}_{(l)}\| = \begin{bmatrix} 0 & 0 & 0 \\ 0 & 0 & 0 \\ 0 & 0 & 2\kappa^2 r^2 \end{bmatrix} \tag{99.7}$$

We first notice from (99.6) and (99.7) that the relation (98.14) again prevails, i.e.,

$$\mathbf{c} = \mathbf{I} - (t - \tau)\,\mathbf{A}_1 + \tfrac{1}{2}(t - \tau)^2\,\mathbf{A}_2 \tag{99.8}$$

Therefore the constitutive equations may again be put into the common form (98.6) or more explicitly

$$\begin{gathered} t^r{}_r = -p \qquad t^\theta{}_\theta = -p + \beta_3 \kappa^2 r^2 \qquad t^z{}_z = -p + 2\beta_2 \kappa^2 r^2 \\ t^r{}_\theta = t^z{}_r = 0 \qquad t^\theta{}_z = \beta_1 \kappa r \end{gathered} \tag{99.9}$$

where

$$\begin{aligned} \beta_1 &\equiv a_{10} + 2 a_{11} \kappa^2 r^2 + 4 a_{12} \kappa^4 r^4 \\ \beta_2 &\equiv a_{01} + \tfrac{1}{2} a_{20} + 2(a_{02} + a_{21}) \kappa^2 r^2 + 4 a_{22} \kappa^4 r^4 \\ \beta_3 &\equiv a_{20} \end{aligned} \tag{99.10}$$

for Rivlin-Ericksen fluids. Here $a_{\lambda\mu}$ are functions of

$$\begin{array}{lll} \operatorname{tr} \mathbf{A}_1{}^2 = 2\kappa^2 r^2 & \operatorname{tr} \mathbf{A}_1{}^3 = 0 & \operatorname{tr} \mathbf{A}_2 = 2\kappa^2 r^2 \\ \operatorname{tr} \mathbf{A}_2{}^2 = 4\kappa^4 r^4 & \operatorname{tr} \mathbf{A}_2{}^3 = 8\kappa^2 r^2 & \operatorname{tr} \mathbf{A}_1 \mathbf{A}_2 = 0 \\ \operatorname{tr} \mathbf{A}_1{}^2 \mathbf{A}_2 = 2\kappa^4 r^4 & \operatorname{tr} \mathbf{A}_1 \mathbf{A}_2{}^2 = 0 & \operatorname{tr} \mathbf{A}_1{}^2 \mathbf{A}_2{}^2 = 4\kappa^6 r^6 \end{array} \tag{99.11}$$

All of these coefficients become identical to those given by (98.7) if we replace $\kappa r$ in (99.11) by $\kappa$.

For simple viscoelastic materials, by analogy, we can obtain the constitutive coefficients $a_{\lambda\mu}$ and $\beta_\lambda$ from (97.8) and (97.10) by replacing $\kappa$ by $\kappa r$. Clearly now these coefficients are also functions of $\kappa r\,(t-\tau)$, in addition to $\kappa r$.

If no body forces are applied to the fluid and the inertia forces are neglected, all of the equations of motion are satisfied except

$$\frac{\partial t^r{}_r}{\partial r} + \frac{1}{r}\,(t^r{}_r - t^\theta{}_\theta) = 0 \tag{99.12}$$

Using (99.9) in (99.12), we find that

$$\frac{\partial p}{\partial r} = -\beta_2\,\kappa^2\,r \tag{99.13}$$

Therefore

$$p = -\int_a^r \beta_2\,\kappa^2\,r\,dr \tag{99.14}$$

if we assume that $t^r{}_r = 0$ at the curved surface $r = a$. Introducing this into (99.9), we determine the stress field completely. Thus the tractions at the plane ends of the cylinder are fully determined and cannot be prescribed arbitrarily. They are equipollent to an axial force $N$ and a torque $M$.

$$\begin{aligned} N &= 2\pi \int_0^a t^z{}_z\,r\,dr = 3\pi \int_0^a \beta_2\,\kappa^2\,r^3\,dr \\ M &= 2\pi \int_0^a t^\theta{}_z\,r^2\,dr = 2\pi \int_0^a \beta_1\,\kappa\,r^3\,dr \end{aligned} \tag{99.15}$$

## 100. HELICAL FLOW OF RIVLIN-ERICKSEN FLUIDS (COUETTE-POISEUILLE FLOW)

Helical flow is a steady laminar flow which can occur in an annular mass of fluid contained between two coaxial circular cylinders rotating about their common axis. Let $R_1$ and $R_2$ ($R_2 > R_1$) denote the radii of the cylinders, and $\Omega_1$ and $\Omega_2$ the corresponding angular velocities. It is assumed that a constant pressure gradient $P$, parallel to the axis of the cylinders, exists in the fluid.

This type of flow includes concentric-pipe flow (Poiseuille flow) in the special case of $\Omega_1 \equiv \Omega_2 \equiv 0$ ($R_1 \equiv 0$) and the Couette flow for $P \equiv 0$.

In rectangular coordinates ($x$, $y$, $z$), with $z$ coinciding with the axis of the cylinders, the velocity profile may be expressed as

$$v_x = -y\,\omega(r) \qquad v_y = x\,\omega(r) \qquad v_z = u(r) \tag{100.1}$$
$$r \equiv \sqrt{x^2 + y^2}$$

With the use of (100.1) the kinematical matrices $\mathbf{A}_K \equiv \mathbf{A}^{(K)}$ given by (93.16) become

$$\mathbf{A}_1 = \begin{bmatrix} -2\frac{xy}{r}\,\acute{\omega} & \frac{x^2-y^2}{r}\,\acute{\omega} & \frac{x}{r}\,\acute{u} \\ \frac{x^2-y^2}{r}\,\acute{\omega} & 2\frac{xy}{r}\,\acute{\omega} & \frac{y}{r}\,\acute{u} \\ \frac{x}{r}\,\acute{u} & \frac{y}{r}\,\acute{u} & 0 \end{bmatrix}$$

$$\text{(100.2)} \quad \mathbf{A}_2 = \begin{bmatrix} 2x^2(\acute{\omega}^2 + \acute{u}^2 r^{-2}) & 2xy(\acute{\omega}^2 + \acute{u}^2 r^{-2}) & 0 \\ 2xy(\acute{\omega}^2 + \acute{u}^2 r^{-2}) & 2y^2(\acute{\omega}^2 + \acute{u}^2 r^{-2}) & 0 \\ 0 & 0 & 0 \end{bmatrix}$$

$$\mathbf{A}_K = 0 \qquad (K > 2)$$

$$\acute{\omega} \equiv \frac{d\omega}{dr} \qquad \acute{u} \equiv \frac{du}{dr}$$

To obtain the physical components of $\mathbf{A}_1$ and $\mathbf{A}_2$ in cylindrical coordinates $(r, \theta, z)$, we now select the direction of the $x$ axis such that $y = 0$ for the point of the fluid considered. Thus, putting $x = r$ and $y = 0$ in (100.2), we get

$$\text{(100.3)} \quad \mathbf{A}_1 = \begin{bmatrix} 0 & r\acute{\omega} & \acute{u} \\ r\acute{\omega} & 0 & 0 \\ \acute{u} & 0 & 0 \end{bmatrix} \qquad \mathbf{A}_2 = \begin{bmatrix} 2(r^2\acute{\omega}^2 + \acute{u}^2) & 0 & 0 \\ 0 & 0 & 0 \\ 0 & 0 & 0 \end{bmatrix}$$

Introducing these into (98.4), we obtain the physical components of the stress tensor in cylindrical coordinates

$$\text{(100.4)} \quad \begin{aligned} t^r{}_r &= -p + (2a_{01} + a_{20})(r^2\acute{\omega}^2 + \acute{u}^2) \\ &\qquad + 4(a_{02} + a_{21})(r^2\acute{\omega}^2 + \acute{u}^2)^2 + 8a_{22}(r^2\acute{\omega}^2 + \acute{u}^2)^3 \\ t^\theta{}_\theta &= -p + a_{20} r^2 \acute{\omega}^2 \qquad t^z{}_z = -p + a_{20}\acute{u}^2 \qquad t^\theta{}_z = a_{20} r \acute{\omega} \acute{u} \\ t^z{}_r &= \acute{u}\,[a_{10} + 2a_{11}(r^2\acute{\omega}^2 + \acute{u}^2) + 4a_{12}(r^2\acute{\omega}^2 + \acute{u}^2)^2] \\ t^r{}_\theta &= r\acute{\omega}\,[a_{10} + 2a_{11}(r^2\acute{\omega}^2 + \acute{u}^2) + 4a_{12}(r^2\acute{\omega}^2 + \acute{u}^2)^2] \end{aligned}$$

where the constitutive coefficients $a_{\lambda\mu}$ are functions of

$$\text{(100.5)} \quad \begin{aligned} &\operatorname{tr}\mathbf{A}_1^2 = 2(r^2\acute{\omega}^2 + \acute{u}^2) \qquad \operatorname{tr}\mathbf{A}_1^3 = 0 \qquad \operatorname{tr}\mathbf{A}_2 = 2(r^2\acute{\omega}^2 + \acute{u}^2) \\ &\operatorname{tr}\mathbf{A}_2^2 = 4(r^2\acute{\omega}^2 + \acute{u}^2)^2 \qquad \operatorname{tr}\mathbf{A}_2^3 = 8(r^2\acute{\omega}^2 + \acute{u}^2)^3 \\ &\operatorname{tr}\mathbf{A}_1\mathbf{A}_2 = 0 \qquad \operatorname{tr}\mathbf{A}_1^2\mathbf{A}_2 = 2(r^2\acute{\omega}^2 + \acute{u}^2)^2 \qquad \operatorname{tr}\mathbf{A}_1\mathbf{A}_2^2 = 0 \\ &\operatorname{tr}\mathbf{A}_1^2\mathbf{A}_2^2 = 4(r^2\acute{\omega}^2 + \acute{u}^2)^3 \end{aligned}$$

which would have the same forms as (98.5) when $r^2\acute{\omega}^2 + \acute{u}^2$ is replaced by $\kappa^2$. From the symmetry of the flow field it follows that $p = p(r, z)$.

For vanishing body forces the equations of motion of a steady flow reduce to

$$\frac{\partial t^r{}_r}{\partial r} + \frac{1}{r}(t^r{}_r - t^\theta{}_\theta) = -\rho\, r\, \omega^2$$

$$\text{(100.6)} \qquad \frac{\partial t^r{}_\theta}{\partial r} + \frac{2}{r}\, t^r{}_\theta = 0 \qquad \frac{\partial t^z{}_r}{\partial r} + \frac{1}{r}\, t^z{}_r + \frac{\partial t^z{}_z}{\partial z} = 0$$

where $\rho$ is the density of the fluid. The pressure gradient is assumed to be constant. Hence

$$\text{(100.7)} \qquad \frac{\partial t^z{}_z}{\partial z} = -P$$

Equations $(100.6)_2$ and $(100.6)_3$ are integrated to give

$$\text{(100.8)} \qquad t^r{}_\theta = \frac{B}{r^2} \qquad t^z{}_r = \tfrac{1}{2} P\, r + \frac{A}{r}$$

where $A$ and $B$ are constants. Employing $t^r{}_\theta$ and $t^z{}_r$ from (100.4), we get two nonlinear first-order differential equations for the determination of functions $\omega\,(r)$ and $u\,(r)$, i.e.,

$$\acute{u}\,[a_{10} + 2\,a_{11}\,(r^2\,\acute{\omega}^2 + \acute{u}^2) + 4\,a_{12}\,(r^2\,\acute{\omega}^2 + \acute{u}^2)^2] = \frac{1}{2} P\, r + \frac{A}{r}$$

$$\text{(100.9)} \qquad \acute{\omega}\,[a_{10} + 2\,a_{11}\,(r^2\,\acute{\omega}^2 + \acute{u}^2) + 4\,a_{12}\,(r^2\,\acute{\omega}^2 + \acute{u}^2)^2] = \frac{B}{r^3}$$

These differential equations must be integrated, subject to conditions $u = 0$ when $r = R_1$ and $r = R_2$; $\omega = \Omega_1$ when $r = R_1$; and $\omega = \Omega_2$ when $r = R_2$.

The remaining equation $(100.6)_1$ with the use of (100.4) gives $\partial p/\partial r$, integrating into

$$\begin{aligned}\text{(100.10)} \quad p = {} & (2\,a_{01} + a_{20})\,(r^2\,\acute{\omega}^2 + \acute{u}^2) + 4\,(a_{02} + a_{21})\,(r^2\,\acute{\omega}^2 + \acute{u}^2)^2 \\ & + 8\,a_{22}\,(r^2\,\acute{\omega}^2 + \acute{u}^2)^3 + \int^r \rho\, r\, \omega^2\, dr \\ & + \int^r \frac{1}{r}\,[2\,a_{01}\,(r^2\,\acute{\omega}^2 + \acute{u}^2) + a_{20}\,\acute{u}^2 \\ & + 4\,(a_{02} + a_{21})\,(r^2\,\acute{\omega}^2 + \acute{u}^2)^2 \\ & + 8\,a_{22}\,(r^2\,\acute{\omega}^2 + \acute{u}^2)^3]\, dr + P\, z + c\end{aligned}$$

where $c$ is a constant of integration. We now can eliminate $p$ from the normal stress components given in (100.4). Hence

$$\begin{aligned} t^r{}_r &= -\int^r \rho\, r\, \omega^2\, dr - \int^r \frac{1}{r} [2\, a_{01}\, (r^2\, \acute{\omega}^2 + \acute{u}^2) \\ &\quad + a_{20}\, \acute{u}^2 + 4\, (a_{02} + a_{21})\, (r^2\, \acute{\omega}^2 + \acute{u}^2)^2 \\ &\quad + 8\, a_{22}\, (r^2\, \acute{\omega}^2 + \acute{u}^2)^3]\, dr - P\, z - c \\ t^\theta{}_\theta &= -a_{20}\, \acute{u}^2 - 2\, a_{01}\, (r^2\, \acute{\omega}^2 + \acute{u}^2) - 4\, (a_{02} + a_{21})\, (r^2\, \acute{\omega}^2 + \acute{u}^2)^2 \\ &\quad - 8\, a_{22}\, (r^2\, \acute{\omega}^2 + \acute{u}^2)^3 - \int^r \rho\, r\, \omega^2\, dr \\ &\quad - \int^r \frac{1}{r} [2\, a_{01}\, (r^2\, \acute{\omega}^2 + \acute{u}^2) + a_{20}\, \acute{u}^2 \\ &\quad + 4\, (a_{02} + a_{21})\, (r^2\, \acute{\omega}^2 + \acute{u}^2)^2 \\ &\quad + 8\, a_{22}\, (r^2\, \acute{\omega}^2 + \acute{u}^2)^3]\, dr - P\, z - c \\ t^z{}_z &= -a_{20}\, r^2\, \acute{\omega}^2 - 2\, a_{01}\, (r^2\, \acute{\omega}^2 + \acute{u}^2) \\ &\quad - 4\, (a_{02} + a_{21})\, (r^2\, \acute{\omega}^2 + \acute{u}^2)^2 \\ &\quad - 8\, a_{22}\, (r^2\, \acute{\omega}^2 + \acute{u}^2)^3 - \int^r \rho\, r\, \omega^2\, dr \\ &\quad - \int^r \frac{1}{r} [2\, a_{01}\, (r^2\, \acute{\omega}^2 + \acute{u}^2) + a_{20}\, \acute{u}^2 \\ &\quad + 4\, (a_{02} + a_{21})\, (r^2\, \acute{\omega}^2 + \acute{u}^2)^2 \\ &\quad + 8\, a_{22}\, (r^2\, \acute{\omega}^2 + \acute{u}^2)^3]\, dr - P\, z - c \end{aligned} \tag{100.11}$$

Neglecting the end effect, for concentric cylinders of length $L$ the pressure head is given by

$$[t^z{}_z]_{z=0} - [t^z{}_z]_{z=L} = P\, L \tag{100.12}$$

The rate of flow $Q$ through the annular region may be calculated by

$$Q = \int_{R_1}^{R_2} 2\, \pi\, r\, u\, dr$$

The difference between the radial tractions acting on the cylindrical walls is given by

$$\begin{aligned} [t^r{}_r]_{r=R_1} - [t^r{}_r]_{r=R_2} &= \int_{R_1}^{R_2} \rho\, r\, \omega^2\, dr \\ &\quad + \int_{R_1}^{R_2} \frac{1}{r} [2\, a_{01}\, (r^2\, \acute{\omega}^2 + \acute{u}^2) + a_{20}\, \acute{u}^2 \\ &\quad + 4\, (a_{02} + a_{21})\, (r^2\, \acute{\omega}^2 + \acute{u}^2)^2 + 8\, a_{22}\, (r^2\, \acute{\omega}^2 + \acute{u}^2)^3]\, dr \end{aligned} \tag{100.13}$$

The azimuthal surface tractions $t^r{}_\theta$ acting on the walls $r = R_1$ and $r = R_2$

are equipollent to equal and opposite torques

$$2\pi R_1^2 [t^r{}_\theta]_{r=R_1} = 2\pi R_2^2 [t^r{}_\theta]_{r=R_2}$$

per unit length of the cylindrical boundaries.

The solution for the special case of *Couette flow* is obtained from the foregoing solution by letting $u \equiv 0$, $P \equiv A \equiv 0$, and that for the case of *longitudinal flow* (*Poiseuille flow*) is obtained by taking $\omega \equiv 0$.

## 101. HELICAL FLOW OF SIMPLE FLUIDS[1]

Simple fluids are characterized by constitutive equations of the form (94.31), i.e.,

$$\text{(101.1)} \qquad \mathbf{t} = \mathbf{F}\,[\underset{\tau=0}{\overset{t}{\mathbf{C}}}(\tau)] \qquad \text{(compressible)}$$

where $\mathbf{F}$ is an objective tensor functional of $\mathbf{C}$ in $0 \leq \tau \leq t$; i.e., it satisfies

$$\text{(101.2)} \qquad \mathbf{Q}\,\mathbf{F}\,[\underset{\tau=0}{\overset{t}{\mathbf{C}}}(\tau)]\,\mathbf{Q}^T = \mathbf{F}\,[\mathbf{Q}\,\underset{\tau=0}{\overset{t}{\mathbf{C}}}(\tau)\,\mathbf{Q}^T]$$

where $\mathbf{Q}$ is any orthogonal tensor and $\mathbf{Q}^T$ is its transpose. For incompressible fluids $\mathbf{t}$ is determined within an arbitrary hydrostatic pressure, i.e.,

$$\text{(101.3)} \qquad \mathbf{t} = -p\,\mathbf{I} + \bar{\mathbf{F}}\,[\underset{\tau=0}{\overset{t}{\mathbf{C}}}(\tau)] \qquad \text{(incompressible)}$$

To remove this indeterminateness, one may also put

$$\text{(101.4)} \qquad \operatorname{tr}\bar{\mathbf{F}}\,[\underset{\tau=0}{\overset{t}{\mathbf{C}}}(\tau)] = 0 \qquad \text{(incompressible)}$$

so that

$$\text{(101.5)} \qquad p = -\tfrac{1}{3}\operatorname{tr}\mathbf{t}$$

In cylindrical coordinates the velocity field of a helical flow is given by

$$\text{(101.6)} \qquad v^r = 0 \qquad v^\theta = \omega(r) \qquad v^z = u(r)$$

subject to the boundary conditions

$$\text{(101.7)} \qquad \begin{aligned} \omega(R_1) = \Omega_1 \qquad \omega(R_2) &= \Omega_2 \\ u(R_1) = u(R_2) &= 0 \end{aligned}$$

where $r = R_1$ and $r = R_2$ $(R_2 > R_1)$ are the walls of the coaxial cylinders whose axes coincide with the $z$ axis of the cylindrical coordinates. Boundary conditions (101.7) state that the fluid adheres to the walls of the

[1] Coleman and Noll [1959*c*].

inner and outer cylinders rotating with angular velocities $\Omega_1$ and $\Omega_2$ respectively.

Consider a particle at time $t$ at a point $r(t)$, $\theta(t)$, $z(t)$. This particle at time $\tau$ ($\tau \leq t$) had coordinates $r(\tau)$, $\theta(\tau)$, $z(\tau)$. To determine this position, we integrate the differential equations

$$\frac{dr}{d\tau} = 0 \qquad \frac{d\theta}{d\tau} = \omega[r(\tau)] \qquad \frac{dz}{d\tau} = u[r(\tau)]$$

This gives

$$r(\tau) = r(t) \qquad \theta(\tau) = \theta(t) - (t - \tau)\,\omega[r(t)]$$
$$z(\tau) = z(t) - (t - \tau)\,u[r(t)] \tag{101.8}$$

Now $C_{KL}(\tau)$ is given by

$$C_{KL}(\tau) = g_{\alpha\beta}\,\chi^{\alpha}{}_{,K}\,\chi^{\beta}{}_{,L} \tag{101.9}$$

For cylindrical coordinates $(r, \theta, z)$ we have

$$\|g_{\alpha\beta}\| = \begin{bmatrix} 1 & 0 & 0 \\ 0 & r^2 & 0 \\ 0 & 0 & 1 \end{bmatrix}$$

Now select

$$\chi^1(\tau) \equiv r(\tau) \qquad \chi^2(\tau) \equiv \theta(\tau) \qquad \chi^3(\tau) \equiv z(\tau)$$

$$X^1 = r(\tau)\Big|_{\tau=0} = r(t) \equiv R$$
$$X^2 = \theta(\tau)\Big|_{\tau=0} = \theta(t) - t\,\omega[r(t)] \equiv \Theta \tag{101.10}$$
$$X^3 = z(\tau)\Big|_{\tau=0} = z(t) - t\,u[r(t)] \equiv Z$$

By use of (101.8) in (101.10) we can express $r(\tau)$, $\theta(\tau)$, and $z(\tau)$ in terms of $R$, $\Theta$, and $Z$ as follows:

$$r(\tau) = R \qquad \theta(\tau) = \Theta + \tau\,\omega(R) \qquad z(\tau) = Z + \tau\,u(R) \tag{101.11}$$

We now get $C_{KL}(\tau)$ through (101.9) and (101.11). Below are given the physical components of this tensor:

$$\mathbf{C} = \begin{bmatrix} 1 + \tau^2(r^2\acute{\omega}^2 + \acute{u}^2) & \tau r \acute{\omega} & \tau \acute{u} \\ \tau r \acute{\omega} & 1 & 0 \\ \tau \acute{u} & 0 & 1 \end{bmatrix} \tag{101.12}$$

where $\acute{\omega} \equiv d\omega/dr$, $\acute{u} \equiv du/dr$. From this it is clear that

$$\mathbf{C} = \mathbf{I} + \tau\,\mathbf{A} + \tau^2\,\mathbf{B} \tag{101.13}$$

where

$$\mathbf{A} = \begin{bmatrix} 0 & r\acute{\omega} & \acute{u} \\ r\acute{\omega} & 0 & 0 \\ \acute{u} & 0 & 0 \end{bmatrix} \qquad \mathbf{B} = \begin{bmatrix} r^2\acute{\omega}^2 + \acute{u}^2 & 0 & 0 \\ 0 & 0 & 0 \\ 0 & 0 & 0 \end{bmatrix} \tag{101.14}$$

Since **C** has the form (101.13) with **A** and **B** independent of $\tau$ and $t$, the functional $\bar{\mathbf{F}}$ appearing in (101.3) will be a function of the two matrices **A** and **B**, i.e.,

$$\mathbf{t} = -p\mathbf{I} + \mathbf{f}(\mathbf{A}, \mathbf{B}) \tag{101.15}$$

which according to (101.4) is subject to

$$\operatorname{tr} \mathbf{f}(\mathbf{A}, \mathbf{B}) = 0 \tag{101.16}$$

It follows from (101.2) that **f** is isotropic, i.e.,

$$\mathbf{Q}\,\mathbf{f}(\mathbf{A}, \mathbf{B})\,\mathbf{Q}^T = \mathbf{f}(\mathbf{Q}\,\mathbf{A}\,\mathbf{Q}^T, \mathbf{Q}\,\mathbf{B}\,\mathbf{Q}^T) \tag{101.17}$$

is valid for any orthogonal tensor **Q**.

Consider now the orthogonal tensor $\mathbf{Q}^*$ having physical components

$$Q^* = \frac{1}{\kappa}\begin{bmatrix} \kappa & 0 & 0 \\ 0 & r\,\acute{\omega} & \acute{u} \\ 0 & -\acute{u} & r\,\acute{\omega} \end{bmatrix} \qquad \kappa \equiv [\acute{u}^2 + (r\,\acute{\omega})^2]^{\frac{1}{2}} \tag{101.18}$$

and set

$$\mathbf{A}^* = \mathbf{Q}^*\mathbf{A}\,\mathbf{Q}^{*T} \qquad \mathbf{B}^* = \mathbf{Q}^*\mathbf{B}\,\mathbf{Q}^{*T} \qquad \mathbf{f}^* = \mathbf{Q}^*\mathbf{f}\,\mathbf{Q}^{*T} \tag{101.19}$$

From (101.14) and (101.18) we obtain

$$\mathbf{A}^* = \kappa\begin{bmatrix} 0 & 1 & 0 \\ 1 & 0 & 0 \\ 0 & 0 & 0 \end{bmatrix} \qquad \mathbf{B}^* = \mathbf{B} = \kappa^2\begin{bmatrix} 1 & 0 & 0 \\ 0 & 0 & 0 \\ 0 & 0 & 0 \end{bmatrix} \tag{101.20}$$

Therefore

$$\mathbf{f}^* = \mathbf{f}(\mathbf{A}^*, \mathbf{B}^*) \tag{101.21}$$

It is not difficult to show that two components of $\mathbf{f}^*$, namely, $f^{*r}{}_z$ and $f^{*\theta}{}_z$, are zero. To this end let us choose **Q** to be

$$\mathbf{Q} = \begin{bmatrix} 1 & 0 & 0 \\ 0 & 1 & 0 \\ 0 & 0 & -1 \end{bmatrix}$$

In this case

$$\mathbf{Q}\,\mathbf{A}^*\mathbf{Q}^T = \mathbf{A}^* \qquad \mathbf{Q}\,\mathbf{B}^*\mathbf{Q}^T = \mathbf{B}^* \qquad \mathbf{Q}\,\mathbf{f}^*\mathbf{Q}^T = \mathbf{f}^*$$

the last of which follows from (101.17) and (101.21). Let $f^{*k}{}_l$ denote the physical components of $\mathbf{f}^*$. Then

$$\mathbf{Q}\,\mathbf{f}^*\mathbf{Q}^T = \begin{bmatrix} f^{*r}{}_r & f^{*r}{}_\theta & -f^{*r}{}_z \\ f^{*\theta}{}_r & f^{*\theta}{}_\theta & -f^{*\theta}{}_z \\ -f^{*z}{}_r & -f^{*z}{}_\theta & f^{*z}{}_z \end{bmatrix}$$

If this matrix is to coincide with $\mathbf{f}^*$, we must have $f^{*r}{}_z = f^{*\theta}{}_z = 0$

Moreover, from (101.16) and (101.21) we have

$$\text{tr}\,\mathbf{f}^* = f^{*r}{}_r + f^{*\theta}{}_\theta + f^{*z}{}_z = 0 \tag{101.22}$$

Since $\mathbf{A}^*$ and $\mathbf{B}^*$ are functions of $\kappa$ alone, it follows from (101.21) and (101.22) that

$$\begin{aligned} f^{*r}{}_r - f^{*z}{}_z &= \sigma_1(\kappa) \qquad & f^{*\theta}{}_\theta - f^{*z}{}_z &= \sigma_2(\kappa) \\ f^{*r}{}_\theta &= \sigma_3(\kappa) \qquad & f^{*r}{}_z = f^{*\theta}{}_z &= 0 \end{aligned} \tag{101.23}$$

where $\sigma_1$, $\sigma_2$, and $\sigma_3$ are *material functions.*

We can further show that $\sigma_3$ is an odd function while $\sigma_1$ and $\sigma_2$ are even functions of $\kappa$. To see this, we now select

$$\mathbf{Q} = \begin{bmatrix} 1 & 0 & 0 \\ 0 & -1 & 0 \\ 0 & 0 & 1 \end{bmatrix}$$

This gives

$$\mathbf{Q}\,\mathbf{A}^*\,\mathbf{Q}^T = -\mathbf{A}^* \qquad \mathbf{Q}\,\mathbf{B}^*\,\mathbf{Q}^T = \mathbf{B}^*$$

so that

$$\mathbf{Q}\,\mathbf{f}^*\,\mathbf{Q}^T = \begin{bmatrix} f^{*r}{}_r & -f^{*r}{}_\theta & 0 \\ -f^{*\theta}{}_r & f^{*\theta}{}_\theta & 0 \\ 0 & 0 & f^{*z}{}_z \end{bmatrix}$$

It is clear that this operation is equivalent to putting $-\kappa$ in place of $\kappa$ in the expressions of $\mathbf{A}^*$ and $\mathbf{B}^*$ in (101.20). Thus through (101.23) we have

$$\sigma_1(-\kappa) = \sigma_1(\kappa) \qquad \sigma_2(-\kappa) = \sigma_2(\kappa) \qquad \sigma_3(-\kappa) = -\sigma_3(\kappa) \tag{101.24}$$

Since, initially, stresses vanish, i.e., $\sigma_1(0) = \sigma_2(0) = \sigma_3(0) = 0$, we therefore see that $\sigma_1$ and $\sigma_2$ are even functions while $\sigma_3$ is an odd function of $\kappa$.

We now apply the inverse operation to $(101.19)_3$ and remember that $\mathbf{Q}^{*T} = \mathbf{Q}^{*-1}$:

$$\mathbf{f} = \mathbf{Q}^{*T}\,\mathbf{f}^*\,\mathbf{Q}^*$$

This gives us $\mathbf{f}$ and hence, through (101.15), $\mathbf{t}$, i.e.,

$$\begin{aligned} f^r{}_r &= t^r{}_r + p = \tfrac{1}{3}[2\,\sigma_1(\kappa) - \sigma_2(\kappa)] \\ f^\theta{}_\theta &= t^\theta{}_\theta + p = -\tfrac{1}{3}\sigma_1(\kappa) + \frac{1}{3\,\kappa^2}(-\acute{u}^2 + 2\,r^2\,\acute{\omega}^2)\,\sigma_2(\kappa) \\ f^z{}_z &= t^z{}_z + p = -\tfrac{1}{3}\sigma_1(\kappa) + \frac{1}{3\,\kappa^2}(2\,\acute{u}^2 - r^2\,\acute{\omega}^2)\,\sigma_2(\kappa) \\ f^r{}_\theta &= t^r{}_\theta = \frac{1}{\kappa}\,r\,\acute{\omega}\,\sigma_3(\kappa) \\ f^\theta{}_z &= t^\theta{}_z = \frac{1}{\kappa^2}\,r\,\acute{\omega}\,\acute{u}\,\sigma_2(\kappa) \\ f^r{}_z &= t^r{}_z = \frac{1}{\kappa}\,\acute{u}\,\sigma_3(\kappa) \end{aligned} \tag{101.25}$$

To determine functions $\acute{u}$, $\acute{\omega}$, and $p$, we must employ the equations of motion which may be written as

$$\frac{\partial f^r{}_r}{\partial r} + \frac{1}{r}(f^r{}_r - f^\theta{}_\theta) - \frac{\partial \Phi}{\partial r} = r\,\rho\,\omega^2$$

$$(101.26) \qquad r\frac{\partial f^r{}_\theta}{\partial r} + 2\,f^r{}_\theta - \frac{\partial \Phi}{\partial \theta} = 0$$

$$\frac{\partial f^r{}_z}{\partial r} + \frac{1}{r}f^r{}_z - \frac{\partial \Phi}{\partial z} = 0$$

$$\Phi \equiv p + \rho\psi$$

where $\psi$ is a body-force potential; i.e., if we use $\mathbf{g}$ for body force per unit mass, then $\mathbf{g} = -\text{grad}\,\psi$.

Equations (101.26) are satisfied if

$$\Phi = -P\,z + h\,(r)$$

$$(101.27) \qquad f^r{}_\theta = \frac{M}{2\,\pi\,r^2} \qquad f^r{}_z = -\tfrac{1}{2}P\,r + \frac{A}{r}$$

$$\acute{h}\,(r) = \frac{\partial f^r{}_r}{\partial r} + \frac{1}{r}(f^r{}_r - f^\theta{}_\theta) + r\,\rho\,\omega^2$$

where $P$, $A$, and $M$ are constants and $h$ is a function of $r$.

It is not difficult to see that $M$ is the torque per unit height required to maintain relative motion of the bounding cylinders, and $P$ is the pressure head per unit length in the axial direction if there are no body forces. The constant $A$ is determined from the boundary conditions as follows. Let

$$(101.28) \qquad \alpha^2\,(r) \equiv \left(\frac{M}{2\,\pi\,r^2}\right)^2 + \left(\frac{A}{r} - \frac{P\,r}{2}\right)^2$$

From $(101.27)_{2,3}$ the expressions for $f^r{}_\theta$ and $f^r{}_z$ from (101.25), and the definition of $\kappa$ from (101.18), we have

$$\alpha^2\,(r) = (f^r{}_\theta)^2 + (f^z{}_r)^2 = \left[\frac{r\,\acute{\omega}}{\kappa}\sigma_3\,(\kappa)\right]^2 + \left[\frac{\acute{u}}{\kappa}\sigma_3\,(\kappa)\right]^2$$

$$= [\sigma_3\,(\kappa)]^2$$

Hence

$$(101.29) \qquad \alpha\,(r) = \sigma_3\,(\kappa) \qquad \kappa = \overset{-1}{\sigma_3}\,[\alpha\,(r)]$$

where $\overset{-1}{\sigma_3}$ denotes the inverse of the function $\sigma_3$. Using $f^r{}_z$ of (101.2 and (101.27), along with (101.29), we find

$$(101.30) \qquad \acute{u} = \left(-\tfrac{1}{2}P\,r + \frac{A}{r}\right)\frac{\overset{-1}{\sigma_3}\,[\alpha\,(r)]}{\alpha\,(r)}$$

ˈhe boundary condition $u(R_1) = u(R_2) = 0$ yields

101.31) $$0 = \int_{R_1}^{R_2} \frac{\overset{-1}{\sigma_3}[\alpha(r)]}{\alpha(r)} \left(-\frac{P}{2} r + \frac{A}{r}\right) dr$$

ˈrom these equations one can solve for $A$ as a function

$$A = A(R_1, R_2, M, P)$$

ᵥhich has a form that depends on the material function $\sigma_3$ only.
From $f^r{}_\theta$ of (101.25), (101.27), and (101.29) we get

101.32) $$\acute{\omega} = \frac{M}{2\pi r^3} \frac{\overset{-1}{\sigma_3}[\alpha(r)]}{\alpha(r)}$$

ˈhus integration of (101.30) and (101.32) with the use of boundary ɔnditions (101.7) gives

.01.33) $$\begin{aligned} u(r) &= \int_{R_1}^{r} \frac{\overset{-1}{\sigma_3}[\alpha(\xi)]}{\alpha(\xi)} \left(-\tfrac{1}{2} P \xi + \frac{A}{\xi}\right) d\xi \\ \omega(r) &= \frac{M}{2\pi} \int_{R_1}^{r} \frac{\overset{-1}{\sigma_3}[\alpha(\xi)]}{\xi^3 \alpha(\xi)} d\xi + \Omega_1 \end{aligned}$$

quations (101.31) and (101.33) determine the velocity profile $\mathbf{v}(r)$ as a nction of $r$, $R_1$, $R_2$, $M$, $P$, and $\Omega_1$. The explicit determination of $\mathbf{v}$ ɛpends only on the function $\sigma_3$.
Volume discharge per unit time, $Q$, is given by

01.34) $$Q = 2\pi \int_{R_1}^{R_2} u(r)\, r\, dr = \pi \int_{R_1}^{R_2} \frac{\overset{-1}{\sigma_3}[\alpha(r)]}{\alpha(r)} \left(\tfrac{1}{2} P r^3 - A r\right) dr$$

ıere the extreme right follows from integration by parts and from 01.30) and (101.31). The difference between the angular velocities of e outer and inner cylinders follows from (101.33) and (101.7).

)1.35) $$\Omega_2 - \Omega_1 = \frac{M}{2\pi} \int_{R_1}^{R_2} \frac{\overset{-1}{\sigma_3}[\alpha(\xi)]}{\xi^3 \alpha(\xi)} d\xi$$

is clear that $\Omega_2 - \Omega_1$ is *not* proportional to $M$ since $\alpha(\xi)$ depends on $P$ d $M$ by (101.28).
By using (101.25), (101.28), (101.29), and (101.32) in $\dot{h}(r)$ of (101.27)

and by integrating, we get

$$
\begin{aligned}
(101.36) \qquad h(r) = {} & \tfrac{2}{3}\sigma_1\{\overset{-1}{\sigma}_3[\alpha(r)]\} - \tfrac{1}{3}\sigma_2\{\overset{-1}{\sigma}_3[\alpha(r)]\} \\
& + \int_{R_1}^{r} \xi^{-1}\sigma_1\{\overset{-1}{\sigma}_3[\alpha(\xi)]\}\,d\xi \\
& - \left(\frac{M}{2\pi}\right)^2 \int_{R_1}^{r} \xi^{-5}\alpha^{-2}(\xi)\,\sigma_2\{\overset{-1}{\sigma}_3[\alpha(\xi)]\}\,d\xi \\
& + \int_{R_1}^{r} \rho\,\xi\,\omega^2(\xi)\,d\xi + C
\end{aligned}
$$

where $\omega$ is given by $(101.33)_2$ and $C$ is a constant which must remain arbitrary on account of the incompressibility of the fluid. From $(101.27)_1$ and $\Phi$ of (101.26) we have

$$
(101.37) \qquad p = \Phi - \rho\psi = -P\,z + h(r) - \rho\psi
$$

Thus through (101.36) and (101.37) the pressure $p$ is determined. The stresses now follow from (101.25)

$$
\begin{aligned}
t^r{}_r = {} & - \int_{R_1}^{r} \xi^{-1}\sigma_1\{\overset{-1}{\sigma}_3[\alpha(\xi)]\}\,d\xi \\
& + \left(\frac{M}{2\pi}\right)^2 \int_{R_1}^{r} \xi^{-5}\alpha^{-2}(\xi)\,\sigma_2\{\overset{-1}{\sigma}_3[\alpha(\xi)]\}\,d\xi \\
& - \int_{R_1}^{r} \rho\,\xi\,\omega^2(\xi)\,d\xi + P\,z + \rho\psi + c \\
t^r{}_r - t^\theta{}_\theta = {} & \sigma_1(\kappa) - \frac{r^2\,\acute{\omega}^2}{\kappa^2}\,\sigma_2(\kappa) \\
= {} & \sigma_1\{\overset{-1}{\sigma}_3[\alpha(r)]\} - \left[\frac{M}{2\pi r^2\alpha(r)}\right]^2 \sigma_2\{\overset{-1}{\sigma}_3[\alpha(r)]\} \\
(101.38) \qquad t^r{}_r - t^z{}_z = {} & \sigma_1(\kappa) - \frac{\acute{u}^2}{\kappa^2}\,\sigma_2(\kappa) \\
= {} & \sigma_1\{\overset{-1}{\sigma}_3[\alpha(r)]\} - \frac{(2\,A\,r^{-1} - P\,r)^2}{4\,\alpha^2(r)}\,\sigma_2\{\overset{-1}{\sigma}_3[\alpha(r)]\} \\
t^\theta{}_r = t^r{}_\theta = {} & \frac{M}{2\pi r^2} \\
t^r{}_z = t^z{}_r = {} & -\tfrac{1}{2}P\,r + \frac{A}{r} \\
t^z{}_\theta = t^\theta{}_z = {} & \frac{M\,(2\,A\,r^{-3} - P\,r^{-1})}{4\pi\,\alpha^2(r)}\,\sigma_2\{\overset{-1}{\sigma}_3[\alpha(r)]\}
\end{aligned}
$$

When the body-force potential $\psi$ is independent of $r$, from $t^r{}_r$ of (101.38 we get the expression for the difference between the normal stresses acti at the outer and inner cylinders

$$t^r{}_r(R_2) - t^r{}_r(R_1) = -\int_{R_1}^{R_2} \xi^{-1}\sigma_1\{\overset{-1}{\sigma}_3[\alpha(\xi)]\}\,d\xi + \left(\frac{M}{2\pi}\right)^2 \int_{R_1}^{R_2} \xi^{-5}\alpha^{-2}(\xi)\,\sigma_2\{\overset{-1}{\sigma}_3[\alpha(\xi)]\}\,d\xi - \int_{R_1}^{R_2} \rho\,\xi\,\omega^2(\xi)\,d\xi \tag{101.39}$$

The foregoing elegant analysis not only illustrates some simple examples of solutions but also supplies us with some important results for theoretical and experimental analysis. Indeed we see that the analysis of helical flow of Rivlin-Ericksen fluids presented in the previous article remains valid for more general simple fluids even though the Rivlin-Ericksen fluids are special cases of simple fluids. It is therefore expected that some approximation theorems exist connecting the constitutive functional equations of simple fluids to the constitutive equations of the Rivlin-Ericksen fluids. Indeed such a theorem has been discovered by Coleman and Noll [1961*b*, art. 7], in which the number of scalar material functions to approximate the constitutive functional of simple fluids is determined by functions evaluated at $R$ different times $\tau_1, \tau_2, \ldots, \tau_R$ in the time interval $0 \le \tau \le t$. See also Coleman and Noll [1960].

Moreover, contrary to expectations, the more general theory such as this provides simpler results. Here we have only three material functions to characterize the helical flow in comparison to the eight functions required to characterize the Rivlin-Ericksen fluids. This is another example of a gratifying contradiction to the popular misconception that a general theory leads to more complicated results. The simplicity gained here is such that one is able to complete the problem including the determination of the velocity field which is left in the form of unsolved differential equations [cf. (100.9)] in the previous article.

The material functions $\sigma_1(\kappa)$, $\sigma_2(\kappa)$, $\sigma_3(\kappa)$ of the present article and the constitutive coefficients $a_{\lambda\mu}(\kappa)$ used in the previous article are connected to each other by

$$\begin{aligned} \sigma_1(\kappa) &= \kappa^2[2a_{01}(\kappa) + a_{20}(\kappa) + 4\kappa^2 a_{02}(\kappa) + 4\kappa^2 a_{21}(\kappa) + 8\kappa^4 a_{22}(\kappa)] \\ \sigma_2(\kappa) &= \kappa^2 a_{20}(\kappa) \\ \sigma_3(\kappa) &= \kappa[a_{10}(\kappa) + 2\kappa^2 a_{11}(\kappa) + 4\kappa^4 a_{12}(\kappa)] \end{aligned} \tag{101.40}$$

In an earlier article Markovitz [1957] classified various rheological theories by introducing four material functions connected with one another in a single equation. With the present work this conjecture now appears to be a reality.

## 102. HYGROSTERIC MATERIALS[1]

The term *hygrosterics* is used specifically for materials having constitutive differential equations of the form (95.15), i.e.,

$$\hat{\mathbf{t}} = \mathbf{f}\,(\mathbf{d}, \mathbf{t}, \rho) \tag{102.1}$$

Here we explicitly indicate the dependence on the mass density $\rho$. For the stress flux we take the form (35.5)

$$\hat{t}^k{}_l = \dot{t}^k{}_l + t^k{}_r\, w^r{}_l - w^k{}_r\, t^r{}_l \tag{102.2}$$

Here $\mathbf{f}$ is a symmetric isotropic tensor function of symmetric matrices, stress $\mathbf{t}$ and deformation rate $\mathbf{d}$. The materials described by (102.1) are homogeneous and isotropic and possess time-independent mechanical properties. In addition, two assumptions may be made:

1. *The function* $\mathbf{f}$ *is a continuously differentiable function of* $\mathbf{t}$, $\mathbf{d}$, *and* $\rho$ *in a suitable neighborhood of* $\mathbf{t} = 0$, $\mathbf{d} = 0$, *and* $\rho = \rho_0$.

2. *For a given density* $\rho$, *the body can be at ease at a certain hydrostatic pressure* $\mathbf{t} = -\bar{p}\,\mathbf{I}$; i.e., *when* $\mathbf{d} = \mathbf{w} = \dot{\mathbf{t}} = 0$, *we have* $\mathbf{t} = -\bar{p}\,\mathbf{I}$ *where*

$$\bar{p} = \bar{p}\,(\rho) \tag{102.3}$$

This is satisfied if $\mathbf{f}$ is a polynomial in $\mathbf{t}$ and $\mathbf{d}$ with continuously differentiable coefficients that are functions of $\rho$ in the neighborhood of $\rho = \rho_0$.

Let $\bar{\mathbf{t}}$ denote the *extra stress* beyond the hydrostatic pressure $\bar{p}$, i.e.,

$$\mathbf{t} = -\bar{p}\,\mathbf{I} + \bar{\mathbf{t}} \tag{102.4}$$

Then

$$\hat{\bar{\mathbf{t}}} = \bar{\mathbf{f}}\,(\mathbf{d}, \bar{\mathbf{t}}, \rho) \tag{102.5}$$

so that

$$\bar{\mathbf{f}}\,(0, 0, \rho) = 0 \tag{102.6}$$

The function $\bar{\mathbf{f}}$ is also an isotropic symmetric polynomial of $\mathbf{d}$ and since $\mathbf{f}$ is a symmetric isotropic polynomial of $\mathbf{d}$ and $\mathbf{t}$. Therefore $\bar{\mathbf{f}}$ can b[e] represented in the form (95.11), i.e.,

$$\begin{aligned} \hat{\bar{\mathbf{t}}} &= \bar{\mathbf{f}}\,(\mathbf{d}, \bar{\mathbf{t}}, \rho) \\ &= a_{00}\,\mathbf{I} + a_{10}\,\mathbf{d} + a_{20}\,\mathbf{d}^2 + a_{01}\,\bar{\mathbf{t}} + a_{02}\,\bar{\mathbf{t}}^2 \\ &\quad + a_{11}\,(\mathbf{d}\,\bar{\mathbf{t}} + \bar{\mathbf{t}}\,\mathbf{d}) + a_{12}\,(\mathbf{d}\,\bar{\mathbf{t}}^2 + \bar{\mathbf{t}}^2\,\mathbf{d}) \\ &\quad + a_{21}\,(\bar{\mathbf{t}}\,\mathbf{d}^2 + \mathbf{d}^2\,\bar{\mathbf{t}}) + a_{22}\,(\mathbf{d}^2\,\bar{\mathbf{t}}^2 + \bar{\mathbf{t}}^2\,\mathbf{d}^2) \end{aligned} \tag{102.7}$$

where $a_{\lambda\mu}$ are scalar polynomials of the joint invariants of $\mathbf{d}$ and $\mathbf{t}$ wit[h]

[1] The main ideas presented in the following articles are based on Noll's work [195

continuously differentiable coefficient functions of $\rho$ in a neighborhood of $\rho = \rho_0$. The joint invariants are

(102.8)
$$\begin{array}{ccc} \operatorname{tr} \mathbf{d} & \operatorname{tr} \mathbf{d}^2 & \operatorname{tr} \mathbf{d}^3 \\ \operatorname{tr} \bar{\mathbf{t}} & \operatorname{tr} \bar{\mathbf{t}}^2 & \operatorname{tr} \bar{\mathbf{t}}^3 \end{array}$$
$$\operatorname{tr} \mathbf{d}\, \bar{\mathbf{t}} \qquad \operatorname{tr} \mathbf{d}\, \bar{\mathbf{t}}^2 \qquad \operatorname{tr} \mathbf{d}^2\, \bar{\mathbf{t}} \qquad \operatorname{tr} \mathbf{d}^2\, \bar{\mathbf{t}}^2$$

From (102.6) and (102.7) it follows that

(102.9)
$$a_{00} = 0$$

for $\mathbf{d} = \hat{\mathbf{t}} = 0$ and $\rho$ arbitrary.

Thermodynamical considerations will undoubtedly impose additional restrictions on the coefficients $a_{\lambda\mu}$. However, no systematic study of these restrictions as yet exists.

Finally, we should like to see the consequence of the axiom of *dimensional invariance.* The constitutive equations contain a number of dimensionally independent constants. These may be identified simply if we replace the dependence on $\rho$ by a dependence on $\bar{p}$ and write

(102.10)
$$\hat{\bar{\mathbf{t}}} = \bar{\mathbf{f}}\,(\mathbf{d}, \bar{\mathbf{t}}, \bar{p})$$

Now we have the physical dimensions of the various tensors

(102.11)
$$[\bar{\mathbf{t}}] = [\bar{p}] = \frac{M}{L\,T^2} \qquad [\mathbf{w}] = [\mathbf{d}] = \frac{1}{T}$$

where $M$, $L$, and $T$ denote mass, length, and time respectively. If we ntroduce two material constants $\mu$ and $\tau$ of dimensions

102.12)
$$[\mu] = \frac{M}{L\,T^2} \qquad [\tau] = T$$

hen (102.10) in terms of dimensionless quantities can be written in the orm

102.13)
$$\hat{\bar{\mathbf{t}}} = \frac{\mu}{\tau}\,\bar{\mathbf{f}}_0\left(\tau\,\mathbf{d}, \frac{\bar{\mathbf{t}}}{\mu}, \frac{\bar{p}}{\mu}\right)$$

here $\bar{\mathbf{f}}_0$ is a dimensionless function. It is now clear that *the materials nder consideration possess only two dimensionally independent moduli.* f instead of $\mu$ one introduces viscosity $\eta$ by

02.14)
$$\eta = \tau\,\mu \qquad [\eta] = \frac{M}{L\,T}$$

en (102.13) becomes

02.15)
$$\hat{\bar{\mathbf{t}}} = \frac{\eta}{\tau^2}\,\bar{\mathbf{f}}_0\left(\tau\,\mathbf{d}, \frac{\tau}{\eta}\,\bar{\mathbf{t}}, \frac{\tau}{\eta}\,\bar{p}\right)$$

By proper choice of $\bar{\mathbf{f}}_0$ it is possible to eliminate one of the dimensional moduli, thus obtaining a special class of the materials. An example of this is provided by hypoelastic materials (see also the following article).

We now collect the basic field equations for hygrosteric materials: namely, the equations of conservation of mass and momenta, and the constitutive equations:

$$\frac{\partial \rho}{\partial t} + (\rho v^k)_{;k} = 0 \tag{102.16}$$

$$\bar{t}^k{}_{l;k} - \frac{\partial \bar{p}}{\partial x^l} + \rho (f_l - \dot{v}_l) = 0 \qquad \bar{t}^k{}_l = \bar{t}_l{}^k \tag{102.17}$$

$$\frac{D}{Dt}\,\bar{t}^k{}_l + \bar{t}^k{}_r\, w^r{}_l - w^k{}_r\, \bar{t}^r{}_l = \bar{f}^k{}_l\,(\mathbf{d}, \bar{\mathbf{t}}, \rho) \tag{102.18}$$

where $\bar{f}^k{}_l$ is given by (102.7) or in component notation by

$$\begin{aligned}\bar{f}^k{}_l \equiv\; & a_{00}\, \delta^k{}_l + a_{10}\, d^k{}_l + a_{20}\, d^k{}_m\, d^m{}_l + a_{01}\, \bar{t}^k{}_l \\ & + a_{02}\, \bar{t}^k{}_m\, \bar{t}^m{}_l + a_{11}\, (d^k{}_m\, \bar{t}^m{}_l + \bar{t}^k{}_m\, d^m{}_l) \\ & + a_{12}\, (d^k{}_m\, \bar{t}^m{}_n\, \bar{t}^n{}_l + \bar{t}^k{}_m\, \bar{t}^m{}_n\, d^n{}_l) \\ & + a_{21}\, (d^k{}_m\, d^m{}_n\, \bar{t}^n{}_l + \bar{t}^k{}_m\, d^m{}_n\, d^n{}_l) \\ & + a_{22}\, (d^k{}_m\, d^m{}_n\, \bar{t}^n{}_p\, \bar{t}^p{}_l + \bar{t}^k{}_m\, \bar{t}^m{}_n\, d^n{}_p\, d^p{}_l)\end{aligned} \tag{102.19}$$

subject to (102.9). In addition, the deformation-rate tensor $\mathbf{d}$ and the spin tensor $\mathbf{w}$ are defined by

$$2\, d_{kl} = v_{k;l} + v_{l;k} \qquad 2\, w_{kl} = v_{k;l} - v_{l;k} \tag{102.20}$$

It is now clear that the behavior of hygrosteric materials can be predicted by solving for ten unknowns $\rho$, $v^k$, $\bar{t}^k{}_l$ from the ten partial differential equations (102.16)–(102.18) subject to appropriate boundary and initial conditions.[2]

*Incompressible Materials.* If a material is susceptible only to motion in which the density at each material point remains constant in time, we say that that material is *incompressible*. Since we have also assumed homogeneity $\rho = \rho_0 =$ const, the pressure is no longer a function of $\rho$ but must be considered a primitive unknown $\bar{p} = p\,(\mathbf{x}, t)$. In this case the basic equations (102.16)–(102.18) reduce to

[2] Arguments advanced in Art. 75 concerning the consistency conditions for the initial stress and the material characterization must of course be considered here too. It is reported that such studies are as yet in the preparation stage (cf. Bernstein, "Differential Equations as Constitutive Relations and Analytic Functionals," in preparation).

$$v^k{}_{;k} = 0$$

(102.21) $$\bar{t}^k{}_{l;k} - \frac{\partial p}{\partial x^l} + \rho\,(f_l - \dot{v}_l) = 0 \qquad \bar{t}^k{}_l = \bar{t}_l{}^k$$

$$\frac{D}{Dt}\,\bar{t}^k{}_l + \bar{t}^k{}_r\,w^r{}_l - w^k{}_r\,\bar{t}^r{}_l = \bar{f}^k{}_l\,(\mathbf{d}, \bar{\mathbf{t}})$$

Addition of an arbitrary pressure (depending on time alone) to $p$ does not change $(102.21)_2$. Therefore the stress is determined to within a uniform time-dependent pressure.

## 103. SPECIAL CLASSES OF HYGROSTERIC MATERIALS

*A body is said to be at rest if the velocity vector* $\mathbf{v} = 0$ *throughout the body. It is said to be at ease if both the velocity* $\mathbf{v}$ *and the stress flux* $\hat{\mathbf{t}}$ *vanish.* A body is at rest without being at ease when $\mathbf{v} = 0$ but $\hat{\mathbf{t}} \neq 0$.

Hygrosteric materials may be divided into two major categories.

1. *Fluent Bodies.* A medium is a fluent body if it can be at ease when the stress is a hydrostatic pressure depending on the density $\rho$ alone, i.e.,

(103.1) $$\mathbf{t} = -\bar{p}\,(\rho)\,\mathbf{I} \qquad (\bar{p} > 0)$$

We therefore have

(103.2) $$\bar{\mathbf{f}}\,(0, 0, \rho) = 0$$

but

(103.3) $$\bar{\mathbf{f}}\,(0, \bar{\mathbf{t}}, \rho) \neq 0 \qquad \text{for } \bar{\mathbf{t}} \neq 0,\ \bar{\mathbf{t}} \equiv \mathbf{t} + \bar{p}\,(\rho)\,\mathbf{I}$$

2. *Resilient Bodies.* A medium is a *resilient* body if it can be at ease for an arbitrary stress within a certain range. In this case the pressure function $\bar{p}$ has no particular meaning, and therefore instead of (102.5) we may use the form

(103.4) $$\hat{\mathbf{t}} = \mathbf{f}\,(\mathbf{d}, \mathbf{t}, \rho)$$

subject to

(103.5) $$\mathbf{f}\,(0, \mathbf{t}, \rho) = 0$$

for a certain range of $\mathbf{t}$ and $\rho$. The function $\mathbf{f}$ in (103.4) will have the same form as that in (102.7) with $\bar{\mathbf{t}}$ appearing in the latter replaced by $\mathbf{t}$.

It is possible that the body may be at ease only when a certain relation between $\rho$ and $\mathbf{t}$ exists, i.e., $\rho = \varphi\,(\mathbf{t})$. In this case (103.5) is replaced by

(103.6) $$\mathbf{f}\,(0, \mathbf{t}, \varphi\,(\mathbf{t})) = 0 \qquad \mathbf{f}\,(0, \mathbf{t}, \rho) \neq 0 \text{ for } \rho \neq \varphi\,(\mathbf{t})$$

This means that at two states of ease having the same stress the density is the same. Alternatively, there is no hysteresis for density, although there may be for strain deviation.

For a *fluent incompressible body* we must have

$$\bar{\mathbf{f}}\,(0, 0) = 0 \qquad \bar{\mathbf{f}}\,(0, \bar{\mathbf{t}}) \neq 0 \qquad \text{for } \bar{\mathbf{t}} \neq 0 \tag{103.7}$$

and for a *resilient incompressible body*

$$\mathbf{f}\,(0, \mathbf{t}) = 0 \qquad \text{for all } \mathbf{t} \text{ in a certain range} \tag{103.8}$$

Many special classes of hygrosteric materials exist. Appropriate constitutive equations are obtained by specializing the general case through the application of the *axiom of dimensional invariance.*

In the same fashion as in Chap. 8 on hypoelasticity we may now classify bodies according to the highest degree of $\mathbf{t}$ and $\mathbf{d}$ contained in the constitutive equations.

1*a*. *Linear Fluent Bodies.* We assume that $\bar{\mathbf{f}}\,(\mathbf{d}, \bar{\mathbf{t}})$ is independent of $\rho$ and is a linear function of $\bar{\mathbf{t}}$ for fixed $\mathbf{d}$ and also a linear function of $\mathbf{d}$ for fixed $\bar{\mathbf{t}}$. Hence $\bar{\mathbf{f}}$ must have the form

$$\hat{\bar{\mathbf{t}}} = \bar{\mathbf{f}}\,(\mathbf{d}, \bar{\mathbf{t}}) \equiv a_{00}\,\mathbf{I} + a_{10}\,\mathbf{d} + a_{01}\,\bar{\mathbf{t}} + a_{11}\,(\mathbf{d}\,\bar{\mathbf{t}} + \bar{\mathbf{t}}\,\mathbf{d}) \tag{103.9}$$

where $a_{\lambda\mu}$ may be expressed as

$$\begin{gathered} a_{00} = \mu_2 \operatorname{tr} \mathbf{d} + \lambda_2 \operatorname{tr} \bar{\mathbf{t}} + \alpha_1 \operatorname{tr} \mathbf{d}\,\bar{\mathbf{t}} + \alpha_4\,(\operatorname{tr} \bar{\mathbf{t}})\,(\operatorname{tr} \mathbf{d}) \\ a_{10} = \mu_1 + \alpha_2 \operatorname{tr} \bar{\mathbf{t}} \qquad a_{01} = \lambda_1 + \alpha_5 \operatorname{tr} \mathbf{d} \\ a_{11} = \alpha_3 \end{gathered} \tag{103.10}$$

where $\lambda_\kappa$, $\mu_\kappa$, and $\alpha_\kappa$ are constants. A fluent body having a constitutive function $\bar{\mathbf{f}}$ of the form (103.9) is called a *linear fluent body.* The constitutive equation for linear fluent bodies is therefore given by

$$\begin{aligned} \hat{\bar{t}}^k{}_l + \bar{t}^k{}_r\,w^r{}_l - w^k{}_r\,\bar{t}^r{}_l & \\ = (\mu_2\,d^r{}_r + \lambda_2\,\bar{t}^r{}_r + \alpha_1\,d^r{}_s\,\bar{t}^s{}_r + \alpha_4\,d^r{}_r\,\bar{t}^s{}_s)\,\delta^k{}_l & \\ + (\mu_1 + \alpha_2\,\bar{t}^r{}_r)\,d^k{}_l + (\lambda_1 + \alpha_5\,d^r{}_r)\,\bar{t}^k{}_l & \\ + \alpha_3\,(\bar{t}^k{}_r\,d^r{}_l + d^k{}_r\,\bar{t}^r{}_l) \qquad \text{(compressible)} & \end{aligned} \tag{103.11}$$

Here the dimensions of the constitutive constants are given by

$$[\mu_\kappa] = \frac{M}{L\,T^2} = [\text{stress}] \qquad [\lambda_\kappa] = \frac{1}{T} \qquad [\alpha_\kappa] = 1$$

Since the body is fluent, we must also have by (103.3)

$$\lambda_2\,\bar{t}^r{}_r\,\delta^k{}_l + \lambda_1\,\bar{t}^k{}_l \neq 0 \qquad \text{for } \bar{t}^k{}_l \neq 0 \tag{103.12}$$

Equality in (103.12) instead of the inequality would be possible for $\lambda_1 \neq 0$ only if $\bar{t}^k{}_l = q\,\delta^k{}_l$, in which case $(3\,\lambda_2 + \lambda_1)\,q = 0$. This can hold or $q \neq 0$ only if $3\lambda_2 + \lambda_1 = 0$. Hence the conclusion is

$$\lambda_1 \neq 0 \qquad 3\lambda_2 + \lambda_1 \neq 0 \tag{103.13}$$

or (103.12) to be valid.

For incompressible materials we have $d^k{}_k = 0$, thus reducing (103.11) to

$$\begin{aligned} \mathring{t}^k{}_l + \bar{t}^k{}_r u^r{}_l - w^k{}_r \bar{t}^r{}_l &= (\lambda_2 \bar{t}^r{}_r + \alpha_1 d^r{}_s \bar{t}^s{}_r)\,\delta^k{}_l + (\mu_1 + \alpha_2 \bar{t}^r{}_r)\, d^k{}_l \\ &\quad + \lambda_1 \bar{t}^k{}_l + \alpha_3 (\bar{t}^k{}_r d^r{}_l + d^k{}_r \bar{t}^r{}_l) \qquad \text{(incompressible)} \end{aligned} \tag{103.14}$$

Equations (103.11) and (103.14) were first given by Noll [1955]. The special case $\alpha_\kappa \equiv 0$ was introduced by Zaremba [1903*a*, *b*].

1*b*. *Viscous Fluids.* Below we sketch the procedure that leads to viscous fluids as a special case of the fluent bodies. In (102.10) we now propose to use a time scale $\tau_2$ for the stress flux $\hat{\mathbf{t}}$ different from the time scale $\tau_1$ used for $\mathbf{d}$. We replace $\hat{\mathbf{t}}, \bar{\mathbf{t}}, \mathbf{d}, \bar{p}$ respectively by nondimensional quantities $\hat{\mathbf{t}}\,\tau_2/\mu, \bar{\mathbf{t}}/\bar{p}, \tau_1\,\mathbf{d}, \bar{p}/\mu, (\bar{p} > 0)$. Upon putting $\eta = \tau_1\,\mu$, this gives

$$\hat{\mathbf{t}} = \frac{\eta}{\tau_1 \tau_2}\, \mathbf{f}_0^* \left(\tau_1\,\mathbf{d}, \frac{\bar{\mathbf{t}}}{\bar{p}}, \frac{\tau_1}{\eta}\,\bar{p}\right) \tag{103.15}$$

We now multiply both sides by $\tau_2$ and let $\tau_2 \to 0$, holding everything else fixed. Hence

$$\mathbf{f}_0^* \left(\tau_1\,\mathbf{d}, \frac{\bar{\mathbf{t}}}{\bar{p}}, \frac{\tau_1}{\eta}\,\bar{p}\right) = 0 \tag{103.16}$$

For fluent bodies by (103.3) we have

$$\mathbf{f}_0^* \left(0, \frac{\bar{\mathbf{t}}}{\bar{p}}, \frac{\tau_1}{\eta}\,\bar{p}\right) \neq 0 \qquad \text{for } \bar{\mathbf{t}} \neq 0 \tag{103.17}$$

We shall in general be able to solve (103.16) for $\bar{\mathbf{t}}/\bar{p}$, obtaining

$$\bar{\mathbf{t}} = \bar{p}\,\mathbf{g}_0 \left(\tau_1\,\mathbf{d}, \frac{\tau_1}{\eta}\,\bar{p}\right) \tag{103.18}$$

This is the constitutive equation of a *Reiner-Rivlin* fluid. This class of fluids therefore contains one time constant. It is a subclass of the general viscous fluids characterized by $\tau_2 = 0$.

If we write (103.18) as

$$\bar{\mathbf{t}} = \bar{p}\,\mathbf{g}_1 \left(\frac{\eta}{\mu}\,\mathbf{d}, \frac{\tau_1}{\eta}\,\bar{p}\right)$$

and let $\tau_1 \to 0$, we obtain a *stokesian fluid* with a constitutive equation of the form

$$\bar{\mathbf{t}} = \bar{p}\,\mathbf{h}_0\left(\frac{\eta}{\mu}\,\mathbf{d}\right) \tag{103.19}$$

Clearly the equations of both Reiner-Rivlin and stokesian fluids are objective. Consequently $\mathbf{g}_0$ and $\mathbf{h}_0$ are isotropic functions.

Finally it is not difficult to see that the classical viscous fluids are special cases of (103.19).

*2a. Hypoelastic Materials.* Consider now the special class of resilient materials whose constitutive equations do not depend on the density $\rho$:

$$\hat{\mathbf{t}} = \mathbf{f}\,(\mathbf{d}, \mathbf{t}) \tag{103.20}$$

In nondimensional form this is expressed as

$$\hat{\mathbf{t}} = \frac{\mu}{\tau}\,\mathbf{f}_0\left(\tau\,\mathbf{d}, \frac{\mathbf{t}}{\mu}\right) \tag{103.21}$$

If (103.21) does not contain a material constant with the dimension of time, the material is called *hypoelastic*. This is possible only if $\tau$ cancels out in the right-hand side. This implies that $\mathbf{f}_0$ is homogeneous of degree one in $\mathbf{d}$. Since $\mathbf{f}_0$ is differentiable near $\mathbf{d} = 0$, it follows that $\mathbf{f}\,(\mathbf{d}, \mathbf{t})$ must be linear in $\mathbf{d}$. Consequently it must be of the form already obtained in Chap. 8.

For the incompressible body, the flux of $\mathbf{t}$ is replaced by the flux of $\mathbf{t} + p\,\mathbf{I}$. Since (103.5) holds and $\mathbf{f}\,(\mathbf{d}, \mathbf{t})$ is homogeneous in $\mathbf{d}$, the hypoelastic materials are resilient bodies.

A theorem due to Noll characterizes such materials by the following property:

THEOREM 1. *A material with a constitutive equation of the form* (103.20) *is hypoelastic if and only if, for a given initial stress, the stress at a final state depends only on the path followed to reach the final state and not upon the rate at which the path is traversed.*

To prove this, all we need is to remark that the replacement of time $t$ in (103.20) by $\chi\,(t)$, where $\chi\,(t)$ is any function of $t$, is equivalent to the replacement of $\dot{\mathbf{t}}$, $\mathbf{w}$, and $\mathbf{d}$ by $\dot{\chi}\,\dot{\mathbf{t}}$, $\dot{\chi}\,\mathbf{w}$, and $\dot{\chi}\,\mathbf{d}$ respectively. Thus if (103.20) holds, then

$$\dot{\chi}\,\hat{\mathbf{t}} = \mathbf{f}\,(\dot{\chi}\,\mathbf{d}, \mathbf{t})$$

if and only if

$$\mathbf{f}\,(\dot{\chi}\,\mathbf{d}, \mathbf{t}) = \dot{\chi}\,\mathbf{f}\,(\mathbf{d}, \mathbf{t})$$

This equation is valid for any $\dot{\chi}$ if and only if $\mathbf{f}\,(\mathbf{d}, \mathbf{t})$ is homogeneous of degree one in $\mathbf{d}$. Hence the proof of the theorem.

The fact that the Cauchy-elastic materials constitute a subclass of hypoelastic materials has already been shown in Art. 75.

## 04. PURE STRESS RELAXATION IN LINEAR FLUENT HYGROSTERIC MATERIALS[1]

In this and in the following two articles we give some simple solutions of problems concerning linear fluent bodies.

Let the body be at rest with a homogeneous mass density

$$\mathbf{v} = 0 \qquad \rho = \rho_0 \tag{104.1}$$

Given an initial constant extra stress

$$\bar{\mathbf{t}}\Big|_{t=0} = \bar{\mathbf{t}}_0 \tag{104.2}$$

we should like to determine the stress $\bar{\mathbf{t}}$ at all times $t > 0$. The equations of continuity and the dynamical equations of motion (for vanishing body forces) are satisfied identically.

The constitutive equations for linear fluent bodies with (104.1) reduce to

$$\mathring{\bar{t}}^k{}_l = \lambda_1 \bar{t}^k{}_l + \lambda_2 \bar{t}^m{}_m \delta^k{}_l \tag{104.3}$$

The solution of these equations subject to (104.2) is given by

$$\bar{t}^k{}_l = (\bar{t}_0{}^k{}_l - \tfrac{1}{3} \bar{t}_0{}^m{}_m \delta^k{}_l) \exp(\lambda_1 t) + \tfrac{1}{3} \bar{t}_0{}^m{}_m \delta^k{}_l \exp[(3\lambda_2 + \lambda_1) t] \tag{104.4}$$

The first term is the deviatoric part, and the second term is a mean pressure. Physically it is natural to make the assumption that

$$\mathbf{t} \to 0 \qquad \text{as } t \to \infty \tag{104.5}$$

This implies that $\lambda_1$ and $3\lambda_2 + \lambda_1$ are negative. Thus writing

$$\tau_d \equiv -\frac{1}{\lambda_1} \qquad \tau_p \equiv -\frac{1}{3\lambda_2 + \lambda_1} \tag{104.6}$$

for the *deviation* and *pressure relaxation times* respectively, we have

$$\bar{t}^k{}_l = (\bar{t}_0{}^k{}_l - \tfrac{1}{3} \bar{t}_0{}^m{}_m \delta^k{}_l) \exp\left(-\frac{t}{\tau_d}\right) + \tfrac{1}{3} \bar{t}_0{}^m{}_m \delta^k{}_l \exp\left(-\frac{t}{\tau_p}\right) \tag{104.7}$$

## 105. HOMOGENEOUS STRESS

Here we treat the problem of hydrostatic extension or compression of linear fluent bodies.[1]

[1] Zaremba [1937, p. 12]. For more general hygrosteric materials see Noll [1955, art. 19].

[1] For the general homogeneous stress of hygrosteric materials see Noll [1955, p. 54]. For hypoelastic materials see Art. 78.

The state of hydrostatic extension or compression may be characterized by

$$\mathbf{v} = h\,(t)\,(\mathbf{z} - \mathbf{z}_0) \qquad \bar{\mathbf{t}} = q\,(t)\,\mathbf{I} \tag{105.1}$$

where $\mathbf{z}$ is the rectangular spatial coordinate, $\mathbf{z}_0$ is a fixed point in the space, and $h\,(t)$ and $q\,(t)$ are two time functions. For $h\,(t) > 0$ we have the hydrostatic extension, and for $h\,(t) < 0$ we have the hydrostatic compression.

Dynamical equations of motion with vanishing body forces are satisfied if and only if $\dot{\mathbf{v}} = 0$. Thus the motion is an accelerationless one. By comparing (105.1) with (78.1), we see that

$$\mathbf{a}\,(t) \equiv h\,(t)\,\mathbf{I} \qquad \mathbf{b}\,(t) \equiv -h\,(t)\,\mathbf{z}_0$$

and these matrix functions satisfy (78.2). Substitution into (78.2) gives

$$h\,(t) = \frac{1}{t + t_0} \qquad t_0 \equiv \frac{1}{h\,(0)}$$

Thus for accelerationless hydrostatic extension or compression we must have

$$\mathbf{v} = \frac{\mathbf{z} - \mathbf{z}_0}{t + t_0} \qquad \bar{\mathbf{t}} = q\,(t)\,\mathbf{I} \tag{105.2}$$

It is now clear that we have

$$\begin{aligned} &0 \le t < \infty \qquad &&\text{if } t_0 > 0 \qquad &&\text{(extension)} \\ &0 \le t < |t_0| \qquad &&\text{if } t_0 < 0 \qquad &&\text{(compression)} \end{aligned} \tag{105.3}$$

The continuity equation with the use of (105.1) reduces to

$$\dot{\rho} + \frac{3\rho}{t + t_0} = 0$$

whose integral is

$$\frac{\rho}{\rho_0} = \frac{1}{(t + t_0)^3} \tag{105.4}$$

which may also be arrived at by use of (76.6) for a zero initial-velocity field.

From (105.2) we have

$$\mathbf{d} = \frac{\mathbf{I}}{t + t_0} \qquad \mathbf{w} = 0 \tag{105.5}$$

Substituting these into the constitutive equations of linear fluent bodies

103.11), we obtain

(105.6) $$\dot{q} = \left[(3\lambda_2 + \lambda_1) + \frac{\beta}{t + t_0}\right] q + \frac{\mu_p}{t + t_0}$$

where

(105.7) $\beta \equiv 3(\alpha_1 + \alpha_2 + \alpha_5 + 3\alpha_4) + 2\alpha_3 \qquad \mu_p \equiv 3\mu_2 + \mu_1$

For the hypoelastic case we have $3\lambda_2 + \lambda_1 = 0$, and (105.6) may be integrated to give

(105.8) $$q = q_0\left(\frac{t}{t_0} + 1\right)^\beta + \frac{\mu_p}{\beta}\left[\left(\frac{t}{t_0} + 1\right)^\beta - 1\right] \qquad (\beta \neq 0)$$
$$q = q_0 + \mu_p \log\left(\frac{t}{t_0} + 1\right) \qquad (\beta = 0)$$

where $$q_0 \equiv q(0)$$

On the other hand, for a fluent body we have, by $(104.6)_2$,

$$3\lambda_2 + \lambda_1 = -\frac{1}{\tau_p} \neq 0 \qquad \tau_p > 0$$

Using this in (105.6) and integrating the result, we find

(105.9) $$\frac{q(\tau)}{\mu_p} = \frac{q_0}{\mu_p}\left(1 + \frac{\tau}{\tau_0}\right)^\beta \exp(-\tau) + g(\tau)$$

where

(105.10) $$g(\tau) \equiv (-\tau - \tau_0)^\beta \exp(-\tau - \tau_0) \int_{-\tau_0}^{-\tau-\tau_0} w^{-1-\beta} e^{-w}\, dw$$
$$\tau \equiv \frac{t}{\tau_p} \qquad \tau_0 \equiv \frac{t_0}{\tau_p}$$

The function $g(\tau)$ can be expressed in terms of incomplete gamma functions defined by[2]

(105.11) $$\gamma(a, x) = \int_0^x w^{a-1} e^{-w}\, dw \qquad (\mathrm{Re}\, a > 0)$$

We may therefore express $g(\tau)$ in terms of this function

(105.12) $$g(\tau) = (-\tau - \tau_0)^\beta [\gamma(-\beta, -\tau - \tau_0) - \gamma(-\beta, -\tau_0)] \exp(-\tau - \tau_0)$$

in the range,[3] $-\infty < \beta < 0$.

[2] A tabulation of the incomplete gamma functions is presented by Pearson [1934].

[3] In the case of $\beta \geq 0$ and $\beta$ = negative nonintegers, the integral in (105.10) is calculated by series expansion of $\exp(-w)$ and by integration termwise. Also for $\beta > 0$ the integral in function $g(\tau)$ can, by integration by parts, be reduced to incomplete gamma functions. For $\beta$ = negative integers integration can be carried out in closed form.

Plots of $g(\tau) = q(\tau)/\mu_p$ for vanishing initial pressure $q_0$ for various values of $\tau_0$ and $\beta$ are given in Figs. 105.1 and 105.2 which respectively represent the extra-stress buildup in time in a hydrostatic compression and in a hydrostatic tension of a linear fluent body. We notice that the body hardens for the hydrostatic compression, finally reaching infinite

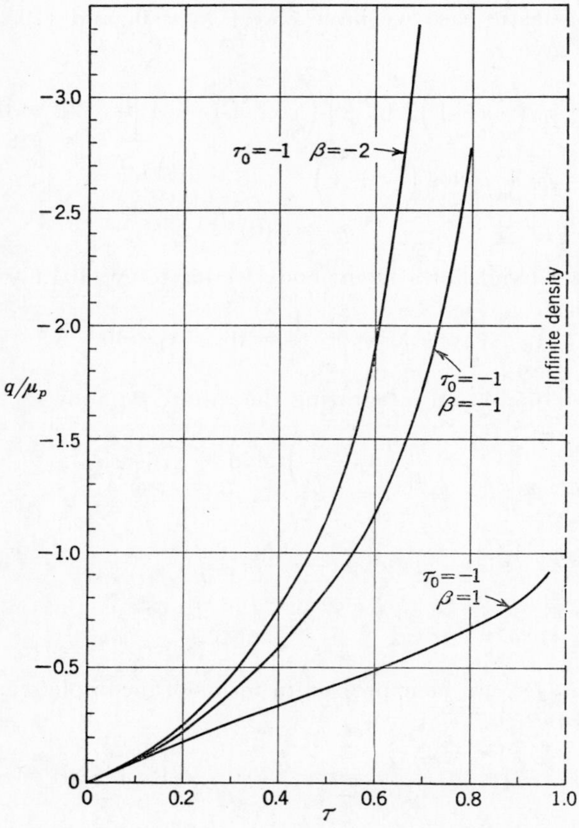


FIG. 105.1. Extra stress buildup in time $t = \tau_p \tau$ in a hydrostatic compression of a linear fluent body.

density at $\tau = -\tau_0$ for $\beta < 0$. For $\beta = 1$ and $\tau_0 = 1$ the hydrostatic extra pressure reaches $\mu_p$ as $\tau \to 1$ from the left. For the hydrostatic tension the extra stress initially builds up. After reaching a maximum, the stress decreases, approaching zero asymptotically as time approaches infinity. This phenomenon is similar to the ones observed in the case of hydrostatic tension of a hypoelastic body (Art. 78). It is a yieldlike phenomenon of instability.

From these results one can also obtain an equation of state of the form

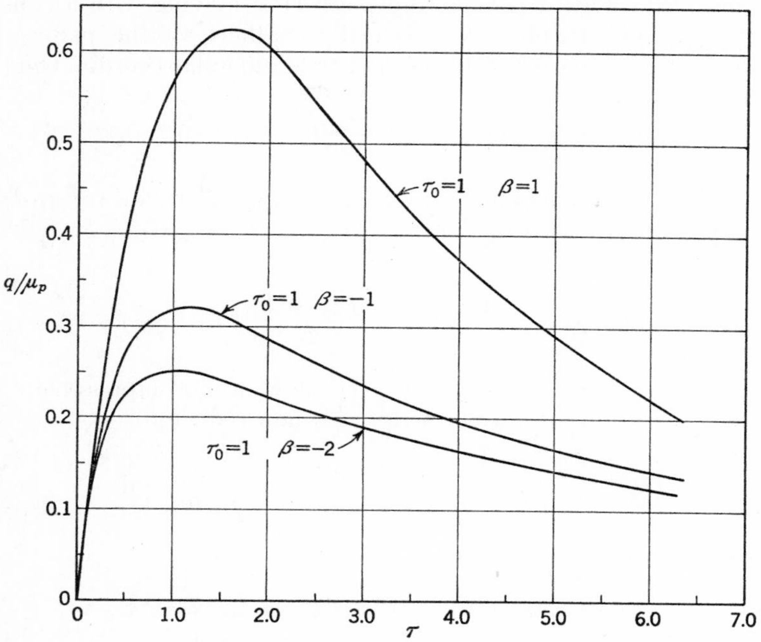


FIG. 105.2. Extra stress buildup in time during a hydrostatic tension of a linear fluent body.

$q = q(\rho)$ where $\rho$ is the density. This is accomplished by eliminating $\tau$ from $q = q(\tau)$ through the use of (105.4). This, however, requires further knowledge of the material constant $\tau_p$; hence it is not carried out here.

## 106. SIMPLE SHEAR FLOW

To obtain a little more insight into the behavior of hygrosteric materials, we consider the case of a simple flow between two parallel plates I and II, Fig. 106.1.

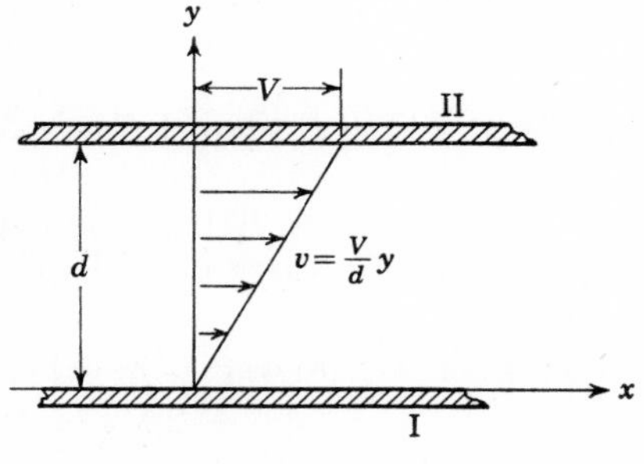


FIG. 106.1. Simple shear flow.

Suppose that plate I is fixed and plate II is moving with a constant velocity $V$. The material is assumed to adhere to the plates. We consider a simple velocity field referred to rectangular coordinates

$$v_x = \frac{V}{d} y \equiv v \qquad v_y = 0 \qquad v_z = 0 \tag{106.1}$$

and, based on our experience through Arts. 79 and 99, we try an extra-stress field characterized by

$$\|\bar{\mathbf{t}}\| = \begin{bmatrix} \bar{t}_{xx} & \bar{t}_{xy} & 0 \\ \cdot & \bar{t}_{yy} & 0 \\ \cdot & \cdot & \bar{t}_{zz} \end{bmatrix} \tag{106.2}$$

where $\bar{\mathbf{t}} = \bar{\mathbf{t}}(y)$. Since $\operatorname{div} \mathbf{v} = 0$, the flow is incompressible. The dynamical equations of motion with $\mathbf{f} \equiv 0$ now reduce to

$$\frac{\partial \bar{t}_{yx}}{\partial y} - \frac{\partial \bar{p}}{\partial x} = 0 \qquad \frac{\partial \bar{t}_{yy}}{\partial y} - \frac{\partial \bar{p}}{\partial y} = 0 \qquad \frac{\partial \bar{p}}{\partial z} = 0 \tag{106.3}$$

A simple analysis shows that

$$\bar{t}_{yx} = -a\,y + b \qquad \bar{p} = -a\,x + \bar{t}_{yy}(y) + c \tag{106.4}$$

where $a$, $b$, and $c$ are constants. The constitutive equations (103.11) for linear fluent bodies give

$$\begin{aligned} 0 &= \lambda_1 \bar{t}_{xx} + \lambda_2 \bar{t} + (\alpha_1 + \alpha_3 + 1)\,\acute{v}\,\bar{t}_{xy} \\ 0 &= \lambda_1 \bar{t}_{yy} + \lambda_2 \bar{t} + (\alpha_1 + \alpha_3 - 1)\,\acute{v}\,\bar{t}_{xy} \\ 0 &= \lambda_1 \bar{t}_{zz} + \lambda_2 \bar{t} + \alpha_1\,\acute{v}\,\bar{t}_{xy} \\ 0 &= \lambda_1 \bar{t}_{xy} + [\mu_1 + \alpha_2 \bar{t} + \alpha_3 (\bar{t}_{xx} + \bar{t}_{yy}) + \bar{t}_{yy} - \bar{t}_{xx}]\,\frac{\acute{v}}{2} \end{aligned} \tag{106.5}$$

where

$$\bar{t} \equiv \bar{t}_{xx} + \bar{t}_{yy} + \bar{t}_{zz} \qquad \text{and} \qquad \acute{v} \equiv \frac{dv}{dy} \tag{106.6}$$

Adding the first three of (106.5), we obtain

$$0 = (\lambda_1 + 3\,\lambda_2)\,\bar{t} + (3\,\alpha_1 + 2\,\alpha_3)\,\acute{v}\,\bar{t}_{xy} \tag{106.7}$$

Since by (103.13) $\lambda_1 \neq 0$, we can calculate $\bar{t}_{xx} + \bar{t}_{yy}$ and $\bar{t}_{xx} - \bar{t}_{yy}$ from $(106.5)_1$ and $(106.5)_2$ and substitute these into $(106.5)_4$. This gives

$$\begin{aligned} 0 = \lambda_1 \bar{t}_{xy} + \tfrac{1}{2}\acute{v}\,\{\mu_1 + \lambda_1^{-1}(\lambda_1 \alpha_2 - 2\,\lambda_2 \alpha_3)\,\bar{t} \\ - 2\,\lambda^{-1}[\alpha_3(\alpha_1 + \alpha_3) - 1]\,\acute{v}\,\bar{t}_{xy}\} \end{aligned} \tag{106.8}$$

Now we may eliminate $\bar{t}$ between (106.7) and (106.8) to obtain

$$\bar{t}_{xy} + \tfrac{1}{2}\, \acute{v}\, (-\eta + 2\, \alpha\, \tau_d^2\, \acute{v}\; \bar{t}_{xy}) = 0 \tag{106.9}$$

where

$$\tau_d \equiv -\lambda_1^{-1} \qquad \eta \equiv \tau_d\, \mu_1 \equiv -\mu_1\, \lambda_1^{-1}$$
$$\alpha \equiv 1 + \frac{2\,\lambda_2\,\alpha_3 - \lambda_1\,\alpha_2}{2\,(\lambda_1 + 3\,\lambda_2)}\,(2\,\alpha_3 + 3\,\alpha_1) - \alpha_3\,(\alpha_1 + \alpha_3) \tag{106.10}$$

We may solve (106.9) for either $\acute{v}$ or $\bar{t}_{xy}$:

$$\begin{aligned} \acute{v} &= \frac{4\,\bar{t}_{xy}}{\eta}\, \frac{1}{1 \pm \sqrt{1 - 16\,\alpha\,\tau_d^2\,\eta^{-2}\,\bar{t}_{xy}^{\,2}}} \\ \bar{t}_{xy} &= \tfrac{1}{2}\,\eta\,\acute{v}\,\frac{1}{1 + \alpha\,\tau_d^2\,\acute{v}^2} \end{aligned} \tag{106.11}$$

The other stresses are then obtained by substituting the value of $\bar{t}$ from (106.7) into $(106.5)_1$–$(106.5)_3$

$$\begin{aligned} \bar{t}_{xx} &= \tau_d\,(-\alpha_0 + \alpha_3 + \alpha_1 + 1)\,\acute{v}\,\bar{t}_{xy} \\ \bar{t}_{yy} &= \tau_d\,(-\alpha_0 + \alpha_3 + \alpha_1 - 1)\,\acute{v}\,\bar{t}_{xy} \\ \bar{t}_{zz} &= \tau_d\,(-\alpha_0 + \alpha_1)\,\acute{v}\,\bar{t}_{xy} \end{aligned} \tag{106.12}$$

where

$$\alpha_0 \equiv \frac{\lambda_2}{\lambda_1 + 3\,\lambda_2}\,(3\,\alpha_1 + 2\,\alpha_3) \tag{106.13}$$

and $\acute{v}$ and $\bar{t}_{xy}$ are as given in (106.11). The solution obtained is valid for arbitrary $y$-dependent stress field (106.2) and velocity $v_1 = v\,(y)$, $v_2 = v_3 = 0$. The flow is a *steady linear flow.*

We now substitute (106.1) to obtain the *simple shear flow.* The shearing stress is then given by

$$\bar{t}_{xy} = \tfrac{1}{2}\,\eta\,\frac{V}{d}\,\frac{1}{1 + \alpha\,\tau_d^2\,(V/d)^2} \tag{106.14}$$

Three cases may be distinguished.

*Case* 1. $\alpha > 0$. In terms of a material constant $\tau_s$ called *shearing yield time,* (106.14) may be expressed as

$$\bar{t}_{xy} = \tfrac{1}{2}\,\eta\,\frac{V}{d}\,\frac{1}{1 + \tau_s^2(V/d)^2} \tag{106.15}$$

$$\tau_s \equiv \sqrt{\alpha}\,\tau_d \tag{106.16}$$

A plot of (106.15) is given in Fig. 106.2. With the increase of velocity of plate II the shearing stress first increases, reaching a maximum at $(V/d)_{\text{cr}} = \tau_s^{-1}$. This is the critical shear at which a *yieldlike phenomenon* occurs, since after this with a further increase of $V/d$ the shearing stress decreases, representing an unstable flow. The critical shear stress is given by

$$(\bar{t}_{xy})_{\text{cr}} = \tfrac{1}{4}\,\eta\,\tau_s^{-1} \tag{106.17}$$

*Case* 2. $\alpha = 0$. In this case the shearing stress is given by

$$\bar{t}_{xy} = \tfrac{1}{2}\,\eta\,\frac{V}{d} \tag{106.18}$$

This is the formula for classical viscous fluids. The tangent line (dash-dot) through the origin in Fig. 106.2 corresponds to this case. This

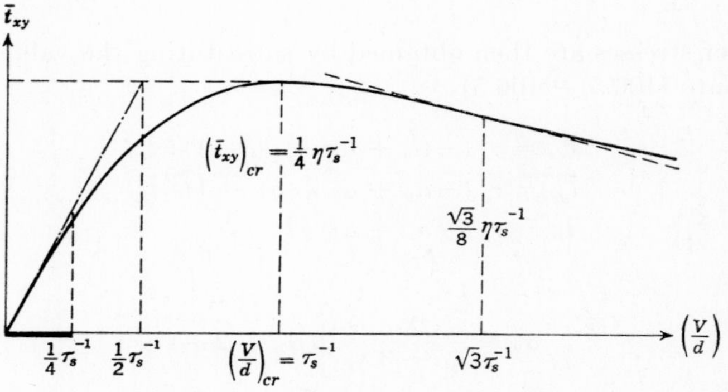


FIG. 106.2. Simple shear ($\alpha > 0$). (*After Noll* [1955])

formula (106.18) may be considered an approximation within 6 per cent in the range $0 < V/d \leq \frac{1}{4}\tau_s^{-1}$.

*Case* 3. $\alpha < 0$. In this case we introduce a *shearing limit time*

$$\acute{\tau}_s \equiv \sqrt{|\alpha|}\,\tau_d \tag{106.19}$$

Now the shearing stress becomes

$$\bar{t}_{xy} = \tfrac{1}{2}\,\eta\,\frac{V}{d}\,\frac{1}{1 - \acute{\tau}_s^{\,2}\,(V/d)^2} \tag{106.20}$$

The graph of this is given in Fig. 106.3. In this case there is a limit value for $(V/d)_{\text{lim}} = \acute{\tau}_s^{-1}$ at which the shearing stress becomes infinite. The materials of this kind are highly resistant to shearing. The second branch of $\bar{t}_{xy}$ for $V/d > \acute{\tau}_s^{-1}$ has no physical meaning.

The tangent line through the origin is the graph for (106.18) representing the classical theory of viscous flow. For the range $0 \leq V/d \leq \frac{1}{4}\acute{\tau}_s^{-1}$ the error of the classical theory formula (106.18) is within 7 per cent of (106.20).

For simple shearing flow the extra stresses are constant, so that from $(106.4)_1$ we have $a = 0$. Through $(106.4)_3$ we also see that $\bar{p} = \bar{t}_{yy} + c = \text{const.}$

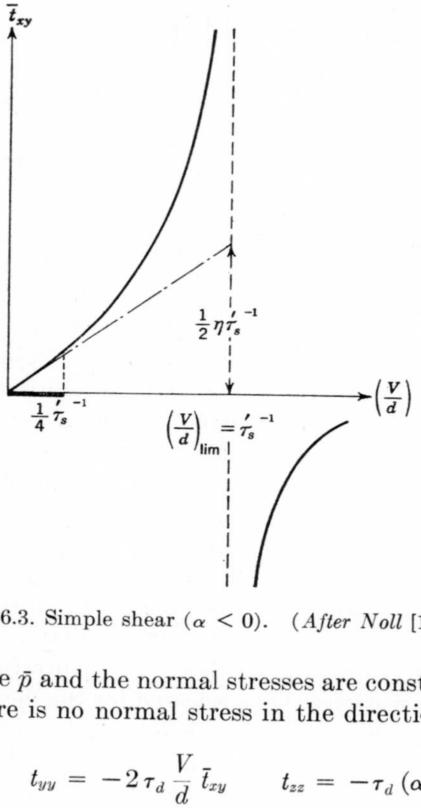


FIG. 106.3. Simple shear ($\alpha < 0$). (*After Noll* [1955])

Since the pressure $\bar{p}$ and the normal stresses are constant, we can select $\bar{p} = \bar{t}_{xx}$ so that there is no normal stress in the direction of flow. Thus

$$(106.21) \quad t_{xx} = 0 \qquad t_{yy} = -2\,\tau_d \frac{V}{d}\,\bar{t}_{xy} \qquad t_{zz} = -\tau_d\,(\alpha_3 + 1)\,\frac{V}{d}\,\bar{t}_{xy}$$

In the classical theory of viscous flow the normal stresses are all zero. Here we find again the *Poynting effect,* which tells us that simple shearing cannot be maintained by a shearing stress alone. Since $\tau_d > 0$, the stress $t_{yy}$ normal to the plates must be compressive. If this is not provided, the plates will spread apart. The stress $t_{zz}$ may be compressive or tensile as $\alpha_3 + 1 > 0$ or $\alpha_3 + 1 < 0$. Experimental or thermodynamical consideration will determine the sign of $\alpha_3 + 1$. Note that both $t_{yy}$ and $t_{zz}$ are of the order of $(V/d)^2$ and may therefore be neglected in a first-order theory such as the classical theory of viscous flow.

# 11

# ELECTROELASTICITY

## 107. SCOPE OF THE CHAPTER

This chapter brings mechanical phenomena into close contact with electrical phenomena. We see here, for the first time, an example of mass and charge interaction. A deformable charge-carrying elastic solid represents the simplest example in which the effect of deformation on the electric field and, conversely, the effect of the electric field on the deformation arise. Deformation of a solid body when subjected to an electric field may be due to *piezoelectric* and/or *electrostrictive* effects. In only the former does there exist the inverse phenomenon: namely, the creation of an electric field by means of deformation. Piezoelectricity is attributable directly to the anisotropy of the medium. Both of these phenomena constitute essential features of *electroelastostatics.*

In Art. 108 we introduce the concepts of charge, electric field, electric displacement, polarization, and their units of measure. The Maxwell-Faraday theory of electrostatics is postulated and formulated in Art. 109 in such a way that its extension to elastic dielectrics can be effected conveniently in the following articles. The powerful formalism of the principle of virtual work has been selected for the derivation of the basic field equations and boundary conditions. In a natural fashion this method leads us to the concepts of the *Maxwell stress tensor,* the local stress tensor, the polarization vector, and the constitutive relations between the last two and the stored energy (Art. 110). A derivation of the constitutive equations from the stored energy is made in the succeeding article. Three different forms employing various strain and polarization invariants and measures are derived. In polynomial approximations of the constitutive equations some of these forms are found to be more convenient. A résumé of basic equations is presented in Art. 112. Pure shear of a polarized isotropic slab, given in Art. 113, illustrates the type of phenomena that the basic equations are capable of predicting, as does the uniform extension of a hollow cylindrical dielectric, given in Art. 114.

In Art. 115 we give a polynomial approximation of the constitutive equations in strain and polarization measures, leading to various-order approximations, the lowest of which is the classical linear theory of *photoelasticity*. We have not elaborated on this point further, however, since photoelasticity is essentially an electrodynamical phenomenon. The last article of the chapter contains a brief account of the anisotropic elastic dielectric, since anisotropy is essential for piezoelectricity. No serious work on the foundations of *electromagnetic elasticity* has yet come into the literature. While *magnetohydrodynamics* is enjoying a new, privileged birth demanded by its various industrial possibilities, its foundation is weak and has not as yet been brought to a level of rigor similar to that of fluid dynamics.

## 108. CHARGE, ELECTRIC FIELD, DIELECTRIC DISPLACEMENT

*Charge.* Existence of *electric charge* is a fundamental postulate of physics which is based on experimental evidence. Existence of electric current is attributed to the motion of charges.

According to modern physics, matter is made up of an aggregate of elementary particles some of which are bound together by interparticle forces while others are free to move. Some of these elementary particles possess, in addition to mass, another *measure* called charge. The electronic charge, expressed by $e = 1.60 \times 10^{-19}$ coulomb, is the smallest possible division of charge. The total charge contained in any spatial volume is some integral multiple of the electronic charge. In the work which follows, however, we shall assume that charge is infinitely divisible, in accordance with the continuum hypothesis.

Matter contains two types of charge: positive charge and negative charge. Experimental evidence supports the postulate that the total charge in any isolated system is conserved: that if an amount of positive charge appears or disappears within the system, an equal amount of negative charge does likewise, so that the algebraic sum of the charge remains constant. This postulate is extremely important in what follows.

Charge may also be characterized as being *free* or *bound*. The negative charges carried by free electrons are examples of the former, while the negative charges carried by electrons which make up the inner electron shells of an atom illustrate the latter.

With this intuitive preparation we now postulate the existence of charge as follows.

*To a spatial region* $\mathcal{V} + \mathcal{S}$ *we assign a quantity called charge with a new dimension Q (called coulomb) independent of M, L, T such that it is additive and invariant under the motion.*[1]

If the charge is absolutely continuous in the region $\mathcal{V} + \mathcal{S}$, then there

[1] For a more general axiomatic approach see Truesdell and Toupin [1960, art. 268].

exist a *volume charge density* $q$ and a *surface charge density* $\omega$ such that the total charge in $\mathcal{V} + \mathcal{S}$ is given by

$$(108.1) \qquad Q = \int_{\mathcal{V}} q\, dv + \int_{\mathcal{S}} \omega\, da \qquad [q] = \frac{Q}{L^3} \qquad [\omega] = \frac{Q}{L^2}$$

*Electric Field.* The *electric vector* $\mathbf{E}$ is a vector field, the magnitude of which is proportional to the force acting on an infinitesimal test body having charge $Q$ inserted in the field. The dimension of $\mathbf{E}$ is

$$(108.2) \qquad [\mathbf{E}] = \frac{\text{force}}{\text{charge}}$$

The line integral

$$(108.3) \qquad \varphi = -\int_{\mathbf{x}_1}^{\mathbf{x}_2} \mathbf{E} \cdot d\mathbf{x}$$

is proportional to the work that must be done against the force field to move a unit charge on a line extending between $\mathbf{x}_1$ and $\mathbf{x}_2$ and is called the *electromotive force, voltage,* or *electric potential* existing between the two points. It is measured by

$$(108.4) \qquad [\varphi] = \frac{\text{force} \times \text{length}}{\text{charge}} = 10^7 \frac{\text{dyne} \times \text{cm}}{\text{coulomb}} = 10^7 \frac{\text{erg}}{\text{coulomb}} = \frac{\text{joule}}{\text{coulomb}} = \text{volt}$$

The conversion of the dimension from the MKSQ system (meter-kilogram-second-coulomb) to the electromagnetic CGS system shows that

$$1 \text{ volt} = 10^8 \text{ CGS units}$$

if we fix $Q$ at

$$1 \text{ coulomb} = \tfrac{1}{10} \text{ CGS units}$$

From (108.3) it is clear that $\varphi$ may depend on the path followed between terminal points $\mathbf{x}_1$ and $\mathbf{x}_2$. For a *conservative field* (lamellar field) we know from mechanics that such a line integral (108.3) should be independent of the path followed. It should, however, depend on the terminal points so that we may speak of the potential between $\mathbf{x}_1$ and $\mathbf{x}_2$ and write (108.3) as

$$(108.5) \qquad \varphi(\mathbf{x}_1) - \varphi(\mathbf{x}_2) = \int_{\mathbf{x}_1}^{\mathbf{x}_2} \mathbf{E} \cdot d\mathbf{x}$$

At a point where $\mathbf{E}(\mathbf{x})$ is continuous, the assumption of a potential field implies that

$$\mathbf{E} = -\operatorname{grad} \varphi \tag{108.6}$$

Clearly for a lamellar field $\mathbf{E}$ when $\mathbf{x}_1 = \mathbf{x}_2$, (108.7) gives

$$\oint_{\mathcal{C}} \mathbf{E} \cdot d\mathbf{x} = 0 \tag{108.7}$$

for any closed curve $\mathcal{C}$.

Electric field $\mathbf{E}(\mathbf{x})$ may possess a discontinuity over the boundary surface of the region. In this case, in addition to (108.6) we must have the boundary condition that the component of $\mathbf{E}$ tangential to the boundary surface $\mathcal{S}$ is continuous, i.e.,

$$[\![\mathbf{E}]\!] \times \mathbf{n} = 0 \tag{108.8}$$

where $[\![\mathbf{E}]\!] \equiv \overset{+}{\mathbf{E}} - \overset{-}{\mathbf{E}}$ denotes, as usual, the jump across $\mathcal{S}$ of $\mathbf{E}$ from exterior ($\overset{+}{\mathbf{E}}$) to interior ($\overset{-}{\mathbf{E}}$), and $\mathbf{n}$ is the exterior normal to $\mathcal{S}$. This and (108.6) may be shown to follow from the generalized Stokes theorem

$$\oint_{\mathcal{C}} \mathbf{E} \cdot d\mathbf{x} = -\int_{\mathcal{L}} [\![\mathbf{E}]\!] \cdot d\mathbf{x} + \int_{\mathcal{A}} \operatorname{curl} \mathbf{E} \cdot d\mathbf{a} \tag{108.9}$$

where $\mathcal{C}$ is a closed curve bounding the surface $\mathcal{A}$ and $\mathcal{L}$ is the intersection line of $\mathcal{A}$ with the boundary surface $\mathcal{S}$ of the body.[1] The vanishing of the left side of (108.9) for every closed $\mathcal{C}$ implies that curl $\mathbf{E}$ and the jump of the component of $\mathbf{E}$ tangential to $\mathcal{S}$ vanish. Hence (108.6) and (108.8) follow.

*Electric Displacement.* Under the influence of the electric field on particles possessing charges there will be exerted certain forces that are proportional to the charge of the particles. Free electrons subject to these forces will be set into motion. Bound particles with positive and negative charges, on the other hand, will be displaced with respect to each other. Matter so strained is said to be *polarized.* A simple model explaining the polarization is the following. In a neutral state the matter may be considered to consist of atoms with nuclei having positive charge $q_0$ and electrons moving around the nucleus with equal amount of negative charge $-q_0$ in such a way that the effective centers of charge coincide. Exceptions to this model occur in permanently polarized bodies. Excluding this latter case, when the matter is subjected to an electric field, the positive charges are displaced with respect to the negative charges. The net transfer of charge across a surface $\mathcal{S}$ of a volume $\mathcal{V}$

[1] This form is obtained by applying the Stokes theorem (A4.24) to each of the two regions of $\mathcal{A}$, separated by $\mathcal{L}$, and adding the results.

is given by

$$Q = \int_{\mathcal{S}} N\, q_0\, \mathbf{d} \cdot d\mathbf{a}$$

$N$ is the number of polarizable atoms per unit volume, and $\mathbf{d}$ is the displacement vector of the positive charges with respect to negative charges. Since the total bound charge in $\mathcal{V}$ was zero originally, the *net polarization charge* $Q_p$ left in $\mathcal{V}$ is therefore given by

$$Q_p = -\oint_{\mathcal{S}} N\, q_0\, \mathbf{d} \cdot d\mathbf{a} = -\oint_{\mathcal{S}} \mathbf{P} \cdot d\mathbf{a} \tag{108.10}$$

where

$$\mathbf{P} = N\, q_0\, \mathbf{d} \tag{108.11}$$

is called the *polarization vector.* When the matter is absent, we have $\mathbf{d} = Q_p = 0$. In this case the total charge consists solely of the free charge that is present in the volume $\mathcal{V}$. It therefore appears reasonable to introduce a vector $\mathbf{D}$ called the *total electric displacement vector* such that

$$\oint_{\mathcal{S}} \mathbf{D} \cdot d\mathbf{a} = Q_f \tag{108.12}$$

where $Q_f$ is the total free charge in $\mathcal{V}$ and

$$\mathbf{D} = \mathbf{P} + \text{vacuum displacement field} \tag{108.13}$$

The vacuum displacement field is therefore included in the surface integral in (108.12). This part is calculated on the basis of an additional assumption that it is proportional to the electric field strength, i.e.,

$$\mathbf{D} = \mathbf{P} + \epsilon_0\, \mathbf{E} \tag{108.14}$$

where $\epsilon_0$ is called the *dielectric constant for vacuum.* For the dimension of $\mathbf{D}$, $\mathbf{P}$, and $\epsilon_0$ we have

$$[\mathbf{D}] = [\mathbf{P}] = \frac{Q}{L^2} \qquad [\epsilon_0] = \frac{Q^2}{L^2\ \text{force}} = \frac{Q^2}{M\, L^3\, T^2} \tag{108.15}$$

We now are ready to lay down the basic postulates of the *Maxwell-Faraday theory of electrostatics.*

## 109. THE MAXWELL-FARADAY THEORY OF ELECTROSTATICS

The Maxwell-Faraday theory of electrostatics is founded on two basic postulates and a constitutive equation:

1. *The Maxwell-Faraday electric field is lamellar.*
2. *The total flux of the electric displacement across any closed two-sided surface $\mathcal{S}$ is equal to the total free charge $Q_f$ within the surface.*

These are expressed respectively by

(109.1) $$\oint_{\mathcal{C}} E^k \, dx_k = 0 \qquad \text{for any closed curve } \mathcal{C}$$

(109.2) $$\oint_{\mathcal{S}} D^k n_k \, da = Q_f \qquad \text{for any closed two-sided surface } \mathcal{S}$$

where **n** is the exterior normal to $\mathcal{S}$.

3. *The form of the constitutive equation depends on the local state of the medium.* For vacuum we have

(109.3) $$D^k = \epsilon_0 E^k \qquad \text{(vacuum)}$$

For a material medium we have polarization, so that the constitutive equation may be expressed as

(109.4) $$D^k - \epsilon_0 E^k = P^k(\mathbf{E}) \qquad \text{(dielectric)}$$

where **P** is the polarization density which vanishes in vacuum and in electrical conductors. In the classical electrostatics of rigid electrically isotropic solids, the constitutive equations are generally taken as linear:

(109.5) $$D^k = \epsilon E^k \qquad \text{or} \qquad P^k = (\epsilon - \epsilon_0) E^k$$

where $\epsilon$ is the dielectric constant for the material medium.

The local state of a dielectric medium may be characterized in part by the value of the polarization. Thus, as we shall see, one may select **P** as one of the independent variables of the state of an elastic dielectric.

Let $\mathcal{R}_d \equiv \mathcal{V}_d + \mathcal{S}_d$ be the region occupied by the dielectric, and let $\mathcal{R}_0 \equiv \mathcal{V}_0 + \mathcal{S}$ be the remainder of the space (Fig. 109.1). We assume that **E** and **D** are continuously differentiable in a region $\mathcal{R} = \mathcal{R}_0 + \mathcal{R}_d$. From (109.1) and the generalized Stokes theorem (108.9), it follows that a scalar potential, called the *electrostatic potential*, $\varphi(\mathbf{x})$, exists such that

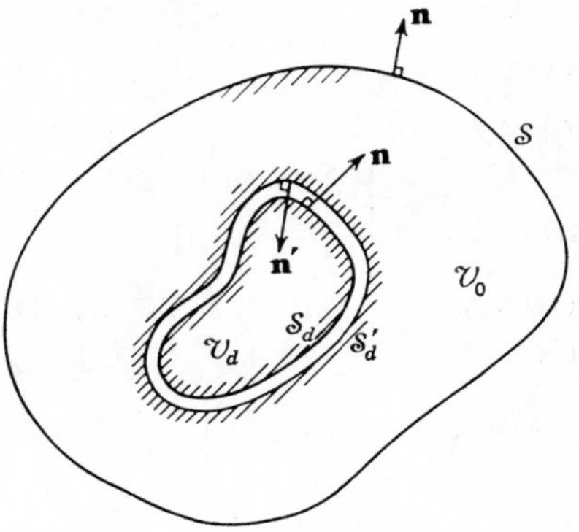

FIG. 109.1

(109.6) $$\begin{aligned} \mathbf{E} &= -\operatorname{grad} \varphi && \text{in } \mathcal{V} \equiv \mathcal{V}_0 + \mathcal{V}_d \\ [\![\nabla\varphi]\!] \times \mathbf{n} &= 0 && \text{on } \mathcal{S}_d \end{aligned}$$

It is also assumed that the normal component of **E** suffers at most a finite discontinuity on $\mathcal{S}_d$. Since addition of constants to $\varphi$ does not alter

**E**, we may, without loss in generality, assume that $\varphi$ is continuous throughout the space.

The total free charge in a region $\mathcal{R}$ is given by

(109.7)
$$Q_f = \int_{\mathcal{V}} q_f \, dv + \oint_{\mathcal{S}_d} \omega_f \, da$$

Here $q_f$ is the volume density of free charge, and $\omega_f$ is the surface density of free charge defined over $\mathcal{S}_d$.

Before proceeding further, we need a generalization of the Green-Gauss theorem to include the effect of surface discontinuities. The Green-Gauss theorem when applied to the two regions $\mathcal{V}_d + \mathcal{S}_d$ and $\mathcal{V}_0 + \mathcal{S} + \mathcal{S}_d'$ (Fig. 109.1), gives

$$\int_{\mathcal{V}_d} \operatorname{div} \mathbf{f} \, dv = \oint_{\mathcal{S}_d} \mathbf{f} \cdot \mathbf{n} \, da$$

$$\int_{\mathcal{V}_0} \operatorname{div} \mathbf{f} \, dv = \oint_{\mathcal{S}_d'} \mathbf{f} \cdot \acute{\mathbf{n}} \, da + \oint_{\mathcal{S}} \mathbf{f} \cdot \mathbf{n} \, da$$

where $\mathbf{n}$ denotes the exterior normal to $\mathcal{S}_d$ and to $\mathcal{S}$, and $\acute{\mathbf{n}}$ is the exterior normal to $\mathcal{S}_d'$. Adding the foregoing equations and letting $\mathcal{S}_d' \to \mathcal{S}_d$, we will have $\acute{\mathbf{n}} = -\mathbf{n}$ and

(109.8)
$$\int_{\mathcal{V}} \operatorname{div} \mathbf{f} \, dv = -\oint_{\mathcal{S}_d} [\![\mathbf{f}]\!] \cdot \mathbf{n} \, da + \oint_{\mathcal{S}} \mathbf{f} \cdot \mathbf{n} \, da$$

We are now ready to apply this generalized form of the Green-Gauss theorem to (109.2). Hence

$$\int_{\mathcal{V}} (\operatorname{div} \mathbf{D} - q_f) \, dv + \oint_{\mathcal{S}_d} ([\![\mathbf{D}]\!] \cdot \mathbf{n} - \omega_f) \, da = 0$$

from which it follows that

(109.9)
$$\operatorname{div} \mathbf{D} = q_f \qquad \text{in } \mathcal{V}$$

(109.10)
$$[\![\mathbf{D}]\!] \cdot \mathbf{n} = \omega_f \qquad \text{on } \mathcal{S}_d$$

Upon use of (109.4) and $(109.6)_1$ these equations may be written as

(109.11)
$$\epsilon_0 \, \varphi_{;}{}^{k}{}_{k} = -q \qquad \text{in } \mathcal{V}$$

(109.12)
$$\epsilon_0 [\![\varphi_{,k}]\!] n^k = -\omega \qquad \text{on any } \mathcal{S}_d$$

where the total volume charge density $q$ and surface charge density $\omega$ are respectively defined by

(109.13)
$$q \equiv q_f - \operatorname{div} \mathbf{P}$$
$$\omega \equiv \omega_f - [\![\mathbf{P}]\!] \cdot \mathbf{n}$$

When $\mathcal{S}_d$ is not a charge-bearing surface, then $\omega_f \equiv 0$.

In the case in which $\mathcal{V} + \mathcal{S}$ does not contain a dielectric, we must set

$P \equiv 0$. Thus the field equations (109.11) subject to the boundary conditions (109.12) apply to any electrostatic field. In addition, $\varphi$ must vanish at infinity, i.e.,

$$\varphi(\mathbf{x}) \to 0 \qquad \text{as } \mathbf{x} \to \infty \tag{109.14}$$

*The field equations* (109.11) *subject to* (109.12) *and* (109.14) *uniquely determine the electrostatic potential* $\varphi(\mathbf{x})$ *where* $\mathbf{P}(\mathbf{x})$ *is prescribed.* Note, however, that the polarization is in general a function of the electric field and cannot be determined in advance. Therefore additional equations relating **P** and **E** are needed. These are the constitutive equations.

The solution of Poisson's equation (109.11) subject to the boundary conditions (109.12) and (109.14) for a prescribed $q$ and $\omega$ is unique and is given by

$$\epsilon_0\,\varphi(\mathbf{X}) = \int_{\mathcal{V}} \frac{q_f}{r}\,dv + \oint_{\mathcal{S}_d} \frac{\omega_f}{r}\,da - \int_{\mathcal{V}} \frac{1}{r} P^k{}_{;k}\,dv + \oint_{\mathcal{S}_d} \frac{1}{r} P^k n_k\,da \tag{109.15}$$

where $r$ is the distance between a point **X** at which the potential is evaluated and the point of integration **x**, i.e.,

$$r = [(r^k - g^k{}_K R^K)(r_k - g^L{}_k R_L)]^{\frac{1}{2}} \tag{109.16}$$

where $r^k - g^k{}_K R^K$ are the components[1] of the position vector $\mathbf{r} - \mathbf{R}$.

The electrostatic potential here is due to two causes: the *extrinsic electric field* ${}_0\mathbf{E}$ and the *Maxwell self electric field* ${}_S\mathbf{E}$. To each of these in (109.5) there corresponds an electrostatic potential ${}_0\varphi$ and ${}_S\varphi$ such that

$$_0\mathbf{E} = -\operatorname{grad} {}_0\varphi \qquad {}_S\mathbf{E} = -\operatorname{grad} {}_S\varphi \tag{109.17}$$

where

$$\begin{aligned} \epsilon_0\,{}_0\varphi &\equiv \int_{\mathcal{V}} \frac{q_f}{r}\,dv + \oint_{\mathcal{S}_d} \frac{\omega_f}{r}\,da \\ \epsilon_0\,{}_S\varphi &\equiv -\int_{\mathcal{V}_d} \frac{1}{r} P^k{}_{;k}\,dv + \oint_{\mathcal{S}_d} \frac{1}{r} P^k n_k\,da \\ \varphi &= {}_0\varphi + {}_S\varphi \end{aligned} \tag{109.18}$$

From (109.18) it is clear that the potential of the self electric field is generated by an equivalent volume distribution of charge $-P^k{}_{;k}$ in $\mathcal{V}_d$ and a surface distribution of charge $P^k n_k$ over the surface $\mathcal{S}_d$ of the dielectric. These are called the *Poisson-Kelvin equivalent charge distributions of a polarized dielectric.*

[1] Here we use $r^k$ and $R^K$ instead of the usual symbols $p^k$ and $P^K$ to denote the components of the position vector so that there will not be a confusion between the polarization vector $P^K$ and the position vector. The shifter $g^k{}_K$ is operative between the coordinates $x^k$ and $X^K$.

Evaluation of the improper integrals in (109.18) and a detailed study of the question of convergence constitute common problems encountered in potential theory (cf. Kellogg [1929]). It suffices to point out that the calculations of the self electric field for the points outside the dielectric may be made by taking the gradient of both sides of $(109.18)_2$ and interchanging the integral and gradient operators, i.e.,

$$(109.19)\qquad \epsilon_0\, {}_S E^K = \int_{\mathcal{V}_d} P^k{}_{;k}\left(\frac{1}{r}\right)_{,}{}^{K} dv - \oint_{\mathcal{S}_d} P^k n_k \left(\frac{1}{r}\right)_{,}{}^{K} da$$

It may be verified through (109.16) that

$$\left(\frac{1}{r}\right)_{,}{}^{K} = -\left(\frac{1}{r}\right)_{,}{}^{k} g^K{}_k$$

By using this, we find

$$P^k{}_{;k}\left(\frac{1}{r}\right)_{,}{}^{K} = -g^K{}_l\left[P^k\left(\frac{1}{r}\right)_{,}{}^{l}\right]_{;k} + g^K{}_l P^k\left(\frac{1}{r}\right)_{;k}{}^{l}$$

Substituting this in place of the integrand of the first integral on the right of (109.19) and using the Green-Gauss theorem to convert the first term to a surface integral, we find

$$(109.20)\qquad \epsilon_0\, {}_S E^K = \int_{\mathcal{V}_d} g^K{}_l P^k\left(\frac{1}{r}\right)_{;k}{}^{l} dv = -\int_{\mathcal{V}_d} P^k\left(\frac{1}{r}\right)_{;k}{}^{K} dv$$

Thus the Maxwell self field at a point outside of the dielectric is given by (109.20), which is a generalization of Coulomb's law. This process cannot be carried out for a point inside the dielectric. For an inside point the integrals in (109.18) must be evaluated first, and then the gradient operation may be carried out to obtain the self electric field. For various other questions concerning the integration of the field equations of the electrostatic field, we refer the reader to standard books in electromagnetic theory, e.g., Stratton [1941], Sommerfeld [1952], Abraham and Becker [1949], and Whittaker [1953].

## 110. PRINCIPLE OF VIRTUAL WORK FOR THE ELASTIC DIELECTRIC[1]

The Maxwell-Faraday electrostatic theory outlined in the previous sections does not take into account the effect of interaction of the local elastic deformation with the electric field. If the polarization (which is the result of the internal relative displacements of the charges) is separated from the mechanical stress (which is the result of the deforma-

[1] Developments contained in this article and the remainder of this chapter are largely based on a report by Eringen [1961] modifying the work of Toupin [1956, 1960].

tion of mass points), we see that the resulting classical electrostatic theory is a theory applicable to rigid bodies. In order to take into account the effect of local elastic deformations, we now propose the following postulates.

1. *The local elastic deformation creates a local electric field* ${}_L\mathbf{E}$ *which is a state function of the local deformation gradients and the polarization vector,* i.e.,

$$(110.1) \qquad {}_L\mathbf{E} = {}_L\mathbf{E}\,(x^k{}_{,K}\,,\, P^k)$$

so that the total electric field at a point $\mathbf{X}$ of an elastic dielectric is given by

$$(110.2) \qquad \mathbf{E} = {}_0\mathbf{E} + {}_S\mathbf{E} + {}_L\mathbf{E} = {}_M\mathbf{E} + {}_L\mathbf{E}\,(x^k{}_{,K}\,,\, P^k)$$

where ${}_M\mathbf{E} \equiv {}_0\mathbf{E} + {}_S\mathbf{E}$ is the Maxwell-Faraday electric field.

The polarization per unit volume $P^k\,(\mathbf{x})$ is defined at each point $\mathbf{x}$ of the deformed and polarized body.[2] Its components in material coordinates, $P^K\,(\mathbf{X})$, are given by

$$(110.3) \qquad P^K\,(\mathbf{X}) = g^K{}_k\, P^k\,(\mathbf{x})$$

2. *The stress tensor at a point depends not only on the local state (short-range forces) but also on the Maxwell electrostatic field (long-range forces).*

3. *The internal energy density function* $\epsilon$ *of deformation and polarization is a state function of the deformation gradient and the polarization,* i.e.,

$$(110.4) \qquad \epsilon = \epsilon\,(x^k{}_{,K}\,,\, P^k)$$

It is clear that the list of state variables may be enlarged, in the same fashion as is done in Chaps. 8 to 10, to include density, metric tensors, higher-order gradients, etc. (cf. Art. 111).

Fortunately the electrostatic theory of elastic bodies, being a static and nondissipative theory, permits the use of the guiding principle of virtual work. The principle of virtual work not only leads to the field equations but also supplies us with the boundary conditions. To apply this principle, we assume that the variables $x^k$, $P^K$, and $\varphi$, in addition to being functions of $\mathbf{X}$, depend on a parameter $\lambda$; i.e., we have

$$(110.5) \qquad \begin{array}{llll} x^k = x^k\,(\mathbf{X}, \lambda) & P^K = P^K\,(\mathbf{X}, \lambda) & \varphi = \varphi\,(\mathbf{X}, \lambda) & \text{(in material)} \\ x^k = x^k\,(\lambda) & \mathbf{P} \equiv 0 & \varphi = \varphi\,(\mathbf{x}, \lambda) & \text{(in vacuum)} \end{array}$$

It is assumed that for $\lambda = 0$ these quantities describe a given state of the body. The *independent variations* of $x^k$, $P^k$, and $\varphi$ are defined as in

[2] Toupin employs the polarization vector per unit mass $\pi^k$ in place of our $P^k$. As we shall see, the use of $P^k$ appears to result in more conventional forms of various quantities such as the Maxwell stress tensor.

Art. 41 by

$$\delta x^k \equiv \frac{\partial x^k}{\partial \lambda}\bigg|_{\mathbf{X}=\text{fixed},\ \lambda=0} d\lambda \qquad \delta P^K \equiv \frac{\partial P^K}{\partial \lambda}\bigg|_{\mathbf{X}=\text{fixed},\ \lambda=0} d\lambda$$

$$\delta \varphi \equiv \frac{\partial \varphi}{\partial \lambda}\bigg|_{\mathbf{X}=\text{fixed},\ \lambda=0} d\lambda \qquad \text{(in material)} \tag{110.6}$$

$$\delta x^k \equiv \frac{dx^k}{d\lambda}\bigg|_{\lambda=0} d\lambda \qquad \delta \mathbf{P} = 0 \qquad \delta \varphi \equiv \frac{\partial \varphi}{\partial \lambda}\bigg|_{\mathbf{x}=\text{fixed},\ \lambda=0} d\lambda$$

$$\text{(in vacuum)}$$

The *principle of virtual work* for the elastic dielectric is now expressed as:

4. *Among all states of stress, electric polarization fields, and potential fields, those satisfying the correct field equations and boundary conditions are determined by the variational equation*

$$-\delta\Sigma - \delta U + \delta^* W = 0 \tag{110.7}$$

where $\delta\Sigma$ and $\delta U$ are respectively the variations of the internal energy and of the electric energy stored in the field, and $\delta^* W$ is the work done by external mechanical and electric forces. An asterisk is placed upon the $\delta$ of the latter quantity to distinguish it from the variation operator $\delta$.

5. *The variations are assumed to obey the axiom of conservation of mass*, i.e.,

$$\delta\,(\rho\, dv) = 0 \tag{110.8}$$

We have by definition

$$\Sigma = \int_{\mathcal{V}} \rho\, \epsilon\,(x^k{}_{,K}\,,\, P^k)\, dv \tag{110.9}$$

Next we express $\delta^* W$ as

$$\delta^* W = \int_{\mathcal{V}} \rho\, f_k\, \delta x^k\, dv + \int_{\mathcal{V}} q\, \delta\varphi\, dv + \oint_{\mathcal{S}} t_{(n)k}\, \delta x^k\, da + \oint_{\mathcal{S}} \omega\, \delta\varphi\, da \tag{110.10}$$

where $q$ and $\omega$ are given by (109.13). Respectively, these integrals are the virtual work associated with the body force, the volume density of total charge, the surface traction, and total surface charge.

What are we to take for the electrostatic energy $U$? In the classical theory the electric energy is given by[3]

$$U = \int_{\mathcal{V}} \int_0^{\mathbf{D}} \mathbf{E} \cdot \delta\mathbf{D}\, dv$$

By use of (109.4) this may be written as

$$U = \tfrac{1}{2} \int_{\mathcal{V}} \epsilon_0\, \mathbf{E}^2\, dv + \int_{\mathcal{V}} \int_0^{\mathbf{P}} \mathbf{E} \cdot \delta\mathbf{P}\, dv \tag{110.11}$$

[3] Cf. Stratton [1941, p. 111].

Guided by this expression, we decide to take[4]

$$\delta U = \tfrac{1}{2}\,\delta \int_{\mathcal{V}} \epsilon_0\, \mathbf{E}^2\, dv + \int_{\mathcal{V}} \mathbf{E}\cdot\delta\mathbf{P}\, dv \tag{110.12}$$

$$= \tfrac{1}{2}\,\delta \int_{\mathcal{V}} \epsilon_0\, g^{kl}\, \varphi_{,k}\, \varphi_{,l}\, dv - \int_{\mathcal{V}} \varphi_{,k}\, \delta P^k\, dv$$

In evaluating the variations, we need the identities

$$\begin{aligned}
\delta(x^k{}_{,K}) &= (\delta x^k)_{;l}\, x^l{}_{,K}\\
\delta(X^K{}_{,k}) &= -(\delta x^l)_{;k}\, X^K{}_{,l}\\
\delta(\varphi_{,k}) &= \delta(\varphi_{,K}\, X^K{}_{,k}) = (\delta\varphi)_{,K}\, X^K{}_{,k} + \varphi_{,K}\,\delta(X^K{}_{,k})\\
&= (\delta\varphi)_{;k} - \varphi_{,l}(\delta x^l)_{;k}\\
\delta(dv) &= (\delta x^k)_{;k}\, dv
\end{aligned} \tag{110.13}$$

In order to outline the procedure, we now carry out the variations of the first term in (110.7), i.e.,

$$-\delta\Sigma = -\delta \int_{\mathcal{V}} \rho\, \epsilon(x^k{}_{,K}, P^k)\, dv = -\int_{\mathcal{V}} \left[\rho \frac{\partial \epsilon}{\partial x^k{}_{,K}}\, \delta(x^k{}_{,K}) + \rho \frac{\partial \epsilon}{\partial P^k}\, \delta P^k\right] dv$$

where we have used (110.8). We now use $(110.13)_1$ to express

$$\rho \frac{\partial \epsilon}{\partial x^k{}_{,K}}\, \delta(x^k{}_{,K}) = \rho \frac{\partial \epsilon}{\partial x^k{}_{,K}}\, (\delta x^k)_{;l}\, x^l{}_{,K} \tag{110.14}$$

$$= \left(\rho \frac{\partial \epsilon}{\partial x^k{}_{,K}}\, x^l{}_{,K}\, \delta x^k\right)_{;l} - \left(\rho \frac{\partial \epsilon}{\partial x^k{}_{,K}}\, x^l{}_{,K}\right)_{;l} \delta x^k$$

and substitute this into the first integral on the right of the previous

[4] This form of electrostatic energy is found to be the correct one for the classical electrostatic theory in which linear constitutive equations (109.5) are valid. In particular, for free space ($\mathbf{P} \equiv 0$) the validity of (110.11) is never questioned. For anisotropic solids and for nonlinear **D-E** relationships however, a great controversy arises regarding the form of the electrostatic stress tensor which results from the choice of $U$. In the latter case the electrostatic stress tensor turns out to be nonsymmetrical.

The proponents of different theories leading to symmetric tensors and the originators of intuitive arguments supporting the legitimacy of the asymmetric tensor have been locked in controversy for over half a century.

Recently this question was reopened by various writers; cf. Marx [1953], Gyorgyi [1954], Marx and Gyorgyi [1954, 1955], and Fano, Chu, and Adler [1960, chap. X and appendix 1]. We need not concern ourselves at present with this controversy. While the form of the purely electrical and purely mechanical parts of the stress tensors are not known and cannot be defined in a unique fashion without further experimental work or a new axiom, our system is closed and the resulting stress tensor is that of Cauchy and is well-defined. For further discussion of the point see also Dunkin and Eringen [1961] and references therein.

equation and use the Green-Gauss theorem (109.8) to obtain

$$(110.15)\quad -\delta\Sigma = \int_{\mathcal{V}} \left[\left(\rho \frac{\partial \epsilon}{\partial x^l{}_{,K}} x^k{}_{,K}\right)_{;k} \delta x^l - \rho \frac{\partial \epsilon}{\partial P^l} \delta P^l\right] dv - \oint_{\mathcal{S}} \rho \frac{\partial \epsilon}{\partial x^l{}_{,K}} x^k{}_{,K} n_k \, \delta x^l \, da + \oint_{\mathcal{S}_d} \left[\!\left[\rho \frac{\partial \epsilon}{\partial x^l{}_{,K}} x^k{}_{,K}\right]\!\right] n_k \, \delta x^l \, da$$

A similar procedure applied to (110.12) gives, with the aid of $(110.13)_6$,

$$(110.16)\quad -\delta U = \int_{\mathcal{V}} (\epsilon_0 \varphi_{;}{}^k{}_k \, \delta\varphi - {}_M t^k{}_{l;k} \, \delta x^l + \varphi_{,k} \, \delta P^k) \, dv + \oint_{\mathcal{S}} (-\epsilon_0 \varphi_{,}{}^k \, \delta\varphi + {}_M t^k{}_{l;k} \, \delta x^l) n_k \, da + \oint_{\mathcal{S}_d} ([\![\epsilon_0 \varphi_{,}{}^k]\!] \, \delta\varphi - {}_M t^k{}_l \, \delta x^l) n_k \, da$$

where

$$(110.17)\quad {}_M t^k{}_l \equiv \epsilon_0 (\varphi_{,}{}^k \varphi_{,l} - \tfrac{1}{2} \varphi_{,}{}^m \varphi_{,m} \delta^k{}_l) = \epsilon_0 (E^k E_l - \tfrac{1}{2} \mathbf{E}^2 \delta^k{}_l)$$

is the *Maxwell stress tensor.*

The principle of virtual work (110.7) now becomes

$$(110.18)\quad 0 = \int_{\mathcal{V}} \left\{\left[\left(\rho \frac{\partial \epsilon}{\partial x^l{}_{,K}} x^k{}_{,K} - {}_M t^k{}_l\right)_{;k} + \rho f_l\right] \delta x^l - \left(\rho \frac{\partial \epsilon}{\partial P^k} - \varphi_{,k}\right) \delta P^k + [(\epsilon_0 \varphi_{,}{}^k - P^k)_{;k} + q_f] \, \delta\varphi\right\} dv$$
$$+ \oint_{\mathcal{S}_d} \left\{\left(\left[\!\left[\rho \frac{\partial \epsilon}{\partial x^l{}_{,K}} x^k{}_{,K} - {}_M t^k{}_l\right]\!\right] n_k + t_{(n)l}\right) \delta x^l + ([\![\epsilon_0 \varphi_{,}{}^k - P^k]\!] n_k + \omega_f) \, \delta\varphi\right\} da$$
$$- \oint_{\mathcal{S}} \left[\left(\rho \frac{\partial \epsilon}{\partial x^l{}_{,K}} x^k{}_{,K} - {}_M t^k{}_l\right) n_k \, \delta x^l + (\epsilon_0 \varphi_{,}{}^k - P^k) n_k \, \delta\varphi\right] da$$

We now let the control surface $\mathcal{S} \to \infty$ and assume that the coefficient of $da$ in the last integral vanish at this limit.[5] Setting the coefficients of $\delta x^l$, $\delta P^k$, and $\delta\varphi$ equal to zero in each of the remaining regions, we obtain

$$(110.19)\quad \left(\rho \frac{\partial \epsilon}{\partial x^l{}_{,K}} x^k{}_{,K} - {}_M t^k{}_l\right)_{;k} + \rho f_l = 0$$

$$(110.20)\quad -\rho \frac{\partial \epsilon}{\partial P^k} + \varphi_{,k} = 0$$

$$(110.21)\quad \epsilon_0 \nabla^2 \varphi - P^k{}_{;k} + q_f = 0 \qquad \text{in } \mathcal{V}_d$$

[5] From this one can deduce what assumptions have been made concerning the order of the stress and electric displacement as a function of distance from the origin, i.e., $\mathbf{t} = O(1/r^2)$, $\mathbf{D} = O(1/r^2)$ as $r \to \infty$.

At every point outside the dielectric we must have

$$-{}_M t^k{}_{l;k} + \rho f_l = 0 \tag{110.22}$$

$$\epsilon_0 \nabla^2 \varphi + q_f = 0 \qquad \text{in } \mathcal{V}_0 = \mathcal{V} - \mathcal{V}_d \tag{110.23}$$

The boundary conditions on $\mathcal{S}_d$ are

$$\left(\rho \frac{\partial \epsilon}{\partial x^l{}_{,K}} x^k{}_{,K} + [\![{}_M t^k{}_l]\!]\right) n_k - t_{(n)l} = 0 \tag{110.24}$$

$$[\![\epsilon_0 \varphi_,{}^k - P^k]\!] n_k + \omega_f = 0 \qquad \text{on } \mathcal{S}_d \tag{110.25}$$

These equations suggest that we may define a *local stress field* ${}_L t^k{}_l$ and a *local electric field* ${}_L E^k$ by

$$\begin{aligned} {}_L t^k{}_l &= \rho \frac{\partial \epsilon}{\partial x^l{}_{,K}} x^k{}_{,K} \\ {}_L E_k &= \rho \frac{\partial \epsilon}{\partial P^k} \end{aligned} \tag{110.26}$$

Since for the Maxwell electric field we have ${}_M\mathbf{E} = -\text{grad } \varphi$, the field equations (110.19)–(110.21) may be transformed into

$$t^k{}_{l;k} + \rho f_l = 0 \tag{110.27}$$

$$ {}_L E_k + {}_M E_k = 0 \tag{110.28}$$

$$\epsilon_0 \nabla^2 \varphi - \text{div } \mathbf{P} + q_f = 0 \qquad \text{in } \mathcal{V}_d \tag{110.29}$$

and the boundary conditions (110.24) and (110.25) may be expressed as

$$[\![t^k{}_l]\!] n_k = 0 \tag{110.30}$$

$$(\epsilon_0 [\![\varphi_,{}^k]\!] + P^k) n_k + \omega_f = 0 \qquad \text{on } \mathcal{S}_d \tag{110.31}$$

where we used the definitions

$$t^k{}_l \equiv {}_L t^k{}_l - {}_M t^k{}_l = \rho \frac{\partial \epsilon}{\partial x^l{}_{,K}} x^k{}_{,K} - {}_M t^k{}_l \tag{110.32}$$

$$\overset{+}{{}_L t^k{}_l} n_k \equiv t_{(n)l} \qquad \overset{-}{{}_L t^k{}_l} \equiv \rho \frac{\partial \epsilon}{\partial x^l{}_{,K}} x^k{}_{,K} \tag{110.33}$$

Here a + superscript represents the value on $\mathcal{S}_d$ when the surface is approached from outside, and a − superscript that when $\mathcal{S}_d$ is approached from inside.

A form equivalent to (110.27) is obtained by carrying out the covariant differentiation in (110.19) and using (110.21). Hence

$$ {}_L t^k{}_{l;k} - q E_l + \rho f_l = 0 \tag{110.34}$$

where $q$ is defined as $(109.13)_1$.

It is of interest to study the two extreme cases: when the electrical effect is absent, clearly the field equations and boundary conditions (110.27)–(110.31) reduce to those of the elasticity theory; on the other hand, when the elastic effect is negligible (i.e., $\epsilon$ is independent of $x^k{}_{,K}$), the field equation (110.19) reduces to

$$\begin{aligned}\rho f_l &= {}_Mt^k{}_{l;k} = \epsilon_0 E^k{}_{;k} E_l \\ &= (q_f - \operatorname{div}\mathbf{P}) E_l = q E_l\end{aligned} \tag{110.35}$$

which indicates that $q\mathbf{E}$ is the electrostatic body force.[6] The boundary conditions (110.30) give the electrostatic surface force

$$t_{(n)l} = [\![{}_Mt^k{}_l]\!] n_k \tag{110.36}$$

The remaining equations (110.28), (110.29), and boundary conditions (110.31) are the usual equations of electrostatics obtained in the previous article.

Equation (110.28) and the constitutive equations $(110.26)_2$ supply us with the constitutive equations for the nonlinear electrostatic field from which the linear theory follows by taking $\epsilon$ as a quadratic polynomial in **P**.

It is not mandatory that we employ the electrostatic stress tensor ${}_Mt^k{}_l$ in order to take into account electrical forces. For example, the stress tensors defined by

$$\begin{aligned}{}_mt^k{}_l &= D^k E_l - \tfrac{1}{2}\mathbf{D}\cdot\mathbf{E}\,\delta^k{}_l \\ t_L{}^k{}_l &= D^k E_l - \tfrac{1}{2}\epsilon_0 E^2 \delta^k{}_l\end{aligned} \tag{110.37}$$

or many other tensors can be employed to replace ${}_Mt^k{}_l$. For each case, of course, the body force $\rho f_l$ takes different forms. The tensor ${}_m\mathbf{t}$ was introduced by Minkowsky and $\mathbf{t}_L$ by Toupin. They are related to ${}_M\mathbf{t}$ by

$$\begin{aligned}{}_Mt^k{}_l &= {}_mt^k{}_l - P^k E_l + \tfrac{1}{2}\mathbf{P}\cdot\mathbf{E}\,\delta^k{}_l \\ &= t_L{}^k{}_l - P^k E_l\end{aligned} \tag{110.38}$$

When these are substituted into (110.27), the terms left over, ${}_m\mathbf{t}$ and $\mathbf{t}_L$, can be combined either with $\rho f_l$ or with ${}_L\mathbf{t}$ to define a new local tensor.

It is clear that the decomposition of the Cauchy stress into mechanical and electrical parts is *not* unique.

Moreover, such decompositions do not have any physical or mathematical significance other than perhaps providing an intuitive guide for construction of the constitutive equations for one or the other equivalent form, at least until the nature of electrical body force is clearly settled. It appears to the present writer that the tensor ${}_L\mathbf{t}$ is the most natural one resulting from the variations of electric energy $U$ and leads to an intuitively correct and simple electrical body force (110.35).

[6] Definition of the electrostatic body force is a question unresolved to date. The question is closely tied with that of the electrostatic stress tensor. See footnote 4, Art. 110, and also the remarks that follow. For definiteness we select the definition given by (110.35).

The principle of virtual work does not supply us with the symmetry of the stress tensor. In a mechanical medium this is obtained as the result of the axiom of balance of moment of momentum (balance of momenta) and the assumption of the nonexistence of couple stress and body couples. By an extension of the theorem proved in Art. 41, however, we see that *the momenta are balanced if the internal energy function* $\epsilon$ *is invariant under rigid rotation of the deformed and polarized dielectric.* Thus, selecting $\nu_{\Gamma}{}^{k}$ as $x^{k}{}_{,K}$ and $P^{k}$, and using the general result (41.24), we obtain

$$\frac{\partial \epsilon}{\partial x^{[k}{}_{,K}} x_{l],K} + \frac{\partial \epsilon}{\partial P^{[k}} P_{l]} = 0$$

Multiplying this equation by $\rho$ and using (110.26), we obtain

$$(110.39) \qquad {}_{L}t^{[kl]} - {}_{L}E^{[k}P^{l]} = 0$$

which expresses the fact that the moment exerted on a particle arising from the local stress is balanced by the moment exerted by the local field ${}_{L}\mathbf{E}$. Clearly then ${}_{L}\mathbf{t}$ is not a symmetric tensor.

The principle of virtual work, with the assumption of the existence of an internal energy function, leads us to the complete field equations and boundary conditions. As in elasticity theory, the elastic dielectric with a stress potential constitutes a special class of materials which may be named *hyperelastic-dielectric materials.* This class of materials falls into a subclass of the more general elastic-dielectric materials of the Cauchy type. For the latter general class the axiom of existence of a strain energy must be replaced by the assumptions

$$(110.40) \qquad {}_{L}\mathbf{t} = {}_{L}\mathbf{t}\,(x^{k}{}_{,K}\,,\, P^{k}) \qquad {}_{L}\mathbf{E} = {}_{L}\mathbf{E}\,(x^{k}{}_{,K}\,,\, P^{k})$$

The principle of objectivity and other invariance requirements may then be used to obtain the final form of the constitutive equations.

## 111. CONSTITUTIVE EQUATIONS OF HYPERELASTIC DIELECTRICS

A *hyperelastic dielectric* is a solid medium characterized by the properties: (1) *its state at each material point* $\mathbf{X}$ *and at time* $t$ *is completely determined by an energy function* $\Sigma \equiv \rho_0\,\epsilon$ *of the form*

$$(111.1) \qquad \Sigma = \Sigma\,(X^{K}, x^{k}, g^{k}{}_{K}, \rho, \mathbf{G}_{K}, x^{k}{}_{,K}\,,\, P^{k})$$

and (2) *it possesses a natural state in which the body is unstressed and unpolarized.*

It therefore is clear that the hyperelastic dielectric is an immediate generalization of the hyperelastic solid with additional state variables $P^{k}$, the polarization.

Reduction of the internal energy function (111.1) to its final form follows the procedure employed in Art. 45. Briefly, by use of the principle of objectivity for rigid translation of the spatial frame, we drop the dependence on **x**. When translation with respect to time is made, we see that $\Sigma$ cannot depend on time. Invariance to an arbitrary rigid rotation $Q^k{}_l(t)$, in the same way as in Art. 45 (3), shows that

$$\Sigma = \Sigma\,(X^K, g^k{}_K, \mathrm{G}_K, Q^k{}_l\, x^l{}_{,K}\,, Q^k{}_l\, P^l) \tag{111.2}$$

Using the theorem of Cauchy enunciated in Art. 45, we see that $\Sigma$ can at most be a function of the following variables:

$$\begin{aligned} C_{KL} &= g_{kl}\, x^k{}_{,K}\, x^l{}_{,L} \\ \Pi_K &\equiv g_{kl}\, x^k{}_{,K}\, P^l \\ P^2 &= g_{kl}\, P^k\, P^l \\ D^M &= \tfrac{1}{2}\,(\det g^N{}_n)\, e_{klm}\, e^{KLM}\, x^k{}_{,K}\, x^l{}_{,L}\, P^m \\ J &= \sqrt{\mathrm{III}_C} \\ \mathrm{G}_K \quad &, \quad X^K \quad , \quad G_{KL} \quad , \quad g^k{}_K \end{aligned} \tag{111.3}$$

Since $\det C^K{}_L = J^2$, and for real motions $0 < J < \infty$, we can eliminate $J$ from this list. Next we make use of (4.4) and (4.5) to find $D^K = J\, X^K{}_{,k}\, P^k$. Consequently $C_{KL}\, D^L = J\, \Pi_K$ or $D^K = J \overset{-1}{C}{}^K{}_L\, \Pi^L$. Hence the dependence of $\Sigma$ on $D^K$ may be dropped.

The coordinate invariance requirement for either set $x^k$ or $X^K$ will show that dependence on $g^k{}_K$ must be excluded since the only absolute scalar that can be formed from $g^k{}_K$ is $G_{KL}$. Therefore we have

$$\Sigma = \Sigma\,(X^K, G_{KL}, \mathrm{G}_K, C_{KL}, \Pi_K, P^2) \tag{111.4}$$

We recall the theorem of algebra which tells us that both $G_{KL}$ and $C_{KL}$ can be reduced to diagonal form by a single coordinate transformation of $X^K$. Thus, in a special coordinate system, we may write

$$\Sigma = \Sigma\,(X^K, \mathrm{G}_K, C_\Gamma, \Pi_K, P^2) \tag{111.5}$$

where $C_\Gamma$ $(\Gamma = 1, 2, 3)$ are the eigenvalues of $C_{KL}$.

From $(111.3)_2$ we solve for $P_k$

$$P_k = X^K{}_{,k}\, \Pi_K \tag{111.6}$$

Forming $P^2$, we see that

$$P^2 = g^{kl}\, X^K{}_{,k}\, X^L{}_{,l}\, \Pi_K\, \Pi_L = \overset{-1}{C}{}^{KL}\, \Pi_K\, \Pi_L \tag{111.7}$$

Therefore, if we wish, we may drop $P^2$ from the arguments of $\Sigma$.

Since also $\overset{-1}{C}_\Gamma = \frac{1}{C_\Gamma}$, we may reduce (111.5) to any one of the forms

$$\Sigma = \Sigma\,(X^K, \mathbf{G}_K, C_{KL}, \Pi_K) \tag{111.8}$$

$$\Sigma = \Sigma\,(X^K, \mathbf{G}_K, \overset{-1}{C}_{KL}, \Pi_K) \tag{111.9}$$

$$\Sigma = \Sigma\,(X^K, \mathbf{G}_K, E_{KL}, \Pi_K) \tag{111.10}$$

For a *homogeneous* medium dependence on $X^K$ drops out. The forms (111.8)–(111.10) are suitable for the determination of local stress and electric fields.

Assuming that in some range of its arguments $\Sigma$ is differentiable with respect to its arguments $\mathbf{C}$, $\overset{-1}{\mathbf{C}}$, $\mathbf{E}$, and $\mathbf{\Pi}$, whichever are in use, one may, in the same way as in Art. 45, obtain various forms of the constitutive equations.

*Generalized Boussinesq's Form.* In this case $\mathbf{C}$ or $\mathbf{E}$ and $\mathbf{\Pi}$ are the basic variables. We have

$$\frac{\partial\Sigma}{\partial x^l{}_{,M}} = \frac{\partial\Sigma}{\partial E_{KL}}\frac{\partial E_{KL}}{\partial x^l{}_{,M}} + \frac{\partial\Sigma}{\partial\Pi_K}\frac{\partial\Pi_K}{\partial x^l{}_{,M}}$$

Now we have

$$\frac{\partial\Pi_K}{\partial x^l{}_{,M}} = \delta^M{}_K\,P_l \tag{111.11}$$

Using this and (45.27) in (110.26), we get

$$_Lt^k{}_l = \frac{\rho}{\rho_0}\left(\frac{\partial\Sigma}{\partial E_{KL}}\,x^k{}_{,K}\,x_{l,L} + \frac{\partial\Sigma}{\partial\Pi_K}\,P_l\,x^k{}_{,K}\right) \tag{111.12}$$

$$_LE^k = \frac{\rho}{\rho_0}\frac{\partial\Sigma}{\partial\Pi_K}\,x^k{}_{,K} \tag{111.13}$$

*Note that for vanishing polarization the constitutive equations* (111.12) *reduce to those of a purely hyperelastic solid* (45.24).

*Isotropic Hyperelastic Dielectric.* In this case we return to (111.5) to obtain further reduction. For isotropic media dependence on the material descriptor $\mathbf{G}_K$ cannot occur. Moreover, if we reverse one of the coordinate axes used to obtain (111.5), we find that $C_\Gamma$ and $P^2$ remain unaltered. However, one of $\Pi_K$ changes sign. Thus the dependence on $\Pi_K$ should occur in even powers of $\Pi_K$. Hence

$$\Sigma = \Sigma\,[X^K, C_\Gamma, (\Pi_K)^2, P^2] \tag{111.14}$$

It can be shown that $C_\Gamma$, $(\Pi_K)^2$, and $P^2$ are single-valued functions of six independent scalar invariants:

$$
\begin{aligned}
\mathrm{I}_C &= \delta^K{}_L\, C^L{}_K \\
\mathrm{II}_C &= \tfrac{1}{2}\, \delta^K{}_L{}^M{}_N\, C^L{}_K\, C^N{}_M \\
\mathrm{III}_C &= \tfrac{1}{6}\, \delta^K{}_L{}^M{}_N{}^P{}_Q\, C^L{}_K\, C^N{}_M\, C^Q{}_P = \det C^K{}_L \\
J_4 &= \Pi_K\, \Pi^K \\
J_5 &= C^K{}_L\, \Pi^L\, \Pi_K \\
J_6 &= P^2
\end{aligned}
\tag{111.15}
$$

Equivalently we may use another set of invariants formed from $\overset{-1}{\mathbf{c}}$ and $\mathbf{P}$, i.e.,

$$
\begin{aligned}
\mathrm{I}_1 &= \mathrm{I} = \mathrm{I}_{\overset{-1}{c}} = \delta^k{}_l\, \overset{-1}{c}{}^l{}_k \\
\mathrm{I}_2 &= \mathrm{II} = \mathrm{II}_{\overset{-1}{c}} = \tfrac{1}{2}\, \delta^k{}_l{}^m{}_n\, \overset{-1}{c}{}^l{}_k\, \overset{-1}{c}{}^n{}_m \\
\mathrm{I}_3 &= \mathrm{III} = \mathrm{III}_{\overset{-1}{c}} = \tfrac{1}{6}\, \delta^k{}_l{}^m{}_n{}^p{}_q\, \overset{-1}{c}{}^l{}_k\, \overset{-1}{c}{}^n{}_m\, \overset{-1}{c}{}^q{}_p \\
\mathrm{I}_4 &= \overset{-1}{c}{}^k{}_l\, P^l\, P_k \\
\mathrm{I}_5 &= \overset{-2}{c}{}^k{}_l\, P^l\, P_k \\
\mathrm{I}_6 &= P^2
\end{aligned}
\tag{111.16}
$$

We may therefore write

$$
\Sigma = \Sigma\,(X^K, \mathrm{I}_\Gamma) \qquad (\Gamma = 1, 2, \ldots, 6)
\tag{111.17}
$$

For a *homogeneous* medium dependence on $X^K$ disappears

$$
\Sigma = \Sigma\,(\mathrm{I}_\Gamma) \qquad \text{(homogeneous isotropic elastic dielectric)}
\tag{111.18}
$$

Assuming that, in some range of values of $\mathrm{I}_\Gamma$, $\Sigma$ is differentiable, from (110.26) and (111.12) we shall have

$$
{}_Lt_k{}^l = \frac{\rho}{\rho_0} \frac{\partial \Sigma}{\partial \mathrm{I}_\Gamma} \frac{\partial \mathrm{I}_\Gamma}{\partial x^k{}_{,K}}\, x^l{}_{,K}
\tag{111.19}
$$

$$
{}_LE_k = \frac{\rho}{\rho_0} \frac{\partial \Sigma}{\partial \mathrm{I}_\Gamma} \frac{\partial \mathrm{I}_\Gamma}{\partial P^k}
\tag{111.20}
$$

Carrying out the indicated differentiations $\partial \mathrm{I}_\Gamma / \partial x^k{}_{,K}$ and $\partial \mathrm{I}_\Gamma / \partial P^k$ from (111.16) and substituting back into these expressions, we find

$$
\begin{aligned}
{}_Lt_k{}^l = 2\,\frac{\rho}{\rho_0} \Bigg[ &\mathrm{III}\, \frac{\partial \Sigma}{\partial \mathrm{III}}\, \delta^l{}_k + \left( \frac{\partial \Sigma}{\partial \mathrm{I}} + \mathrm{I}\, \frac{\partial \Sigma}{\partial \mathrm{II}} \right) \overset{-1}{c}{}^l{}_k \\
&- \frac{\partial \Sigma}{\partial \mathrm{II}}\, \overset{-2}{c}{}^l{}_k + \frac{\partial \Sigma}{\partial \mathrm{I}_4}\, \overset{-1}{c}{}^l{}_m\, P^m\, P_k \\
&+ \frac{\partial \Sigma}{\partial \mathrm{I}_5}\, \overset{-2}{c}{}^l{}_m\, P^m\, P_k + \frac{\partial \Sigma}{\partial \mathrm{I}_5}\, \overset{-1}{c}{}^l{}_m\, \overset{-1}{c}{}^n{}_k\, P_n\, P^m \Bigg]
\end{aligned}
\tag{111.21}
$$

$$(111.22) \qquad {}_LE^k = 2\frac{\rho}{\rho_0}\left(\frac{\partial\Sigma}{\partial \mathrm{I}_4}\overset{-1}{c}{}^k{}_l + \frac{\partial\Sigma}{\partial \mathrm{I}_5}\overset{-2}{c}{}^k{}_l + \frac{\partial\Sigma}{\partial \mathrm{I}_6}\delta^k{}_l\right)P^l$$

An alternative form displaying a close resemblance to the purely elastic solid is obtained by using the Cayley-Hamilton theorem (47.9) for the tensor $\overset{-1}{\mathbf{c}}$ to eliminate $\overset{-2}{\mathbf{c}}$ from our equation. Hence

$$(111.23) \qquad {}_Lt^l{}_k = \frac{2\rho}{\rho_0}\left[\frac{\partial\Sigma}{\partial \mathrm{I}}\overset{-1}{c}{}^l{}_k + \left(\mathrm{III}\frac{\partial\Sigma}{\partial \mathrm{III}} + \mathrm{II}\frac{\partial\Sigma}{\partial \mathrm{II}}\right)\delta^l{}_k\right.$$
$$- \mathrm{III}\frac{\partial\Sigma}{\partial \mathrm{II}}c^l{}_k + \left(\frac{\partial\Sigma}{\partial \mathrm{I}_4} + \mathrm{I}\frac{\partial\Sigma}{\partial \mathrm{I}_5}\right)\overset{-1}{c}{}^l{}_m P^m P_k$$
$$\left. - \mathrm{II}\frac{\partial\Sigma}{\partial \mathrm{I}_5}P^l P_k + \mathrm{III}\frac{\partial\Sigma}{\partial \mathrm{I}_5}c^l{}_m P^m P_k + \frac{\partial\Sigma}{\partial \mathrm{I}_5}\overset{-1}{c}{}^l{}_m \overset{-1}{c}{}^n{}_k P_n P^m\right]$$

$$(111.24) \qquad {}_LE^k = \frac{2\rho}{\rho_0}\left[\left(\frac{\partial\Sigma}{\partial \mathrm{I}_4} + \mathrm{I}\frac{\partial\Sigma}{\partial \mathrm{I}_5}\right)\overset{-1}{c}{}^k{}_l + \left(\frac{\partial\Sigma}{\partial \mathrm{I}_6} - \mathrm{II}\frac{\partial\Sigma}{\partial \mathrm{I}_5}\right)\delta^k{}_l\right.$$
$$\left. + \mathrm{III}\frac{\partial\Sigma}{\partial \mathrm{I}_5}c^k{}_l\right]P^l$$

A third form suitable for polynomial approximations is obtained as follows. We start with the stored-energy function (111.9). For isotropic media this $\Sigma$ shall depend on the invariants $\mathrm{I}_{\overset{-1}{C}}$, $\mathrm{II}_{\overset{-1}{C}}$, $\mathrm{III}_{\overset{-1}{C}}$, $\Pi_K \Pi^K$, $\overset{-1}{C}{}^K{}_L \Pi^L \Pi_K$, and $\overset{-2}{C}{}^K{}_L \Pi^L \Pi_K$. Of these the first three may be replaced by $\mathrm{I}_c$, $\mathrm{II}_c$, $\mathrm{III}_c$. By (111.6) and (111.7) we find that

$$\begin{aligned} \overset{-1}{C}{}^K{}_L \Pi^L \Pi_K &= P^2 \\ (111.25) \qquad \overset{-2}{C}{}^K{}_L \Pi^L \Pi_K &= c^k{}_l P^l P_k \\ \Pi_K \Pi^K &= \overset{-1}{c}{}^k{}_l P^l P_k \end{aligned}$$

If one uses (47.9) to eliminate $\overset{-1}{c}{}^k{}_l$ in the last, we find that $\Sigma$ may be expressed as

$$(111.26) \qquad \Sigma = \Sigma\,(X^K, \mathrm{I}_c, \mathrm{II}_c, \mathrm{III}_c, K_4, K_5, K_6)$$

where $\mathrm{I}_c$, $\mathrm{II}_c$, $\mathrm{III}_c$ are the invariants of $\mathbf{c}$ and

$$\begin{aligned} K_4 &= c^k{}_l P^l P_k \\ (111.27) \qquad K_5 &= \overset{2}{c}{}^k{}_l P^l P_k \\ K_6 &= \mathrm{I}_6 = P^2 \end{aligned}$$

Now carrying out the indicated differentiations in (111.19) and

(111.20) with these new arguments, we find

$$(111.28) \quad {}_Lt^l{}_k = -\frac{2\rho}{\rho_0}\Bigg[\mathrm{III}_c \frac{\partial\Sigma}{\partial \mathrm{III}_c}\,\delta^l{}_k + \left(\frac{\partial\Sigma}{\partial \mathrm{I}_c} + \mathrm{I}_c\frac{\partial\Sigma}{\partial \mathrm{II}_c}\right) c^l{}_k - \frac{\partial\Sigma}{\partial \mathrm{II}_c}\, c^l{}_m\, c^m{}_k + \frac{\partial\Sigma}{\partial K_4}\, c^r{}_k\, P_r\, P^l + \frac{\partial\Sigma}{\partial K_5}\,(\overset{2}{c}{}^r{}_k\, P_r\, P^l + c^r{}_k\, c^l{}_s\, P_r\, P^s)\Bigg]$$

$$(111.29) \quad {}_LE^k = \frac{2\,\rho}{\rho_0}\left(\frac{\partial\Sigma}{\partial K_4}\, c^k{}_r\, P^r + \frac{\partial\Sigma}{\partial K_5}\,\overset{2}{c}{}^k{}_r\, P^r + \frac{\partial\Sigma}{\partial K_6}\, P^k\right)$$

We have used such relations as

$$(111.30) \quad \frac{\partial c_{rs}}{\partial x^k{}_{,K}} = -c_{sk}\, X^K{}_{,r} - c_{rk}\, X^K{}_{,s}$$

which is obtained by the chain rule of differentiation.

$$\frac{\partial c_{rs}}{\partial x^k{}_{,K}} = \frac{\partial c_{rs}}{\partial X^M{}_{,n}}\,\frac{\partial X^M{}_{,n}}{\partial x^k{}_{,K}} \qquad \frac{\partial}{\partial x^k{}_{,K}}\,(X^M{}_{,n}\, x^n{}_{,N}) = 0$$

where $\partial c_{rs}/\partial X^M{}_{,n}$ is given by an equation preceding (45.35) and $\partial X^M{}_{,n}/\partial x^k{}_{,K}$ follows from the second of the foregoing equations, i.e.,

$$(111.31) \quad \frac{\partial X^M{}_{,n}}{\partial x^k{}_{,K}} = -X^M{}_{,k}\, X^K{}_{,n}$$

Other forms using other equivalent invariants are of course possible.

Let us immediately note that the first three terms in (111.23) and (111.28) are identical to those obtained for a purely elastic solid, (47.11) and (47.5) respectively. Therefore *for vanishing polarization the constitutive equations of the isotropic hyperelastic dielectric reduce to those of an isotropic hyperelastic solid.*

The constitutive equations (111.21) and (111.22) or equivalent forms (111.23) and (111.24) or (111.28) and (111.29), together with the field equations and the boundary conditions (110.27)–(110.29), constitute the basic equations of the nonlinear theory of the deformable isotropic hyperelastic dielectric.

While the various exact forms of the constitutive equations are equivalent to each other, polynomial approximations in strain and polarization measures for these different forms lead to different approximate constitutive equations. Hence any of the foregoing three sets may provide a basis for an approximate theory. The linearized forms which provide the lowest-degree terms (in strain and polarization measures) in a polynomial approximation naturally give the same thing for all three sets.

## 112. BASIC EQUATIONS OF HOMOGENEOUS ISOTROPIC HYPERELASTIC DIELECTRICS

*Basic Field Equations:*

$$t^k{}_{l;k} + \rho f_l = 0 \tag{112.1}$$

$$_L E_k - \varphi_{,k} = 0 \tag{112.2}$$

$$\epsilon_0 \nabla^2 \varphi - \operatorname{div} \mathbf{P} = -q_f \qquad \text{in } \mathcal{V}_d \tag{112.3}$$

*Boundary Conditions on the Surface of a Dielectric:*

$$[\![ t^k{}_l ]\!] n_k = 0 \tag{112.4}$$

$$[\![ \epsilon_0 \varphi,^k - P^k ]\!] n_k + \omega_f = 0 \qquad \text{on } \mathcal{S}_d \tag{112.5}$$

where the Cauchy stress tensor $\mathbf{t}$ is defined by

$$\begin{aligned} t^k{}_l &\equiv {_L t^k{}_l} - {_M t^k{}_l} \\ {_M t^k{}_l} &\equiv \epsilon_0 \left(\varphi,^k \varphi_{,l} - \tfrac{1}{2} \varphi,^m \varphi_{,m} \delta^k{}_l\right) \end{aligned} \tag{112.6}$$

and $_L\mathbf{t}$ and $_L\mathbf{E}$ are given by the constitutive equations.

A boldface bracket $[\![ \; ]\!]$ indicates the discontinuity across the surface; i.e., the limiting values of the quantity enclosed as the surface is approached from the exterior minus the limiting value as the surface is approached from the interior. By definition (110.33), the exterior and interior values of the local stress are

$$_L \overset{+}{t}{}^k{}_l n_k \equiv t_{(n)l} \qquad _L \overset{-}{t}{}^k{}_l \equiv \rho \frac{\partial \epsilon}{\partial x^l{}_{,K}} x^k{}_{,K} \tag{112.7}$$

where $t_{(n)l}$ is the surface traction.

*Constitutive Equations (Isotropic Dielectric).* Here we give the expression of $_L\mathbf{t}$ and $_L\mathbf{E}$. Expression of $\mathbf{t}$ follows from the defining equation $(112.6)_1$.

$$\begin{aligned} {_L t^k{}_l} = \frac{2\rho}{\rho_0} \Bigg[ & \mathrm{III} \frac{\partial \Sigma}{\partial \mathrm{III}} \delta^k{}_l + \left( \frac{\partial \Sigma}{\partial \mathrm{I}} + \mathrm{I} \frac{\partial \Sigma}{\partial \mathrm{II}} \right) \overset{-1}{c}{}^k{}_l - \frac{\partial \Sigma}{\partial \mathrm{II}} \overset{-2}{c}{}^k{}_l \\ & + \frac{\partial \Sigma}{\partial \mathrm{I}_4} \overset{-1}{c}{}^k{}_m P^m P_l + \frac{\partial \Sigma}{\partial \mathrm{I}_5} \overset{-2}{c}{}^k{}_m P^m P_l + \frac{\partial \Sigma}{\partial \mathrm{I}_5} \overset{-1}{c}{}^k{}_m \overset{-1}{c}{}^n{}_l P_n P^m \Bigg] \end{aligned} \tag{112.8}$$

$$_L E^k = \frac{2\rho}{\rho_0} \left( \frac{\partial \Sigma}{\partial \mathrm{I}_4} \overset{-1}{c}{}^k{}_l + \frac{\partial \Sigma}{\partial \mathrm{I}_5} \overset{-2}{c}{}^k{}_l + \frac{\partial \Sigma}{\partial \mathrm{I}_6} \delta^k{}_l \right) P^l \tag{112.9}$$

The stress, electric, and polarization fields of a deformed and polarized elastic dielectric must satisfy the foregoing field equations, boundary conditions, and constitutive equations.

In the following article we illustrate the solution of these equations for a simple problem.

## 113. SIMPLE SHEAR OF A POLARIZED DIELECTRIC[1]

Consider an infinite homogeneous isotropic slab of width $a$ (Fig. 113.1). Select $x^k$ and $X^K$ as the same rectangular coordinate system $(x, y, z)$ and $(X, Y, Z)$. Consider a simple shear deformation of the slab characterized by

$$x = X + KY \qquad y = Y \qquad z = Z \tag{113.1}$$

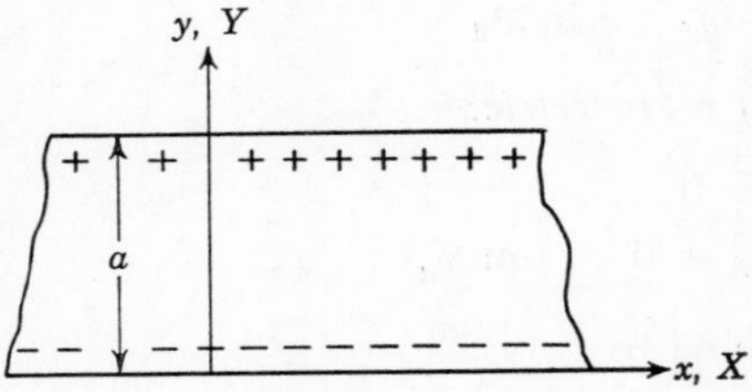


FIG. 113.1. Polarized elastic slab.

where the constant $K$ is the measure of the shear. Suppose that the dielectric polarization is the constant vector

$$\mathbf{P} = (P_x, P_y, 0) \tag{113.2}$$

We should like to determine the stress and electric fields in the dielectric.

The deformation tensor $\overset{-1}{\mathbf{c}}$ has already been given by (52.22).

$$\|\overset{-1}{c}{}^{kl}\| = \|\overset{-1}{c}{}^{k}{}_{l}\| = \begin{bmatrix} 1+K^2 & K & 0 \\ K & 1 & 0 \\ 0 & 0 & 1 \end{bmatrix}$$

$$\|\overset{-2}{c}{}^{k}{}_{l}\| = \begin{bmatrix} 1+3K^2+K^4 & K(2+K^2) & 0 \\ K(2+K^2) & 1+K^2 & 0 \\ 0 & 0 & 1 \end{bmatrix} \tag{113.3}$$

The invariants obtained using (111.16) are

$$\begin{aligned} \mathrm{I} &= \mathrm{II} = 3 + K^2 \\ \mathrm{III} &= 1 \\ \mathrm{I}_4 &= (1+K^2)P_x^2 + 2KP_xP_y + P_y^2 \\ \mathrm{I}_5 &= (1+3K^2+K^4)P_x^2 + 2K(2+K^2)P_xP_y + (1+K^2)P_y^2 \\ \mathrm{I}_6 &= P^2 = P_x^2 + P_y^2 \end{aligned} \tag{113.4}$$

Since $\mathrm{III} = 1$, the deformation is isochoric; hence $\rho = \rho_0$. Through (112.5) we have

$$\epsilon_0\,({}_ME_y - {}_0E_y) = -P_y \qquad \text{at } y = a \tag{113.5}$$

Electrostatic field equation (112.3) with $q_f = 0$ is satisfied identically for a constant ${}_M\mathbf{E} = -\operatorname{grad}\varphi$. Through the foregoing boundary condi-

[1] Present analysis modifies that of Toupin [1956, art. 12].

tion and the continuity of tangential components of the electric field across the boundary, we see that the Maxwell electric field is given by

$$(113.6)\quad \begin{aligned} {}_M\mathbf{E} &= -\text{grad}\,\varphi = ({}_0E_x,\, {}_0E_y - \epsilon_0^{-1} P_y,\, {}_0E_z) \qquad (0 < y < a) \\ {}_M\mathbf{E} &= [{}_0E_x,\, {}_0E_y,\, {}_0E_z] \qquad (0 < y \text{ and } y > a) \end{aligned}$$

Since $\overset{-1}{\mathbf{c}}$ and $\mathbf{P}$ are constant fields, the Cauchy stress tensor $\mathbf{t}$ is constant, and for vanishing body forces the field equations (112.1) are satisfied identically. From (112.2) and (113.6) it follows that

$$(113.7)\quad \begin{aligned} &{}_LE_x + {}_0E_x = 0 \qquad {}_LE_y + {}_0E_y - (P_y/\epsilon_0) = 0 \\ &{}_LE_z + {}_0E_z = 0 \qquad (0 < y < a) \end{aligned}$$

are the conditions of equilibrium. Calculating ${}_L\mathbf{E}$ from (112.9), (113.3), and (113.4) and substituting into (113.7), we find

$$(113.8)\quad \begin{aligned} {}_0E_x &= -2\left\{[(1 + K^2)\,P_x + K\,P_y]\,\frac{\partial\Sigma}{\partial \mathrm{I}_4} + [(1 + 3\,K^2 + K^4)\,P_x \right. \\ &\qquad \left. + K\,(2 + K^2)\,P_y]\,\frac{\partial\Sigma}{\partial \mathrm{I}_5} + P_x\,\frac{\partial\Sigma}{\partial \mathrm{I}_6}\right\} \\ {}_0E_y &= \frac{P_y}{\epsilon_0} - 2\left\{(K\,P_x + P_y)\,\frac{\partial\Sigma}{\partial \mathrm{I}_4} + [K\,(2 + K^2)\,P_x \right. \\ &\qquad \left. + (1 + K^2)\,P_y]\,\frac{\partial\Sigma}{\partial \mathrm{I}_5} + P_y\,\frac{\partial\Sigma}{\partial \mathrm{I}_6}\right\} \\ {}_0E_z &= 0 \end{aligned}$$

The stress tensor ${}_L\mathbf{t}$ is calculated from (112.8) and (113.3):

$$(113.9)\quad \begin{aligned} {}_Lt_{xx} &= 2\,(1 + K^2)\,\frac{\partial\Sigma}{\partial \mathrm{I}} + 2\,(2 + K^2)\,\frac{\partial\Sigma}{\partial \mathrm{II}} + 2\,\frac{\partial\Sigma}{\partial \mathrm{III}} \\ &\quad + 2\,[(1 + K^2)\,P_x^2 + K\,P_x\,P_y]\,\frac{\partial\Sigma}{\partial \mathrm{I}_4} \\ &\quad + 2\,[(2 + 5\,K^2 + 2\,K^4)\,P_x^2 \\ &\qquad + (4\,K + 3\,K^3)\,P_x\,P_y + K^2\,P_y^2]\,\frac{\partial\Sigma}{\partial \mathrm{I}_5} \\ {}_Lt_{yy} &= 2\,\frac{\partial\Sigma}{\partial \mathrm{I}} + 4\,\frac{\partial\Sigma}{\partial \mathrm{II}} + 2\,\frac{\partial\Sigma}{\partial \mathrm{III}} + 2\,(K\,P_x\,P_y + P_y^2)\,\frac{\partial\Sigma}{\partial \mathrm{I}_4} \\ &\quad + 2\,[K^2\,P_x^2 + (4\,K + K^3)\,P_x\,P_y + (2 + K^2)\,P_y^2]\,\frac{\partial\Sigma}{\partial \mathrm{I}_5} \\ {}_Lt_{zz} &= 2\,\frac{\partial\Sigma}{\partial \mathrm{I}} + 2\,(2 + K^2)\,\frac{\partial\Sigma}{\partial \mathrm{II}} + 2\,\frac{\partial\Sigma}{\partial \mathrm{III}} \\ {}_Lt_{xy} &= 2\,K\left(\frac{\partial\Sigma}{\partial \mathrm{I}} + \frac{\partial\Sigma}{\partial \mathrm{II}}\right) + 2\,[(1 + K^2)\,P_x\,P_y + K\,P_y^2]\,\frac{\partial\Sigma}{\partial \mathrm{I}_4} \\ &\quad + 2\,[(1 + K^2)\,K\,P_x^2 + (2 + 5\,K^2 + K^4)\,P_x\,P_y \\ &\qquad + (3\,K + K^3)\,P_y^2]\,\frac{\partial\Sigma}{\partial \mathrm{I}_5} \\ {}_Lt_{xz} &= {}_Lt_{yz} = 0 \end{aligned}$$

For the Maxwell stress tensor, through $(112.6)_2$ and (113.6), we get

$$
\begin{aligned}
{}_Mt_{xx} &= \epsilon_0 \left({}_0E_x{}^2 - \tfrac{1}{2}\mathbf{E}^2\right) \\
{}_Mt_{yy} &= \epsilon_0 \left({}_0E_y{}^2 - \tfrac{1}{2}\mathbf{E}^2 - 2\,{}_0E_y \frac{P_y}{\epsilon_0} + \frac{P_y{}^2}{\epsilon_0{}^2}\right) \\
{}_Mt_{zz} &= \epsilon_0 \left({}_0E_z{}^2 - \tfrac{1}{2}\mathbf{E}^2\right) \\
{}_Mt_{xy} &= {}_Mt_{yx} = \epsilon_0\, {}_0E_x \left({}_0E_y - \frac{P_y}{\epsilon_0}\right) \\
{}_Mt_{yz} &= {}_Mt_{zy} = \epsilon_0 \left({}_0E_y - \frac{P_y}{\epsilon_0}\right) {}_0E_z \\
{}_Mt_{zx} &= {}_Mt_{xz} = \epsilon_0\, {}_0E_z\, {}_0E_x \\
\mathbf{E}^2 &= {}_0E_x{}^2 + \left({}_0E_y - \frac{P_y}{\epsilon_0}\right)^2 + {}_0E_z{}^2
\end{aligned}
\tag{113.10}
$$

Now the Cauchy stress $\mathbf{t}$ is obtained by

$$\mathbf{t} = {}_L\mathbf{t} - {}_M\mathbf{t}$$

Let us first of all note that the first three terms in the expression of the stress components ${}_L\mathbf{t}$ are identical in form to (52.24) given for the simple elastic shear. Thus for zero polarization the present solution is the same as that given for the simple elastic shear.

Next we may calculate the tractions which must be applied to the face $y = a$ in order to maintain the equilibrium. These are given by

$$t_{(y)k} = {}_Lt^l{}_k\, n_l + [\![{}_Mt^l{}_k]\!]\, n_l$$

From (113.10) we find that

$$[\![{}_Mt^l{}_k]\!]\, n_l = \pm\left({}_0E_x P_y,\ {}_0E_y P_y - \frac{1}{2\,\epsilon_0} P_y{}^2,\ {}_0E_z P_y\right) \tag{113.11}$$

where the positive sign holds for $y = a$ and the negative for $y = 0$.

The total tractions on the face $y = a$ are given by

$$
\begin{aligned}
t_{(y)x} &= {}_Lt_{yx} + {}_0E_x P_y \\
t_{(y)y} &= {}_Lt_{yy} + {}_0E_y P_y - \frac{1}{2\,\epsilon_0{}^2} P_y{}^2 \\
t_{(y)z} &= {}_0E_z P_y
\end{aligned}
\tag{113.12}
$$

where ${}_Lt_{yy}$ and ${}_Lt_{yx}$ are given by $(113.9)_2$ and $(113.9)_4$ respectively. At the surface $y = 0$ the tractions are equal in magnitude and opposite in direction to those indicated in (113.12).

Similarly the tractions on a deformed face which originally was the undeformed face $X =$ const can be obtained. The procedure for this is similar to that given in Art. 52. Hence it is omitted here.

The solution is now complete. A number of special features of the solution are to be noted:

1. Let us find out under what conditions it is possible to eliminate the longitudinal component ${}_0E_x$ of the extrinsic electric field.

According to $(113.8)_1$ we see that for a specified energy function $\Sigma$, we have

$$ {}_0E_x = {}_0E_x\,(P_x, P_y, K) \tag{113.13} $$

Suppose now $P_y$ and $K$ have specified values but $P_x$ may be left to our choice. For a given $K$ there is always the purely elastic solution obtained by setting $P_x = P_y = 0$. If the derivative $\partial\,{}_0E_x/\partial\,P_x$ is nonzero and continuous in some neighborhood of this zero solution, the implicit function theorem states that a nonzero solution of ${}_0E_x = 0$ exists for

$$ P_x = P_x\,(P_y, K) \tag{113.14} $$

In this case the elastic dielectric is subjected to an external electric field ${}_0\mathbf{E}$ which is *normal* to the faces of the slab. The polarization $\mathbf{P}$ will now have a component $P_x$ parallel to the faces of the slab for nonzero values of $K$. This will give rise to an extrinsic body moment of the form

$$ \|m^{kl}\| = \begin{bmatrix} 0 & P_x\,{}_0E_y & 0 \\ -P_x\,{}_0E_y & 0 & 0 \\ 0 & 0 & 0 \end{bmatrix} \tag{113.15} $$

tending to rotate the slab about the $z$ axis.

2. From the expression (113.12) for the stress tensor it is clear that a state of simple shear deformation cannot be maintained by shearing surface loads alone. In addition to a shearing load we need to supply a normal load so as to keep the width of the slab unchanged. The effect which makes it necessary to supply this normal load is known as the *Poynting effect.* Clearly the Poynting effect encountered in the purely elastic case is modified by the additional terms involving the polarization. Even when the elastic part of the stresses is set equal to zero (by assuming that $\Sigma$ is independent of I, II, and III), we shall still have the part due to electric polarization. The lowest-order term in $P_x$ and $P_y$ of this part is of second degree.

We also need a hydrostatic pressure in order to keep the volume unchanged, as is clear from the existence of nonzero $t_{zz}$. This is the *Kelvin effect.*

The sign of the Kelvin effect, i.e., whether it tends to elongate or shorten the body, is again left open. To settle this question, thermodynamic or equivalent considerations are needed.

3. For a vanishing shear angle the normal component $t_{(y)x}$ of the tractions at $y = 0$ depends on the polarization components to at least

second degree. This is the well-known *electrostrictive effect.* In addition, there exist cross terms involving both the shear angle $K$ and the polarization components $P_y$ and $P_x$.

If one assumes, as is reasonable, that $P_x$ is of the same order as the shear angle $K$, this cross effect is of at least second order; hence it cannot occur in a first-order theory. The sign of these effects again requires the knowledge of certain inequalities for thermodynamic stability.

Finally, for the solution of a similar problem concerning a homogeneously deformed and polarized ellipsoid, the reader is referred to Toupin [1956, Art. 12].

## 114. UNIFORM EXTENSION OF A HOLLOW CYLINDRICAL DIELECTRIC[1]

A thick incompressible circular cylindrical shell, carrying a uniform surface charge at the inner surface, is elongated uniformly in the axial direction (Fig. 114.1). We should like to determine the electrostatic field and the stress tensor. The cylindrical coordinates $(r, \theta, z)$ are employed.

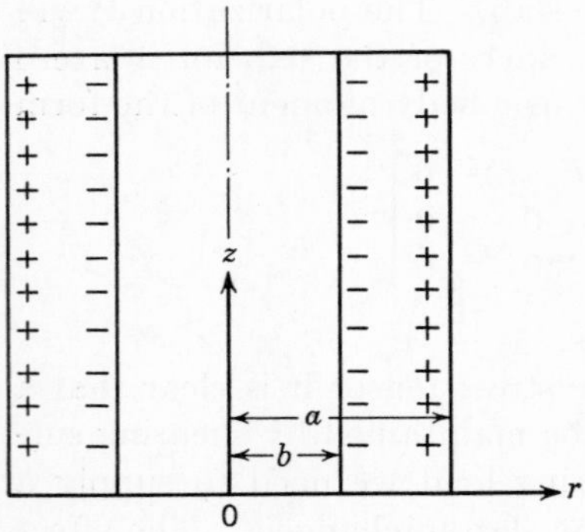


FIG. 114.1. Cylindrical dielectric.

To determine the electrostatic field we must solve the field equation

$$(114.1) \qquad \epsilon_0 \nabla^2 \varphi = \operatorname{div} \mathbf{P} - q_f$$

in the three regions $r < b$, $b < r < a$, and $r > a$ subject to the boundary conditions that the component of the electric field tangential to the boundary surface is continuous and that

$$(114.2) \qquad [\![ \epsilon_0 \varphi,^k - P^k ]\!] n_k + \omega_f = 0$$

We assume that the electric field and polarization have single components, i.e.,

$$\mathbf{E} = [E(r), 0, 0], \mathbf{P} = [P(r), 0, 0].$$

In the region $r < b$ we have $\mathbf{P} = q_f = 0$. At $r = 0$, $\varphi$ is bounded. Hence the appropriate solution of (114.1) is

$$(114.3) \qquad \varphi = A = \text{const} \qquad r < b$$

In the region $b < r < a$ we have $q_f = 0$ and (114.1) is

$$\frac{1}{r} \epsilon_0 (r \varphi,_r),_r = \frac{1}{r} [r P(r)],_r$$

[1] Eringen [1961, Art. 7].

ntegrating once, we have

$$\epsilon_0 \, \varphi_{,r} = P\,(r) + \frac{B_1}{r}$$

where $B_1$ is a constant. Since there is no electric field in the $z$ direction, we also have $\varphi_{,z} = 0$, and owing to symmetry $\varphi_{,\theta} = 0$. Therefore

$$\epsilon_0 \, \varphi = B_1 \log r + \int^r P\,(\xi)\, d\xi + B_2 \tag{114.4}$$

where $B_2$ is a constant.

In the region $r > a$ we have $\mathbf{P} = q_f = 0$, and the appropriate solution of (114.1) is

$$\epsilon_0 \, \varphi = C_1 \log r + C_2 \tag{114.5}$$

where $C_1$ and $C_2$ are constants, of which, without loss in generality, $C_2$ may be taken to be zero.

The boundary conditions (114.2) applied to the boundaries $r = a$ and $= b$ give

$$B_1 = C_1 = -b\,\omega_f$$

Hence the electrostatic potentials in the three regions are given by

$$\begin{aligned} \varphi &= A && r < b \\ \epsilon_0 \, \varphi &= -b\,\omega_f \log r + \int^r P\,(\xi)\, d\xi + B_2 && b < r < a \\ \epsilon_0 \, \varphi &= -b\,\omega_f \log r && r > a \end{aligned} \tag{114.6}$$

The unknown constants $A$ and $B_2$ are immaterial for the electric and stress fields.

The Maxwell electric field is given by ${}_M\mathbf{E} = -\operatorname{grad} \varphi$, and the Maxwell stress tensor follows from $(112.6)_2$. Hence

$$\begin{aligned} {}_M E^r &= \frac{1}{\epsilon_0}\left[\frac{b\,\omega_f}{r} - P\,(r)\right] \\ {}_M E^\theta &= {}_M E^z = 0 \\ {}_M t^r{}_r &= -\,{}_M t^\theta{}_\theta = -\,{}_M t^z{}_z = \frac{1}{2\,\epsilon_0}\left[\frac{b\,\omega_f}{r} - P\,(r)\right]^2 \\ {}_M t^r{}_\theta &= {}_M t^r{}_z = {}_M t^\theta{}_z = 0 \end{aligned} \tag{114.7}$$

Next we determine the local electric and stress fields. To this end we assume a deformation field:

$$r = \mu\, R \qquad \theta = \Theta \qquad z = \lambda\, Z \tag{114.8}$$

which characterizes a uniform axial elongation (if $\lambda > 1$) accompanied by a uniform contraction (if $\mu < 1$). Here $R, \Theta, Z$ are the cylindrical coordinates of a point before deformation, $r, \theta, z$ are the coordinates of the same point after deformation, and $\lambda$ and $\mu$ are respectively the constant stretches in the axial and radial directions. By use of (4.8) and (4.15) we calculate the deformation tensors

$$\|c^k{}_l\| = \begin{bmatrix} 1/\mu^2 & 0 & 0 \\ 0 & 1/\mu^2 & 0 \\ 0 & 0 & 1/\lambda^2 \end{bmatrix} \qquad \|\overset{-1}{c}{}^k{}_l\| = \begin{bmatrix} \mu^2 & 0 & 0 \\ 0 & \mu^2 & 0 \\ 0 & 0 & \lambda^2 \end{bmatrix}$$

For an incompressible medium $\mathrm{III} = \mu^4 \lambda^2 = 1$ or $\mu^2 = \dfrac{1}{\lambda}$, so that

$$\|c^k{}_l\| = \begin{bmatrix} \lambda & 0 & 0 \\ 0 & \lambda & 0 \\ 0 & 0 & 1/\lambda^2 \end{bmatrix} \qquad \|\overset{-1}{c}{}^k{}_l\| = \begin{bmatrix} 1/\lambda & 0 & 0 \\ 0 & 1/\lambda & 0 \\ 0 & 0 & \lambda^2 \end{bmatrix} \tag{114.9}$$

The invariants are

$$\begin{gathered} \mathrm{I} = \frac{2}{\lambda} + \lambda^2 \qquad \mathrm{II} = \frac{1}{\lambda^2} + 2\lambda \qquad \mathrm{III} = 1 \qquad \mathrm{I}_4 = \frac{1}{\lambda} P_r{}^2 \\ \mathrm{I}_5 = \frac{1}{\lambda^2} P_r{}^2 \qquad \mathrm{I}_6 = P_r{}^2 \end{gathered} \tag{114.10}$$

as may be easily verified through (111.16).

By use of constitutive equations (112.9) we obtain the local electric field

$$\begin{gathered} {}_LE^r = 2\left(\frac{1}{\lambda}\frac{\partial\Sigma}{\partial \mathrm{I}_4} + \frac{1}{\lambda^2}\frac{\partial\Sigma}{\partial \mathrm{I}_5} + \frac{\partial\Sigma}{\partial \mathrm{I}_6}\right) P\,(r) \\ {}_LE^\theta = {}_LE^z = 0 \end{gathered} \tag{114.11}$$

According to (112.2) this must be equal to the negative of the Maxwell electric field, so that

$$2\,\epsilon_0 \left(\frac{1}{\lambda}\frac{\partial\Sigma}{\partial \mathrm{I}_4} + \frac{1}{\lambda^2}\frac{\partial\Sigma}{\partial \mathrm{I}_5} + \frac{\partial\Sigma}{\partial \mathrm{I}_6}\right) P = -\frac{b\,\omega_f}{r} + P \tag{114.12}$$

When the form of $\Sigma$ is known, from this equation we can determine $P\,(r)$ as a function of $r$ and $\lambda$, i.e.,

$$P = P\,(r, \lambda) \tag{114.13}$$

The local stress tensor now follows from the constitutive equations similar to (112.8) for the incompressible dielectric:

$$
(114.14)\quad
\begin{aligned}
{}_Lt^r{}_r &= -p + 2\left[\frac{1}{\lambda}\frac{\partial\Sigma}{\partial \mathrm{I}} + \left(\lambda + \frac{1}{\lambda^2}\right)\frac{\partial\Sigma}{\partial \mathrm{II}} + \left(\frac{1}{\lambda}\frac{\partial\Sigma}{\partial \mathrm{I}_4} + \frac{2}{\lambda^2}\frac{\partial\Sigma}{\partial \mathrm{I}_5}\right)P^2\right] \\
{}_Lt^\theta{}_\theta &= -p + 2\left[\frac{1}{\lambda}\frac{\partial\Sigma}{\partial \mathrm{I}} + \left(\lambda + \frac{1}{\lambda^2}\right)\frac{\partial\Sigma}{\partial \mathrm{II}}\right] \\
{}_Lt^z{}_z &= -p + 2\lambda\left(\lambda\frac{\partial\Sigma}{\partial \mathrm{I}} + 2\frac{\partial\Sigma}{\partial \mathrm{II}}\right) \\
{}_Lt^r{}_\theta &= {}_Lt^r{}_z = {}_Lt^\theta{}_z = 0
\end{aligned}
$$

The Cauchy stress tensor $\mathbf{t}$ is now given by

$$
(114.15)\qquad \mathbf{t} = {}_L\mathbf{t} - {}_M\mathbf{t}
$$

The equations of force equilibrium with the vanishing body force are

$$
(114.16)\quad
\begin{aligned}
&\frac{\partial t^r{}_r}{\partial r} + \frac{1}{r}(t^r{}_r - t^\theta{}_\theta) = 0 \\
&\frac{\partial t^\theta{}_\theta}{\partial \theta} = 0 \qquad \frac{\partial t^z{}_z}{\partial z} = 0
\end{aligned}
$$

Since $\Sigma$ is a function of $r$ alone, from the last two equations of (114.16) it follows that $p = p(r)$, and the first of (114.16) may be integrated to give

$$
\begin{aligned}
p(r) - p_0 = {}& 2\left[\frac{1}{\lambda}\frac{\partial\Sigma}{\partial \mathrm{I}} + \left(\lambda + \frac{1}{\lambda^2}\right)\frac{\partial\Sigma}{\partial \mathrm{II}} + \left(\frac{1}{\lambda}\frac{\partial\Sigma}{\partial \mathrm{I}_4} + \frac{2}{\lambda^2}\frac{\partial\Sigma}{\partial \mathrm{I}_5}\right)P^2\right] \\
& - \frac{1}{2\,\epsilon_0}\left(\frac{b\,\omega_f}{r} - P\right)^2 + \int^r \frac{1}{r}\left[2\left(\frac{1}{\lambda}\frac{\partial\Sigma}{\partial \mathrm{I}_4} + \frac{2}{\lambda^2}\frac{\partial\Sigma}{\partial \mathrm{I}_5}\right)P^2 \right. \\
& \left. - \frac{1}{\epsilon_0}\left(\frac{b\,\omega_f}{r} - P\right)^2\right] dr
\end{aligned}
$$

where $p_0$ is a constant which can be determined from the boundary condition on either the inner or the outer surface. Suppose that the outside surface $r = a$ is clear from tractions; then $t^r{}_r(a) = 0$. Hence

$$
p_0 = -\int^a \frac{1}{r}\left[2\left(\frac{1}{\lambda}\frac{\partial\Sigma}{\partial \mathrm{I}_4} + \frac{2}{\lambda^2}\frac{\partial\Sigma}{\partial \mathrm{I}_5}\right)P^2 - \frac{1}{\epsilon_0}\left(\frac{b\,\omega_f}{r} - P\right)^2\right] dr
$$

Substitution of $p$ into (114.14) now gives

$$
(114.17)\quad
\begin{aligned}
{}_Lt^r{}_r &= \frac{1}{2\,\epsilon_0}\left(\frac{b\,\omega_f}{r} - P\right)^2 + \int_r^a \frac{1}{r}\left[2\left(\frac{1}{\lambda}\frac{\partial\Sigma}{\partial \mathrm{I}_4} + \frac{2}{\lambda^2}\frac{\partial\Sigma}{\partial \mathrm{I}_5}\right)P^2 - \frac{1}{\epsilon_0}\left(\frac{b\,\omega_f}{r} - P\right)^2\right] dr \\
{}_Lt^r{}_r - {}_Lt^\theta{}_\theta &= 2\left(\frac{1}{\lambda}\frac{\partial\Sigma}{\partial \mathrm{I}_4} + \frac{2}{\lambda^2}\frac{\partial\Sigma}{\partial \mathrm{I}_5}\right)P^2 \\
{}_Lt^z{}_z - {}_Lt^\theta{}_\theta &= -2\left(\frac{1}{\lambda} - \lambda^2\right)\left(\frac{\partial\Sigma}{\partial \mathrm{I}} + \frac{1}{\lambda}\frac{\partial\Sigma}{\partial \mathrm{II}}\right) \\
{}_Lt^r{}_\theta &= {}_Lt^r{}_z = {}_Lt^\theta{}_z = 0
\end{aligned}
$$

Clearly the internal surface is not free of tractions now. In fact, on the inner surface there acts a uniform radial traction.

$$t^r{}_r = \int_b^a \frac{1}{r}\left[2\left(\frac{1}{\lambda}\frac{\partial \Sigma}{\partial \mathrm{I}_4} + \frac{2}{\lambda^2}\frac{\partial \Sigma}{\partial \mathrm{I}_5}\right)P^2 - \frac{1}{\epsilon_0}\left(\frac{b\,\omega_f}{r} - P\right)^2\right]dr \tag{114.18}$$

For vanishing surface charge we have $\omega_f = P = 0$, and we obtain the elasticity solution

$$\begin{aligned} t^r{}_r &= t^\theta{}_\theta = t^r{}_\theta = t^r{}_z = 0 \\ t^z{}_z &= -2\left(\frac{1}{\lambda} - \lambda^2\right)\left(\frac{\partial \Sigma}{\partial \mathrm{I}} + \frac{1}{\lambda}\frac{\partial \Sigma}{\partial \mathrm{II}}\right) \end{aligned} \tag{114.19}$$

We observe several new phenomena that are not present in an unpolarized elastic cylinder subject to uniform extension: (1) uniform extension is not possible by the application of a uniform axial load alone; (2) in addition to an axial load distributed in a particular fashion that depends on the characteristic of material and the charge, we must apply to the inner surface a uniform load; (3) the cylinder is radially stressed with a radius-dependent stress and is subjected to a radius-dependent hoop stress.

*Special Cases.* To get a more definite idea with regard to the magnitude and the distribution of local stress, we now consider a material characterized by a stored energy which is linear in the invariants, i.e.,

$$\Sigma = \alpha_1(\mathrm{I} - 3) + \alpha_2(\mathrm{II} - 3) + \alpha_4\mathrm{I}_4 + \alpha_5\mathrm{I}_5 + \alpha_6\mathrm{I}_6$$

Through (114.12) we obtain

$$\begin{aligned} P &= -K_1\frac{b\,\omega_f}{r} \\ K_1 &= \left[\epsilon_0\left(\frac{2}{\lambda}\alpha_4 + \frac{2}{\lambda^2}\alpha_5 + 2\,\alpha_6\right) - 1\right]^{-1} \end{aligned} \tag{114.20}$$

Through (114.11), (114.17), and (114.20) we get

$$\begin{aligned} {}_LE^r &= -\left[\epsilon_0 - \left(\frac{2}{\lambda}\alpha_4 + \frac{2}{\lambda^2}\alpha_5 + 2\,\alpha_6\right)^{-1}\right]^{-1}\frac{b\,\omega_f}{r} \\ {}_LE^\theta &= {}_LE^z = 0 \\ {}_Lt^r{}_r &= (1 + K_1)^2\frac{b^2\,\omega_f{}^2}{2\,\epsilon_0}\frac{1}{r^2} + \left[\left(\frac{2}{\lambda}\alpha_4 + \frac{4}{\lambda^2}\alpha_5\right)K_1{}^2 \right. \\ &\qquad \left. - \frac{1}{\epsilon_0}(1 + K_1)^2\right]\frac{b^2\,\omega_f{}^2}{4}\left(\frac{1}{r^4} - \frac{1}{a^4}\right) \end{aligned} \tag{114.21}$$

$$\begin{aligned} {}_Lt^r{}_r - {}_Lt^\theta{}_\theta &= 2\left(\frac{1}{\lambda}\alpha_4 + \frac{2}{\lambda^2}\alpha_5\right)\frac{K_1{}^2\,b^2\,\omega_f{}^2}{r^2} \\ {}_Lt^z{}_z - {}_Lt^\theta{}_\theta &= -2\left(\frac{1}{\lambda} - \lambda^2\right)\left(\alpha_1 + \frac{1}{\lambda}\alpha_2\right) \\ {}_Lt^r{}_\theta &= {}_Lt^r{}_z = {}_Lt^\theta{}_z = 0 \end{aligned} \tag{114.22}$$

Finally we remark that the situation is unchanged if the charge distribution at the inner surface is replaced by an applied external radial electric field ${}_0E_r$ such that at the inner surface $\epsilon_0\,{}_0E_r = \omega_f$.

## 115. POLYNOMIAL APPROXIMATIONS

Problems concerning the finite deformations and polarization of an elastic dielectric are very difficult to treat. For a large class of dielectric materials the elastic deformation cannot become large before yield or fracture occurs. This allows polynomial approximations of basic equations in strain measures. Below we give the lowest-order approximations in terms of infinitesimal strain $\tilde{\mathbf{e}}$. To accomplish this, we transform the constitutive equations (111.28) and (111.29) into ones containing the strain measure $\mathbf{e}$. To this end we employ (9.29)

$$\text{(115.1)}\qquad \begin{aligned} \mathrm{I}_c &= 3 - 2\,\mathrm{I}_e \\ \mathrm{II}_c &= 3 - 4\,\mathrm{I}_e + 4\,\mathrm{II}_e \\ \mathrm{III}_c &= 1 - 2\,\mathrm{I}_e + 4\,\mathrm{II}_e - 8\,\mathrm{III}_e \end{aligned}$$

and

$$\text{(115.2)}\qquad \begin{aligned} K_4 &= 2\,\bar{\mathrm{I}}_4 - \bar{\mathrm{I}}_6 \\ K_5 &= 4\,\bar{\mathrm{I}}_5 - 2\,K_4 - \bar{\mathrm{I}}_6 \\ K_6 &= \mathrm{I}_6 = \bar{\mathrm{I}}_6 \end{aligned}$$

where

$$\text{(115.3)}\qquad \begin{aligned} \bar{\mathrm{I}}_4 &= e^k{}_r\,P^r\,P_k \\ \bar{\mathrm{I}}_5 &= e^k{}_r\,e^r{}_s\,P_k\,P^s \\ \bar{\mathrm{I}}_6 &= P^2 \end{aligned}$$

The stored-energy function may now be approximated by

$$\text{(115.4)}\qquad \begin{aligned} \Sigma = {} & \alpha_0\,\mathrm{I}_e + \alpha_1\,\mathrm{I}_e{}^2 + \alpha_2\,\mathrm{II}_e + \alpha_3\,\bar{\mathrm{I}}_6 + \alpha_4\,\bar{\mathrm{I}}_4 \\ & + \alpha_5\,\bar{\mathrm{I}}_6\,\mathrm{I}_e + \alpha_6\,\bar{\mathrm{I}}_5 + \alpha_7\,\bar{\mathrm{I}}_6\,\mathrm{I}_e{}^2 + \alpha_8\,\bar{\mathrm{I}}_6\,\mathrm{II}_e \\ & + \alpha_9\,\bar{\mathrm{I}}_4\,\mathrm{I}_e + \alpha_{10}\,\bar{\mathrm{I}}_6{}^2 + \alpha_{11}\,\mathrm{I}_e{}^3 + \alpha_{12}\,\mathrm{I}_e\,\mathrm{II}_e \\ & + \alpha_{13}\,\mathrm{III}_e + \alpha_{14}\,\bar{\mathrm{I}}_6{}^2\,\mathrm{I}_e + \alpha_{15}\,\bar{\mathrm{I}}_6{}^3 \end{aligned}$$

which contains all terms up to and including third order in $\mathbf{e}$ and $P^2$. Using (115.1) and (115.2), we calculate

$$\begin{aligned} \frac{\partial\Sigma}{\partial\mathrm{I}_c} &= \frac{\partial\Sigma}{\partial\mathrm{I}_e}\frac{\partial\mathrm{I}_e}{\partial\mathrm{I}_c} + \frac{\partial\Sigma}{\partial\mathrm{II}_e}\frac{\partial\mathrm{II}_e}{\partial\mathrm{I}_c} + \frac{\partial\Sigma}{\partial\mathrm{III}_e}\frac{\partial\mathrm{III}_e}{\partial\mathrm{I}_c} \\ &= -\frac{1}{2}\frac{\partial\Sigma}{\partial\mathrm{I}_e} - \frac{1}{2}\frac{\partial\Sigma}{\partial\mathrm{II}_e} - \frac{1}{8}\frac{\partial\Sigma}{\partial\mathrm{III}_e} \\ \frac{\partial\Sigma}{\partial\mathrm{II}_c} &= \frac{1}{4}\frac{\partial\Sigma}{\partial\mathrm{II}_e} + \frac{1}{8}\frac{\partial\Sigma}{\partial\mathrm{III}_e} \end{aligned}$$

$$\frac{\partial \Sigma}{\partial \mathrm{III}_c} = -\frac{1}{8}\frac{\partial \Sigma}{\partial \mathrm{III}_e}$$

$$\frac{\partial \Sigma}{\partial K_4} = \frac{1}{2}\left(\frac{\partial \Sigma}{\partial \bar{\mathrm{I}}_4} + \frac{\partial \Sigma}{\partial \bar{\mathrm{I}}_5}\right)$$

$$\frac{\partial \Sigma}{\partial K_5} = \frac{1}{4}\frac{\partial \Sigma}{\partial \bar{\mathrm{I}}_5}$$

$$\frac{\partial \Sigma}{\partial K_6} = \frac{1}{2}\frac{\partial \Sigma}{\partial \bar{\mathrm{I}}_4} + \frac{1}{4}\frac{\partial \Sigma}{\partial \bar{\mathrm{I}}_5} + \frac{\partial \Sigma}{\partial \bar{\mathrm{I}}_6}$$

Now substitute (115.4) into the right-hand sides of these expressions and carry the results into (111.28) and (111.29). Retaining the linear terms in **e** and replacing them by $\tilde{\mathbf{e}}$, and retaining quadratic terms in **P**, after some lengthy manipulations we find[1]

$$(115.5)\quad {}_Lt^k{}_l = [a_0 + (\lambda + a_3 P^2)\,\tilde{e}^m{}_m + a_2 P^2 + a_1 \tilde{e}^m{}_n P_m P^n]\,\delta^k{}_l + (2\,\mu + a_4 P^2)\,\tilde{e}^k{}_l + [a_5 - (a_1 + a_5)\,\tilde{e}^m{}_m]\,P^k P_l + a_6\,\tilde{e}^m{}_l P_m P^k + (2\,a_5 + a_6)\,\tilde{e}^k{}_m P^m P_l$$

$$(115.6)\quad {}_LE^k = [-a_7 + (2\,a_1 + 2\,a_2 + a_7)\,\tilde{e}^m{}_m]\,P^k + 2\,a_5\,\tilde{e}^k{}_m P^m$$

where the relations of $\alpha_\kappa$ to $a_\kappa$ are

$$(115.7)\quad \begin{aligned} &a_0 \equiv \alpha_0 \qquad \lambda \equiv -\alpha_0 + 2\,\alpha_1 + \alpha_2 \qquad a_1 \equiv \alpha_9 \qquad a_2 \equiv \alpha_5\\ &a_3 \equiv -\alpha_5 + 2\,\alpha_7 + \alpha_8 \qquad 2\,\mu \equiv -2\,\alpha_0 - \alpha_2 \qquad a_4 \equiv -2\,\alpha_5 - \alpha_8\\ &a_5 \equiv -\alpha_4 - 2\,\alpha_6 \qquad a_6 \equiv 2\,\alpha_4 + 5\,\alpha_6\\ &a_7 \equiv -2\,(\alpha_3 + \alpha_4 + \alpha_6)\end{aligned}$$

Both ${}_L\mathbf{t}$ and ${}_L\mathbf{E}$ vanish with $\tilde{\mathbf{e}}$ and **P** if we take $\alpha_0 = 0$. Thus constitutive equation (115.5) contains a constant initial pressure field.

From (115.5) there follows the antisymmetric part of the local stress tensor

$$(115.8)\quad {}_Lt^{[kl]} = 2\,a_5\,\tilde{e}^{[k}{}_m P^{l]} P^m$$

The constitutive equations (115.5) and (115.6) are linear in $\tilde{\mathbf{e}}$ and of second order in $P^k$. Polynomial approximations containing higher-degree terms in $\tilde{\mathbf{e}}$ and **P** may be obtained in a similar fashion.

In the approximation (115.4) for the stored energy leading to constitutive equations (115.5) and (115.6), the terms having coefficients from $\alpha_{10}$

[1] The present result is arrived at in a way different from the method used by Toupin [1956, art. 16]. Toupin treats the anisotropic dielectric first and takes the strain measures **E** and $_\rho\mathbf{\Pi}$ as primitive variables. Afterwards, by introducing isotropic tensors of various orders (up to six), he obtains his constitutive equations (16.2 and 16.7), which have the same form as ours given below. They contain the same number of independent constants. We find his approach more indirect and somewhat more lengthy.

to $\alpha_{15}$ inclusive do not contribute to the stress and electric field. We may therefore set these equal to zero. By use of (115.7) the stored-energy function may then be expressed as

$$(115.9)\quad \Sigma = \rho_0\,\epsilon = a_0\,\mathrm{I}_e + \frac{\lambda + 2\,\mu + 3\,a_0}{2}\,\mathrm{I}_e^2 - (2\,\mu + 2\,a_0)\,\mathrm{II}_e + (3\,a_5 + a_6 - \tfrac{1}{2}\,a_7)\,\bar{\mathrm{I}}_6 - (5\,a_5 + 2\,a_6)\,\bar{\mathrm{I}}_4 + a_2\,\bar{\mathrm{I}}_6\,\mathrm{I}_e + (2\,a_5 + a_6)\,\bar{\mathrm{I}}_5 + \tfrac{1}{2}\,(3\,a_2 + a_3 + a_4)\,\bar{\mathrm{I}}_6\,\mathrm{I}_e^2 - (2\,a_2 + a_4)\,\bar{\mathrm{I}}_6\,\mathrm{II}_e + a_1\,\bar{\mathrm{I}}_4\,\mathrm{I}_e$$

Further specialization of the quasi-linear constitutive equations (115.5) and (115.6) is possible by dropping the products of strain and polarization. Thus for a zero initial stress ($a_0 = 0$)

$$(115.10)\quad {}_Lt^k{}_l = \lambda\,\tilde{e}^m{}_m\,\delta^k{}_l + 2\,\mu\,\tilde{e}^k{}_l + a_2\,P^2\,\delta^k{}_l + a_5\,P^k\,P_l$$

$$(115.11)\quad {}_LE^k = -a_7\,P^k$$

If one further uses the equilibrium condition ${}_ME + {}_LE = 0$, the local stress becomes

$$(115.12)\quad {}_Lt^{kl} = \lambda\,\tilde{e}^m{}_m\,g^{kl} + 2\,\mu\,\tilde{e}^k{}_l + A\;{}_ME^2\,g^{kl} + B\;{}_ME^k\,E^l$$

where $A$ and $B$ are material constants. This result was obtained by Stratton [1941, pp. 140–146] from an energy principle attributed to Helmholtz and Korteweg.

The expression for the stored energy (115.9) corresponding to the approximation (115.10) and (115.11) is

$$(115.13)\quad \Sigma = \rho_0\,\epsilon = \tfrac{1}{2}\,(\lambda + 2\,\mu)\,\mathrm{I}_e^2 - 2\,\mu\,\mathrm{II}_e + (3\,a_5 - \tfrac{1}{2}\,a_7)\,\bar{\mathrm{I}}_6 - 5\,a_5\,\bar{\mathrm{I}}_4 + a_2\,\bar{\mathrm{I}}_6\,\mathrm{I}_e + 2\,a_5\,\bar{\mathrm{I}}_5 + \tfrac{3}{2}\,a_2\,\bar{\mathrm{I}}_6\,\mathrm{I}_e^2 - 2\,a_2\,\bar{\mathrm{I}}_6\,\mathrm{II}_e$$

## 116. ANISOTROPIC DIELECTRICS

Anisotropic elastic-dielectric solids exhibit a certain important phenomenon that is eliminated in isotropic solids. This is the piezoelectric effect which in Voigt's theory of piezoelectricity is based on constitutive equations of linearly anisotropic elastic dielectrics.

In nature, materials are found to possess certain symmetries based on the arrangements of their atoms and molecules with respect to each other. A crystalline solid possesses *point symmetry* that can be fully characterized by the invariant property for its stored-energy function under a *finite subgroup* of the orthogonal group of transformations of the material coordinates. On the other hand, in elasticity theory one finds *transverse isotropy* or some other types of anisotropy which require the invariance under a *continuous subgroup* of the orthogonal group. For example, one may mention the state of the elastic solid inhomogeneously deformed from an isotropic natural state.

Here we consider the anisotropy as a material characteristic referred to its natural state. *If the characteristic group of the material symmetry of the natural state of an elastic dielectric is a proper subgroup of the orthogonal group, we say that the dielectric is anisotropic.* The material symmetry of the natural state of crystals is described by thirty-two finite crystal groups.[1]

For an anisotropic elastic dielectric the stored energy function may be expressed by any one of (111.8)–(111.10). Alternative representations have been used in the literature[2] replacing $\mathbf{G}_K$ by material descriptor tensors $H_\Gamma{}^{KLM\cdots}$ of any order which, under the proper subgroup characteristic of the material symmetry in the natural state, leave $\Sigma$ invariant; e.g., we may write

$$(116.1) \qquad \Sigma = \Sigma\,(X^K, E_{KL}, \Pi_K, H_\Gamma{}^{KLM\cdots}) \qquad (\Gamma = 1, 2, \ldots)$$

Selection of the number of these descriptors depends on the number of state variables and the type of anisotropy. Toupin uses a polynomial approximation of the form

$$(116.2) \qquad \Sigma = H_0{}^K \Pi_K + H_1{}^{KL} \Pi_K \Pi_L + H_2{}^{KL} E_{KL} + H_3{}^{KLMN} E_{KL} E_{MN} + H_4{}^{KLM} E_{KL} \Pi_M + H_5{}^{KLMN} E_{KL} \Pi_M \Pi_N + H_6{}^{KLMNP} E_{KL} E_{MN} \Pi_P + H_7{}^{KLMNPQ} E_{KL} E_{MN} \Pi_P \Pi_Q$$

Upon substituting this into (111.21) and (111.22), we find approximate constitutive equations for the anisotropic dielectric. Below we give the simplest of these for the linear case

$$(116.3) \qquad {}_Lt^{kl} = 4\, H_3{}^{klmn}\, \tilde{e}_{mn} + 2\, H_4{}^{klm}\, P_m$$

$$(116.4) \qquad {}_LE^k = 2\, H_1{}^{km}\, P_m + H_4{}^{mnk}\, \tilde{e}_{mn}$$

where $H_\Gamma{}^{\cdots}$ $(\Gamma = 1, 3, 4)$ are material constants. For static equilibrium ${}_L\mathbf{E} + {}_M\mathbf{E} = 0$. Since in the linear theory the difference between the Cauchy stress tensor $\mathbf{t}$ and ${}_L\mathbf{t}$ is negligible, we may write (116.3) and (116.4) in the form

$$(116.5) \qquad t^{kl} = c^{klmn}\, \tilde{e}_{mn} + q^{klm}\, P_m$$

$$(116.6) \qquad -\,\epsilon_0\, {}_ME^k = \overset{-1}{\chi}{}^{km}\, P_m + p^{mnk}\, \tilde{e}_{mn}$$

where

$$c^{klmn} = 4\, H_3{}^{klmn} \qquad q^{klm} = 2\, H_4{}^{klm}$$
$$\overset{-1}{\chi}{}^{kl} = 2\, \epsilon_0\, H_1{}^{kl} \qquad p^{klm} = \epsilon_0 H_4{}^{klm}$$

[1] For references in connection with anisotropic elastic solids see footnote 4, Art. 45

[2] Cf. Toupin [1956, art. 14], Doyle and Ericksen [1956], Ericksen and Rivlin [1954] and Smith and Rivlin [1958].

elations (116.5) and (116.6) were first given by Voigt. These equaons, together with the field equation, constitute the foundation of the near theory of *piezoelectricity*. Since in elasticity theory the static and ynamic forms of the constitutive equations are the same, (116.5) and 16.6) are used in the dynamical problem of piezoelectricity. Toupin ave more general expressions involving quadratic terms in $\tilde{\mathbf{e}}$ and **P** f. [1956, art. 15, footnote 2]). He also obtained the isotropic form of ese relations, which we derived in the preceding article in a different ay.

The theory of electromagnetic elastic solids is in a prenatal state. If e exclude the foregoing account, the theory of finite deformations emains untouched. While there is extensive work presently being roduced in the sister field, magnetohydrodynamics, the foundation is not ell-understood. Linear theories can be said to have had sufficient xploration, but even in these limiting cases many vital questions remain nanswered or side-stepped. Theoretical and experimental questions oncerning electromagnetomechanical body forces, stress tensors, omenta, boundary conditions, and the foundation of moving electroagnetic media are still in the state of their nineteenth-century conoversy. For this reason we avoid presenting a chapter on electroagnetic fluids, although this was our early intention because of their ecent popularity among physicists, mathematicians, and engineers. or the benefit of interested readers we cite the following few recent works this area.

Toward a general theory of constitutive equations of continuum physics e cite Pipkin and Rivlin [1959] and Rivlin [1960*b*]. For the electroagnetic-field theories we have Truesdell and Toupin [1960, art. F], tratton [1941], Sommerfeld [1952], Abraham and Becker [1949], Whitker [1953], Fano, Chu, and Adler [1960], Goldstein [1960], Kottler 922], Van Dantzig [1934, 1937], and Schouten and Haantjes [1934].

For specific materials in magneto-gas dynamics and plasma physics e cite Elsasser [1956], Alfvén [1950], Spitzer [1956], Cowling [1957], and rummond [1961]. See also the survey articles by Mawardi [1959] and andshoff [1961] and the references contained therein.

APPENDIX

# TENSOR ANALYSIS

## A1. INTRODUCTION

In this appendix we present a brief account of tensor calculus, a prerequisite to an understanding of the main text.

Tensors are recognized by their invariant property under transformations of the reference frame. Like vectors, tensors possess components referred to a frame of reference. The laws of transformation of these components upon the change of the reference frame characterize these objects. Their precise definition is given in Art. A3. Because of the invariant properties of these objects they are particularly suited to the description of natural laws. Indeed, the laws of nature must be independent of the reference frame used.

We cite the following important advantages in favor of their use: (1) tensors provide a powerful method for the derivation of basic equations; (2) because of their invariant properties upon coordinate transformation, the equations obtained are universal in nature; i.e., they are valid in any coordinate system; (3) economic use of symbols and symmetric appearance makes them perfectly suited for a neat bookkeeping system; (4) the equations obtained suggest the unification of different ideas and the generalization of particular ideas.

The following references constitute a brief library for further study by readers desiring various degrees of sophistication. For beginners we recommend Jeffreys [1931], Michal [1947], Weatherburn [1938], Sokolnikoff [1951], Spain [1956], and Coburn [1955]. For readers at an intermediate level, Eisenhart [1926], Appell [1926], Levi-Civita [1927], McConnell [1931], Brillouin [1938], and Synge and Schild [1949] are suggested. For more advanced readers we suggest Weyl [1923], Thomas [1934], Veblen [1933], Schouten [1951], [1954], Schouten and Kulk [1949], and Yano [1957].

## A2. CURVILINEAR COORDINATES

Let $z^k$ or $z^1, z^2, z^3$ be the rectangular coordinates of a point $P(\mathbf{z})$. three functions

$$x^k = x^k(z^1, z^2, z^3) \qquad (k = 1, 2, 3) \tag{A2.1}$$

in a neighborhood of $\mathbf{z}$ possess a *unique* inverse

$$z^k = z^k(x^1, x^2, x^3) \tag{A2.2}$$

we say that $P$ has curvilinear coordinates $x^k$. Generally, from ge metrical considerations (A2.2) would be written down. It can then b shown[1] that its unique inverse (A2.1) exists if the $z^k$ have continuo first-order derivatives and if the jacobian

$$J \neq 0 \tag{A2.3}$$

in a neighborhood of $P$, where

$$J = \left|\frac{\partial z^k}{\partial x^l}\right| = \begin{vmatrix} \partial z^1/\partial x^1 & \partial z^1/\partial x^2 & \partial z^1/\partial x^3 \\ \partial z^2/\partial x^1 & \partial z^2/\partial x^2 & \partial z^2/\partial x^3 \\ \partial z^3/\partial x^1 & \partial z^3/\partial x^2 & \partial z^3/\partial x^3 \end{vmatrix} \tag{A2.4}$$

For a fixed $z^1$, $z^2$, or $z^3$ the transformation (A2.2) gives surfaces, calle *curvilinear surfaces,* which intersect at a point. The intersection line any two curvilinear surfaces defines a *curvilinear line* so that through point $P$ there pass three noncoincident curvilinear lines defining th coordinates of $P$ (Fig. A2.1).

*Example* 1. *Cylindrical Coordinates.* The cylindrical coordinates[2] are defined by their relations to the rectangular coordinates $z^k$:

$$z^1 = x^1 \cos x^2 \qquad z^2 = x^1 \sin x^2 \qquad z^3 = x^3 \tag{A2.5}$$

Thus the jacobian $J$ is

$$J = \begin{vmatrix} \cos x^2 & -x^1 \sin x^2 & 0 \\ \sin x^2 & x^1 \cos x^2 & 0 \\ 0 & 0 & 1 \end{vmatrix}$$

Hence a unique inverse to (A2.5) exists everywhere excluding the $x^3$ ax $(x^1 = 0)$ where $J = 0$. In fact,

$$x^1 = \sqrt{(z^1)^2 + (z^2)^2} \qquad x^2 = \arctan\frac{z^2}{z^1} \qquad x^3 = z^3 \tag{A2.6}$$

[1] Cf. Widder [1947, p. 47].

[2] The commonly used notation for $x^1$, $x^2$, $x^3$ is $r$, $\theta$, $z$ respectively.

e coordinate surfaces are circular cylinders having the $x^3$ axis as their is, vertical planes through the $x^3$ axis, and planes perpendicular to the axis (Fig. A2.2).

*Base vectors* $\mathbf{g}_k\ (x^1, x^2, x^3)$ are defined by

$$\mathbf{g}_k = \frac{\partial \mathbf{p}}{\partial x^k} = \frac{\partial z^m}{\partial x^k}\,\mathbf{i}_m \qquad \text{2.7)}$$

here $\mathbf{p} = z^m\,\mathbf{i}_m$ is the position vector of a point $p$, and the diagonally

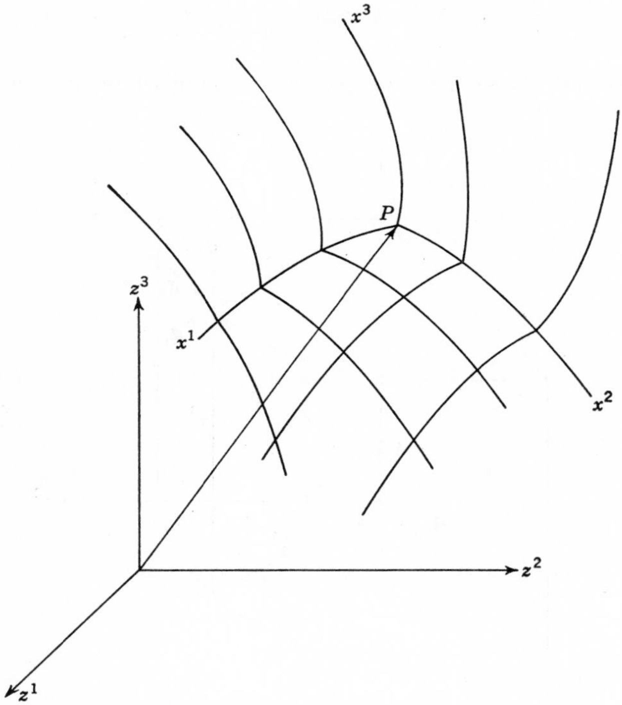


FIG. A2.1. Curvilinear coordinates.

peated index $m$ indicates summation over the range $m = 1, 2, 3$. This mmation convention is used throughout the text.

By multiplying both sides of (A2.7) by $\partial x^k/\partial z^l$, we solve for $\mathbf{i}_m$:

$$\mathbf{i}_m = \frac{\partial x^k}{\partial z^m}\,\mathbf{g}_k \qquad \text{2.8)}$$

st as the rectangular base vectors $\mathbf{i}_m$ lie on the $z^m$ axes, it is clear from

(A2.7) that $\mathbf{g}_k$ are tangential to the curvilinear lines $x^k$ (see Fig. A2.2). From (A2.5) and (A2.7) we find, for instance, that in cylindrical coordinates we have

$$\begin{aligned} \mathbf{g}_1 &= (\cos x^2)\,\mathbf{i}_1 + (\sin x^2)\,\mathbf{i}_2 \\ \mathbf{g}_2 &= -(x^1 \sin x^2)\,\mathbf{i}_1 + (x^1 \cos x^2)\,\mathbf{i}_2 \\ \mathbf{g}_3 &= \mathbf{i}_3 \end{aligned} \tag{A2.9}$$

*The fundamental metric tensor* $g_{kl}$ is defined by

$$g_{kl}(\mathbf{x}) = \mathbf{g}_k \cdot \mathbf{g}_l = \frac{\partial z^m}{\partial x^k}\frac{\partial z^n}{\partial x^l}\,\delta_{mn} \tag{A2.10}$$

where $\delta_{mn}$ is the Kronecker symbol, which is 1 when $m = n$ and zero otherwise.

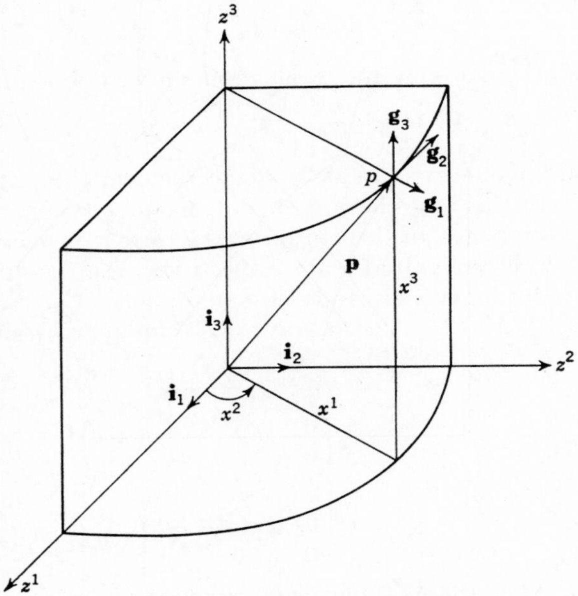


FIG. A2.2. Cylindrical coordinates.

For the infinitesimal vector $d\mathbf{p}$ we have

$$d\mathbf{p} = \frac{\partial \mathbf{p}}{\partial x^k}\,dx^k = \mathbf{g}_k\,dx^k \tag{A2.11}$$

Therefore the square of the line element is calculated by

$$ds^2 = d\mathbf{p} \cdot d\mathbf{p} = g_{kl}\,dx^k\,dx^l \tag{A2.12}$$

In general, curvilinear coordinates are not mutually orthogonal since

$$\mathbf{g}_k \cdot \mathbf{g}_l = g_{kl} \neq 0 \qquad k \neq l$$

that is, mixed components of $\mathbf{g}$; $g_{12}, g_{23}, g_{31}$ are not all zero.

The reciprocal base vectors $\mathbf{g}^k(x)$ are the solution of the system

(A2.13) $$\mathbf{g}^k \cdot \mathbf{g}_l = \delta^k{}_l$$

where $\delta^k{}_l$ is the Kronecker symbol. It can be verified that the unique solution of (A2.13) is

(A2.14) $$\mathbf{g}^k = g^{kl}\,\mathbf{g}_l$$

where

(A2.15) $$g^{kl}(\mathbf{x}) = \frac{\text{cofactor } g_{kl}}{g}$$

$$g \equiv \det g_{kl}$$

From (A2.14), by taking the scalar product, we find that

(A2.16) $$g^{kl} = \mathbf{g}^k \cdot \mathbf{g}^l \qquad \delta^k{}_l = g^{km}\,g_{ml}$$

When coordinate curves are orthogonal, then the directions of $\mathbf{g}^k$ and $\mathbf{g}_k$ coincide. In this case the mixed components $g^{kl} = g_{kl} = 0$, $(k \neq l)$.

The base vectors $\mathbf{g}_k$ and their reciprocals $\mathbf{g}^k$ are, in general, not of unit magnitude. Their magnitudes are respectively $\sqrt{g_{\underline{kk}}}$ and $\sqrt{g^{\underline{kk}}}$, where an underscore for indices suspends the summation.

Using (A2.9), (A2.10), (A2.14), and (A2.15) for cylindrical coordinates, we find

(A2.17)
$$\|g_{kl}\| = \begin{bmatrix} 1 & 0 & 0 \\ 0 & (x^1)^2 & 0 \\ 0 & 0 & 1 \end{bmatrix}$$

$$\|g^{kl}\| = \begin{bmatrix} 1 & 0 & 0 \\ 0 & 1/(x^1)^2 & 0 \\ 0 & 0 & 1 \end{bmatrix}$$

$$\mathbf{g}^1 = \mathbf{g}_1 \qquad \mathbf{g}^2 = \frac{1}{(x^1)^2}\,\mathbf{g}_2 \qquad \mathbf{g}^3 = \mathbf{g}_3 = \mathbf{i}_3$$

Hence $\mathbf{g}_1$ and $\mathbf{g}_3$ have unit magnitudes while $\mathbf{g}_2$ and $\mathbf{g}^2$ have magnitudes $x^1$ and $1/x^1$ respectively.

Any vector $\mathbf{v}$ can be expressed in terms of its parallel projections along $\mathbf{g}_k$ and $\mathbf{g}^k$ by writing

(A2.18) $$\mathbf{v} = v^k\,\mathbf{g}_k = v_k\,\mathbf{g}^k$$

Note that the components $v^k$ and $v_k$ of $\mathbf{v}$ are in general different. They are identical *only* in rectangular coordinates. Components $v^k$ and $v_k$ a respectively called *contravariant* and *covariant* components of $\mathbf{v}$. B multiplying (A2.18) scalarly by $\mathbf{g}^l$ and $\mathbf{g}_l$, we see that they are related each other by

$$v^k = g^{kl} v_l \qquad v_k = g_{kl} v^l \tag{A2.19}$$

Thus, when either $v_k$ or $v^k$ is known, we can obtain the other by (A2.1 as long as the metric tensor $g_{kl}$ is known. This process is known as th *raising* and *lowering of the indices.*

## A3. VECTORS AND TENSORS

DEFINITION 1. *A function* $\phi(x^1, x^2, x^3)$ *is called an absolute scalar upon transformation of coordinates* $x^k = x^k(\acute{x}^1, \acute{x}^2, \acute{x}^3)$ *it does not change i original value,* i.e.,

$$\phi(x^1(\acute{\mathbf{x}}), x^2(\acute{\mathbf{x}}), x^3(\acute{\mathbf{x}})) \equiv \acute{\phi}(\acute{x}^1, \acute{x}^2, \acute{x}^3) = \phi(x^1, x^2, x^3) \tag{A3.1}$$

An example of an absolute scalar is the temperature at a point, for it h the same value in all coordinate systems.

DEFINITION 2. *Quantities* $A^k(\mathbf{x})$ *are called contravariant components of vector (or, simply, a contravariant vector) if under coordinate transformati* $x^k = x^k(\acute{x}^1, \acute{x}^2, \acute{x}^3)$ *they transform according to the rule*

$$\acute{A}^k(\acute{\mathbf{x}}) = A^m(\mathbf{x}) \frac{\partial \acute{x}^k}{\partial x^m} \qquad \text{(contravariant vector)} \tag{A3.2}$$

Here $\acute{A}^k$ are the components of the same vector referred to coordinat $\acute{x}^k$. An example of a contravariant vector is the differential; i.e., $A^k \equiv dx$ since according to the chain rule of differentiation we have

$$d\acute{x}^k = \frac{\partial \acute{x}^k}{\partial x^m} dx^m$$

which follows the rule (A3.2).

DEFINITION 3. *Similarly* $A_k(\mathbf{x})$ *are called covariant components of vector (or, simply, a covariant vector) if they obey the transformation law*

$$\acute{A}_k(\acute{\mathbf{x}}) = A_m(\mathbf{x}) \frac{\partial x^m}{\partial \acute{x}^k} \qquad \text{(covariant vector)} \tag{A3.3}$$

An example of a covariant vector is the partial derivative of an absolu scalar; i.e., $A_m \equiv \partial\phi/\partial x^m$, since

$$\frac{\partial \phi}{\partial \acute{x}^k} = \frac{\partial \phi}{\partial x^m} \frac{\partial x^m}{\partial \acute{x}^k}$$

which obeys the law (A3.3).

DEFINITION 4. *The quantities* $A^{kl}(\mathbf{x})$, $A_{kl}(\mathbf{x})$, *and* $A^k{}_l(\mathbf{x})$ *are respective called contravariant, covariant, and mixed tensors of second order if they obey the transformation rules:*

$$\acute{A}^{kl}(\acute{\mathbf{x}}) = A^{mn}(\mathbf{x}) \frac{\partial \acute{x}^k}{\partial x^m} \frac{\partial \acute{x}^l}{\partial x^n} \qquad \text{(contravariant tensors)}$$

(A3.4) $$\acute{A}_{kl}(\acute{\mathbf{x}}) = A_{mn}(\mathbf{x}) \frac{\partial x^m}{\partial \acute{x}^k} \frac{\partial x^n}{\partial \acute{x}^l} \qquad \text{(covariant tensors)}$$

$$\acute{A}^k{}_l(\acute{\mathbf{x}}) = A^m{}_n(\mathbf{x}) \frac{\partial \acute{x}^k}{\partial x^m} \frac{\partial x^n}{\partial \acute{x}^l} \qquad \text{(mixed tensors)}$$

Examples of these tensors are $g^{kl}$, $g_{kl}$, and $\delta^k{}_l$ introduced in Art. A2, as may be easily verified. Higher-order tensors are defined by extending these rules.

*Relative scalars, vectors,* and *tensors of weight N* are defined in a fashion similar to (A3.1)–(A3.4) except that on the right side of these expressions we have a coefficient $|\partial x^r/\partial \acute{x}^s|^N$, e.g.,

$$\phi(\acute{\mathbf{x}}) = \left|\frac{\partial x^r}{\partial \acute{x}^s}\right|^N \phi(\mathbf{x}) \qquad \text{(relative scalar)}$$

(A3.5) $$\acute{A}_k(\acute{\mathbf{x}}) = \left|\frac{\partial x^r}{\partial \acute{x}^s}\right|^N A_m(\mathbf{x}) \frac{\partial x^m}{\partial \acute{x}^k} \qquad \text{(relative covariant vector)}$$

$$\acute{A}^k{}_l(\acute{\mathbf{x}}) = \left|\frac{\partial x^r}{\partial \acute{x}^s}\right|^N A^m{}_n(\mathbf{x}) \frac{\partial \acute{x}^k}{\partial x^m} \frac{\partial x^n}{\partial \acute{x}^l} \qquad \text{(relative mixed tensor)}$$

*Addition. Two tensors of the same order and type may be added to (or subtracted from) each other to obtain a new tensor.*

$$C^k{}_{lm} = A^k{}_{lm} + B^k{}_{lm}$$

It is easy to prove that the result is also a tensor of the same order and type.

*Multiplication. The outer product of two tensors is obtained by simply multiplying their components.* This operation gives a new tensor whose order is the sum of those of the multipliers:

(A3.6) $$C_{lm}{}^k = A_{lm} B^k$$

*In a mixed tensor the operation of equating a subscript to a superscript is called contraction.* A contraction decreases the order of a tensor by two. Thus $C_{lm}{}^m$ and $C_{mk}{}^m$ are two contractions of $C_{lk}{}^m$. *The inner product* is obtained from the outer product by contraction:

$$C_{ml}{}^m = A_{ml} B^m$$

The tensor character is easily tested by use of the *quotient rule* embodied in the two theorems given below.

THEOREM 1. *If $A_k$ is an arbitrary covariant vector and $A_k X^k$ is invariant,* i.e.,

$$A_k X^k = \acute{A}_k \acute{X}^k$$

*then $X^k$ is a contravariant vector.*

THEOREM 2. *If $A_k$ is an arbitrary covariant vector and $B^l = X^{kl} A_k$ is a contravariant vector, then $X^{kl}$ is a contravariant tensor of second order.*

A corollary to this theorem is: If $A_k$ and $B_l$ are arbitrary covariant vectors and $X^{kl} A_k B_l$ is an invariant, then $X^{kl}$ is a second-order contravariant tensor. When $X^{kl}$ is symmetric, i.e., $X^{kl} = X^{lk}$, then the invariance of $X^{kl} A_k A_l$ suffices for $X^{kl}$ to be a second-order contravariant tensor. For example, according to (A2.12) we have

$$ds^2 = g_{kl}\, dx^k\, dx^l$$

where the left side is invariant, $dx^k$ is a contravariant vector, and $g_{kl}$ is symmetric; hence $g_{kl}$ is a covariant tensor of second order. This result is also apparent from (A2.10) or its analogue for arbitrary curvilinear coordinates $\acute{x}^k$, i.e.,

$$\acute{g}_{kl}(\acute{\mathbf{x}}) = g_{mn}(\mathbf{x}) \frac{\partial x^m}{\partial \acute{x}^k} \frac{\partial x^n}{\partial \acute{x}^l} \tag{A3.7}$$

By use of the metric tensors $g_{kl}$ and $g^{kl}$ one may *raise* or *lower* the indices of higher-order tensors. Thus, for example, we may write

$$A^k_{\cdot l} = g^{mk} A_{ml} \tag{A3.8}$$

where a dot is inserted in place of the index raised. Often this dot is ignored in writing. Similarly

$$A_l^{\cdot k} = g^{km} A_{lm} \tag{A3.9}$$

Note that the mixed tensors in (A3.8) and (A3.9) are not necessarily the same. Both indices are raised by repeating this process

$$A^{kl} = g^{km} g^{ln} A_{mn} = g^{km} A_m^{\ l} = g^{ln} A^k_{\ n} \tag{A3.10}$$

When $A_{kl}$ is symmetrical, then $A^{kl}$ is also symmetrical. In this case $A^k_{\ l} = A_l^{\ k}$ and the relative position of indices becomes unimportant.

The lowering of indices is accomplished by use of $g_{kl}$, e.g.,

$$\begin{aligned} A^k_{\ l} &= g_{lm} A^{km} \qquad A_l^{\ k} = g_{lm} A^{mk} \\ A_{kl} &= g_{lm} A_k^{\ m} = g_{km} A^m_{\ l} = g_{km} g_{ln} A^{mn} \end{aligned} \tag{A3.11}$$

In this way we see that upon raising the indices of $A_{kl}$ to $A^{kl}$ and then lowering again, we obtain the same tensor. The tensors obtained by raising and lowering indices are called *associated tensors*.

*Physical Components.* The components of a tensor do not in general have the same units. For example, let $\mathbf{u} = u^k \mathbf{g}_k$ be a displacement vector with contravariant tensor components $u^k$ referred to cylindrical coordinates. Since

$$|\mathbf{g}_1| = \sqrt{g_{11}} = 1 \qquad |\mathbf{g}_2| = \sqrt{g_{22}} = x^1 \qquad |\mathbf{g}_3| = \sqrt{g_{33}} = 1$$

we see that if $\mathbf{u}$ is measured in length $L$, then the dimensions of $u^1$ and $u^3$ are $L$, but the dimension of $u^2$ is $L/L = 1$. By taking parallel projections of vectors on unit vectors lying along the coordinate curves, we define the physical components of vectors. Thus if we write

$$\mathbf{u} = u^{(k)}\,\mathbf{e}_k \tag{A3.12}$$

where $\mathbf{e}_k$ are the unit vectors, i.e.,

$$\mathbf{e}_k \equiv \frac{\mathbf{g}_k}{\sqrt{g_{\underline{kk}}}} \tag{A3.13}$$

then the components $u^{(k)}$ are called physical components of $\mathbf{u}$. Writing

$$\mathbf{u} = u^k \mathbf{g}_k = u^{(k)}\,\mathbf{e}_k$$

we see that the tensor and physical components are related to each other by

$$u^{(k)} = u^k \sqrt{g_{\underline{kk}}} \qquad u^k = \frac{u^{(k)}}{\sqrt{g_{\underline{kk}}}} \tag{A3.14}$$

If we want to replace $u_k$ by its physical component, we lower the index of $u^k$, i.e.,

$$u_k = g_{kl}\,u^l = \sum_l g_{kl}\,\frac{u^{(l)}}{\sqrt{g_{ll}}} \tag{A3.15}$$

An equally consistent definition for physical components may be based on parallel projection on unit vectors along $\mathbf{g}^k$. Here the choice is made in favor of $\mathbf{e}_k$ lying along $\mathbf{g}_k$ which are tangential to coordinate curves $x^k$.

The foregoing definition can be carried over to higher-order tensors. To this end, use is made of the vector equations in which the tensors appear. For instance, consider the second-order tensor $t^k{}_l$ involved in

$$t^k = t^k{}_l\,n^l \tag{A3.16}$$

in which $t^k$ and $n^l$ are contravariant vectors. Now replace $t^k$ and $n^l$ by their expressions in terms of their physical components in the forn (A3.14)₂

$$\frac{1}{\sqrt{g_{\underline{kk}}}} t^{(k)} = \sum_l \frac{1}{\sqrt{g_{ll}}} t^k{}_l n^{(l)}$$

or write

$$t^{(k)} = \sum_l t^k{}_l \sqrt{g_{\underline{kk}}/g_{ll}}\, n^{(l)} = t^{(k)}{}_{(l)}\, n^{(l)}$$

which defines the *right physical components*

(A3.17) $$t^{(k)}{}_{(l)} = t^k{}_l \sqrt{g_{\underline{kk}}/g_{\underline{ll}}} = t_{ml}\, g^{km} \sqrt{g_{\underline{kk}}/g_{\underline{ll}}}$$

From this we solve for

(A3.18) $$t^k{}_l = t^{(k)}{}_{(l)} \sqrt{g_{\underline{ll}}/g_{\underline{kk}}}$$

By lowering and raising indices, we also have

(A3.19) $$t_{kl} = \sum_m g_{km}\, t^{(m)}{}_{(l)} \sqrt{g_{\underline{ll}}/g_{mm}}$$
$$t^{kl} = \sum_m g^{ml}\, t^{(k)}{}_{(m)} \sqrt{g_{mm}/g_{\underline{kk}}}$$

Instead of (A3.16) we may start with

(A3.20) $$t^k = t_l{}^k n^l$$

In this case the foregoing process results in *left physical components* $t_{(l)}{}^{(k)}$

(A3.21) $$t_{(l)}{}^{(k)} = t_l{}^k \sqrt{g_{\underline{kk}}/g_{ll}} \qquad t_l{}^k = t_{(l)}{}^{(k)} \sqrt{g_{\underline{ll}}/g_{\underline{kk}}}$$

(A3.22) $$t_{kl} = \sum_m g_{ml}\, t_{(k)}{}^{(m)} \sqrt{g_{\underline{kk}}/g_{mm}}$$
$$t^{kl} = \sum_m g^{km}\, t_{(m)}{}^{(l)} \sqrt{g_{mm}/g_{\underline{ll}}}$$

Since the tensors $t^k{}_l$ and $t_l{}^k$ are related to each other by

$$t^k{}_l = g^{km}\, g_{ln}\, t_m{}^n$$

by substituting (A3.18) and (A3.21)₂, we find the relation between right and left physical components

(A3.23) $$t_{(l)}{}^{(k)} = \sum_{m,n} \sqrt{g_{mm}\, g_{\underline{kk}}/g_{\underline{ll}}\, g_{nn}}\; g^{km}\, g_{ln}\, t^{(n)}{}_{(m)}$$

For a symmetric tensor the left and the right physical components are identical. For an orthogonal coordinate system, on the other hand,

$t^{(k)}{}_{(l)} = t_{(k)}{}^{(l)}$. *Thus, for symmetric tensors referred to orthogonal curvilinear coordinates, the right and the left physical components are identical and each possess symmetric matrices.* For orthogonal curvilinear coordinates we therefore have

$$t^{(k)}{}_{(l)} = t_{(k)}{}^{(l)} = \sqrt{g_{\underline{kk}}/g_{\underline{ll}}}\, t^{k}{}_{l} = \sqrt{g_{\underline{ll}}/g_{\underline{kk}}}\, t_{k}{}^{l}$$

$$= \sqrt{g_{\underline{kk}}\, g_{\underline{ll}}}\, t^{kl} = \frac{1}{\sqrt{g_{\underline{kk}}\, g_{\underline{ll}}}}\, t_{kl} \tag{A3.24}$$

The method developed above can be applied without any difficulty in obtaining the physical components of higher-order tensors.

## A4. TENSOR CALCULUS

Unlike the rectangular unit vectors $\mathbf{i}_k$, the base vectors $\mathbf{g}_k$ and $\mathbf{g}^k$ are functions of curvilinear coordinates $x^k$. Therefore in differentiation and integration of vectors these base vectors cannot be treated as constants. We have

$$\frac{\partial \mathbf{g}_k}{\partial x^l} = \frac{\partial}{\partial x^l}\left(\frac{\partial \mathbf{p}}{\partial x^k}\right) = \frac{\partial^2 z^m}{\partial x^l\, \partial x^k}\, \mathbf{i}_m$$

Upon replacing $\mathbf{i}_m$ by its equal given by (A2.8), we may write this as

$$\frac{\partial \mathbf{g}_k}{\partial x^l} = \begin{Bmatrix} m \\ kl \end{Bmatrix} \mathbf{g}_m \tag{A4.1}$$

where

$$\begin{Bmatrix} m \\ kl \end{Bmatrix} = \frac{\partial^2 z^n}{\partial x^k\, \partial x^l}\, \frac{\partial x^m}{\partial z^n} \tag{A4.2}$$

are known as the *Christoffel symbols of the second kind. Christoffel symbols of the first kind* are defined by

$$[kl,m] = g_{mn} \begin{Bmatrix} n \\ kl \end{Bmatrix} \qquad \text{or} \qquad \begin{Bmatrix} m \\ kl \end{Bmatrix} = g^{mn}\, [kl,n] \tag{A4.3}$$

By use of (A2.10) it is not difficult to show that

$$[kl,m] = \tfrac{1}{2}\left(\frac{\partial g_{km}}{\partial x^l} + \frac{\partial g_{lm}}{\partial x^k} - \frac{\partial g_{kl}}{\partial x^m}\right) \tag{A4.4}$$

Christoffel symbols of both kinds are symmetric with respect to the two paired indices $kl$, i.e.,

$$\begin{Bmatrix} m \\ kl \end{Bmatrix} = \begin{Bmatrix} m \\ lk \end{Bmatrix} \qquad [kl,m] = [lk,m] \tag{A4.5}$$

A result, similar to (A4.1), is that

$$\frac{\partial \mathbf{g}^m}{\partial x^l} = -\begin{Bmatrix} m \\ lk \end{Bmatrix} \mathbf{g}^k \tag{A4.6}$$

By use of (A4.1) and (A4.6) one can obtain partial derivatives of vectors. For example,

$$\frac{\partial \mathbf{u}}{\partial x^k} = \frac{\partial}{\partial x^k}(u^m \mathbf{g}_m) = \frac{\partial u^m}{\partial x^k}\mathbf{g}_m + u^m \frac{\partial \mathbf{g}_m}{\partial x^k} = \left(\frac{\partial u^m}{\partial x^k} + \begin{Bmatrix} m \\ kl \end{Bmatrix} u^l\right)\mathbf{g}_m$$

when (A4.1) is employed. This may be abbreviated by

$$\frac{\partial \mathbf{u}}{\partial x^k} = u^m{}_{;k}\,\mathbf{g}_m \tag{A4.7}$$

thus defining the *covariant partial derivative of a contravariant vector with respect to* $g_{kl}$

$$u^m{}_{;k} \equiv \frac{\partial u^m}{\partial x^k} + \begin{Bmatrix} m \\ kl \end{Bmatrix} u^l \tag{A4.8}$$

The covariant partial derivative of a covariant vector, $u_{m;k}$, is obtained by using $\mathbf{u} = u_m\,\mathbf{g}^m$ in the foregoing operation. Hence

$$\frac{\partial \mathbf{u}}{\partial x^k} = u_{m;k}\,\mathbf{g}^m \tag{A4.9}$$

where

$$u_{m;k} \equiv \frac{\partial u_m}{\partial x^k} - \begin{Bmatrix} l \\ mk \end{Bmatrix} u_l \tag{A4.10}$$

*In rectangular coordinates Christoffel symbols vanish identically, thus reducing covariant partial differentiation to the usual partial differentiation.*

For illustrative purposes we give below the Christoffel symbols and covariant derivative of a vector in cylindrical coordinates. These are obtained by using (A2.17) in (A4.3), (A4.4), and (A4.8).

$$[12,2] = [21,2] = x^1 \qquad [22,1] = -x^1 \qquad \text{all other } [kl,m] = 0$$

$$\begin{Bmatrix} 2 \\ 12 \end{Bmatrix} = \begin{Bmatrix} 2 \\ 21 \end{Bmatrix} = \frac{1}{x^1} \qquad \begin{Bmatrix} 1 \\ 22 \end{Bmatrix} = -x^1 \qquad \text{all other } \begin{Bmatrix} m \\ kl \end{Bmatrix} = 0 \tag{A4.11}$$

$$u^1{}_{;1} = \frac{\partial u^1}{\partial x^1} \qquad u^1{}_{;2} = \frac{\partial u^1}{\partial x^2} - x^1 u^2 \qquad u^1{}_{;3} = \frac{\partial u^1}{\partial x^3}$$

$$u^2{}_{;1} = \frac{\partial u^2}{\partial x^1} + \frac{1}{x^1}u^2 \qquad u^2{}_{;2} = \frac{\partial u^2}{\partial x^2} + \frac{1}{x^1}u^1 \qquad u^2{}_{;3} = \frac{\partial u^2}{\partial x^3} \tag{A4.12}$$

$$u^3{}_{;k} = \frac{\partial u^3}{\partial x^k} \qquad (k = 1, 2, 3)$$

Covariant partial differentiation of higher-order tensors with respect to $g_{kl}$ is defined in a similar fashion, i.e.,

$$
\begin{aligned}
A^{kl}{}_{;m} &\equiv \frac{\partial A^{kl}}{\partial x^m} + \begin{Bmatrix} k \\ mn \end{Bmatrix} A^{nl} + \begin{Bmatrix} l \\ mn \end{Bmatrix} A^{kn} \\
A^{k}{}_{l;m} &\equiv \frac{\partial A^{k}{}_{l}}{\partial x^m} - \begin{Bmatrix} n \\ lm \end{Bmatrix} A^{k}{}_{n} + \begin{Bmatrix} k \\ mn \end{Bmatrix} A^{n}{}_{l} \qquad \text{(A4.13)} \\
A_{kl;m} &\equiv \frac{\partial A_{kl}}{\partial x^m} - \begin{Bmatrix} n \\ km \end{Bmatrix} A_{nl} - \begin{Bmatrix} n \\ lm \end{Bmatrix} A_{kn}
\end{aligned}
$$

The covariant derivative of a tensor is another tensor of degree one higher.

Applying the rules (A4.13) to $g_{kl}$ and $g^{kl}$, one obtains *Ricci's theorem*

$$g_{kl;m} = g^{kl}{}_{;m} = 0 \qquad \text{(A4.14)}$$

*Therefore in the process of covariant differentiation $g_{kl}$ and $g^{kl}$ are unaffected;* i.e., we may freely move them in and out of the covariant differentiation sign, e.g.,

$$
\begin{aligned}
A^{k}{}_{;l} &= (g^{km} A_m)_{;l} = g^{km} A_{m;l} \\
A_{k;l} &= (g_{km} A^m)_{;l} = g_{km} A^{m}{}_{;l}
\end{aligned}
$$

It is simple to show that the product law of differentiation holds for the covariant differentiation, e.g.,

$$(A^k B_{lm})_{;r} = A^{k}{}_{;r} B_{lm} + A^k B_{lm;r}$$

A useful result that can be proved by differentiation is

$$\frac{\partial}{\partial x^k} (\log \sqrt{g}) = \begin{Bmatrix} m \\ mk \end{Bmatrix} \qquad g \equiv \det g_{kl} \qquad \text{(A4.15)}$$

The *gradient* (grad) of an absolute scalar $\phi$ and the *divergence* (div) and *curl* of an absolute vector $\mathbf{A}$ are defined by

$$
\begin{aligned}
\text{grad } \phi &\equiv \frac{\partial \phi}{\partial x^k} \mathbf{g}^k \\
\text{div } \mathbf{A} &\equiv A^{k}{}_{;k} \qquad \text{(A4.16)} \\
\text{curl } \mathbf{A} &\equiv \epsilon^{klm} A_{m;l} \mathbf{g}_k
\end{aligned}
$$

where

$$\epsilon^{klm} = \frac{e^{klm}}{\sqrt{g}} \qquad \text{(A4.17)}$$

is the $\epsilon$ symbol with $e^{klm}$ being the usual permutation symbol, i.e.,

$$e^{klm},\ e_{klm} = \begin{cases} 1 & \text{when } klm \text{ is an even permutation of 123} \\ -1 & \text{when } klm \text{ is an odd permutation of 123} \\ 0 & \text{otherwise} \end{cases} \tag{A4.18}$$

Therefore

$$e^{123} = e^{231} = e^{312} = 1$$
$$e^{213} = e^{132} = e^{321} = -1 \qquad \text{all other } e^{klm} = 0$$

Similar to (A4.17) we have the covariant $\epsilon$ symbol

$$\epsilon_{klm} = e_{klm}\sqrt{g} \tag{A4.19}$$

The operators in (A4.16) are invariant under general transformation of coordinates. Sometimes it is more convenient to use the operator $\boldsymbol{\nabla}$, defined by

$$\boldsymbol{\nabla} \equiv \mathbf{g}^k \frac{\partial}{\partial x^k} \tag{A4.20}$$

By use of $\boldsymbol{\nabla}$ we may express (A4.16) as

$$\begin{aligned} \text{grad}\ \phi &\equiv \boldsymbol{\nabla}\phi = \mathbf{g}^k \frac{\partial \phi}{\partial x^k} \\ \text{div}\ \mathbf{A} &\equiv \boldsymbol{\nabla} \cdot \mathbf{A} = \mathbf{g}^k \cdot \frac{\partial}{\partial x^k}(A^l \mathbf{g}_l) = \mathbf{g}^k \cdot \mathbf{g}_l A^l{}_{;k} \\ &= A^k{}_{;k} = \frac{1}{\sqrt{g}} \frac{\partial}{\partial x^k}(\sqrt{g}\, A^k) \\ \text{curl}\ \mathbf{A} &\equiv \boldsymbol{\nabla} \times \mathbf{A} = \mathbf{g}^k \frac{\partial}{\partial x^k} \times (A_l \mathbf{g}^l) = \mathbf{g}^k \times \mathbf{g}^l A_{l;k} \\ &= \epsilon^{klm} A_{m;l}\, \mathbf{g}_k \end{aligned} \tag{A4.21}$$

The last expression of div **A** may be obtained as follows:

$$\begin{aligned} A^k{}_{;k} &= \frac{\partial A^k}{\partial x^k} + \begin{Bmatrix} k \\ km \end{Bmatrix} A^m = \frac{\partial A^k}{\partial x^k} + A^k \frac{\partial}{\partial x^k}(\log \sqrt{g}) \\ &= \frac{1}{\sqrt{g}} \frac{\partial}{\partial x^k}(\sqrt{g}\, A^k) \end{aligned}$$

where we have used (A4.15).

The laplacian $\nabla^2$ in curvilinear coordinates is obtained from

$$\begin{aligned} \nabla^2 \phi &= \text{div grad}\ \phi = \left(g^{kl} \frac{\partial \phi}{\partial x^l}\right)_{;k} = g^{kl}\left(\frac{\partial \phi}{\partial x^l}\right)_{;k} \\ &= \frac{1}{\sqrt{g}} \frac{\partial}{\partial x^k}\left(\sqrt{g}\, g^{kl} \frac{\partial \phi}{\partial x^l}\right) \end{aligned} \tag{A4.22}$$

The *Green-Gauss* and *Stokes* theorems of vector analysis are expressed as

(A4.23) $$\iiint_{\mathcal{V}} \operatorname{div} \mathbf{u}\, dv = \iint_{\mathcal{S}} \mathbf{u} \cdot \mathbf{n}\, da \qquad \text{(Green-Gauss)}$$

(A4.24) $$\iint_{\mathcal{S}} \operatorname{curl} \mathbf{A} \cdot \mathbf{n}\, da = \oint_{\mathcal{C}} \mathbf{A} \cdot d\mathbf{p} \qquad \text{(Stokes)}$$

where $\mathbf{n}$ is the exterior normal to the surface $\mathcal{S}$. In component notation these may be expressed as

(A4.25) $$\iiint_{\mathcal{V}} u^k{}_{;k}\, dv = \iiint_{\mathcal{V}} \frac{1}{\sqrt{g}} \frac{\partial}{\partial x^k} (\sqrt{g}\, u^k)\, dv = \iint_{\mathcal{S}} u^k n_k\, da$$

(A4.26) $$\iint_{\mathcal{S}} \epsilon^{klm} n_k A_{m;l}\, da = \oint_{\mathcal{C}} A_k\, dx^k$$

Below we list expressions of the metric tensor, Christoffel symbols, gradient, divergence, curl, and laplacian for general orthogonal curvilinear coordinates, cylindrical coordinates, and spherical coordinates for reference.

*Orthogonal Curvilinear Coordinates* ($g_{kl} = 0,\ k \neq l$):

$$ds^2 = g_{11}(dx^1)^2 + g_{22}(dx^2)^2 + g_{33}(dx^3)^2$$

$$g^{\underline{kk}} = \frac{1}{g_{\underline{kk}}} \qquad \mathbf{g}^k = g^{\underline{kk}}\, \mathbf{g}_{\underline{k}} \qquad g = g_{11}\, g_{22}\, g_{33}$$

(A4.27) $$\begin{Bmatrix} l \\ \underline{kk} \end{Bmatrix} = -\frac{1}{2\, g_{\underline{ll}}} \frac{\partial g_{\underline{kk}}}{\partial x^l} \qquad \begin{Bmatrix} k \\ \underline{k}l \end{Bmatrix} = \frac{\partial}{\partial x^l} (\log \sqrt{g_{\underline{kk}}})$$

$$\begin{Bmatrix} k \\ \underline{kk} \end{Bmatrix} = \frac{\partial}{\partial x^k} (\log \sqrt{g_{\underline{kk}}}) \qquad \begin{Bmatrix} k \\ lm \end{Bmatrix} = 0 \qquad (k \neq l \neq m)$$

$$\operatorname{grad} \phi = \frac{1}{\sqrt{g_{11}}} \frac{\partial \phi}{\partial x^1} \mathbf{e}_1 + \frac{1}{\sqrt{g_{22}}} \frac{\partial \phi}{\partial x^2} \mathbf{e}_2 + \frac{1}{\sqrt{g_{33}}} \frac{\partial \phi}{\partial x^3} \mathbf{e}_3$$

$$\operatorname{div} \mathbf{A} = (g_{11}\, g_{22}\, g_{33})^{-\frac{1}{2}} \left[ \frac{\partial}{\partial x^1} (\sqrt{g_{22}\, g_{33}}\, A^{(1)}) + \frac{\partial}{\partial x^2} (\sqrt{g_{33}\, g_{11}}\, A^{(2)}) + \frac{\partial}{\partial x^3} (\sqrt{g_{11}\, g_{22}}\, A^{(3)}) \right]$$

(A4.28) $$\begin{aligned} \operatorname{curl} \mathbf{A} = {} & (g_{22}\, g_{33})^{-\frac{1}{2}} \left[ \frac{\partial}{\partial x^2} (\sqrt{g_{33}}\, A^{(3)}) - \frac{\partial}{\partial x^3} (\sqrt{g_{22}}\, A^{(2)}) \right] \mathbf{e}_1 \\ & + (g_{33}\, g_{11})^{-\frac{1}{2}} \left[ \frac{\partial}{\partial x^3} (\sqrt{g_{11}}\, A^{(1)}) - \frac{\partial}{\partial x^1} (\sqrt{g_{33}}\, A^{(3)}) \right] \mathbf{e}_2 \\ & + (g_{11}\, g_{22})^{-\frac{1}{2}} \left[ \frac{\partial}{\partial x^1} (\sqrt{g_{22}}\, A^{(2)}) - \frac{\partial}{\partial x^2} (\sqrt{g_{11}}\, A^{(1)}) \right] \mathbf{e}_3 \end{aligned}$$

$$\nabla^2 \phi = (g_{11}\, g_{22}\, g_{33})^{-\frac{1}{2}} \left[ \frac{\partial}{\partial x^1} \left( \frac{\sqrt{g_{22}\, g_{33}}}{\sqrt{g_{11}}} \frac{\partial \phi}{\partial x^1} \right) + \frac{\partial}{\partial x^2} \left( \frac{\sqrt{g_{33}\, g_{11}}}{\sqrt{g_{22}}} \frac{\partial \phi}{\partial x^2} \right) + \frac{\partial}{\partial x^3} \left( \frac{\sqrt{g_{11}\, g_{22}}}{\sqrt{g_{33}}} \frac{\partial \phi}{\partial x^3} \right) \right]$$

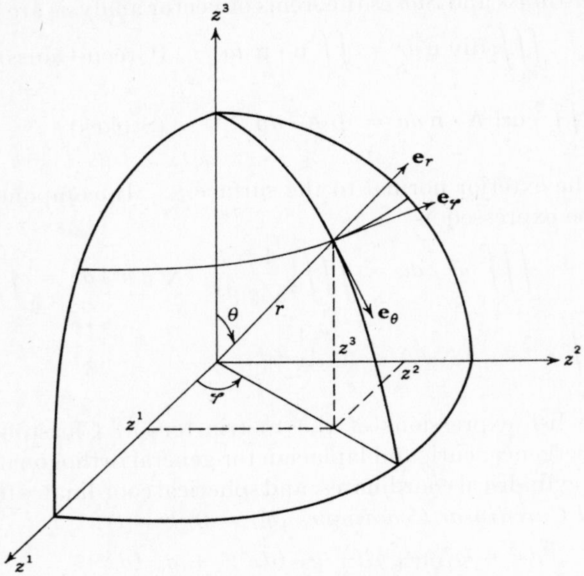


FIG. A4.1. Spherical coordinates.

where $A^{(k)} = A^k \sqrt{g_{\underline{kk}}}$ are the physical components of the vector $\mathbf{A}$ and $\mathbf{e}_k \equiv \mathbf{g}_k/\sqrt{g_{\underline{kk}}}$.

*Cylindrical Coordinates* $(r, \theta, z)$ are defined in terms of rectangular coordinates $z^k$ [we use $x^1 \equiv r$, $x^2 \equiv \theta$, $x^3 \equiv z$, $A^{(1)} \equiv A_r$, $A^{(2)} \equiv A_\theta$, $A^{(3)} \equiv A_z$].

$$z^1 = r\cos\theta \qquad z^2 = r\sin\theta \qquad z^3 = z$$

$$ds^2 = dr^2 + r^2\,d\theta^2 + dz^2$$

$$g_{11} = g^{11} = g_{33} = g^{33} = 1 \qquad g_{22} = \frac{1}{g^{22}} = r^2$$

$$\begin{Bmatrix} 2 \\ 12 \end{Bmatrix} = \begin{Bmatrix} 2 \\ 21 \end{Bmatrix} = \frac{1}{r} \qquad \begin{Bmatrix} 1 \\ 22 \end{Bmatrix} = -r \qquad \text{all other} \begin{Bmatrix} k \\ lm \end{Bmatrix} = 0$$

(A4.29)

$$\operatorname{grad}\phi = \frac{\partial\phi}{\partial r}\,\mathbf{e}_r + \frac{1}{r}\frac{\partial\phi}{\partial\theta}\,\mathbf{e}_\theta + \frac{\partial\phi}{\partial z}\,\mathbf{e}_z$$

$$\operatorname{div}\mathbf{A} = \frac{1}{r}\frac{\partial}{\partial r}(r\,A_r) + \frac{1}{r}\frac{\partial A_\theta}{\partial\theta} + \frac{\partial A_z}{\partial z}$$

$$\operatorname{curl}\mathbf{A} = \left(\frac{1}{r}\frac{\partial A_z}{\partial\theta} - \frac{\partial A_\theta}{\partial z}\right)\mathbf{e}_r + \left(\frac{\partial A_r}{\partial z} - \frac{\partial A_z}{\partial r}\right)\mathbf{e}_\theta + \left[\frac{1}{r}\frac{\partial}{\partial r}(r\,A_\theta) - \frac{1}{r}\frac{\partial A_r}{\partial\theta}\right]\mathbf{e}_z$$

$$\nabla^2\phi = \frac{\partial^2\phi}{\partial r^2} + \frac{1}{r}\frac{\partial\phi}{\partial r} + \frac{1}{r^2}\frac{\partial^2\phi}{\partial\theta^2} + \frac{\partial^2\phi}{\partial z^2}$$

*Spherical Coordinates* $(r, \theta, \varphi)$ are defined by (Fig. A4.1):

$$z^1 = r \sin \theta \cos \varphi \qquad z^2 = r \sin \theta \sin \varphi \qquad z^3 = r \cos \theta$$

$$g_{11} = g^{11} = 1 \qquad g_{22} = \frac{1}{g^{22}} = r^2 \qquad g_{33} = \frac{1}{g^{33}} = r^2 \sin^2 \theta$$

$$g_{kl} = 0 \qquad (k \neq l)$$

$$\begin{Bmatrix} 1 \\ 22 \end{Bmatrix} = -r \qquad \begin{Bmatrix} 1 \\ 33 \end{Bmatrix} = -r \sin^2 \theta \qquad \begin{Bmatrix} 2 \\ 12 \end{Bmatrix} = \frac{1}{r}$$

$$\begin{Bmatrix} 2 \\ 33 \end{Bmatrix} = -\sin \theta \cos \theta \qquad \begin{Bmatrix} 3 \\ 13 \end{Bmatrix} = \frac{1}{r}$$

$$\begin{Bmatrix} 3 \\ 23 \end{Bmatrix} = \cot \theta \qquad \text{all other} \begin{Bmatrix} k \\ lm \end{Bmatrix} = 0$$

(A4.30) $$\operatorname{grad} \phi = \frac{\partial \phi}{\partial r} \mathbf{e}_r + \frac{1}{r} \frac{\partial \phi}{\partial \theta} \mathbf{e}_\theta + \frac{1}{r \sin \theta} \frac{\partial \phi}{\partial \varphi} \mathbf{e}_\varphi$$

$$\operatorname{div} \mathbf{A} = \frac{1}{r^2} \frac{\partial}{\partial r} (r^2 A_r) + \frac{1}{r \sin \theta} \frac{\partial}{\partial \theta} (A_\theta \sin \theta) + \frac{1}{r \sin \theta} \frac{\partial A_\varphi}{\partial \varphi}$$

$$\operatorname{curl} \mathbf{A} = \frac{1}{r \sin \theta} \left[ \frac{\partial}{\partial \theta} (A_\varphi \sin \theta) - \frac{\partial A_\theta}{\partial \varphi} \right] \mathbf{e}_r + \left[ \frac{1}{r \sin \theta} \frac{\partial A_r}{\partial \varphi} - \frac{1}{r} \frac{\partial}{\partial r} (r A_\varphi) \right] \mathbf{e}_\theta + \frac{1}{r} \left[ \frac{\partial}{\partial r} (r A_\theta) - \frac{\partial A_r}{\partial \theta} \right] \mathbf{e}_\varphi$$

$$\nabla^2 \phi = \frac{1}{r^2} \frac{\partial}{\partial r} \left( r^2 \frac{\partial \phi}{\partial r} \right) + \frac{1}{r^2 \sin \theta} \frac{\partial}{\partial \theta} \left( \sin \theta \frac{\partial \phi}{\partial \theta} \right) + \frac{1}{r^2 \sin^2 \theta} \frac{\partial^2 \phi}{\partial \varphi^2}$$

## A5. RIEMANN-CHRISTOFFEL CURVATURE TENSOR

According to a theorem of calculus the order of mixed partial differentiation is unimportant, i.e.,

$$\frac{\partial^2 \phi}{\partial x^1 \partial x^2} = \frac{\partial^2 \phi}{\partial x^2 \partial x^1}$$

We ask the question: Under what conditions do second-order covariant derivatives commute; that is, when can we write

$$A_{k;lm} = A_{k;ml}$$

To find the answer to this question, we take the covariant derivative of

(A5.1) $$A_{k;l} = A_{k,l} - \begin{Bmatrix} r \\ kl \end{Bmatrix} A_r$$

i.e.,

$$A_{k;lm} = (A_{k,l})_{,m} - \begin{Bmatrix} r \\ km \end{Bmatrix} A_{r;l} - \begin{Bmatrix} r \\ lm \end{Bmatrix} A_{k;r}$$

Using (A5.1), this reduces to

$$(A5.2)\qquad A_{k;lm} = A_{k,lm} - \begin{Bmatrix} r \\ kl \end{Bmatrix}_{,m} A_r - \begin{Bmatrix} r \\ kl \end{Bmatrix} A_{r,m} - \begin{Bmatrix} r \\ km \end{Bmatrix} A_{r,l} + \begin{Bmatrix} r \\ km \end{Bmatrix} \begin{Bmatrix} s \\ rl \end{Bmatrix} A_s - \begin{Bmatrix} r \\ lm \end{Bmatrix} A_{k,r} + \begin{Bmatrix} r \\ lm \end{Bmatrix} \begin{Bmatrix} s \\ kr \end{Bmatrix} A_s$$

If we interchange the indices $l$ and $m$ and subtract the result from (A5.2), we get

$$(A5.3)\qquad A_{k;lm} - A_{k;ml} = \left( \begin{Bmatrix} r \\ km \end{Bmatrix}_{,l} - \begin{Bmatrix} r \\ kl \end{Bmatrix}_{,m} + \begin{Bmatrix} s \\ km \end{Bmatrix} \begin{Bmatrix} r \\ sl \end{Bmatrix} - \begin{Bmatrix} s \\ kl \end{Bmatrix} \begin{Bmatrix} r \\ sm \end{Bmatrix} \right) A_r$$

Here $A_r$ is an arbitrary vector, and the left side of (A5.3) is a covariant tensor of third order. Hence, according to the quotient law, the coefficient of $A_r$ on the right must be a fourth-order tensor, i.e.,

$$(A5.4)\qquad R^r{}_{klm} \equiv \begin{Bmatrix} r \\ km \end{Bmatrix}_{,l} - \begin{Bmatrix} r \\ kl \end{Bmatrix}_{,m} + \begin{Bmatrix} s \\ km \end{Bmatrix} \begin{Bmatrix} r \\ sl \end{Bmatrix} - \begin{Bmatrix} s \\ kl \end{Bmatrix} \begin{Bmatrix} r \\ sm \end{Bmatrix}$$

is a tensor once contravariant and three times covariant. This tensor is called the *Riemann-Christoffel* tensor. It is independent of the choice of $A_r$, and is formed from the metric tensor $g_{kl}$. To indicate the latter point sometimes we may write $R^{(g)r}{}_{klm}$. Equation (A5.3) now reads

$$(A5.5)\qquad A_{k;lm} - A_{k;ml} = R^r{}_{klm} A_r$$

It is now clear that the following theorem may be stated.

THEOREM. *Cross-covariant derivatives of any vector are equal if and only if the Riemann-Christoffel tensor vanishes identically.*

By lowering the contravariant index, we define a tensor called the *curvature tensor*.

$$(A5.6)\qquad R_{klmn} = g_{kr} R^r{}_{lmn} = \tfrac{1}{2} (g_{kn,lm} + g_{lm,kn} - g_{km,ln} - g_{ln,km}) + g^{rs} ([lm,s]\,[kn,r] - [ln,s]\,[km,r])$$

Extension of (A5.5) to higher-order tensors is made in an obvious fashion. For example, for a second-order tensor we find

$$(A5.7)\qquad A_{kl;mn} - A_{kl;nm} = A_{kr} R^r{}_{lmn} + A_{rl} R^r{}_{kmn}$$

Both tensors $R^k{}_{lmn}$ and $R_{klmn}$ possess a number of symmetry and skew-symmetry properties. It can easily be shown that in $n$-dimensional space there exist $n^2 (n^2 - 1)/12$ components of $R_{klmn}$. In three dimensions the nonvanishing components are $R_{1212}$, $R_{1313}$, $R_{2323}$, $R_{1213}$, $R_{2123}$, and $R_{3132}$. In two dimensions the only nonvanishing component is $R_{1212}$.

By taking the covariant derivative of the Riemann-Christoffel tensors using (A4.13) and (A5.4), we can show that

$$R^k{}_{lmn;r} + R^k{}_{lnr;m} + R^k{}_{lrm;n} = 0 \tag{A5.8}$$

$$R_{klmn;r} + R_{klnr;m} + R_{klrm;n} = 0 \tag{A5.9}$$

These identities are known as *Bianchi's identities.*

The Riemann-Christoffel tensor is a measure of the curvature of the space. Because of this, a space in which this tensor vanishes is called a *flat space*. *In euclidean space the Riemann-Christoffel tensor vanishes identically.* Consequently euclidean space is a flat space. For further details on other related subjects we refer the reader to references cited in Art. A1.

## A6. TWO-POINT TENSOR FIELDS

DEFINITION 1. *Quantities $A^k{}_K(\mathbf{x}, \mathbf{X})$ that transform like tensors with respect to indices $k$ and $K$ upon the transformation of each of the two sets of coordinates $x^k$ and $X^K$ are called two-point tensors.* Thus if

$$\acute{x}^k = \acute{x}^k(\mathbf{x}) \qquad \acute{X}^K = \acute{X}^K(\mathbf{X}) \tag{A6.1}$$

are differentiable coordinate transformations, and if

$$\acute{A}^k{}_K(\acute{\mathbf{x}}, \acute{\mathbf{X}}) = A^m{}_M(\mathbf{x}, \mathbf{X}) \frac{\partial \acute{x}^k}{\partial x^m} \frac{\partial X^M}{\partial \acute{X}^K} \tag{A6.2}$$

then $A^k{}_K$ is an absolute two-point tensor field. As an example of a two-point tensor field we cite *shifters*, which are defined by

$$g^k{}_K(\mathbf{x}, \mathbf{X}) \equiv \mathbf{g}^k(\mathbf{x}) \cdot \mathbf{G}_K(\mathbf{X}) \qquad g^K{}_k(\mathbf{x}, \mathbf{X}) \equiv \mathbf{G}^K(\mathbf{X}) \cdot \mathbf{g}_k(\mathbf{x}) \tag{A6.3}$$

where $\mathbf{g}_k(\mathbf{x})$ and $\mathbf{G}_K(\mathbf{X})$ are respectively the base vectors in curvilinear coordinates $x^k$ and $X^K$, and $\mathbf{g}^k(\mathbf{x})$ and $\mathbf{G}^K(\mathbf{X})$ are their reciprocals. A second example is provided by displacement gradients

$$x^k{}_{,K}(\mathbf{X}) \equiv \frac{\partial x^k}{\partial X^K} \qquad X^K{}_{,k}(\mathbf{x}) \equiv \frac{\partial X^K}{\partial x^k} \tag{A6.4}$$

To see the two-point-tensor character of $x^k{}_{,K}$ we transform the coordinates according to (A6.1); then, by chain rule of differentiation,

$$\frac{\partial \acute{x}^k}{\partial \acute{X}^K} = \frac{\partial \acute{x}^k}{\partial x^m} \frac{\partial x^m}{\partial X^M} \frac{\partial X^M}{\partial \acute{X}^K}$$

which has the form (A6.2).

Higher-order two-point tensors and their various generalizations, such as relative two-point tensors, and multiple-point tensors are defined similarly.

DEFINITION 2. *Total covariant differentiation of a two-point-tensor field* $A^k{}_K(\mathbf{x}, \mathbf{X})$, *when* $\mathbf{x}$ *is related to* $\mathbf{X}$ *by a mapping* $\mathbf{x} = \mathbf{x}(\mathbf{X})$, *is defined by*

$$A^k{}_{K:L} \equiv A^k{}_{K;L} + A^k{}_{K;l}\, x^l{}_{,L} \tag{A6.5}$$

where $A^k{}_{K;L}$ denotes the covariant partial derivative of $A^k{}_K$ with respect to the metric $G_{KL}$ of coordinates $X^K$ with $\mathbf{x}$ regarded fixed, and $A^k{}_{K;l}$ is that with respect to the metric $g_{kl}$ of $x^k$ with $\mathbf{X}$ fixed, i.e.,

$$A^k{}_{K;L} = \frac{\partial A^k{}_K}{\partial X^L} - \begin{Bmatrix} M \\ LK \end{Bmatrix} A^k{}_M$$

$$A^k{}_{K;l} = \frac{\partial A^k{}_K}{\partial x^l} + \begin{Bmatrix} k \\ lm \end{Bmatrix} A^m{}_K$$

Therefore

$$A^k{}_{K:L} = \frac{\partial A^k{}_K}{\partial X^L} - \begin{Bmatrix} M \\ LK \end{Bmatrix} A^k{}_M + \left( \frac{\partial A^k{}_K}{\partial x^l} + \begin{Bmatrix} k \\ lm \end{Bmatrix} A^m{}_K \right) \frac{\partial x^l}{\partial X^L} \tag{A6.6}$$

Applying this rule to $x^k{}_{,K}(\mathbf{X})$, we find that

$$(x^k{}_{,K})_{:L} = \frac{\partial^2 x^k}{\partial X^L\, \partial X^K} - \begin{Bmatrix} M \\ LK \end{Bmatrix} \frac{\partial x^k}{\partial X^M} + \begin{Bmatrix} k \\ lm \end{Bmatrix} \frac{\partial x^m}{\partial X^K} \frac{\partial x^l}{\partial X^L} \tag{A6.7}$$

We note that (A6.5) generalizes the total derivative of a scalar function of two variables $\phi(x, X)$ subject to $x = x(X)$; i.e.,

$$\frac{d\phi}{dX} = \frac{\partial \phi}{\partial x} \frac{dx}{dX} + \frac{\partial \phi}{\partial X}$$

Total covariant differentiation obeys the formal rules of covariant differentiation. Thus for example

$$g_{kl:M} = g^k{}_{K:M} = G_{KL:m} = 0 \tag{A6.8}$$

$$(A^k{}_K\, B^L{}_l)_{:M} = A^k{}_{K:M}\, B^L{}_l + A^k{}_K\, B^L{}_{l:M}$$

etc. Thus we see that the metric tensors and shifters can be moved in and out of a covariant total differentiation as if they were constant, i.e.,

$$(g^k{}_K\, A^K{}_l)_{:m} = g^k{}_K\, A^K{}_{l:m} \tag{A6.9}$$

$$(g^{kl}\, A^K{}_l)_{:m} = g^{kl}\, A^K{}_{l:m}$$

For further accounts of the subject and for other references we refer the reader to Ericksen's article in Truesdell and Toupin [1960, appendix].

# BIBLIOGRAPHY

*Parenthetical numbers following the entries indicate the articles in which text references are made.*

Abraham, M., and R. Becker [1949]: "The Classical Theory of Electricity and Magnetism," 2d ed., Hafner Publishing Company, New York. (109, 116)

Adkins, J. E. [1955]: Some General Results in the Theory of Large Elastic Deformations, *Proc. Roy. Soc. (London)*, (**A**) **231**: 75–90. (59)

Adkins, J. E. [1956*a*]: Finite Plane Deformation of Thin Elastic Sheets Reinforced with Inextensible Cords, *Phil. Trans. Roy. Soc. London*, (**A**) **249**: 125–150. (59)

Adkins, J. E. [1956*b*]: Cylindrically Symmetrical Deformations of Incompressible Elastic Materials Reinforced with Inextensible Cords, *J. Rational Mech. and Analysis*, **5**: 189–202. (59)

Adkins, J. E. [1958]: A Reciprocal Property of the Finite Plane Strain Equations, *J. Mech. and Phys. Solids*, **6**: 267–275. (59)

Adkins, J. E., A. E. Green, and G. C. Nicholas [1954]: Two-dimensional Theory of Elasticity for Finite Deformations, *Phil. Trans. Roy. Soc. London*, (**A**) **247**: 279–306. (56)

Adkins, J. E., A. E. Green, and R. T. Shield [1953]: Finite Plane Strain, *Phil. Trans. Roy. Soc. London*, (**A**) **246**: 181–213. (56, 57)

Adkins, J. E., and R. S. Rivlin [1952]: Large Elastic Deformations of Isotropic Materials. IX. The Deformation of Thin Shells, *Phil. Trans. Roy. Soc. London*, (**A**) **244**: 505–531. (61)

Adkins, J. E., and R. S. Rivlin [1955]: Large Elastic Deformations of Isotropic Materials. X. Reinforcement by Inextensible Cords, *Phil. Trans. Roy. Soc. London*, (**A**) **248**: 201–223. (59)

Alfvén, H. [1950]: "Cosmical Electrodynamics," Oxford University Press, New York. (116)

Appell, P. [1926]: "Traité de mécanique rationelle," vol. 5, Gauthier-Villars, Paris. (A1)

Ariano, R. [1930]: Deformazioni finite di sistemi continui isotropi, *Rend. Ist. Lombardo Sci.*, (2) **63**: 740–754. (47)

Armanni, G. [1915]: Sulle deformazioni finite dei solidi elastici isotropi, *Nuovo cimento*, (6) **10**: 427–447. (54)

Baker, M., and J. L. Ericksen [1954]: Inequalities Restricting the Form of the Stress-deformation Relations for Isotropic Elastic Solids and Reiner-Rivlin Fluids, *J. Wash. Acad. Sci.*, **44**: 33–35. (47, 48)

Barta, J. [1957]: On the Non-linear Elasticity Law, *Acta Tech. Acad. Sci. Hung.*, **18**: 55–65. (47)

Bateman, H. [1932]: Ch. 3, I. General Physical Properties of Viscous Fluid; II. Motion of an Incompressible Viscous Fluid; IV. Compressible Fluids, Report of the Committee on Hydrodynamics, *Bull. Nat. Research Council* (*U.S.*), no. 84. (63)

Bernstein, B. [1960*a*]: Hypo-elasticity and Elasticity, *Arch. Rational Mech. and Analysis*, **6**: 90–104. (73, 75)

Bernstein, B. [1960*b*]: Relations between Hypo-elasticity and Elasticity, *Trans. Soc. Rheol.*, **4**: 23–28. (73)

Bernstein, B., and J. L. Ericksen [1958]: Work Functions in Hypo-elasticity, *Arch. Rational Mech. and Analysis*, **1**: 396–409. (75)

Biot, M. A. [1955]: Variational Principles in Irreversible Thermodynamics with Application to Viscoelasticity, *Phys. Rev.*, **97**: 1463–1469. (39, 40)

Bland, D. R. [1960]: "The Theory of Linear Viscoelasticity," Pergamon Press, Inc., New York. (91)

Bland, D. R., and P. M. Naghdi [1958]: A Compressible Elastic, Perfectly Plastic Wedge, *J. Appl. Mechanics*, **25**: 239–242. (88)

Bôcher, M. [1952]: "Introduction to Higher Algebra," 16th printing, The Macmillan Company, New York. (45)

Boltzmann, L. [1874]: Zur Theorie der elastischen Nachwirkung, *Sitzber. Akad. Wiss. Wien*, **70**: 275–306; *Wiss. Abhandl.*, **1**: 616–639. (92)

Bordoni, P. G. [1955]: On the Exact Relation between the Specific Heats of an Elastic Solid, *J. Rational Mech. and Analysis*, **4**: 975–981. (39)

Born, M. [1921]: Kritische Betrachtungen zur traditionellen Darstellung der Thermodynamik, *Physik. Z.*, **22**: 218–224, 249–254, 282–286. (39)

Born, M., and K. Huang [1954]: "Dynamical Theory of Crystal Lattices," Oxford University Press, New York. (43)

Boussinesq, J. [1868]: Sur l'influence des frottements dans les mouvements régulières des fluides, *J. Math. Pures Appl.*, (2) **13**: 377–438. (48)

Boussinesq, J. [1870]: Note complémentaire au mémoire sur les ondes liquides périodiques, présenté le 29 novembre 1869, et approuvé par l'Académie le 21 fevrier 1870—Établissement de relations générales et nouvelles entre l'énergie interne d'un corps fluide ou solide, et ses pressions ou forces élastiques, *Compt. Rend. Acad. Sci. Paris*, **71**: 400–402. (45)

Boussinesq, J. [1872]: Théorie des ondes liquides périodiques, *Mém. Divers Savants*, **20**: 509–615. (45)

Braun, I., and M. Reiner [1952]: Problems of cross-viscosity, *Quart. J. Mech. Appl. Math.*, **5**: 42–53. (64, 65, 67)

Bridgman, P. W. [1923]: The Compressibility of Thirty Metals as a Function of Pressure and Temperature, *Proc. Am. Acad. Arts Sci.*, **58**: 163–242. (84)

Bridgman, P. W. [1948]: The Compression of 39 Substances to 100,000 kg/cm$^2$, *Proc. Am. Acad. Arts Sci.*, **76**: 55–70. (59)

Brillouin, L. [1925]: Les Lois de l'élasticité sous forme tensorielle valable pour des coordonnées quelconques, *Ann. Phys.*, (**10**) **3**: 251–298. (34, 45)

Brillouin, L. [1928]: Les Lois de l'élasticité en coordonnées quelconques, *Proc. Intern. Congr. Math. Toronto* (1924), **2**: 73–97. (34, 45)

Brillouin, L. [1938]: "Les Tenseurs en mécanique et en élasticité," Masson et Cie, Paris. (A1)

Brillouin, M. [1888]: Chaleur spécifique pour une transformation quelconque et thermodynamique, *J. Phys. Theor. Appl.*, (2) **7**: 148–152. (39)

Burgers, J. M. [1948]: Non-linear Relations between Viscous Stresses and Instantaneous Rate of Deformation as a Consequence of Slow Relaxations, *Proc. koninkl. Ned. Akad. Wetenschap.*, **51**: 787–792. (70)

Caldonazzo, B. [1947]: Sui moti liberi di un mezzo continuo, *Ann. di Mat.*, (4) **26**: 43–55. (76)

Caprioli, L. [1955]: Su un criterio per l'esistenza dell'energia di deformazione, *Boll. Un. Mat. Ital.*, (3) **10**: 481–483. (47, 75)

Carathéodory, C. [1909]: Untersuchungen über die Grundlagen der Thermodynamik, *Math. Ann.*, **67**: 355–386. (39)

Carathéodory, C. [1925]: Über die Bestimmung der Energie und der absoluten Temperatur mit Hilfe von reversiblen Prozessen, *Berlin Akad. Wiss.*, 39–47. (39)

Carnot, S. [1824]: Réflexions sur la puissance mortice du feu et les machines propres à développer cette puissance, *École Norm. Super. Ann. Sci.*, (2) **1**: 393–457 (1872). (37)

Cauchy, A. L. [1823]: Recherches sur l'équilibre et mouvement intérieur des corps solides ou fluides, élastiques ou non élastiques, *Bull. Soc. Philomath.*, 9–13; *Œuvres*, (2) **2**: 300–304. (45)

Cauchy, A. L. [1827*a*]: De la pression ou tension dans un corps solide, *Ex. de Math.*, **2**: 42–56; *Œuvres*, (2) **7**: 60–78. (32)

Cauchy, A. L. [1827*b*]: Sur les relations qui existent dans l'état d'équilibre d'un corps solide ou fluide entre les pressions ou tensions et les forces accélératrices, *Ex. de Math.*, **2**: 108–111; *Œuvres*, (2) **7**: 141–145. (32)

Cauchy, A. L. [1828]: Sur les équations qui expriment les conditions d'équilibre ou les lois du mouvement intérieur d'un corps solide, élastique, ou non élastique, *Ex. de Math.*, **3**: 160–187; *Œuvres*, (2) **8**: 195–226. (32, 45)

Cauchy, A. L. [1829]: Sur l'équilibre et le mouvement intérieur des corps considérés comme des masses continues, *Ex. de Math.*, **4**: 293–319; *Œuvres*, (2), **9**: 342–369. (27, 45, 72)

Cauchy, A. L. [1850]: Mémoire sur les systèmes isotropes des points matériels, *Mem. Acad. Sci.*, **22**: 615; *Œuvres*, (1) **2**: 351. (45)

Chapman, S., and T. G. Cowling [1952]: "The Mathematical Theory of Non-uniform Gases," Cambridge University Press, New York. (43, 69)

Clausius, R. [1854]: Über eine veränderte Form des zweiten Hauptsatzes der mechanischen Wärmetheorie, *Ann. Physik*, **93**: 481–506; *Abhandl.*, **1**: 126–154. (40)

Clausius, R. [1862]: Über die Anwendung des Satzes von der Äquivalenz der Verwandlungen auf die innere Arbeit, *Vjschr. nat. Ges. Zürich*, **7**: 48–95; *Ann. Physik*, **116**: 73–112; *Abhandl.*, **1**: 242–279. (40)

Clausius, R. [1865]: Über verschiedene für die Anwendung bequeme Formen der Hauptgleichungen der mechanischen Wärmetheorie, *Vjschr. nat. Ges. Zürich*, **10**: 1–59; *Ann. Physik*, **125**: 353–400; *Abhandl.*, **2**: 1–44. (40)

Coburn, N. [1955]: "Vector and Tensor Analysis," The Macmillan Company, New York. (A1)

Coleman, B. D., and W. Noll [1959*a*]: On the Thermostatics of Continuous Media, *Arch. Rational Mech. and Analysis,* **4**: 97–128. (39, 47)

Coleman, B. D., and W. Noll [1959*b*]: On Certain Steady Flows of General Fluids, *Arch. Rational Mech. and Analysis,* **3**: 289–303. (64, 92)

Coleman, B. D., and W. Noll [1959*c*]: Helical Flow of General Fluids, *J. Appl. Phys.,* **30**: 1508–1512. (92, 101)

Coleman, B. D., and W. Noll [1960]: An Approximation Theorem for Functionals, with Applications in Continuum Mechanics, *Arch. Rational Mech. and Analysis,* **6**: 355–370. (92, 101)

Coleman, B. D., and W. Noll [1961*a*]: Foundations of Linear Viscoelasticity, *Revs. Modern Phys.,* **33**: 239–249. (91, 94)

Coleman, B. D., and W. Noll [1961*b*]: Recent Results in the Continuum Theory of Viscoelastic Fluids, *Ann. N.Y. Acad. Sci.,* **89**: 672–714. (92, 94, 101)

Copeland, L. E., and M. Mooney [1948]: The Thermodynamics of a Strained Elastomer. III. The Thermal Coefficient of Modulus and Statistical Theory of Elasticity, *J. Appl. Phys.,* **19**: 450–455. (60)

Cosserat, E. and F. [1896]: Sur la théorie de l'élasticité, *Ann. Toulouse,* **10**: 1–116. (14, 34, 45)

Cosserat, E. and F. [1909]: "Théorie des corps déformables," Paris; in O. D. Khvol'son, "*Traité de physique,*" translation by E. Davaux, 2d ed., vol. 2, Hermann & Cie, Paris (1909), pp. 953–1173. (40, 41, 45)

Cotter, B. A., and R. S. Rivlin [1955]: Tensors Associated with Time-dependent Stress, *Quart. Appl. Math.,* **13**: 177–182. (72, 92)

Cowling, T. G. [1957]: "Magnetohydrodynamics," Interscience Publishers, Inc., New York. (116)

Criminale, W. O., Jr., J. L. Ericksen, and G. L. Filbey, Jr. [1958]: Steady Shear Flow of Non-Newtonian Fluids, *Arch. Rational Mech., and Analysis,* **1**: 410–417. (68)

Crossland, B. [1954]: The Effect of Fluid Pressure on the Shear Properties of Metals, *Proc. Inst. Mech. Engrs. (London),* **169**: 935–944. (84)

De Groot, S. R. [1952]: "Thermodynamics of Irreversible Processes," North-Holland Publishing Company, Amsterdam. (39, 40)

Doyle, T. C., and J. L. Ericksen [1956]: Nonlinear Elasticity, *Advances Appl. Mech.,* **4**: 53–115. (45, 54, 60, 116)

Drucker, D. C. [1950]: "Stress-strain Relations in the Plastic Range—a Survey of Theory and Experiment," U.S. Office of Naval Research Technical Report, Contract N7-onr-358, Graduate Division of Applied Mathematics, Brown University. (83)

Drucker, D. C. [1951]: A More Fundamental Approach to Plastic Stress-strain Relations, *Proc. 1st U.S. Natl. Congr. Appl. Mech.,* 487–491. (84)

Drucker, D. C. [1960]: Plasticity, in "Structural Mechanics—Proceedings of the First Symposium on Naval Structural Mechanics," pp. 407–455, Pergamon Press, Inc., New York. (83)

Drummond, J. E. [1961]: "Plasma Physics," McGraw-Hill Book Company, Inc., New York. (116)

Duhem, P. [1901]: Recherches sur l'hydrodynamique, *Ann. Toulouse,* (2) **3**:

315–377, 379–431; **4** [1902]: 101–169; **5** [1903]: 5–61, 197–255, 353–404; Separate reprints, Gauthier-Villars, Paris, 2 vols. [1903], [1904]. (40, 63)

Duhem, P. [1903]: Sur la propagation des ondes dans un milieu parfaitement élastique affecté de defórmations finies, *Compt. Rend. Acad. Sci. Paris,* **136:** 1379–1381. (58)

Duhem, P. [1911]: "Traité d'énergétique," Gauthier-Villars, Paris, 2 vols. (41)

Dunkin, J. W., and A. C. Eringen, [1961]: "On the Propagation of Waves in an Electromagnetic Elastic Solid," U.S. Office of Naval Research Technical Report No. 18, Contract Nonr-1100(02), Purdue University. (110)

Dupont, Y. [1933]: Thermodynamique invariantive des systèmes élastiques, *Bull. Sci. Acad. Roy. Belg.,* (5) **19:** 1167–1179. (98)

Eckart, C. [1940]: The Thermodynamics of Irreversible Processes, *Phys. Rev.,* (2) **58:** 267–275, 924. (39)

Ehrenfest-Afanassjewa, T. [1925]: Zur Axiomatisierung des zweiten Hauptsatzes der Thermodynamik, *Z. Physik,* **33:** 933–945; **34:** 638. (39)

Eisenhart, L. P. [1926]: "Riemannian Geometry," Princeton University Press, Princeton, N.J. (A1)

Eisenhart, L. P. [1947]: "Differential Geometry," Princeton University Press, Princeton, N.J. (75)

Elsasser, W. M. [1956]: Hydromagnetic Dynamo Theory, *Revs. Modern Phys.,* **28:** 135–163. (116)

Ericksen, J. L. [1953]: On the Propagation of Waves in Isotropic Incompressible Perfectly Elastic Materials, *J. Rational Mech. and Analysis,* **2:** 329–337. (58)

Ericksen, J. L. [1954]: Deformations Possible in Every Isotropic, Incompressible, Perfectly Elastic Body, *Z.A.M.P.,* **v:** 466–489. (59)

Ericksen, J. L. [1955]: A Consequence of Inequalities Proposed by Baker and Ericksen, *J. Wash. Acad. Sci.,* **45:** 268. (47, 48)

Ericksen, J. L. [1956]: Overdetermination of the Speed in Rectilinear Motion of Non-Newtonian Fluids, *Quart. Appl. Math.,* **14:** 318–321. (68)

Ericksen, J. L. [1958]: Hypo-elastic Potentials, *Quart. J. Mech. Appl. Math.,* **11:** 67–72. (75)

Ericksen, J. L. [1960*a*]: Anisotropic Fluids, *Arch. Rational Mech. and Analysis,* **4:** 231–237. (48, 92, 94)

Ericksen, J. L. [1960*b*]: Transversely Isotropic Fluids, *Kolloid-Zeitschrift,* **173–2:** 117–122. (48, 92, 94)

Ericksen, J. L. [1960*c*]: Theory of Anisotropic Fluids, *Trans. Soc. Rheol.,* **4:** 29–39. (48, 92, 94)

Ericksen, J. L. [1960*d*]: A Vorticity Effect in Anisotropic Fluids, *J. Polymer Sci.,* **47:** 327–331. (48, 92, 94)

Ericksen, J. L. [1960*e*]: The Behavior of Certain Viscoelastic Materials in Laminar Shearing Motions, in J. T. Bergen (editor), "Viscoelasticity: Phenomenological Aspects," Academic Press, Inc., New York. (98)

Ericksen, J. L., and R. S. Rivlin, [1954]: Large Elastic Deformations of Homogeneous Anisotropic Materials, *J. Rational Mech. and Analysis,* **3:** 281–301. (57, 59, 116)

Ericksen, J. L., and R. A. Toupin, [1956]: Implications of Hadamard's Conditions for Elastic Stability with Respect to Uniqueness Theorems, *Canadian J. Math.*, **8**: 432–436. (59)

Ericksen, J. L., and C. Truesdell, [1958]: Exact Theory of Stress and Strain in Rods and Shells, *Arch. Rational Mech. and Analysis*, **1**: 295–323. (3)

Eringen, A. C. [1954]: Mimeo notes on "Elastic Wave Propagation," Purdue University. (6, 14, 60)

Eringen, A. C. [1960]: Irreversible Thermodynamics and Continuum Mechanics, *Phys. Rev.*, **117**: 1174–1183. (39, 40, 48, 69)

Eringen, A. C. [1961]: "On the Foundations of Electroelastostatics," U.S. Office of Naval Research Technical Report No. 19, Contract Nonr-1100(02), Purdue University. (110, 114)

Eringen, A. C. [1964]: "Theory of Continuous Media," John Wiley & Sons, Inc., New York. (9, 34, 39, 40, 41, 43, 48, 51, 69, 91)

Euler, L. [1770]: Sectio secunda de principiis motus fluidorum, *Novi. Comm. Acad. Sci. Petrop.* **14** (1769), 270–386; *Opera Omnia*, (2) **13**: 73–153. (21)

Fano, R. M., L. J. Chu, and R. B. Adler [1960]: "Electromagnetic Fields, Energy, and Forces," John Wiley & Sons, Inc., New York. (110, 116)

Finger, J. [1894*a*]: Über die allgemeinsten Beziehungen zwischen die Deformationen und den zugehörigen Spannungen in aeolotropen und isotropen Substanzen, *Sitzber. Akad. Wiss. Wien*, (**IIa**) **103**: 1073–1100. (4, 45, 47)

Finger, J. [1894*b*]: Das Potential der innern Kräfte und die Beziehungen zwischen den Deformationen und den Spannungen in elastisch isotropen Körpern bei Berücksichtigung von Gliedern, die bezüglich der Deformationselemente von dritter, beziehungsweise zweiter Ordnung sind, *Sitzber. Akad. Wiss. Wien*, (**IIa**) **103**: 163–200, 231–250. (45)

Fresnel, A. [1868]: Second supplément au mémoire sur la double réfraction (1822), *Œuvres*, **2**: 369–442. (32)

Freudenthal, A. M., and H. Geiringer, [1958]: The Mathematical Theories of the Inelastic Continuum, in "Handbuch der Physik," vol. vi, pp. 229–433, Springer-Verlag, Berlin. (83)

Garner, F. H., and A. H. Nissan [1946]: Rheological Properties of High-viscosity Solutions of Long Molecules, *Nature*, **158**: 634–635. (66, 70)

Garner, F. H., A. H. Nissan, and G. F. Wood [1950]: Thermodynamics and Rheological Behavior of Elastoviscous Systems under Stress, *Phil. Trans. Roy. Soc. London*, (**A**) **243**: 37–66. (66, 70)

Geiringer, H. [1953]: Some Recent Results in the Theory of an Ideal Plastic Body, *Advances Appl. Mech.*, **3**: 197–294. (83)

Gent, A. N., and P. B. Lindley [1959]: Internal Rupture of Bonded Rubber Cylinders in Tension, *Proc. Roy. Soc. (London)*, (**A**) **249**: 195–205. (61)

Gent, A. N., and R. S. Rivlin [1952]: Experiments on the Mechanics of Rubber, *Proc. Phys. Soc. (London)*, (**B**) **65**: 118–121, 487–501, 645–648. (61)

Gent, A. N., and A. G. Thomas [1958]: Forms for the Stored (Strain) Energy Function for Vulcanized Rubber, *J. Polymer Sci.*, **28**: 625–628. (61)

Gibbs, J. W. [1873]: A Method of Geometrical Representation of the Thermodynamic Properties of Substances by Means of Surfaces, *Trans. Conn. Acad. Arts Sci.*, **2**: 382–404. (39)

Gibbs, J. W. [1875]: On the Equilibrium of Heterogeneous Substances, *Trans. Conn. Acad. Arts Sci.*, **3**: 108–248, 343–534; *Works*, **1**: 55–353. (41, 45)

Goldstein, S. [1960]: "Lectures on Fluid Mechanics," Interscience Publishers, Inc., New York, chap. 3. (116)

Goodier, J. N., and W. A. Shaw [1957]: "Large (Second Order) Torsion of Elastic Bars," U.S. Office of Naval Research Technical Report No. 108, Stanford University. (53)

Gosiewski, W. [1890]: O naturze ruchu wewnatrz elementu plynnego, *Pamietnik Akad. Krakow, mat-przyv.*, **17**: 135–142. (21)

Grad, H. [1958]: Principles of Kinetic Theory of Gases, in "Handbuch der Physik," vol. XII, 205–293, Springer-Verlag, Berlin. (43)

Green, A. E. [1955]: Finite Elastic Deformation of Incompressible Isotropic Bodies, *Proc. Roy. Soc. (London)*, (**A**) **227**: 271–278. (54)

Green, A. E. [1956*a*]: Hypo-elasticity and Plasticity, *Proc. Roy. Soc. (London)*, (**A**) **234**: 46–59. (79, 80, 83, 89, 90)

Green, A. E. [1956*b*]: Hypo-elasticity and Plasticity. II, *J. Rational Mech. and Analysis*, **5**: 725–734. (79, 83, 89)

Green, A. E. [1956*c*]: Simple Extension of Hypo-elastic Body of Grade Zero, *J. Rational Mech. and Analysis*, **5**: 637–642. (81)

Green, A. E., and J. E. Adkins [1960]: "Large Elastic Deformations and Non-linear Continuum Mechanics," Oxford University Press, New York. (45, 51, 59, 61, 95)

Green, A. E., and R. S. Rivlin [1956]: Steady Flow of Non-Newtonian Fluids through Tubes, *Quart. Appl. Math.*, **14**: 299–308. (68)

Green, A. E., and R. S. Rivlin [1957]: The Mechanics of Non-linear Materials with Memory, Part I, *Arch. Rational Mech. and Analysis*, **1**: 1–21. (46, 92)

Green, A. E., and R. S. Rivlin [1960]: The Mechanics of Non-linear Materials with Memory, Part III, *Arch. Rational Mech. and Analysis*, **4**: 387–404. (92)

Green, A. E., R. S. Rivlin, and R. T. Shield [1952]: General Theory of Small Elastic Deformations Superposed on Finite Elastic Deformations, *Proc. Roy. Soc. (London)*, (**A**) **211**: 128–154. (60)

Green, A. E., R. S. Rivlin, and A. J. M. Spencer [1959]: The Mechanics of Non-linear Materials with Memory, Part II, *Arch. Rational Mech. and Analysis*, **3**: 82–90. (92)

Green, A. E., and R. T. Shield [1950]: Finite Elastic Deformation of Incompressible Isotropic Bodies, *Proc. Roy. Soc. (London)*, (**A**) **202**: 407–419. (53)

Green, A. E., and E. W. Wilkes [1953]: A Note on the Finite Extension and Torsion of a Circular Cylinder of Compressible Elastic Isotropic Material, *Quart. J. Mech. Appl. Math.*, **6**: 240–249. (59)

Green, A. E., and E. W. Wilkes [1954]: Finite Plane Strain for Orthotropic Bodies, *J. Rational Mech. and Analysis*, **3**: 713–723. (55, 59)

Green, A. E., and W. Zerna [1954]: "Theoretical Elasticity," Oxford University Press, New York. (47, 52, 53, 59, 60)

Green, G. [1839]: On the Laws of Reflection and Refraction of Light at the Common Surface of Two Non-crystallized Media, *Trans. Cambridge Phil. Soc.*, **7**: 1–24; *Papers*, 245–269. (45)

Green, G. [1841]: On the Propagation of Light in Crystallized Media, *Trans. Cambridge Phil. Soc.*, **7**: 121–140; *Papers*, 293–311. (45)

Green, H. S. [1952]: "The Molecular Theory of Fluids," North-Holland Publishing Company, Amsterdam. (43)

Greensmith, H. W., and R. S. Rivlin [1951]: Measurements of the Normal Stress Effect in Solutions of Polyisobutylene, *Nature,* **168:** 664–665. (67)

Greensmith, H. W., and R. S. Rivlin [1954]: The Hydrodynamics of Non-Newtonian Fluids. III. The Normal Stress Effect in High-polymer Solutions, *Phil. Trans. Roy. Soc. London,* (**A**) **245:** 399–428. (67, 70)

Gumbrell, S. M., L. Mullins, and R. S. Rivlin [1953]: Departures of the Elastic Behavior of Rubbers in Simple Extension from the Kinetic Theory, *Trans. Faraday Soc.,* **49:** 1495–1505. (60)

Gyorgyi, G. [1954]: The Motion of the Center of Energy and the Energy Impulse Tensor of Electromagnetic Fields in Dielectrics, *Acta Phys. Hung.,* **4:** 121–131. (110)

Hadamard, J. [1903]: "Leçons sur la propagation des ondes et les équations de l'hydrodynamique," Hermann & Cie, Paris. (58)

Hamel, G. [1912]: "Elementare Mechanik," Teubner, Verlagsgesellschaft, mbh, Stuttgart. (45)

Hayes, M., and R. S. Rivlin [1960]: "Propagation of a Plane Wave in an Isotropic Elastic Material Subjected to Pure Homogeneous Deformations," U.S. Office of Naval Research Technical Report, Contract Nonr 562(10) NR-064-406. (59, 60)

Hellinger, E. [1914]: Die allgemeinen Ansätze der Mechanik der Kontinua, *Enz. Math. Wiss.,* **4:** 602–694. (40, 41)

Helmholtz, H. [1858]: Über Integrale der hydrodynamischen Gleichungen, welche den Wirbelbewegungen entsprechen, *J. Reine Angew. Math.,* **55:** 25–55. (10)

Hetényi, M. I., (editor) [1950]: "Handbook of Experimental Stress Analysis," John Wiley & Sons, Inc., New York. (61)

Hilbert, D. [1907]: "Mechanik der Continua," manuscript notes by W. Marshall in Purdue University Library. (39)

Hill, R. [1950]: "Mathematical Theory of Plasticity," Oxford University Press, New York. (80, 83)

Hill, R. [1956]: The Mechanics of Quasi-static Plastic Deformation in Metals, in "Surveys in Mechanics," Cambridge University Press, New York. (83)

Hill, R. [1957]: On Uniqueness and Stability in the Theory of Finite Elastic Strain, *J. Mech. and Phys. Solids,* **5:** 229–241. (59)

Hille, E., and R. S. Phillips [1957]: "Functional Analysis and Semi-groups," American Mathematical Society Colloquium Publications, vol. XXXI, New York. (94)

Hirschfelder, J. O., C. F. Curtiss, and R. B. Bird [1954]: "Molecular Theory of Gases and Liquids," John Wiley & Sons, Inc., New York. (43)

Hodge, P. G., Jr. [1958]: The Mathematical Theory of Plasticity, in J. N. Goodier and P. G. Hodge, Jr., "Elasticity and Plasticity," John Wiley & Sons, Inc., New York. (83)

Jaumann, G. [1911]: Geschlossenes System physikalischer und chemischer Differenzialgesetze, *Sitzber. Akad. Wiss. Wien,* (**IIa**) **120:** 385–530. (39, 41, 72)

Jaumann, G. [1918]: Physik der kontinuierlichen Medien, *Denkschr. Akad. Wiss. Wien,* **95:** 461–562. (41)

Jeffreys, H. [1931]: "Cartesian Tensors," Cambridge University Press, New York. (A1)

John, F. [1960]: Plane Strain Problems for a Perfectly Elastic Material of Harmonic Type, *Comm. Pure Appl. Math.*, **13**: 239–296. (59)

Joule, J. P. [1843]: On the Caloric Effects of Magneto-electricity and on the Mechanical Value of Heat, *Phil. Mag.*, (3) **23**: 263–276, 347–355, 435–443; *Papers*, **1**: 123–159. (37)

Kellogg, O. D. [1929]: "Foundations of Potential Theory," Frederick Ungar Publishing Co., New York. (99, 109)

Kelvin. See Thomson, W.

Kirchhoff, G. [1852]: Über die Gleichungen des Gleichgewichts eines elastischen Körpers bei nicht unendlich kleinen Verschiebungen seiner Teile, *Sitzber. Akad. Wiss. Wien*, **9**: 762–773. (34, 45, 60)

Kittel, C. [1956]: "Introduction to Solid State Physics," 2d ed., John Wiley & Sons, Inc., New York. (43)

Koh, S. L., and A. C. Eringen [1962]: "On the Foundations of Non-linear Thermoviscoelasticity," U.S. Office of Naval Research Technical Report, Contract Nonr-1100(02), Purdue University. (92)

Koiter, W. T. [1960]: General Theorems for Elastic-plastic Solids, in "Progress in Solid Mechanics," North-Holland Publishing Company, Amsterdam, vol. 1, chap. 4. (83, 84)

Kottler, F. [1922]: Maxwell'sche Gleichungen und Metrik, *Sitzber. Acad. Wiss. Wien*, **(IIa) 131**: 119–146. (116)

Lamb, H. [1945]: "Hydrodynamics," 6th ed., Dover Publications, New York. (24)

Landshoff, R. K. M. [1961]: Magneto-fluid-dynamic Waves, *Appl. Mechanics Revs.*, **14**: 339–344. (116)

Langlois, W. [1957]: Steady Flow of Slightly Visco-elastic Fluids, Doctoral dissertation, Graduate Division of Applied Mathematics, Brown University. (68)

Levi-Civita, T. [1927]: "The Absolute Differential Calculus," Blackie & Son, Ltd., Glasgow. (A1)

Lévy, M. [1869]: Rapport sur un mémoire de M. Maurice Lévy, relatif à l'hydrodynamique des liquides homogènes, particulièrement à leur écoulement rectiligne et permanent, (St. Venant), *Compt. Rend. Acad. Sci. Paris*, **68**: 582–592. (48)

Lévy, M. [1870]: Mémoire sur les équations générales des mouvements intérieurs des corps solides ductiles au delà des limites où l'élasticité pourrait les ramener à leur premier état, *Compt. Rend. Acad. Sci. Paris*, **70**: 1323–1325. (83)

Lichtenstein, L. [1929]: "Grundlagen der Hydromechanik," Springer-Verlag, Berlin. (58, 59)

Lodge, A. S. [1951]: On the Use of Convected Coordinate Systems in the Mechanics of Continuous Media, *Proc. Cambridge Phil. Soc.*, **47**: 575–584. (27)

Lohr, E. [1917]: Entropieprinzip und geschlossenes Gleichungssystem, *Denkschr. Akad. Wiss. Wien*, **93**: 339–421. (39, 41)

Love, A. E. H. [1892]: "A Treatise on the Mathematical Theory of Elasticity," 1st ed., Cambridge University Press, New York; 4th ed. [1944], Dover Publications, New York. (10, 45, 61)

McConnell, A. J. [1931]: "Applications of the Absolute Differential Calculus," Blackie and Son, Ltd., Glasgow. (A1)

Markovitz, H. [1957]: Normal Stress Effect in Polyisobutylene Solutions. II. Classification and Application of Rheological Theories, *Trans. Soc. Rheol.*, **1**: 37–52. (68, 70, 91, 101)

Markovitz, H., and R. B. Williamson [1957]: Normal Stress Effect in Polyisobutylene Solutions. I. Measurements in a Cone and Plate Instrument, *Trans. Soc. Rheol.*, **1**: 25–36. (68, 70)

Marx, G. [1953]: The Electromagnetic Field in Moving Anisotropic Media, *Acta Phys. Hung.*, **3**: 75–94. (110)

Marx, G., and G. Gyorgyi [1954]: The Energy Impulse Tensor of the Electromagnetic Field and the Ponderomotive Forces in Dielectrics, *Acta Phys. Hung.*, **3**: 213–242. (110)

Marx, G., and G. Gyorgyi [1955]: The Energy Impulse Tensor of Electromagnetic Fields in Dielectrics, *Ann. Physik*, **6**: 241–256. (110)

Mason, P., and N. Wookey, (editors) [1958]: "The Rheology of Elastomers," Pergamon Press, Inc., New York. (43)

Mawardi, O. K. [1959]: Magnetohydrodynamics—A Survey of the Literature, *Appl. Mechanics Revs.*, **12**: 443–446. (116)

Maxwell, J. C. [1867]: On the Dynamical Theory of Gases, *Phil. Trans. Roy. Soc. London*, (**A**) **157**: 49–88; *Papers*, **2**: 26–78; *Phil. Mag.*, (4) **35**: 129–145, 185–217. (92)

Meixner, J. [1941]: Zur Thermodynamik der Thermodiffusion, *Ann. Physik*, (**5**) **39**: 333–356. (39)

Meixner, J. [1943]: Zur Thermodynamik der irreversiblen Prozesse, *Z. Physik. Chem.*, (B) **53**: 235–263. (39)

Merrington, A. C. [1943*a*]: Measurement of Anomalous Viscosity by the Capillary Tube Method, *Nature*, **152**: 214–215. (70)

Merrington, A. C. [1943*b*]: Flow of Visco-elastic Materials in Capillaries, *Nature*, **152**: 663. (65, 70)

Michal, A. D. [1927]: Functionals of $r$-Dimensional Manifolds Admitting Continuous Groups of Point Transformations, *Trans. Am. Math. Soc.*, **29**: 612–646. (3)

Michal, A. D. [1947]: "Matrix and Tensor Calculus," John Wiley & Sons, Inc. New York. (3, A1)

Mimura, Y. [1931]: On the Foundation of the Second Law of Thermodynamics, *J. Hiroshima Univ.*, **1**: 43–53. (39)

Mises, R. von [1913]: Mechanik der festen Körper im plastischdeformablen Zustand, *Gött. Nachr.*, 582–592. (83)

Mooney, M. [1931]: Explicit Formulas for Slip and Fluidity, *J. Rheol.*, **2**: 210–222. (63)

Mooney, M. [1940]: A Theory of Large Elastic Deformation, *J. Appl. Phys.*, **11**: 582–592. (51, 60, 61)

Mooney, M. [1948]: The Thermodynamics of a Strained Elastomer. I. General Analysis, *J. Appl. Phys.*, **19**: 434–444. (60)

Mooney, M. [1951]: Secondary Stresses in Viscoelastic Flow, *J. Colloid Sci.*, **6**: 96–107. (70)

Moreau, J. J. [1949]: Sur l'interprétation tourbillonaire des surfaces de glissement, *Compt. Rend. Acad. Sci. Paris*, **228**: 1923–1925. (59)

Moreau, J. J. [1953]: Bilan dynamique d'un écoulement rotationel, *J. Math. Pures Appl.*, (9) **31**: 355–375, **32**: 1–78. (59)

Murch, S. A., and P. M. Naghdi [1958]: On the Infinite Elastic, Perfectly Plastic Wedge under Uniform Surface Tractions, *Proc. 3d U.S. Natl. Congr. Appl. Mech.*, 611–624. (88)

Murnaghan, F. D. [1937]: Finite Deformations of an Elastic Solid, *Am. J. Math.*, **59**: 235–260. (9, 45, 60)

Murnaghan, F. D. [1951]: "Finite Deformation of an Elastic Solid," John Wiley & Sons, Inc., New York. (59)

Naghdi, P. M. [1957]: Stresses and Displacements in an Elastic-plastic Wedge, *J. Appl. Mechanics*, **24**: 98–104. (88)

Naghdi, P. M. [1958]: On Plane Stress Solution of an Elastic, Perfectly Plastic Wedge, *J. Appl. Mechanics*, **25**: 407–410. (88)

Naghdi, P. M. [1960]: Stress-strain Relations in Plasticity and Thermoplasticity, in "Plasticity—Proceedings of the Second Symposium on Naval Structural Mechanics," Pergamon Press, Inc., New York. (83, 84)

Naghdi, P. M., and W. L. Wainwright [1961]: On the Time Derivative of Tensors in Mechanics of Continua, *Quart. Appl. Math.*, **19**: 95–109. (22)

Neumann, C. [1860]: Zur Theorie der Elastizität, *J. Reine Angew. Math.*, **57**: 281–318. (45)

Noll, W. [1955]: On the Continuity of the Solid and Fluid States, *J. Rational Mech. and Analysis*, **4**: 3–81. (22, 27, 48, 73, 75, 92, 94, 102, 103, 104, 105, 106)

Noll, W. [1957]: "On the Foundations of the Mechanics of Continuous Media," Carnegie Institute of Technology Report No. 17, Air Force Office of Scientific Research. (27, 30, 92)

Noll, W. [1958]: A Mathematical Theory of the Mechanical Behavior of Continuous Media, *Arch. Rational Mech. and Analysis*, **2**: 197–226. (27, 92, 94)

Noll, W. [1959]: The Foundations of Classical Mechanics in the Light of Recent Advances in Continuum Mechanics, in "The Axiomatic Method, with Special Reference to Geometry and Physics" (1957), North-Holland Publishing Company, Amsterdam, pp. 266–281. (27)

Novozhilov, V. V. [1948]: "Foundations of the Nonlinear Theory of Elasticity," English Translation, Graylock Press (1953), Rochester, N.Y. (6, 10, 14, 60)

Oldroyd, J. G. [1950]: On the Formulation of Rheological Equations of State, *Proc. Roy. Soc.* (*London*), (**A**) **200**: 523–541. (27, 64, 72, 98)

Patterson, G. N. [1956]: "Molecular Flow of Gases," John Wiley & Sons, Inc., New York. (63)

Pearson, L. [1934]: "Tables of the Incomplete Γ-function," Cambridge University Press, New York. (105)

Piola, G. [1833]: La meccanica de' corpi naturalmente estesi trattata col calcolo delle variazioni, *Opusc. Mat. Fis. di Diversi Autori. Milano. Guisti*, **1**: 201–236. (4, 34)

Piola, G. [1836]: Nuova Analisi per tutte le questioni della meccanica molecolare, *Mem. Mat. Fis. Soc. Ital. Modena*, **21**: 155–321. (4, 34)

Piola, G. [1848]: Intorno alle equazioni fondamentali del movimento di corpi qualsivogliono, considerati secondo la naturale loro forma e costituzione (1845), *Mem. Mat. Fis. Soc. Ital. Modena,* **24**: 1–186. (34)

Pipkin, A. C., and R. S. Rivlin [1959]: The Formulation of Constitutive Equations in Continuum Physics. I, *Arch. Rational Mech. and Analysis,* **4**: 129–144. (45, 92, 116)

Pipkin, A. C., and R. S. Rivlin [1961]: "Small Deformations Superposed on Large Deformations in Materials with Fading Memory," U.S. Office of Naval Research Technical Report C11-66, Contract Nonr-562(10), Brown University; *Arch. Rational Mech. and Analysis,* **8**: 297–308. (59)

Poincaré, H. [1892]: "Leçon sur la théorie de l'élasticité," G. Carré, Paris. (45)

Prager, W. [1938]: On Isotropic Materials with Continuous Transition from Elastic to Plastic State, *Proc. 5th Intern. Congr. Appl. Mech.,* Cambridge, Mass., 234–237. (85)

Prager, W. [1955]: The Theory of Plasticity: a Survey of Recent Achievements, *Proc. Inst. Mech. Engrs. (London),* **169**: 41–57. (83)

Prager, W. [1959]: "An Introduction to Plasticity," Addison-Wesley Publishing Company, Reading, Mass. (83)

Prager, W., and P. G. Hodge [1951]: "Theory of Perfectly Plastic Solids," John Wiley & Sons, Inc., New York. (83)

Prandtl, L. [1924]: Spannungsverteilung in plastischen Körpern, *Proc. 1st Intern. Congr. Appl. Mech.,* Delft, 43. (86)

Prigogine, I. [1947]: "Étude thermodynamique des phénomènes irréversibles," Dunod-Desoer, Paris and Liège. (39)

Reiner, M. [1931]: Slippage in a Non-Newtonian Liquid, *J. Rheol.,* **2**: 337–350. (63)

Reiner, M. [1932*a*]: Die Berechnung des Einflusses einer festen Wand auf den Aggregatzustand einer Flüssigkeit aus Viskositätsmessungen, *Physik. Z.,* **33**: 499–502. (63)

Reiner, M. [1932*b*]: Haftet eine Flussigkeit an einer Wand, die sie nicht benetzt?, *Z. Physik,* **79**: 139–140. (63)

Reiner, M. [1945]: A Mathematical Theory of Dilatancy, *Am. J. Math.,* **67**: 350–362. (48)

Reiner, M. [1948]: Elasticity beyond the Elastic Limit, *Am. J. Math.,* **70**: 433–446. (70)

Reiner, M. [1951]: The Theory of Cross-elasticity (in Hebrew with English summary), *Hebrew Inst. Technol. Haifa Sci. Publ.,* **4**: 15–30. (53)

Reiner, M. [1960]: "Deformation, Strain and Flow," 2d ed., Interscience Publishers, Inc., New York. (66)

Reiner, M., G. W. Scott Blair, and H. B. Hawley [1949]: The Weissenberg Effect in Sweetened Condensed Milk, *J. Soc. Chem. Ind. (London),* **68**: 327–328. (66, 70)

Reuss, A. [1930]: Berücksichtigung der elastischen Formänderung in der Plastizitätstheorie, *Z.A.M.M.,* **10**: 266–274. (86)

Rivlin, R. S. [1947*a*]: Hydrodynamics of Non-Newtonian Fluids, *Nature,* **160**: 611–613. (48)

Rivlin, R. S. [1947*b*]: Torsion of a Rubber Cylinder, *J. Appl. Phys.,* **18**: 444–449. (61)

Rivlin, R. S. [1948*a*]: Large Elastic Deformations of Isotropic Materials. I. Fundamental Concepts, *Phil. Trans. Roy. Soc. London,* (**A**) **240**: 459–490. (45)

Rivlin, R. S. [1948*b*]: Large Elastic Deformations of Isotropic Materials. III. Some Simple Problems in Cylindrical Polar Co-ordinates, *Phil. Trans. Roy. Soc. London,* (**A**) **240**: 509–525. (45)

Rivlin, R. S. [1948*c*]: Large Elastic Deformations of Isotropic Materials. IV. Further Developments of the General Theory, *Phil. Trans. Roy. Soc. London,* (**A**) **241**: 379–397. (45, 47, 52, 53)

Rivlin, R. S. [1948*d*]: The Hydrodynamics of Non-Newtonian Fluids. I, *Proc. Roy. Soc. (London),* (**A**) **193**: 260–281. (64, 66)

Rivlin, R. S. [1949*a*]: Large Elastic Deformations of Isotropic Materials. V. The Problem of Flexure, *Proc. Roy. Soc. (London),* (**A**) **195**: 463–473. (15, 55)

Rivlin, R. S. [1949*b*]: Large Elastic Deformations of Isotropic Materials. VI. Further Results in the Theory of Torsion Shear and Flexure, *Phil. Trans. Roy. Soc. London,* (**A**) **242**: 173–195. (53, 55)

Rivlin, R. S. [1949*c*]: The Hydrodynamics of Non-Newtonian Fluids. II, *Proc. Cambridge Phil. Soc.,* **45**: 88–91. (63)

Rivlin, R. S. [1955*a*]: Further Remarks on the Stress-deformation Relations for Isotropic Materials, *J. Rational Mech. and Analysis,* **4**: 681–702. (73, 95)

Rivlin, R. S. [1955*b*]: Plane Strain of a Net Formed by Inextensible Cords, *J. Rational Mech. and Analysis,* **4**: 951–974. (59)

Rivlin, R. S. [1956]: Solution of Some Problems in the Exact Theory of Viscoelasticity, *J. Rational Mech. and Analysis,* **5**: 179–188. (70, 92, 94, 98, 100)

Rivlin, R. S. [1960*a*]: Some Topics in Finite Elasticity, in "Proceedings of the First Symposium on Naval Structural Mechanics," Pergamon Press, Inc., New York, 169–198. (45)

Rivlin, R. S. [1960*b*]: The Formulation of Constitutive Equations in Continuum Physics. II, *Arch. Rational Mech. and Analysis,* **4**: 262–272. (92, 95, 116)

Rivlin, R. S., and J. L. Ericksen [1955]: Stress-deformation Relations for Isotropic Materials, *J. Rational Mech. and Analysis,* **4**: 323–425. (19, 92, 96)

Rivlin, R. S., and D. W. Saunders [1951]: Large Elastic Deformations of Isotropic Materials. VII. Experiments on the Deformation of Rubber, *Phil. Trans. Roy. Soc. London,* (**A**) **243**: 251–288. (47, 52, 61)

Rivlin, R. S., and D. W. Saunders [1952]: The Free Energy of Deformation for Vulcanized Rubber, *Trans. Faraday Soc.,* **48**: 200–206. (61)

Rivlin, R. S., and A. G. Thomas [1951]: Large Elastic Deformations of Isotropic Materials. VIII. Strain Distribution around a Hole in a Sheet, *Phil. Trans. Roy. Soc. London,* (**A**) **243**: 289–298. (61)

Roberts, J. E. [1953]: Pressure Distribution in Liquids in Laminar Shearing Motion and Comparison with Predictions from Various Theories, *Proc. 2d Intern. Congr. Rheol.,* 91–98. (67, 68, 70)

St. Venant, A.-J.-C. B. de [1844]: Sur les pressions qui se développent à l'intérieur des corps solides lorsque les déplacements de leur points, sans altérer l'élasticité, ne peuvent cependant pas être considérés comme trèspetits, *Bull. Soc. Philomath.,* **5**: 26–28. (60)

St. Venant, A.-J.-C. B. de [1847]: Mémoire sur l'équilibre des corps solides, dans les limites de leur élasticité, et sur les conditions de leur résistance, quand les déplacements ne sont pas trèspetits, *Compt. Rend. Acad. Sci. Paris,* **24**: 260–263. (60)

St. Venant, A.-J.-C. B. de [1863]: Mémoire sur la distribution des élasticités autour de chaque point d'un solide ou d'un milieu de contexture quelconque, particulièrement lorsqu'il est amorphe sans être isotrope, *J. Math. Pures Appl.,* (2) **8**: 257–295, 353–430. (60)

St. Venant, A.-J.-C. B. de [1870]: Mémoire sur l'établissement des équations différentielles des mouvements intérieurs opérés dans les corps solides ductiles au delà des limites où l'élasticité pourrait les ramener à leur premier état, *Compt. Rend. Acad. Sci. Paris,* **70**: 473–480. (83)

St. Venant, A.-J.-C. B. de [1871]: Mémoire sur l'établissement des équations différentielles des mouvements intérieurs opérés dans les corps solides ductiles au delà des limites où l'élasticité pourrait les ramener à leur premier état, *J. Math. Pures Appl.,* **16**: 308–316. (83)

St. Venant, A.-J.-C. B. de [1872*a*]: Sur l'intensité des forces capables de déformer, avec continuité des blocs ductiles, cylindriques, pleins ou évidés et placés dans diverses circonstances, *Compt. Rend. Acad. Sci. Paris,* **74**: 1009–1015. (83)

St. Venant, A.-J.-C. B. de [1872*b*]: Sur un complément à donner à une des équations présentées par M. Lévy pour les mouvements plastiques qui sont symétriques autour d'un même axe, *Compt. Rend. Acad. Sci. Paris,* **74**: 1083–1087. (83)

Schouten, J. A. [1951]: "Tensor Analysis for Physicists," Oxford University Press, New York. (45, A1)

Schouten, J. A. [1954]: "Ricci-calculus," 2d ed., Springer-Verlag, Berlin. (A1)

Schouten, J. A., and J. Haantjes [1934]: Über die konforminvariente Gestalt der Maxwellschen Gleichungen und der elektromagnetischen Impulsenergiegleichungen, *Physica,* **1**: 869–872. (116)

Schouten, J. A., and W. V. D. Kulk [1949]: "Pfaff's Problem and Its Generalizations," Oxford University Press, New York. (A1)

Seitz, F. S. [1940]: "The Modern Theory of Solids," McGraw-Hill Book Company, Inc., New York. (43)

Serrin, J. [1959]: Mathematical Principles of Classical Fluid Mechanics, in "Handbuch der Physik," vol. VIII/1, pp. 125–263, Springer-Verlag, Berlin. (63)

Signorini, A. [1942]: Deformazioni elastiche finite: elasticità di 2° grado, *Atti 2° Cong. Mat. Ital. Rome* 1940, 56–71. (60)

Signorini, A. [1943]: Transformazioni termoelastiche finite, Memoria 1ª *Ann. di Mat.,* (4) **22**: 33–143. (14, 15)

Signorini, A. [1945]: Recenti progressi della teoria delle transformazioni termoelastiche finite, *Atti del Conv. Mat.* (1942), Rome. (60)

Signorini, A. [1949*a*]: On Finite Deformations of an Elastic Solid, *Proc. 7th Intern. Congr. Appl. Mech.,* (1948), **4**: 237–247. (60)

Signorini, A. [1949*b*]: Transformazioni termoelastiche finite, Memoria 2ª, *Ann. di Mat.,* (4) **30**: 1–72. (60)

Smith, G. F., and R. S. Rivlin [1957]: Stress-deformation Relations for Anisotropic Solids, *Arch. Rational Mech. and Analysis,* **1**: 107–112. (45)

Smith, G. F., and R. S. Rivlin [1958]: The Strain-energy Function for Anisotropic Elastic Materials, *Trans. Am. Math. Soc.*, **88**: 175–193. (45, 116)

Sokolnikoff, I. S. [1951]: "Tensor Analysis: Theory and Applications," John Wiley & Sons, Inc., New York. (9, A1)

Sokolnikoff, I. S. [1956]: "Mathematical Theory of Elasticity," McGraw-Hill Book Company, Inc., New York. (33)

Sokolovskii, V. V. [1946]: "Theory of Plasticity," Moscow, 1946, 1950, 1952; revised German edition, Verlag Technik, Berlin; 1955. (83)

Sommerfeld, A. [1952]: "Electrodynamics," Academic Press, Inc., New York. (109, 116)

Spain, B. [1956]: "Tensor Calculus," 2d ed., Interscience Publishers, Inc., New York. (A1)

Spencer, A. J. M., and R. S. Rivlin [1959*a*]: The Theory of Matrix Polynomials and Its Application to the Mechanics of Isotropic Continua, *Arch. Rational Mech. and Analysis*, **2**: 309–336. (95)

Spencer, A. J. M., and R. S. Rivlin [1959*b*]: Finite Integrity Bases for Five or Fewer Symmetric 3 × 3 Matrices, *Arch. Rational Mech. and Analysis*, **2**: 435–446. (95)

Spencer, A. J. M., and R. S. Rivlin [1960]: Further Results in the Theory of Matrix Polynomials, *Arch. Rational Mech. and Analysis*, **3**: 214–230. (95)

Spitzer, L. [1956]: "Physics of Fully Ionized Gases," Interscience Publishers, Inc., New York. (116)

Stokes, G. G. [1845]: On the Theories of the Internal Friction of Fluids in Motion, and the Equilibrium and Motion of Elastic Solids, *Trans. Cambridge Phil. Soc.*, **8**: (1844–1849), 287–319. (21, 48)

Stone, D. E. [1957]: On Nonexistence of Rectilinear Motion in Plastic Solids and Non-Newtonian Fluids, *Quart. Appl. Math.*, **15**: 257–262. (68)

Stratton, J. A. [1941]: "Electromagnetic Theory," McGraw-Hill Book Company, Inc., New York. (109, 110, 115, 116)

Synge, J. L., and A. Schild [1949]: "Tensor Calculus," University of Toronto Press, Toronto. (A1)

Thomas, A. G. [1955]: The Departures from the Statistical Theory of Rubber Elasticity, *Trans. Faraday Soc.*, **51**: 569–582. (61)

Thomas, T. Y. [1934]: "Differential Invariants of Generalized Spaces," Cambridge University Press, New York. (A1)

Thomas, T. Y. [1953]: Singular Surfaces and Flow Lines in the Theory of Plasticity, *J. Rational Mech. and Analysis*, **2**: 339–381. (59)

Thomas, T. Y. [1954]: Interdependence of the Yield Condition and the Stress-strain Relations for Plastic Flow, *Proc. Natl. Acad. Sci. U.S.*, **40**: 593–597. (83, 84)

Thomas, T. Y. [1955*a*]: On the Structure of the Stress-strain Relations, *Proc. Natl. Acad. Sci. U.S.*, **41**: 716–720. (27, 35, 72, 83)

Thomas, T. Y. [1955*b*]: Kinematically Preferred Coordinate Systems, *Proc. Natl. Acad. Sci. U.S.*, **41**: 762–770 (27, 35, 72)

Thomas, T. Y. [1955*c*]: Combined Elastic and Prandtl-Reuss Stress-strain Relations, *Proc. Natl. Acad. Sci. U.S.*, **41**: 720–726. (83, 85, 86)

Thomas, T. Y. [1955*d*]: Combined Elastic and von Mises Stress-strain Relations, *Proc. Natl. Acad. Sci. U.S.*, **41**: 908–910. (83, 85)

Thomas, T. Y. 1956]: Isotropic Materials Whose Deformation and Distortion Energies Are Expressible by Scalar Invariants, *Proc. Natl. Acad. Sci. U.S.*, **42**: 603–608. (75)

Thomas, T. Y. [1957*a*]: Extended Compatibility Conditions for the Study of Surfaces of Discontinuity in Continuum Mechanics, *J. Math. Mech.*, **6**: 311–322, 907–908. (59)

Thomas, T. Y. [1957*b*]: Deformation Energy and the Stress-strain Relations for Isotropic Materials, *J. Math. and Phys.*, **4**: 335–350. (75)

Thomas, T. Y. [1961]: "Plastic Flow and Fracture in Solids," Academic Press, Inc., New York. (83)

Thomson, W. (Lord Kelvin) [1863]: Dynamical Problems Regarding Elastic Spheroidal Shells and Spheroids of Incompressible Liquid, *Phil. Trans. Roy. Soc. London*, (**A**) **153**: 583–616; *Papers*, **3**: 351–394. (45)

Thomson, W. (Lord Kelvin), and P. G. Tait [1867]: "Treatise on Natural Philosophy," Cambridge University Press, New York, part I. (10)

Timoshenko, S. P., and J. N. Goodier [1951]: "Theory of Elasticity," McGraw-Hill Book Company, Inc., New York. (88)

Tolotti, C. [1943]: Deformazioni elastiche finite onde ordinare di discontinuta e caso tipico di solidi elastici isotropi, *Rend. di Mat. e delle sue Applic.*, **4**, (5[a]), 34–59. (58)

Toupin, R. A. [1956]: The Elastic Dielectric, *J. Rational Mech. and Analysis*, **5**: 849–915. (3, 10, 41, 110, 113, 115, 116)

Toupin, R. A. [1960]: Stress Tensors in Elastic Dielectrics, *Arch. Rational Mech. and Analysis*, **5**: 440–452. (110)

Trefftz, E. [1931]: Über die Ableitung der Stabilitätskriterien des elastischen Gleichgewichtes aus der Elastizitätstheorie endlicher Deformationen, *Proc. 3d Intern. Congr. Appl. Mech.*, **3**: 44–50. (34)

Treloar, L. R. G. [1943]: The Elasticity of a Network of Long Chain Molecules, *Trans. Faraday Soc.*, **39**: 36–41, 241–246. (61)

Treloar, L. R. G. [1948]: Stresses and Birefringence in Rubber Subjected to General Homogeneous Strain, *Proc. Phys. Soc.* (*London*), (**B**) **60**: 135–144. (60)

Treloar, L. R. G. [1958]: "The Physics of Rubber Elasticity," 2d ed., Oxford University Press, New York. (43, 61)

Truesdell, C. [1949*a*]: A New Definition of a Fluid. I. The Stokesian Fluid, *Proc. 7th Intern. Congr. Appl. Mech.* (1948), **2**: 351–364; U.S. Naval Research Laboratory Report No. P-3457; *J. Math. Pures Appl.*, (9) **29**: 215–244, (1950). (48)

Truesdell, C. [1949*b*]: "A New Definition of a Fluid. II. The Maxwellian Fluid," U.S. Naval Research Laboratory Report No. P-3553; *J. Math. Pures Appl.*, (9) **30**: 111–158. (48)

Truesdell, C. [1952]: The Mechanical Foundations of Elasticity and Fluid Dynamics, *J. Rational Mech. and Analysis*, **1**: 125–300; **3**: 593–616. (45, 47, 48, 49, 60, 63, 64)

Truesdell, C. [1954]: The Kinematics of Vorticity, *Indiana Univ. Sci. Ser.* N. **19.** (24)

Truesdell, C. [1955*a*]: The Simplest Rate Theory of Pure Elasticity, *Comm. Pure Appl. Math.*, **8**: 123–132. (27, 72, 76, 79, 80)

Truesdell, C. [1955*b*]: Hypo-elasticity, *J. Rational Mech. and Analysis*, **4**: 83–133, 1019–1020. (27, 72, 78, 79, 80)

Truesdell, C. [1956]: Hypo-elastic Shear, *J. Appl. Phys.*, **27**: 441–447. (79, 89, 90)

Truesdell, C. [1958]: Geometric Interpretation for the Reciprocal Deformation Tensors, *Quart. Appl. Math.*, **15**: 434–435. (12)

Truesdell, C. [1961]: General and Exact Theory of Waves in Finite Elastic Strain, *Arch. Rational Mech. and Analysis*, **8**: 263–296. (58)

Truesdell, C., and R. Toupin [1960]: The Classical Field Theories, in "Handbuch der Physik" vol. III/1, Springer-Verlag, Berlin. (2, 10, 13, 21, 34, 39, 41, 44, 59, 105, 108, 116)

Tsien, H. [1946]: Superaerodynamics, Mechanics of Rarefied Gases, *J. Aeronaut. Sci.*, **13**: 653–664. (63)

Van Dantzig, D. [1934]: The Fundamental Equations of Electromagnetism, Independent of Metrical Geometry, *Proc. Cambridge Phil. Soc.*, **30**: 421–427. (116)

Veblen, O. [1933]: "Invariants of Quadratic Differential Forms," Cambridge University Press, New York. (A1)

Voigt, W. [1889]: Über die innere Reibung der festen Körper, insbesondere der Kristalle, *Abhandl. Ges. Wiss. Göttingen*, **36**: no. 1. (92)

Voigt, W. [1892]: Über innere Reibung fester Körper, insbesondere der Metalle, *Ann. Phys.*, (**2**) **47**: 671–693. (92)

Voigt, W. [1900]: "Rapports présentés au Congrès International de Physique," vol. 1, Charles Édouard Guillaume et L. Poincaré (eds.) Gauthier-Villars, Paris. (45)

Voigt, W. [1928]: "Lehrbuch der Kristallphysik," Teubner Verlagsgessellschaft, mbH, Stuttgart. (45)

Volterra, V. [1907]: Sur l'équilibre des corps élastiques multiplement connexes, *Ann. Ecole Normale*, (3) **24**: 401–517. (57)

Volterra, V. [1930]: "Theory of Functionals and Integral and Integro-differential Equations," Blackie & Son, Glasgow. (92)

Weatherburn, C. E. [1938]: "Riemannian Geometry and the Tensor Calculus," Cambridge University Press, New York. (A1)

Weissenberg, K. [1946]: Geometry of Rheological Phenomena, *Conf. of British Rheol. Club*, London. (70)

Weissenberg, K. [1947]: A Continuum Theory of Rheological Phenomena, *Nature*, **159**: 310–311. (66, 70)

Weissenberg, K. [1949]: Abnormal Substances and Abnormal Phenomena of Flow, *Proc. Intern. Congr. Rheol.* (1948), I-29-I-46. (66, 70)

Weyl, H. [1923]: "Mathematische Analyse des Raumsproblems," Springer-Verlag, Berlin. (A1)

Weyl, H. [1946]: "The Classical Groups, Their Invariants and Representations," Princeton University Press, Princeton, N.J. (45, 46)

Whaples, G. [1952]: Carathéodory's Temperature Equations, *J. Rational Mech. and Analysis*, **1**: 301–307. (39)

Whittaker, E. T. [1953]: "A History of the Theories of Aether and Elasticity," Nelson, London. (109, 116)

Widder, D. V. [1947]: "Advanced Calculus," Prentice-Hall, Inc., Englewood Cliffs, N.J. (A2)

Wood, G. F., A. H. Nissan, and F. H. Garner [1947]: Viscometry of Soap-in-hydrocarbon Systems, *J. Inst. Petrol.*, **33**: 71–94. (66, 70)

Yano, K. [1957]: "The Theory of Lie Derivatives and Its Applications," North-Holland Publishing Company, Amsterdam. (A1)

Zaremba, S. [1903*a*]: Sur une généralisation de la théorie classique de la viscosité, *Bull. Intern. Acad. Sci. Cracovie*, 380–403. (92, 103)

Zaremba, S. [1903*b*]: Sur une forme perfectionée de la théorie de la relaxation, *Bull. Intern. Acad. Sci. Cracovie*, 594–614. (27, 72, 92, 103)

Zaremba, S. [1937]: Sur une conception nouvelle des forces intérieures dans un fluide en mouvement, *Mem. Sci. Math.*, no. 82. (27, 92, 104)

Zorawski, K. [1901]: Über gewisse Änderungsgeschwindigkeiten von Linienelementen bei der Bewegung eines continuierlichen materiellen Systems, *Bull. Intern. Acad. Sci. Cracovie*, 486–499. (21)

# INDEX